Science has been triumphant in understanding the material universe and applying the laws of nature in the development of new technologies for humanity's benefit. But it has achieved this at the price of neglecting other equally important areas, such as mental and spiritual experience. There is a now a dawning realisation—as evidenced by the emergence of the post-materialist science movement—that science must expand beyond the material domain. One needs a new paradigm and a key feature of this must be the realization that *consciousness* is a fundamental, rather than incidental, feature of the Universe.

The unique achievement of this work is to put this endeavour in a proper conceptual and historical context. For while the search for an expanded paradigm might be viewed as a recent development, it has also been the basis of esoteric traditions—in particular, the perennial philosophy—and occult sciences which go back a thousand years and stem from a variety of both Eastern and Western cultures. Many books have focussed on extending science towards perennial philosophy but without making a link with the occult sciences. Other books have focused on occult sciences without making a link with modern science. They are therefore like two outstretched hands which do not quite connect. This work completes the connection, rather like the two hands in the famous picture by Michelangelo.

This is a *magnum opus* in every sense of the word. For its thousand pages, spread over three volumes, are not just about the link between traditional and esoteric science. They are also about the many connections between the worlds of matter, mind and spirit. While everyone has a foot in all three worlds, most of us are mainly drawn to just one because success in life—be it on the scientific, artistic or mystical fronts—usually requires narrowly-focussed dedication. However, a full understanding of the universe must embrace all three worlds and Edi Bilimoria is one of the few people with the breadth of vision and width of knowledge required to expound on this. The result is a work which will surely play a vital role in bridging the chasms between matter, mind and spirit.

BERNARD CARR, *Emeritus Professor of Mathematics and Astronomy,*
Queen Mary University of London, and President of the Scientific and Medical Network

This work presents a comprehensive, lucid and well-written overview, with careful attention to detail and yet full of far-ranging and potentially transformative ideas.

RUPERT SHELDRAKE PHD, *biologist and author of* The Science Delusion

It is refreshing to read a masterly study of consciousness written by an author who roots his arguments in a profound grasp of esoteric wisdom. It is not simply that such wisdom conveys profound insights for understanding the essence of consciousness. Of far greater importance is the skill that Edi Bilimoria brings in clarifying our place in the vast panorama of which we are a part. There is nothing more pressing in our day than this challenge for us to act in synergy with the planet (and, in more esoteric terms, the macrocosm). Bilimoria shows that the ancient axiom that "man is the measure of all things" can be revitalised in the context of contemporary science. And he brings an encyclopaedic grasp of modern physics, neuroscience, and psychology to support his supremely optimistic view that consciousness is fundamental to reality. This is an insight whose time has come, and Bilimoria shows himself to be a diligent and creative guide to what a post-materialist understanding of consciousness will mean for us all.

B LES LANCASTER, *Professor Emeritus of Transpersonal Psychology,*
Liverpool John Moores University and Director, the Alef Trust

Unfolding Consciousness is a remarkable tour de force through spiritual meanders of esoteric traditions, from East and West, and their dialogue with modern science. It is as fascinatingly provocative, as it is informative—and it will equally challenge the scientist, the philosopher, and the artist. In contemporary, unpretentious language, it takes the reader from the spiritual mission of humanity to the principles of the universe (and back), with careful consideration of both scientific evidence and metaphysical subtleties; and underneath it all, it seeks the traces of consciousness, in all its forms. Just like its main theme—ourselves, and our rapport to the universe—this is not an *easy* work; nor should it be. It is an *important* work, which is worth taking time to engage with.

DR ANA-MARIA PASCAL, MBA, PHD, SFHEA,
Director, Liberal Arts Programmes,
Associate Professor in Philosophy and Public Ethics, Provost's Group, Regent's University London

When you consider the scope, width and erudition of this work, it is not surprising that it took its author over 20 years to complete. Most philosophical books take a single view of the problem of consciousness, either scientific or philosophical, but Edi Bilimoria takes a much wider, more inclusive view. Who am I? is the underlying question of *Volume I: A Panoramic Survey – Science Contrasted with the Perennial Philosophy on Consciousness and Man*, which provides an overview of the field, highlighting both the value of science and its limitations as a tool for examining the deeper problems of life and consciousness, and makes the case for the perennial philosophy as a bridge to reach a greater understanding of these areas. In *Volume II: Peering Down the Microscope – Man's Internal Landscapes*, Bilimoria manages the seemingly impossible task of finding common ground in the mass of beliefs and practices, old and new, from diverse, cultures, religions and philosophies, to demonstrate an overlap and unifying doctrine even on such issues as post-mortem existence and re-birth and the complexities of the human mind. *Volume III: Gazing Through the Telescope – Man is the Measure of All Things* is even more ambitious in its aim to show how the human being fits into the grand scheme of the Universe, to examine the question of emergence from the spiritual to the material, from the implicate order to its explicate expression. It draws on the insights of symbolism and mysticism, and the deepest teachings of occultism to explain the nature of consciousness. In this twenty-first century, an era in which science is our dominant paradigm and is playing an ever increasing part in our technology and our lives, this work helps to adjust the balance and resolve the conflicts between science and religion on issues like evolution and purpose, the nature of consciousness, and what it truly means to be a human being as opposed to an animated robot or a biological mechanism.

This is a complex work, but each chapter opens with a synopsis and closes with a summary of the principal themes which are extremely helpful and means that despite their complexity, the three volumes are always easy to understand and follow. I would recommend this trilogy to anyone who wants a broad overview of the various traditions which have led to the current Western understanding of man's place in the Universe

> PETER FENWICK *was a senior lecturer at King's College, London, where he worked as a consultant at the Institute of Psychiatry. He was the Consultant Neuropsychiatrist and Neuropsychologist at the Maudsley and John Radcliffe hospitals. He worked with the Mental Health Group at the University of Southampton, and held a visiting professorship at the Riken Neurosciences Institute in Japan. He is President Emeritus of the* Scientific and Medical Network.

Undoubtedly, we live in historic times. The multitude of surrounding crises, both in everyday life and in the analyses of the experts, testify to this. In such crucial times it is important that men of goodwill raise their voice and thus raise the collective consciousness of humanity. This is the only way we can overcome. Via his trilogy, the author raises exactly such a voice. By a brilliant tour de force, he provides us with a masterpiece that elucidates the origins of science and technology, historically and ontologically, and relates them to the ultimate philosophical quest of perennial philosophy. It also shows why we got it wrong and where. As the author informs us, meticulously, science, in multiple instances, was lured away from truth towards scientism and utilitarianism blinded by its own great power. The trilogy at hand offers a way out by detailing exactly how we can correct this route of mindless exploitation and bring science back on track, back to its quest for the truth. The author is brilliantly clear on that: we treat nature as we treat ourselves, therefore to emerge alive from the crises we have put ourselves into we have to rediscover the sacredness of nature, in nature and in us. It is for this reason that Edi Bilimoria's work will prove a much needed historic work in historic times.

> VASILEIOS BASIOS (BSc, MSc, PhD)
> *PhD in Physics of Complex Systems, University of Brussels (ULB)*

Unfolding Consciousness

Exploring the Living Universe and Intelligent Powers in Nature and Humans

Volume I

A Panoramic Survey –
Science Contrasted with the Perennial
Philosophy on Consciousness and Man

EDI BILIMORIA, DPhil, FIMechE, FEI, FRSA

SHEPHEARD
WALWYN
PUBLISHERS

First published in 2022 by Shepherd-Walwyn (Publishers) Ltd
107 Parkway House, Sheen Lane, London SW14 8LS
www.shepheardwalwyn.com
www.ethicaleconomics.org.uk

British Library Cataloguing in Publication Data
A catalogue record of this book is available from the British Library

ISBN: 978-08-5683-536-0

Copyedit by Elizabeth Medler
Typeset by Ian Wileman

Printed and bound through
s|s|media limited, Rickmansworth, Hertfordshire

Dedication

As spoken by a wise man of the East known only to a few: 'Not one of the Great Teachers allowed this Truth—the transcendent answer to the worldly malaise, material and psychological, of the day—to be soiled by the lure of establishing any earthly Utopia, or his life-energy to be wasted in inventing techniques and systems for dealing with the muddlement and evil of the world's politics, economics and unregenerate everyday life at their own level. Each of them saw with unerring insight that man the world over is himself the prolific spawner of ubiquitous ugliness and suffering, and that there is only one way to redeem the world situation: the way of purity and truth, wisdom and love; the way of the unselfed, of the transformed man. It is each man's personal responsibility to realize this.'

This work is the writer's heartfelt tribute and obeisance to the illimitable sages of the Orient and the Occident who have epitomized the noblest endeavours of humanity, in Philosophy and Science, Religion and Art, thus ever illuminating a Path for mankind through the darkness and turbulence of the mundane world towards his true empyrean abode—should we but listen to their words.

Acknowledgements

In being able to bring to fruition a trilogy with a gestation period of nearly two decades I tender grateful thanks to many well-wishers and supporters.

First and foremost, I am deeply indebted to Anthony Werner, Owner, until comparatively recently, of Shepheard-Walwyn (Publishers) Ltd, who agreed to publish my work. I can only hope that the end result has justified his early conviction. The Editorial Director, Mirella Lombardo, and Marketing Manager, Tracey Kerrigan, have taken up the mantle in a splendid way and it has been a pleasure to have worked with them.

Immense gratitude and thanks are due to David Lorimer for kindly providing a generous Foreword and reviewing an early draft of the complete work. I can think of no one better equipped to do this. David's breadth of knowledge and immense erudition—spanning the whole range of science, spirituality, and philosophy—is second to none. Incorporating his numerous suggestions and comments for improving and enriching my work have provided me with countless hours of enjoyable headaches!

Then to Elizabeth Medler for her painstaking copyediting, insightful suggestions, and ever-active involvement in the message of my work; her expertise in transforming my several angular sentences into elegant narrative; for restraining my penchant for overly long sentences, curtailing my obsessive drive for punctiliousness; and for facilitating communication with my publisher.

Next to Ian Wileman for his inordinate patience, expertise and great care in typesetting a difficult manuscript.

I flatter myself with the thought that to have my publisher, reviewer, copyeditor, and typesetter all in sync with the esoteric and philosophical theme of my work cannot be a matter of coincidence. The synchronicity of Shepheard-Walwyn, David Lorimer, Elizabeth Medler, and Ian Wileman has been a rare privilege and a huge relief. And here I must also include educationalist and designer, writer and lecturer Leon Conrad, not only for some invaluable advice on editorial matters but, above all, in his role as a catalyst in putting me in touch with my publisher.

With well over two thousand references in these Volumes, the advice and assistance from George Timcke, my associate since 'Channel Tunnel days', in organizing and formatting this material has been invaluable. Then I must thank Cyrus Bilimoria for producing excellent diagrams from poor quality scanned images; and to Stephan Fowler of Artefact Design for assistance with images and credits. Gratitude is extended to Taposhri Ganguly, and to Beverley Winkler and Bourchier for their help with indexing the three Volumes.

Much appreciation is extended to my friends and colleagues at work: Taz Sinhal for providing me with a crucial source reference that I had been seeking for years, which constituted the foundation of major sections of Volume III; Adrian Rifat for insightful discussions and comments on the current world situation in the light of science and spiritual values; and Sophia Mirza for substantial input to the pure mathematics sections of the Mathematical Codicil to Volume III.

Thanks are due to the Theosophical Society in Australia for permission to reproduce some of the material I was researching in my role as Education Manager.

Whereas all images are fully credited and, where appropriate, rights and permissions obtained, especial thanks are due to the Theosophical Publishing House, India for permission to use several images from their various publications; likewise, to the Bhaktivedanta Book Trust International for permission to use pictures from one of their publications.

Immense thanks to all who generously gave of their time to provide generous endorsements: Associate Professor Ana-Maria Pascal of Regent's University, London; Dr Peter Fenwick, President Emeritus of the Scientific and Medical Network; Professor Bernard Carr, Emeritus Chairman and current President of the Scientific and Medical Network; Dr Vasileios Basios, Senior Researcher of Université Libre de Bruxelles, Brussels; Professor Les Lancaster, Liverpool John Moores University and Director, the Alef Trust; and Dr Rupert Sheldrake, biologist, researcher, and internationally acclaimed author. Their combined support and encouragement are gratefully acknowledged.

I seem now to have lost count of how many Saturday evenings I must have spent endlessly proof reading and checking my manuscript over dinner at The Withies Inn, England's finest free house with a fairy-tale garden dating from the sixteenth century. I thank all the staff for being so welcoming and uplifting my spirits.

Above all, the inspiration I have received from those great sages of the Orient and the Occident, along with the luminaries in science, religion, philosophy, and art, as cited in this work, and my debt of gratitude to them cannot be put into words. By their personal example, these Great Ones have shown that the confusion and darkness of this mundane world can be dispelled by the Light of their wisdom to reveal a bright and abundant life, should we but heed their words—spoken and unspoken. I can only hope that this work will encourage those few truly earnest students of life and wisdom to drink deeply of the springs at their source and discover the truths for themselves.

A Personal Note to Readers

These Volumes comprise three stages of an exploratory journey through the diverse terrain of consciousness. Consciousness can neither be subjected to intellectual dissection upon the rack of discursive ratiocination and vindicated by what is fashionably known as a 'critical argument'; nor can it be put into a box with a neat descriptive label. If I were permitted to mention what I regard as a unique feature of this work it would be this: There are splendid books on science, religion, occult science, philosophy, and art; but few that have brought these diverse streams under a single overarching theme comprising a single body of integral Wisdom, whilst pointing to their Source. Allied to this, a constant theme of these Volumes is the universality of the Mystery teachings of all cultures and religions. That does not mean they are all the same, by any means, but they are in harmony and confluence one with the other and also with enlightened Science. This is not science in the narrow sense, as regarded by the mainstream, namely the knowledge of phenomena and the objective world, appreciable to our physical senses, but Science in its larger and truer sense which has its seat in the noumenal (the final causes of all things) from which it surveys the phenomenal, the things we see all around us. This Science discloses the radiant Truth because it is free from all man-made accretions and superstitions.

Always accepting that in the mundane world the practical application of Truth means that it is sometimes hard to distinguish the wood from the trees in terms of its multifaceted expressions, some of which are very partitive indeed, in the spirit of genuine seeker, I have endeavoured to remain open to exploring Truth throughout, holding on firmly to Ariadne's Golden Thread amidst the convoluted twists and turns of the labyrinth. To this end, I have avoided the all-too-common tendency amongst writers of stating 'the truth' on any particular subject as a *fait accompli*, then seeking to justify the conclusion with arguments and references. Rather, I have sought to be witness, seeing the various aspects of the subject matter in the round, so as to argue *towards* the Truth but to leave the reader entirely free to come to his or her conclusions.

Above all, few books have attempted the challenge of this work—to show, with chapter and verse, how innumerable conundrums in mainstream science can be resolved in the light of the *philosophia perennis*—the eternal Wisdom; and, in some cases, to show how the latter can be corroborated by the inferences and evidence from modern science. In this sense, these Volumes may be seen as a successor to my earlier book *The Snake and the Rope: Problems in Western Science Resolved by Occult Science* (ISBN 81-7059-484-7 (HC), 2006).

Those few books that respond to the above demands are so abstruse as to leave the modern reader, used to a literary diet of small books and short, bite-sized, sentences exhausted by the labour. In a work like this, the unity and cohesion between the broad range and diversity of subjects covered is of major import. To that end, I have spared no effort to render the material accessible and easy to navigate. The Introductory contains abstracts of each Chapter and these contain their own synopsis, sidenotes, footnotes, and postlude leading on organically to the next.

Complex chapters are provided with a route map. Many important references are from arcane sources and may be difficult for the researcher to obtain or locate; therefore, with a view to facilitating research, these have been supplied with alternative references and online websites. Moreover, given the wide range of material, proper names have their provenance, role and dates (correct to 2021) outlined. This is important for reason that readers may then appreciate quotes and expositions in the context and epoch in which they were provided. Another feature is that the philosophic and scientific portions are fully up to date. Thus, the work ranges from the ancient to the avant-garde.

In the wake of over half a century of intense involvement and participation in spiritual societies and musical circles, contemporaneous with a working life in diverse roles across numerous industries, I ask the reader's indulgence in permitting me to pass on four observations hard-won through experience.

First, the need to transcend—never jettison—intellect in order to arrive at even an approximate semblance of truth. We live in a world where reality is ascribed to the surface appearance and 'thing-ness' of objects; however the noumenal (*thing-in-itself*) essences have more reality than their phenomenal, objective counterparts. We cannot approach truth merely through science and the intellect. Great music and art—the eloquence of Mozart, the timelessness of Schubert, the majesty of Beethoven—can sometimes draw an aspirant closer to his Source than a dozen books might do—even the one he happens to be reading! To that end, I am unconditionally and utterly convinced as to the ubiquity and primacy of consciousness. Moreover, all my research leads to the same conclusion, namely—that consciousness is transmitted through the human being and filtered by the brain, its instrument of expression. This is, of course, contrary to the current virtually unanimous mainstream neuroscience diktat that thought is produced, or generated, by the brain, and consciousness is nothing more than a distracting epiphenomenon—'ghost in the machine'—explained away by physical processes. Be that as it may, in my view, whereas there is never any question of artificial intelligence overtaking human intelligence (as leading computationalists and entrepreneurs confidently assert), I regard the blurring of the two by virtue of the increasingly rampant glorification of the former, along with the 'machinization' of human intelligence with the promise of a digital afterlife together with researching gene reprogramming in order to live for ever, as some of the most pernicious trends in contemporary mainstream science consciousness research. With notable exceptions, sadly, such research is still driven by materialistic concepts underpinned by unsupportable presuppositions, at the cost of reality and Truth. On a brighter note, there is a burgeoning movement amongst increasing numbers of enlightened scientists and philosophers investigating such research evidence that has been ignored or dismissed because it is philosophically incompatible with materialism. In this we see reflected a heartening attempt to build bridges between spirit, mind, and matter. This movement argues for global dialogue about a science of consciousness without restricting consciousness just to a sub-discipline of mainstream neuroscience. It further proposes that consciousness can give us direct access to the deeper structures of reality and therefore stresses the importance of coupling the normal theoretical third person perspective approach to consciousness studies with the experiential, first-person perspective.

Second, the indispensable need always to main a universal outlook, which demands a plurality of approaches and universality of outlook which draws on diverse wisdom streams, but always endeavouring to discover their unifying thread and seeking out their Source. Sectarianism and its twin, dogma, are the greatest curses that have blighted not only religion, the obvious example, but, albeit more covertly, science, philosophy, and esotericism no less. I maintain that there is absolutely no one book, teacher or teaching, of any epoch, that can be upheld as an absolute gold standard of Truth. For example, musicians the world over revere Bach; but no musician would ever enter into interminable debates over whether Bach was the final authority over, say, Haydn, Mozart or Beethoven, or whether, to wit, Beethoven's fugues were merely borrowed from those of Bach. Still less would musicians engage in prolonged, acrimonious debates over whether the Romantic era was inferior to the Classical era, which happened to come first. That sectarian attitudes, like poisonous mushrooms, pervade spiritual societies which are always founded on the basis of *truth wherever it leads*, is quite deplorable. To maintain such a stance (promulgated in the guise of upholding the 'purity' of the original teachings) is nothing short of fundamentalism and indicative of weak minds—the equivalent of religious orthodoxy. Attempting to establish an ultimate 'Church of Truth' based on one authority, whose say-so is propped up by its self-appointed popes or archbishops, would be an affront to Truth. Furthermore, Truth is best served by both intellect and intuition—the way of science in hand with the path of mysticism. Depending on the context, the proportion of each will vary, but in any situation, either one is not a substitute for the other. By a judicious balance combining heart, mind and will, any propensity towards arrogance stemming from an over reliance on the intellect would be tempered; and any over emphasis on the feeling side, leading to gullibility, hyper-sensitivity and sentimentality, would be moderated.

Third, it is a huge mistake to believe (as I credulously did for some decades) that members of spiritual organisations are, by definition, a 'cut above' the common folk in terms of their generosity, sincerity, and altruism. Human nature, in general, is always the same and I have personally experienced genuinely fraternal behaviour as much from those in the wide world of industry, from friends and colleagues who would not have (or want to have) any clue about such subjects as theosophy or esoteric science, let alone occultism, as from those few in spiritual organisations. Whereas politics, corruption, and skulduggery are nothing new to commercial organisations, they are no less extant and, in fact, more insidious in spiritual or esoteric societies than the secular world, for reason that such societies were set up for the express purpose of promulgating Truth and therefore have a sacred duty in this respect which, if departed from, for self-seeking motives, constitutes a greater Fall and dereliction of duty than would be the case in ordinary secular life. Clearly, the amount of backbiting and infighting in such societies— amongst those who profess such things as brotherhood and universal love—is an adulteration and falling away from the nobility of the ideals and spiritual vision of their founders. As Mahatma Gandhi counselled, the best way to change society (let alone the world) is first to start with oneself—and that is rarely achieved merely by piously quoting long passages about 'service to humanity' from sacred texts or revered books at public lectures.

Finally, the need to listen to all but to maintain one's own counsel. 'Art thou able to walk alone?' was a testing question once put to a contemporary sage and philosopher in his younger days. Those who are not sure about how to answer might care to take to heart this extract from another adept: 'Be prepared for loneliness. It is the law. This must be endured and passed… [Additionally] have patience. Endurance is one of the characteristics [of the aspirant].' Whatever societies we may or may not belong to, we can listen to all but must ultimately walk our own path—alone. On that score over the last decade, I have been in the constant company of my ever-faithful friend—solitude. So those amongst my acquaintances, most likely unaware of my acute need for seclusion in writing this work, cannot be entirely blamed for mistaking my necessarily excessive demands for protracted solitude with unfriendliness and aloofness.

As this work is about the perennial philosophy—the eternal Wisdom—and our claim that, by its very nature it provides the solution to the problems that beset any age, given that the COVID-19 pandemic was the backdrop for part of the time as this work was being written, how does the perennial philosophy shine a light on such watershed moments in history? First, we need to be clear that we are not claiming that this Wisdom had foreseen and analysed every complexity or detail of this, or any other generation, but that from an understanding of the fundamental verities of life comes the method and correct solution, and the means, to cope intelligently with those great cultural, intellectual, moral, and social problems which, in their unsolved state, confront the humanity of all times, as the past century of political unrest, terrorist violence (often in the name of religion), ecological disasters, and the recent pandemic bears ample witness. In other words, we have all the tools we need to solve our problems, if we can but grasp these verities of life and work with Prometheus (foresight) as well as learn from our mistakes through Epimetheus (hindsight).

Has this sea-change in all our lives caused by the pandemic raised the possibility of living in a better way—a less materialistic and more environmental way—a way in which Nature is regarded as a living being rather than a resource to be plundered? We have sophisticated tools at our disposal for strategic foresight and analysing emerging trends and risks. And we have massive resources—financial, material, and scientific. We also have global institutions, such as the World Health Organization, the World Bank, the International Monetary Fund, and worldwide humanitarian networks. *The building blocks exist to build a resilient, sustainable and adaptable future for all. But do we have the wisdom and the will to act on what we know?* This is where the perennial philosophy plays an indispensable part in the necessary refining and evolution of man's character by showing us that, primarily, the solution lies in a reformation of man's nature, and only secondarily in economic, technological or social schemes. A solution at the physical level will not address the underlying causes. We have only to look at world history to realize for ourselves that, without exception, the great sages, since time immemorial, have sounded the clarion call to man to *Know Himself*. Not one of these luminaries wasted his life-energy in preaching the lure of any earthly Utopia by inventing techniques and systems for dealing with the confusion and evil of the world's politics, economics, and daily life at the routine and everyday level. With unerring insight, each of them saw the futility of the conventional economic or technological way of dealing with problems, when it is, in fact, man himself, the world over, who creates the ugliness and misery around him, which he then attempts to remedy by changing outer structures. Those with wisdom know that there is only one way to redeem the world situation and that is through a change in the *inner* structure of man—that is, through his mindset, the way of the *transformed* man—the *inner* revolution in the mind and not its brutal counterpart in the external world that has spilt rivers of blood and caused untold suffering.

What can we glean from the perennial philosophy in the current global climate? Its fundamental tenet is the intrinsic unity, interrelationship, and interconnection of all life forms in nature, at all levels ranging from the physical to the spiritual, from the mightiest galaxy to the minutest speck of matter, even to a virus, to wit. This is really tantamount to saying that all existence is essentially, one, organic and *living* Being which may be called by the popular but overloaded term 'God', or 'Brahman', or by the term we prefer, 'Divine Consciousness'. All beings and all life, organic and so-called inorganic, thus belong together in that we are all the various aspects of one single Being, like the many, almost identical, images which a multi-faceted diamond reflects of the same *one* object. This is not something that can be proven by ratiocination or is logically deducible. But it is accessible through mysticism and metaphysics, as evinced not only by the great sages, philosophers, and artists since time immemorial but equally by legendary scientists of all ages, past and present. And what better evidence (albeit at the physical level) is there of the fragile interconnectedness of all life forms and livelihoods than the pandemic? Local communities have, in general, become more closely bonded as one large extended family, but have the nations of the world come any closer to this realization of unity? It is to be doubted, especially in the light of the warning by the Director-General of the World Health Organization that 'the world is on the brink of a catastrophic moral failure'. Why? Owing to the 'me first' strategy to secure vaccines that many countries have adopted, whereby 'vaccine nationalism' has resulted in unequal access to vaccines (*RSA Journal*, Issue 2, June 2021, pages 16, 17).

Another cardinal teaching of the perennial wisdom is the coexistence of the spiritual, mental (intellectual), and physical worlds; and that man inhabits, and must live in, all three worlds. Has the excessive focus on purely materialistic concepts and solutions resulted in the present imbalance due to an over dependence on technological schemes at the expense of spiritual insights? Thus, has mainstream science caused as many problems as it tries to solve? Are vaccines and other physical measures, not to be decried, nevertheless, the sole means of dealing with a problem on many levels?

There are bound to be other pandemics in future so what will it take to prepare for future disasters? They must all be approached in the light of the eternal Wisdom which teaches us that the plethora of health and social problems that currently beset individuals, societies, and nations would be greatly alleviated were this simple fact realized: that man (like all other creatures) is the outcome of Divine Ideation and his body the product of Divine Forces sculpted by Divine Handicraft.

Today we are deluged with countless books that contribute little, or nothing, to public improvement and merely represent recreational reading or argumentative discourse, dealing with scandal, gossip, and all kinds of social prejudices, conceits, and a fascination for the 'cancel culture' that typifies our age. Clearly, society in general is paying the price of a decline in culture, moral standards, and mental health due to consuming the intellectual equivalent of junk food.

On the other hand, there is no dearth of scholarly books and papers nowadays on broad matters of consciousness and its relation to science and spirituality. This is a welcome development but the current trend in serious literature seems to be heading, to my mind, towards increasing specialization, or populism, in the interests of making the subject user-accessible, resulting, in many cases, with presentation at the expense of content. The consciousness–science–spirituality bandwagon trundles along on three well-oiled wheels! So, to those who might find my work overly cumbersome or abstruse, I can only respond by quoting a passage from a book by the great nineteenth century German philosopher Arthur Schopenhauer:

> I part with the book with deep seriousness, in the sure hope that sooner or later it will reach those to whom alone it can be addressed; and for the rest, patiently resigned that the same fate should, in full measure, befall it, that in all ages has, to some extent, befallen all knowledge, and especially the weightiest knowledge of the truth, to which only a brief triumph is allotted between the two long periods in which it is condemned as paradoxical or disparaged as trivial. The former fate is also want to befall its author. But life is short, and truth works far and lives long: let us speak the truth.[i]

Who wrote this work is of lesser consequence than the fact that it had to be, and was, written. Well over a decade of protracted effort in producing it has provided little pleasure but boundless joy—anyone who has been involved in strenuous creative endeavour will need no explanation of what I mean. May you the reader, however, reap both in abundance.

Contacting the writer: If this work has touched you in some way and you would like to share your reflections, your comments would be welcome. Any faults are mine and have nothing to do with the subject matter of science, spirituality or occult science; so if you have spotted any obvious omissions and/or errors, do please contact the writer: edibil@btinternet.com; or visit the publisher's website: shepheardwalwyn.com; general enquiries: books@shepheardwalwyn.com.

---

i Arthur Schopenhauer, *Die Welt als Wille und Vorstellung* [The World as Will and Representation], trans. R. B. Haldane and J. Kemp, 1st edn Leipzig, Germany: Vorrede, 1819; 7th edn, California, US: CreateSpace Independent Publishing Platform, 2015, page 9.

About the Author

Edi Bilimoria DPhil, FIMechE, FEI, FRSA

Born in India and educated at the universities of London, Sussex and Oxford, Edi Bilimoria presents an unusual blend of experience in the fields of science, the arts and philosophy.

Professionally, Edi is an award-winning engineer and was a consultant to the petrochemical, oil and gas, transport, and construction industries. He was Project Manager and Head of Design for major innovative projects such as the Channel Tunnel, London Underground systems, and offshore installations. He also worked in safety and environmental engineering and management for several Royal Navy projects, including the Queen Elizabeth Aircraft Carrier and the fleet of River-class offshore patrol vessels.

A student of the perennial philosophy for over half a century, Edi has given courses and lectured extensively in the UK, and internationally in California, the Netherlands, India, and Australia. He has organized and chaired conferences in order to encourage the cross fertilization of ideas in the fields of science, religion and practical philosophy. He worked as Education Manager for the Theosophical Society in Australia developing courses and study papers, researching, lecturing and organizing international conferences; as well as supervising the Research Library, National Media Library, National Members Lending Library and the development of the website.

Edi has published extensively in the disciplines of science, engineering and the esoteric philosophy. His book *The Snake and the Rope* was awarded a prize by the Scientific and Medical Network on which he now serves as a Board Director, and an Adviser to the Galileo Commission of the Network. Edi is also a Trustee and a Council Member of the Francis Bacon Society.

An enthusiastic glider pilot for many years, Edi is a choral singer and a dedicated pianist of concert standard.

Summary

The benefit of Edi's work in science and engineering is that it has enabled him to understand and approach interdisciplinary problems in an innovative, lateral-thinking manner under time and budgetary constraints. It has also provided the necessary team-working, supervision and management skills with the opportunity to actuate eternal principles on an organizational level, in line with his belief that spirituality is reserved not only for quiet retreats, but also applies to daily working life.

The outcome of Edi's involvement in music and the perennial philosophy is a discernment of the higher laws governing all life and existence, at all levels, and the necessity of striving to live with integrity according to this realization.

Foreword

David Lorimer

You hold in your hand a magisterial treatise, the fruit of a lifetime of careful study and reflection by a man who is also a consulting engineer and concert level pianist inspired not only by Liszt and Beethoven but also, in the context of this work, by Sir Isaac Newton and Erwin Schrödinger, whose scope as scientist and thinker was far greater and deeper than commonly understood. A glance through the detailed contents of the three volumes immediately gives the reader an impression of its comprehensive approach to the subject matter of what a human being is and what life is about.

Culturally, we are dominated—especially in the West—by science and technology with its prevailing philosophy that mind is an emergent property of matter and that everything can or will ultimately be explained in material terms. To doubt this proposition is to risk branding as a heretic and undermine one's reputation as a 'serious scientist', as many have found to their cost, notably in our time Dr Rupert Sheldrake, Nobel laureate Professor Brian Josephson FRS, Dr Peter Fenwick and Dr Eben Alexander among many others. This tendency is not new and can also be exemplified in the nineteenth century by attacks on such leading scientists as Sir William Crookes FRS and President of the Royal Society, Sir Oliver Lodge FRS, Alfred Russel Wallace FRS and Sir William Barrett FRS for their active interest in psychical research.

The Theosophical Society was also founded in this era—1875—and its three declared objects are highly relevant to this study, especially as the author has drawn deeply on this tradition, which he knows very well:

❖ To form a nucleus of the universal brotherhood of humanity, without distinction of race, creed, sex, caste or colour.

❖ To encourage the comparative study of religion, philosophy and science.

❖ To investigate unexplained laws of nature and the powers latent in humanity.

The second and third objects are particularly relevant here in the author's quest to bring together into a coherent framework key findings of religion, philosophy and science as well as investigating unexplained laws of nature and the powers latent in humanity in terms of subtle anatomy going beyond brain and physical body and exerting causal influence from the inside out. Our current scientific tendency is to examine everything from the outside in and assume that causality also operates in this manner in that matter gives rise to mind and brain to consciousness.

Historically, this reflects the 17th-century classification of quantitative and measurable aspects of reality as primary and qualitative or subjective aspects as secondary. As Michael Aeschliman points out in his book *The Restitution of Man* in 1983, this has momentous consequences in terms of what is now known as scientism, that is, materialism as an ideology: 'the ultimate effect of scientism is to dissolve the absolute qualitative distinction between persons and things—the very heart of the metaphysical tradition of *sapientia* — reducing persons to things, denying man's rational soul and his transcendence of the physical, giving him a value no higher than that of a camel or a stone or any other part of nature. This reduction of the human category to the natural runs parallel with a whole series of reductions from quality to quantity, from value to fact, from rational to empirical.' Scientists tend to take this new perspective for granted unless they become aware that scientism is in fact philosophy not science. One cannot get away from metaphysics, as Aldous Huxley observed in his book *Ends and Means* in 1937: 'it is impossible to live without metaphysics. The choice that is given is not between some kind of metaphysics and no metaphysic: it is always between a good metaphysic and a bad metaphysic'. What the author has in mind in this work is a more adequate and comprehensive metaphysic.

In his seminal work published in 1924—*The Metaphysical Foundations of Modern Science*— E. A. Burtt observes that 'just as it was thoroughly natural for mediaeval thinkers to view nature as subservient to man's knowledge, purpose and destiny; so now it has become natural to view her as existing and operating in her own self-contained independence, and so far as the ultimate relationship to her is clear at all, to consider his knowledge and purpose somehow produced by, and wholly dependent on her.' 'Natural' in this context means normal and taken for granted. Taking up this point, the historian and Orientalist Patricia Crone (quoted in *Sufism*, by Alexander Knysh, p. 231) says: 'People see things from their own perspective, much of what they say adds up to comforting ideas or outright propaganda for themselves and the groups to which they belong. They believe their own propaganda because they cannot see that this is what it is: the bias is invisible because the angle which produces it is felt as normal, not as a perspective peculiar to a special group (you cannot see it unless you stand outside it).'[i]

This is not surprising, as the historian Marshall Hodgson observes: 'Scholarly pre-commitments manifest themselves in the questions the scholar poses and in the type of category he uses, where, indeed, bias is especially hard to track down because it is hard to suspect the very terms one uses, which seem so innocently neutral.' The key phrase is the last one 'innocently neutral' as the lens through which one peers is naïvely assumed to represent underlying reality when it is precisely that: an abstract representation or model. A good example from modern neuroscience and philosophy is the formulation by the cognitive scientist and philosopher David Chalmers of the 'hard problem of consciousness' where he asks how the brain generates consciousness, thus implicitly assuming that the brain does in fact generate consciousness, which may not in fact be true as William James pointed out over 100 years ago when he observed that the relationship between brain and consciousness might not be 'productive' (the brain produces consciousness) but rather transmissive or permissive (the brain transmits or permits consciousness)—a view becoming more popular among cutting-edge neuroscientists and philosophers represented in such scholarly books emanating from the University of Virginia as *Irreducible Mind* and *Beyond Physicialism*.

The philosopher and mathematician Alfred North Whitehead FRS, FBA was well aware of the relationship between science and philosophy: 'Modern scholarship and modern science reproduce the same limitations as dominated the bygone Hellenistic people, and the bygone Scholastic epoch. They canalise thought and observation within predetermined limits, based

---

i Alexander Knysh, *Sufism: A New History of Islamic Mysticism*, Princeton University Press, 2017.

upon inadequate metaphysical assumptions dogmatically assumed. The modern assumptions differ from older assumptions, not wholly for the better. They exclude from rationalistic thought more of the final values of existence.' His key point is that the underlying philosophy or metaphysical assumptions constitute the predetermined limits he refers to and that these are dogmatically mostly unconsciously assumed, as C. G. Jung also warned when he said that the basic error of every worldview is its remarkable tendency to pretend to be the truth of things themselves, whereas it is actually only a name which we give to things. Hence an explanation—literally an unfolding—can only reflect the assumptions implicit in the question, as already noted in the example above of the hard problem of consciousness.

Whitehead introduces an important distinction relevant to this study between what he calls the observational order and the conceptual order. The observational order is 'constituted by the direct, immediate discriminations of particular observations' while the conceptual order 'is constituted by our general way of conceiving the Universe'—the central point here is that 'the observational order is invariably interpreted in terms of the concepts supplied by the conceptual order... We inherit in observational order, namely types of things which we do in fact discriminate; and we inherit conceptual order, namely a rough system of ideas in terms of which we do in fact interpret.'

The reader will find in these volumes a thoroughgoing and justifiably polemical critique of the conceptual order supplied by scientism as well as a systematic elaboration of a deeper and more comprehensive conceptual order based on the author's understanding of occult science and the principles of the perennial philosophy. Distinctive features of this work are comprehensive accounts of the universality of the perennial wisdom from the East and the West, ancient and modern, their self-consistent philosophy and methodology, and the manner in which they reveal the hidden laws and processes of nature that throw light on such areas as: paranormal phenomena, the subtle bodies of a human being, evolution considered from the mental and spiritual perspectives, death as transition and not extinction of consciousness, and most importantly, the nature of mind and the unfolding of consciousness from the implicate order to its explication in the world of matter.

The result is the re-establishment of the dignity of the human being and human life beyond the reductionist and mechanical categories of modern science. Importantly, this includes purpose, a category removed with Aristotle's final causes when science decided to focus on the instrumental and efficient causality of *how*, while at the same time eliminating the possibility of an ultimate *why* – thus effectively removing the qualitative, subjective aspect of human life, that is consciousness itself. The irony, not lost on such thinkers as Mary Midgley and Rupert Sheldrake, is that the formulation of scientific theories presupposes consciousness, as Descartes implicitly realised in his famous cogito – 'I think therefore I am'.

During the 1990s the author was a key member of the Science and Esoteric Knowledge Group of the *Scientific and Medical Network* (www.scimednet.org). The work of this group sought to extend the metaphysical framework of science to include consciousness, spirituality and so-called paranormal phenomena that are not amenable to materialistic explanations. In the brilliant analysis and exposition of this well illustrated and fully referenced work, the reader will find a comprehensive explanation of how religion and spirituality, science and philosophy can complement each other. He provides a systematic metaphysical framework that extends rather than contradicts science and its spirit. In doing so, he overcomes the limitations of materialistic scientism to introduce a wider and deeper context that is also meaningful in terms of the nature of human life. In this sense, this work is a magnificent work of metaphysical reconstruction and moral reorientation, a vital enterprise in our era of rising mental distress arguably correlated with the idea that economic prosperity and celebrity are the royal highways to happiness and that human life is merely a chance accident in an ultimately meaningless universe. The author demonstrates that this view is very limited and partial, providing a firmer and more extensive basis for a positive philosophy of life.

As he himself explains:

'1. nature is not simply a fortuitous concurrence of atoms that happened to self-assemble themselves according to blind, mechanical laws in the fullness of time;

2. since there are invisible and unseen worlds all under the governance of divine law that have barely been understood or approached by modern science;

3. moreover, there is an accumulated and uninterrupted wisdom that constitutes the archaic truths which are the basis of all religions and sciences since antiquity to the present day.'

Prepare to embark on an intellectual and spiritual odyssey that will open up new vistas and immensely enhance your understanding of many branches of science and philosophy as well as of the perennial philosophy and the deeper aspects of esotericism, symbolism, mythology, and allegory. I know of no other work of such scope and depth relating to the ultimate questions raised by human existence both in terms of our origins and destiny.

David Lorimer is Chair of the Galileo Commission and International Programme Director of the Scientific and Medical Network, Editor of *Paradigm Explorer* since 1986, and author and editor of over a dozen books, most recently *A Quest for Wisdom.*

Outline Contents for the Four Volumes

Detailed Contents for Volume I

List of Illustrations and Tables for Volume I

Abbreviations

CW-'Volume number'	*The Collected Writings* – in Fifteen Volumes by H. P. Blavatsky, compiled by Boris de Zirkoff: Volumes I to VI, The Theosophical Publishing House, Wheaton, Illinois, US, 1988 (Third Edition) to 1975 (Second Edition); Volumes VII to XV, The Theosophical Publishing House, Adyar, Madras, India, 1975 (Second Edition) to 1991.
IU-'Volume number'	*Isis Unveiled* – Two Volume Set by H. P. Blavatsky, edited by Boris de Zirkoff, The Theosophical Publishing House, First Quest Edition, 1994.
KT	*The Key to Theosophy* by H. P. Blavatsky, Theosophical Publishing House, London, 1968.
ML	*The Mahatma Letters to A. P. Sinnett* (in chronological sequence), compiled, numbered, arranged, and annotated by Virginia Hanson, The Theosophical Publishing House, Adyar, First Edition, 1998.
NPB-'Volume number'	*The Notebooks of Paul Brunton* – in Sixteen Volumes by Paul Brunton, Larson Publications, for Paul Brunton Philosophic Foundation, 1984 to 1988.
SD-'Volume number'	*The Secret Doctrine* – Three Volume Set by H. P. Blavatsky, edited by Boris de Zirkoff, The Theosophical Publishing House, First Quest Edition, 1993.
STA	*The Secret Teachings of All Ages* by Manly P. Hall, Diamond Jubilee Edition, Los Angeles, Philosophical Research Society, 1988.
TSGLOSS	Theosophical Glossary by H. P. Blavatsky, Theosophical Publishing Society, 1892.
VS	*The Voice of the Silence* by H. P. Blavatsky, introductory by Boris de Zirkoff, The Theosophical Publishing House, Second Quest Edition, 1992.

For example, *CW*-XII means *The Collected Writings*, Volume XII.
Likewise, for *IU-*, *NPB-*, and *SD-*

Exordium

The Universe is a thought of the Deity. Since this ideal thought-form has overflowed into actuality, and the world born thereof has realized the plan of its creator, it is the calling of all thinking beings to rediscover in this existent whole the original design.
— *Friedrich von Schiller*

Our age is proud of the progress it has made in men's intellectual development… and certainly, we should take care not to make the intellect our goal. It cannot lead, it can only serve…This characteristic is reflected in the qualities of its priests, the intellectuals. The intellect has a sharp eye for methods and tools, but is blind to ends and values.
— *Albert Einstein*

The scientific picture of the real world around me is very deficient. It gives a lot of factual information…but it is ghastly silent about all and sundry that is really near to our heart, that really matters to us. We do not belong to this material world that science constructs for us.
— *Erwin Schrödinger*

Verily, just as serpents close their ears, so do men close their eyes to the light of truth.
— *Galileo to Kepler*

Man was not made for science, but science by man, who remains more and greater than his creations.
— *Sir Francis Walshe*

Indissolubly linked with thought and action, love is their common mainspring and, hence, their common bond.
— *Louis de Broglie*

Atheism is so senseless and odious to mankind that it never had many professors.
— *Sir Isaac Newton*

The commonest failing is the sectarian spirit in which people diminish themselves by rejecting others.
— *Gottfried Wilhelm von Leibniz*

By materialists I mean those who are, so to speak, mentally retarded by virtue of wilful refusal, despite all evidence, to admit the possibility of nonphysical life.
— *E. Lester Smith*

Science, especially through psychology, shines its brilliant light on the afterlife and instead of illuminating it causes it to shrink and die, revealing its core: anxiety.
— *Peter Atkins*, epitomizing the virtually unanimous belief of establishment science.

Consciousness does not vanish when the functions of the brain and body cease.
— *Ervin László*, exemplifying the burgeoning insights of enlightened science.

How wretchedly inadequate is the theoretical physicist as he stands before Nature.
— *Albert Einstein*

Thirty years have passed since I published an account of experiments tending to show that outside our scientific knowledge there exists a Force exercised by intelligence differing from the ordinary intelligence common to mortals.
— *Sir William Crookes*

Current mainstream science, however, makes unscientific assumptions, even while assuming that they make no assumptions. To take one example, there is no single shred of evidence that matter gives rise to consciousness.
— *Iain McGilchrist*

The inability to identify any physical location of memory in the brain is one of the greatest clues that materialism is a failed worldview.   — *Eben Alexander*

❧ ❧ ❧

By analogy with a pianist and a piano, the mind corresponds to the pianist and the brain to the piano. If either pianist or piano is inadequate, so will be the music.
                                                                                              — *D. M. A. Leggett*

Physical man is the musical instrument, and the Ego, the performing artist. The potentiality of perfect melody of sound, is in the former—the instrument—and no skill of the latter can awaken a faultless harmony out of a broken or badly made instrument. Physical man may … be a priceless Stradivarius, or a cheap and cracked fiddle, or again a mediocrity between the two, in the hands of the Paganini who ensouls him.
                                                                                              — *H. P. Blavatsky*

Man is essentially a permanent and immortal principle; only his bodies pass through the cycle of birth and death. The immortal is the reality; the mortal is the unreality. During each period of earth life, reality thus dwells in unreality, to be liberated from it temporarily by death and permanently by illumination.   — *Manly P. Hall*

Life, like a dome of many-coloured glass, Stains the white radiance of eternity.
                                                                                              — *Percy Bysshe Shelley*

❧ ❧ ❧

The visible world is part of a more spiritual universe [and] union with that higher universe is our true end.   — *William James*

Visible life is explained by the invisible causes.   — *Rudolf Steiner*

The realm of the unseen is the realm of cause. The realm of the seen is the realm of effect.
                                                                                              — *Ralph Waldo Trine*

The Universe is worked and *guided* from *within outwards*; and man—the microcosm and miniature copy of the macrocosm—is the living witness to this Universal Law, and to the mode of its action.   — *H. P. Blavatsky*

The whole course of evolution bears witness to the principle of dying for the sake of life.
                                                                                              — *Jalaluddin Rumi*

Give up thy life, if thou would'st live.   — *H. P. Blavatsky*

To strive for the unattainable, towards Truth, Beauty and Goodness—irrespective of how our weaknesses put restrictions on our endeavours—and to try to approach our Maker.   — *Franz Liszt*

There is no loftier mission than to approach the Godhead more nearly than other mortals and by means of that contact to spread the rays of the Godhead through the human race.   — *Ludwig van Beethoven*

In seeking out truth, a man is faced with many stones too heavy for him to overturn. But he should never leave untouched any stone that lies within his capacity to overturn.
                                                                                              — *Edi Bilimoria*

The soul of man is immortal, and its future is the future of a thing whose growth and splendour has no limit.   — *Mabel Collins* in *Light on the Path*

Science can discover many things but will never be able to fill the emptiness in the life of an individual, can never give him the knowledge of self which is essential to peace and happiness. In knowledge of Self alone lies happiness.   — *Manly P. Hall*

Truth is the offspring of silence and unbroken meditation.   — *Sir Isaac Newton*

The truth needed for immediate and provisional use may be learned from books and teachers, but the truth of the ultimate revelation can be learned only from and within oneself by meditation.   — *Paul Brunton*

Proem:
The Purpose and Justification for this Work

Three kinds of progress are significant for culture: progress in knowledge and technology; progress in the socialization of man; progress in spirituality. The last is the most important.

Dr Albert Schweitzer[1]

There is an ancient tale about a pretentious scholar who approached the Greek philosopher, mathematician, and astronomer, Thales of Miletus (624 BC–546 BC) hoping to baffle him with all sorts of bewildering questions about God, the universe, and man. 'What is the easiest of all things?' our sophist inquired. 'To give advice' came the reply from the Miletian sage.[i] Then hoping to wrong-foot the sage he asked, 'And what is the most difficult of all things?' 'To Know Thyself!' came the unequivocal rejoinder.

Ruins of forecourt of the Temple of Apollo at Delphi, where γνῶθι σεαυτόν (Know Thyself) was said to be inscribed

Image Credit: Babis Kosmidis/CC-BY-SA-3.0

---

i To which the writer would like to add: 'To cast opinions upon subjects of which one has very little knowledge, much like empty vessels making the most noise.'

Inscribed in the pronaos (forecourt) of the Temple of Apollo at Delphi are the words: 'Know Thyself' (Greek: γνῶθι σεαυτόν).[ii] The same aphorism has been rendered as 'Man, Know Thyself' by other Greek sages like Pythagoras and Socrates.

Self discovery counts above all else

This work is therefore not about giving advice! It is concerned with that most difficult of all injunctions which the worldly wise rarely bother to understand or to which they render but a shallow, surface meaning. But a considered response to this wise exhortation of the Delphic Oracle is worth infinitely more than all worldly riches because just these two (or three) simple words, whose brevity far outweighs their profundity, impart the clue to resolving the myriad problems that have beset humanity since the dawn of time. As affirmed in the epigraph, technical progress and the rapid dissemination of knowledge do indeed represent progress, likewise, the integration of our common humanity into our culture and society; but the most important progress of all is in the fundamentals of Self-discovery, that is, reading the Book of our own Life to discover our deepest, innermost core—who we truly are—as Albert Schweitzer OM (1875–1965), the German (later French), theologian, organist, philosopher, physician, and medical missionary in Africa was at pains to point out. Once we know ourselves deeply, we become more profoundly human because in that knowing we meet all other beings.

Since the dawn of time, the exhortation by sages of all ages and cultures to *know ourselves*, and thereby to know humanity and the world of which we are a part, is, of course, a perennial entreaty. It would be presumptuous indeed to profess to have found the ultimate dictum. However, we may claim in this work to have advanced a few small footsteps towards this supreme, but never-ending quest of Self-enquiry. But what is meant by the disarmingly simple injunction, 'Know Thyself'? Does it refer merely to our body, which obviously assumes that we are just our body and nothing else? Or does the totality of our being comprise our physical body as well as subtle bodies on higher levels than the physical—giving us form and expression at those levels—all subsumed under the guidance of an overarching master principle? This master principle, we aver, is none other than *Consciousness*. In this work then, we deal with the unfolding of Consciousness—the primary principle of all existence—and its expression through various bodies, subtle and material, on all planes of being from the divine and spiritual to the material and physical. Our scope of enquiry and terms of reference will embrace the universal, ageless wisdom and the corroboration of some of its tenets by modern science.

It is important to understand what is meant by the universal, ageless wisdom. This wisdom is known under a variety of terms, all conveying the essential meaning of eternal truth. This corpus of wisdom addresses the oneness of all life, and the intrinsic divinity of all that exists—it is the root of all religions, sciences, and philosophies that have burgeoned like magnificent fruits from the branches emanating from the central trunk of the Tree of Wisdom. As the term implies, it is the unbounded wisdom of all ages and all times; it can be discerned in the doctrines of the East and the West, from antiquity to the present. Amongst the many appellations given to this universal wisdom through the ages we cite: *philosophia perennis*, the phrase coined by the German philosopher, mathematician, historian, and inventor Gottfried Wilhelm Leibniz FRS (1646–1716), then adopted as the *Perennial Philosophy* by Aldous Huxley (1894–1963), the novelist and philosopher nominated nine

---

ii This version is according to Pausanias, the Greek explorer and geographer of the second century AD, who lived in the time of the Roman Emperors Hadrian, Antoninus Pius, and Marcus Aurelius.

times for the Nobel Prize in Literature;[2] the *religio perennis* by the Swiss philosopher and metaphysicist, Frithjof Schuon (1907–1998); the *Ancient Wisdom* ('ancient' in the sense of being eternal, or ageless, not obsolete); the *Eternal Wisdom*; *theosophia*, or *theosophy*; the *Mystery Teachings*; *Gupta-Vidyā*, the Sanskrit term meaning *Divine Wisdom*; and *prisca sapientia*, the Latin term for *sacred wisdom* used by one of the Royal Society's most illustrious presidents, Sir Isaac Newton (1642–1726, Julian calendar), in reference to this accumulated store of ancient wisdom. Rudiments of the *ageless wisdom* (another common term) may be found scattered among the folklore of aboriginals and so-called primitive peoples in every region of the globe; moreover, it informs the core teaching of the world religions and constitutes the matrix of the laws of science as we shall see.

The universal, ageless wisdom is known under a variety of similar terms

A more specific reference to this universal wisdom is *occult science*. The term *occult* simply means 'hidden' from the Latin 'to hide'; hence the science of the secrets of nature—otherwise known as the Hermetic or Esoteric Sciences. Alchemy is a science to which Newton devoted his life. It is an aspect of the universal occult science and means the *chemistry of the invisible, or hidden aspect of the laws of nature*. As the term 'occult science' is invariably misunderstood, we shall consider its meaning in depth as we proceed.

There is a strong overlap of meaning in the above terms, but there are also subtle nuances that convey fine differences and shades of distinction. However, to avoid confusion caused by a plethora of terms, 'Perennial Philosophy' in its original and authentic rendering of '*philosophia perennis*'—which is virtually synonymous with 'Eternal Wisdom'—will be used throughout this work as a generalizing term. (When a different term is used, it will be for a specific reason in order to point to a subtle distinction of meaning.) We have chosen this term over the others for two good reasons. First, the term '*perennis*' signifies the eternal nature of this Philosophy and its everlasting application to nature and to all people everywhere. The evergreen characteristic of perennialism was elegantly voiced by Dr Schweitzer.[3] He likened it to a tree that annually bears the same type of fruit—but never exactly the same fruit, symbolizing that the universal wisdom—ever One in essence—must periodically be given new expression and communicated in an updated idiom to suit the epoch in question. Second, in order to underline the attribute of 'love of wisdom' denoted by '*philosophia*', derived from the compound *philo-* 'loving' and *sophia* 'wisdom'. The *philosophia perennis* encompasses the Mystery Teachings imparted in the Mystery Schools of the arcane centres of learning of the Orient and the Occident, from ancient times to the present.

Perennialism ~ the tree of perpetual fruit

The underlying self-consistency and unity in the diverse expositions of the *philosophia perennis* are cardinal features to grasp. So, it is encumbent upon the writer to explain, carefully, what is meant by unity in the context of the *philosophia perennis* tradition.

The Meaning and Significance of Unity

The assumed unity of the *philosophia perennis* is not without criticism from some leading academics on the grounds that transpersonal psychologists—the American Ken Wilber (b.1949) being one—maintain that such a position, 'confines the multiplicity of spiritual expressions to a single, unilinear sequence of spiritual development.'[4]

A more robust criticism of the idea of the unity of the *philosophia perennis* comes from the British academic R. C. Zaehner (1913–1974), Spalding Professor of Eastern Religions and Ethics, elected to succeed the celebrated professor Sir Sarvepalli Radhakrishnan (1888–1975), who had resigned to become Vice-President (later President) of India. As stated in *The Routledge Companion to the Study of Religion*,[5] Zaehner rejects the view, maintained by some writers, most notably Aldous Huxley, that mysticism represents a common core or thread that can be discerned in all of the major religions of the world, both in the East and in the West; that hence, as the uniting factor behind all religions, mysticism therefore constitutes a perennial philosophy, which occurs in diverse religious and cultural settings throughout human history. Zaehner identifies three distinct categories of mysticism, namely:

Multiple academic categories of mysticism preclude *philosophia perennis* as a uniting factor

1. theistic (the experience of loving communion or union with a personal God);
2. monistic (absorptive experience of an undifferentiated unity transcending space and time);
3. panenhenic (nature mysticism, or experience of the oneness of nature, one's self included).[6, 7]

In his view, these categories are too dissimilar to be reconciled to a common core.

To debate the merits of Zaehner's arguments is not our purpose. But we are entitled to speculate as to whether Zaehner actually experienced any of the mystical states that he eloquently wrote about[iii]—and to supply a contrasting viewpoint from a Nobel laureate. In his celebrated lectures at Trinity College, Dublin, in February 1943, the legendary Austrian physicist Erwin Schrödinger ForMemRS (1887–1961) summarized the unique experiences of mystics throughout the ages thus:

Erwin Schrödinger perceives harmony of mystical experience

> The mystics of many centuries, independently, yet in perfect harmony with each other […] have described, each of them, the unique experience of his or her life in terms that can be condensed in the phrase: DEUS FACTUS SUM (I have become God).[8]

Any true understanding of the unity of the *philosophia perennis* and mystical experiences must therefore come from an *experience* (Schrödinger being one of the finest exemplars among scientists), and not from an academic approach to mysticism regarded as an object of intellectual study and enquiry.

Knowledge *in itself* far surpasses knowledge *about* something

---

In view of the above, what is meant by unity in the context of the *philosophia perennis*? It does not mean similarity, nor even the

Unity is attested through mystical experience; not by intellectual discourse

experience of being bound by a common purpose, like an army or a sports team. Unity is not the same as uniformity or unification in the sense of an amalgamation or union. Nor is it even a matter of consilience as defined by the American biologist and naturalist Edward O. Wilson (*b.* 1929) as 'literally a "jumping together" of knowledge by the linking of facts and fact-based theory across disciplines to create a common groundwork of explanation.'[9] Crucially, and paradoxically, unity in the truest sense of the term, admits of infinite diversity. Some analogies from mundane life may help to convey the meaning.

---

iii The writer vividly recalls a lecture by the Indian-born concert pianist, Cambridge scientist, and philosopher Phiroz Mehta (1902–1994) who recounted an incident after an erudite talk on yoga by R. C. Zaehner, when a diminutive Hindu lady from the audience asked, 'Have you actually *practised* yoga?' Being an honest man, the learned professor had to admit that he hadn't. This tale underscores the limits and the limitations of the intellectual–academic approach to religion and philosophy: *it is much easier to give a lecture on how to get to heaven, so to speak, than it is to heed the actual signposts and walk to heaven.*

Consider a necklace of several beads. The individual beads may be of different colours, shapes or sizes, but they are strung together as one entity. Unity does not lie in the common characteristics of all the beads (such as their roundness or hardness), but in the fact of the thread passing through all of them stringing them together as a complete entity—one necklace. Another example would be many writers dipping their pens into a common inkwell to write about a theme in common. Each would write in his or her own handwriting with possibly only a limited overlap of ideas with the others, but with the same ink. Here unity lies in the ink, not in the combination of various concepts or individual expositions in different languages. The ink is always *one* substance, the expositions from the same inkwell may be innumerable: thus, the One admits of the Many; and unity is open to plurality and infinite diversity. Finally, consider the individual bones of the human skeleton. No two bones are exactly the same, nor are they all held together by a single muscle or sinew. However, they all interconnect and interrelate to function as an organism. Unity here lies in the structure and functioning of the human frame, not in its individual components viewed in combination.

Unity subsumes diversity

Drawing upon these analogies, then, the individual expositions of the *philosophia perennis* are extremely varied in their content, focus, doctrines, and expression. Despite the extremely varied language and expression in widely different cultures and historical epochs over vast expanses of time, it is still possible to discern the single thread passing through them that reconciles and unites them as one universal and self-consistent body of wisdom on the common theme of spiritual awakening and realization. One of the finest examples of the underlying unity of the great religious paths of both West and East is the fundamental harmony between the enigmatic *Book of Revelation* and the *Sāṁkhya philosophy* of ancient India. This, and several other instances of unity, will become plain as we proceed, being a central theme periodically stressed throughout this work.

Reason and Justification for the Work

At this juncture, readers may quite justifiably ask three pressing questions:

1. Is there anything to replace the scope and power of science? In any case, doesn't science nowadays provide all the answers, and if not just yet, will it not do so soon, given the enormous strides that it is now making?

2. Aren't there enough books ranging from the popular to the academic, not to mention the abstruse, on this kind of subject already, so why do we need yet more books of this kind? What purpose does it serve over and above all others? What's so unique or special about this work?

Does science provide adequate answers?

3. And what message is this work trying to convey?

If Science Won't Eventually Provide Us with All the Answers, Then What Will?

In answer to the first question, we have only to look at the unhappy and frustrated condition of large swathes of humanity in the present strife-torn world to realize the disastrous effects of being without any kind of anchoring philosophy or moral compass in life.

Science and technology on their own are poor substitutes—holding out the promise of a sort of gilded dreamland of virtual possibilities which puts many people at the mercy of their passions and baser instincts for want of higher principles to guide their lives. The chaotic conditions now prevailing, exacerbated by negative journalism, should convince all, other than the most superficially minded, about the sheer inadequacy of the predominantly money-oriented, worldly philosophy of life. This secular approach to life, particularly in the affluent West, has been promulgated by the media and politicians as a utopia to aspire to. A higher philosophy must obviously be based on wisdom, not utilitarian ideologies.

The inner state of a person counts far more than outer conditions

This is the reason why none of the sages and philosophers from the Orient or the Occident, from bygone days to modern times, ever allowed the self-realization of truth to be sullied by the lure of an earthly utopia. They realized that true happiness is never the lot of the spiritually impoverished man. Neither did they waste their time and energy inventing technologies, social schemes or business models for dealing with the turmoil and malice of the world's politics, economics, and physical conditions at their own level. Each one of them saw with unerring insight that it was unregenerate man the world over— spiritually impoverished man—who was himself the prolific spawner of the ubiquitous cruelty and suffering around him; and so it is through man himself, through his character, not his acquisitions or possessions, that the way must be found to redeem the world situation: the way of truth, wisdom, and love—*the transformed man*.[10] However, none of these luminaries ever preached a diet of material poverty or self-mortification as the highway to truth. Supremely practical, they understood the value of material existence and its enjoyment; but their counsel was always the same: evils result from ignorance of our true spiritual nature—ignorance of SELF. Even though this knowledge of the inner, spiritual life was disseminated to the public mainly on the plane of the intellect (except for the deeper message reserved for the few dedicated disciples), the allegorical and metaphorical nature of the *philosophia perennis* is more than enough to convey a good idea of the true nature of life and the means for self-realization.

It is upon this realization that our true happiness depends. This in turn is contingent primarily on our inner condition and the way we think (witness the mindfulness programmes and happiness training courses proliferating in the West), and only secondarily on outward material and economic factors. One of many initiatives is *Action for Happiness* (AfH) founded in 2010 in the UK. His Holiness the Dalai Lama (*b.*1935) is its patron, and at the time of writing this work, it has a Facebook following of 475,000. Moreover, 59,000 people in 168 countries having taken its pledge 'to create more happiness and less unhappiness in the world around me'.[11] AfH has helped launch 'happy cafes' and 1000 happiness clubs all over the country, many in run-down areas. An American counterpart is *Project Happiness* which has 1.6 million Facebook fans. This movement seems to be gaining global momentum. What is the deep message? Clearly, this is saying, in a nutshell, that the more we know ourSELVES, the happier we will be.

Unsurprisingly, the movement has also attracted adverse criticism. One such criticism is to be found in an article entitled 'The sad truth about the Action for Happiness movement'. Written for a UK national newspaper by a reader in clinical psychology at the University of East London, it argues that it is a flawed assumption that the source of unhappiness lies inside our heads, and that the real problems are structural to do with income inequality first.[12] But this contention is symptomatic of a predominantly theoretical approach to psychology, especially from a sociological viewpoint.

Major Turnarounds in Science

As noted above, people these days tend to attribute the final word of authority to science: what science proves must be true and facts are only facts if they bear the stamp of scientific approval. But it is easy to forget (or conveniently dismiss) two important points. First, that science is a 'movable feast'. What was taken as gospel truth has been completely overturned in the light of new discoveries. The Polish physicist and Rockefeller fellow at Cambridge University, Leopold Infeld (1898–1968) put it in a nutshell when he said: 'Scientific theories arise, develop and perish. They have their span of life, with its success and triumphs, only to give way later to new ideas and a new outlook.'[13] There are innumerable examples on the large scale and in the miniature. Take the universe, once regarded as being static, it is now deemed to be expanding; Mars, once confidently declared by astronomers as being entirely arid, is now known to contain water and harbour microorganisms; moreover, it is actively being considered as a destination for future space tourism;[iv] in 1895 aeroplane flight was declared to be impossible by the President of the Royal Society of London (Lord Kelvin OM), but eight years later the Wright brothers took their home-built flying machine to the sandy dunes of Kitty Hawk and took off into the history books; molecular biology of the 1970s asserted that environmental factors and our thoughts cannot affect our genes, but epigenetics,[v] albeit mooted in the 1940s, is nowadays showing, increasingly, that this is simply not the case, that external and environmental factors can 'switch' genes on or off, controlling when and where genes are expressed. Many more such examples of major turnarounds in science are cited and fully referenced in this work.

Examples of significant U-turns in science

Science Itself Demolishes Scientific Materialism

The second point is the uncomfortable fact that this very science that has established the groundwork and laid the foundations of materialism has also provided the facts that have demolished scientific materialism—referring of course to quantum science. Simply put, materialism is the concept that regards physical matter as constituting the fundamental essence of the universe; hence *all* phenomena, including those of mind (such as thoughts, memories, and dreams) are entirely due to material agencies. The fatal flaws in this

Science is a series of closer approximations towards truth. There is no final terminus.

---

iv Grainy black and white images beamed back to Earth by the NASA Mariner 4 probe in 1965 showing a crated, lifeless surface prompted *The New York Times* to declare the Red Planet to be a 'dead planet'; but in 2004, NASA's rovers found evidence of ancient oceans and streams, and of ice beneath the surface; and in 2018, the car-sized Curiosity rover found organic deposits trapped in mudstone 3.5 billion years ago. NASA's Perseverance rover landed on Mars in February 2021 in order to study habitability on Mars, seek out signs of past microbial life, collecting and caching core rock and 'soil' samples, and preparing for future human missions by 2030. The rover carried the Mars Helicopter, Ingenuity, which may achieve a 'Wright Brothers moment' by testing the first powered flight on the Red Planet. Other high-profile missions have also reached Mars: China's Tianwen-1 is due to land a rover in May or June 2021 and the Emirates Mars mission achieved orbital insertion in February 2021.[14]

v Epigenctics is the study of cellular and physiological trait variations that are caused not by changes in the DNA sequence as in molecular biology, but from the interaction between genetic makeup and the environment (phenotypic variations).

contention of science will be developed fully in this work. But few scientists seem to be aware of (or will admit to) this subtle irony of fate, and that is because their approach is almost exclusively intellectual and so lacking in that higher intelligence that comes from the light of intuition.

But How Many Scientists Admit This?

It is therefore paradoxical, one could almost say comical, to see scientists spending their entire lives studying the universe and the structure of the atom, the intricacies of the plant and animal kingdom, and the nature of the human body and brain, all in the minutest, most painstaking detail, yet virtually oblivious to that which holds and reveals, within its deeper recesses, the greatest and most profound secrets of the universe—the nature of their own selves. Can it be said that doctors, nurses, and surgeons are ministering to the health of the whole person when they ignore the inner self and focus only on the physical body?

Whereas mainstream science can hardly disagree with what the best of science has discovered through its own methods of theoretical analysis and laborious experimentation, yet the deeper philosophical and metaphysical implications have barely penetrated the still predominant paradigm of science. Let us pause and look at the supreme irony of the current situation.

Modern Science Opens a Window on to the Perennial Philosophy

The two pillars supporting the edifice of modern science are relativity theory and quantum physics. When it comes to addressing the basic reality of existence (in line with the *philosophia perennis*, as we shall see later), both have contributed in no small measure to shifting the emphasis from matter to mind. Relativity—in particular, Einstein's famous energy-mass equation—has dispensed with the concept of matter and energy as an intrinsic, non-interconvertible duality. Furthermore, it has demolished the notion of matter *per se* as the primary stuff of reality, matter being regarded in this new physics as crystallized energy, so to speak. Energy can take the form of visible light, as from a light bulb or invisible waves, like radio waves. Hence, 'imprisoned light', or 'bottled-up waves' are other fanciful terms used to express the essential idea that matter is the form taken by energy and not an independent or distinct entity in its own right. As expressed by the English physicist, astronomer, and mathematician Sir James Jeans OM FRS (1877–1946), 'The tendency of modern physics is to resolve the whole material universe into waves, and nothing but waves. These waves are of two kinds: bottled-up waves, which we call matter, and unbottled waves, which we call radiation or light.' Regarding the so-called annihilation of matter, continues Jeans, 'the process is merely that of unbottling imprisoned wave-energy and setting it free to travel through space.' What then are the implications of this new physics? 'These concepts reduce the whole universe to a world of light, potential or existent, so that the whole story of its creation can be told with perfect accuracy and completeness in the six words: "God said, *Let there be light*".'[15] Now comes another seminal insight from the great scientist:

> The stream of human knowledge is heading towards a non-mechanical reality; the universe begins to look more like a great thought than a great machine. Mind no longer

Science demonstrates the non-materiality of matter

appears to be an accidental intruder into the realm of matter; we are beginning to suspect that we ought rather to hail it as a creator and governor of the realm of matter.[16]

The primacy of mind rather than matter was strongly endorsed by Jeans's contemporary, the English physicist, mathematician, Astronomer Royal, and Plumian Professor of Astronomy and Experimental Philosophy at Cambridge, Sir Arthur Eddington OM FRS (1882–1944). In his Gifford Lectures delivered at the University of Edinburgh between January and March 1927, Eddington pronounced:

> The universe is of the nature of a thought or sensation in a universal Mind.[17]

What is this saying about the old idea of the clockwork universe promulgated by post-Newtonian scientists like the French mathematician and astronomer Pierre Simon Laplace (1749–1827), but wrongly ascribed to Newton?

The discoveries of quantum physics, even more startling than relativity theory to the concepts of classical science, have recognized mind and consciousness as primary qualities (not as the products of matter) in order to make sense of quantum experiments. The founder of quantum physics, the German Nobel laureate Max Planck ForMemRS (1858–1947) says:

> As a man who has devoted his whole life to the most clearheaded science, to the study of matter, I can tell you as a result of my research about the atoms this much: There is no matter as such! All matter originates and exists only by virtue of a force which brings the particles of an atom to vibration and holds this most minute solar system of the atom together. We must assume behind this force the existence of a conscious and intelligent mind. This mind is the matrix of all matter.[18]

Quantum physics points to the primacy of mind

Another Nobel physicist, Hungarian-born American Eugene Wigner FRS (1902–1995) has declared:

> It will remain remarkable, in whatever way our future concepts may develop, that the very study of the external world led to the scientific conclusion that the content of the consciousness is an ultimate reality.[19]

Note, carefully, the words 'the scientific conclusion'. We could go on in this vein, but must rest our case with the words of yet another Nobel physicist, Erwin Schrödinger, mentioned earlier:

> Consciousness cannot be accounted for in physical terms. For consciousness is absolutely fundamental. It cannot be accounted for in terms of anything else.[20]

But that would imply that consciousness is an ultimate element of reality—a theme that will be taken up fully later.

If Not Materialism, Then What?

Note that the above statements are not saying that there is a realm of matter contained within that of energy, or waves: it is that the latter are the only reality and that matter is its form or appearance. Put slightly differently, there is no physical world contained within a non-physical world of consciousness and mind, but that there is *only* the realm of consciousness and mind with the apparently physical world an appearance, or form, of the mental world. All this is not a merely speculative hypothesis; it is based on the conclusions of modern science.

But have the profound implications coming from what may certainly be regarded as the triumph of modern physics percolated into the corpus of the scientific and the medical community? Unfortunately, they have not. Despite all these unequivocal assertions about the primacy of consciousness from legendary scientists based, not upon their conjectures, but upon decades of sophisticated theory and rigorous, repeatable experiments, the vast majority of scientists nowadays still regard a mechanical reality based on matter as the fundamental essence of the universe and existence. The logical corollary of this is that mind and consciousness are the products of material interactions. In the main, then, establishment science is still steeped in this materialistic and mechanistic paradigm. We shall consider in-depth its ontological basis as we progress, but in simple terms it advocates the viewpoint that all life and existence can be explained in terms of, and ultimately reduced to, the laws of physics and chemistry, which deal with physical matter and its interactions as the fundamental reality.

Contemporary
mainstream
science still
wedded to
classical
materialism

Neuroscience and neurobiology are burgeoning subjects of research and enquiry, spurred by the enormous advances in medical technology and brain imaging techniques, such as functional magnetic resonance imaging, computer tomography, and electroencephalography. Notwithstanding the benefits accruing from increased understanding of brain neurological mechanisms—not to be disparaged—this massive research effort is based on the materialistic assumption that the physical brain generates, i.e. produces, consciousness. Hence, by equating the mind with the brain there is currently a frantic effort to find a physical basis, or neural correlate of consciousness and mind (notwithstanding that in a series of interviews with great scientists published in *The Observer* in 1931, Schrödinger explicitly asserted that 'consciousness cannot be accounted for in physical terms' as quoted above). The very subject single-mindedly dedicated to the workings of the mind—neuroscience—is neglecting mind, its own *raison d'être*, wholesale. Are these scientists confusing or conflating mind with its mode of expression? But there are exceptions. Schrödinger was an all too rare example of a scientist who was also deeply versed in the philosophy of the Indians and the Greeks. Hence his assertions should be taken with utmost seriousness having the added weight of insight from the union of science with the *philosophia perennis*.

But other than such rare instances of scientists also steeped in the *philosophia perennis*, the mainstream scientist investigates innumerable natural processes empirically and is undoubtedly struck by the seeming intelligence and order that appear to underlie these processes; but he stops at this point and desists from asking the deeper question: 'Why?' Hence, he is unable to comprehend the inner significance of the process, or shirks from investigating further, for example, the American physicist John Wheeler (1911–2008) who refrained from enquiring into the deeper implications of the 'Many-Worlds' interpretation of the results of quantum experiments (which he himself played a major role in developing) because 'it carries too great a load of metaphysical baggage'.[21] (The Many-Worlds interpretation of quantum mechanics holds that all possible outcomes of quantum measurements are physically realized in some 'world' or universe. Accordingly, it posits that there are many worlds that exist in parallel with our own.)

By contrast, the knowledge gained through occultism (nature's hidden laws), albeit sometimes lacking the detailed and technical information forming part of scientific knowledge, makes our conception much more meaningful and richer by illuminating the inner guiding forces and intelligence which underlie all natural processes and phenomena. Recall

Planck's forthright scientific conviction that mind is the matrix of matter, the latter being the theatre of consciously directed force. His remarks were presaged, however, over half a century earlier by the principal founder of the modern Theosophical movement, the Russian philosopher and occultist H. P. Blavatsky (1831–1891) in *The Secret Doctrine*, a monumental tome of occult science, which affirms that the 'infinite divisibility of atoms resolves matter into simple centres of force, *i.e.*, precludes the possibility of conceiving matter as an *objective* substance.'[22] The great German Nobel physicist Albert Einstein ForMemRS (1879–1955) is reputed to have possessed a copy of *The Secret Doctrine* and was deeply struck by the above quote[23]—see the Endnote for more details.

Einstein's likely contact with occult science

Given Einstein's alleged familiarity with aspects of occult science through *The Secret Doctrine*, we need to take to heart his *philosophical* insights emerging from his theory of relativity. He beautifully illustrates the difference between what is true, and what is really true. In his own words:

> I think we often draw a distinction between what is *true* and what is *really true*. A statement which does not profess to deal with anything except appearances may be true; a statement which is not only true but deals with the realities beneath the appearances is *really true*. [All italics in original.]

> We can only know the relative truth; the Real Truth is known only to the Universal Observer.[24]

Einstein discerned universality of Truth above relative truths

Let us reflect on two major points arising from the above insight by the great scientist. First, who is the 'Universal Observer'? It is what is known by all sorts of names, such as the 'Almighty', generally referring to an omniscient deity, or that much misconstrued and overused term 'God'. From our standpoint it is Divine Consciousness, that state of Omniscience, or All-Knowingness, which is unconditional, eternal, and universal.

Second, what we can know about literally any subject is always limited by what we do not know and therefore have omitted. Such partial knowledge may be quite unavoidable and is certainly needed for practical existence. But the student of the *philosophia perennis* soon realizes, as did Einstein, that nothing can be known fully and for certain if it is studied, in however much detail, in isolation, without seeing it as a part of the Whole. This is the viewpoint of the 'Universal Observer'—and its relation to the Whole from which all things arise. *THIS, IN A NUTSHELL, IS THE WHOLE BASIS OF THE PERENNIAL PHILOSOPHY WHICH, TO REITERATE, DEALS WITH THE REALITIES BENEATH AND BEHIND APPEARANCES.*

Noumenal essences have more reality than their objective counterparts

The pursuit of intellectual knowledge for its own sake, which is so fashionably the way of science, is therefore alluring only to those who are not aware of, or choose to ignore, the inner life and the great mysteries of life that challenge us daily on all sides. To revert to the previous example, the frantic research nowadays to find a neural correlate of sensation associated with a physical basis for consciousness is concentrated almost exclusively on the physical brain—as if a human being, in his entirety, were nothing other than a brain walking on two legs. That most mysterious and sublimely intimate organ, the heart, is almost completely ignored (other than recent research into neurocardiology). The *philosophia perennis* the world over—whether we look to the Greeks, Egyptians or Indians—disseminates the cardinal teaching about the heart in relation to the whole constitution of the human being. But mainstream science chooses to disdain such teachings about the crucial role of the heart in our emotional, feeling, and conscious nature.

Exclusively intellectual knowledge can be sterile

How can science, then, ever hope to acquire even a partial, let alone a complete, understanding of consciousness by such neglect of the central organ in the human body? Dissecting with the scalpel or analysing with the intellect in limited areas is often confused with rigour. It has nothing to do with it. Rigour implies a complete understanding of the whole and the relation of the parts to the whole.

Nevertheless, science is here to stay. It would be both foolish and ungrateful to castigate its spectacular success willy-nilly. Our aim, therefore, is never to ignore or discard science but to raise it to a higher metaphysic, meaning a higher standpoint, in order to understand the 'how and why' and not just the 'what' of existence, something that will become much clearer as we proceed.

What Then is so Special about this Work Amongst All Others?

Regarding the second question, posed earlier, about the uniqueness of this work, it is the manner in which the diverse esoteric and spiritual traditions from both the West and the East (constituting the underlying worldview of the *philosophia perennis*) have been brought together and, when pertinent, interfaced with modern science. Accordingly, our overall approach has been as follows:

1. explaining the essence of the *philosophia perennis* in a modern idiom;

2. whilst supporting our affirmations by such evidence as is publicly available;

3. moreover, elaborating these ideas in a progressive fashion, applying its theories and facts with direct inferences, when possible, deduced from, and corroborated by, the evidence furnished by modern, cutting-edge science.

Philosophia perennis ~ the universal solvent

The outcome is a broadening and contextualizing of science beyond its existing metaphysical limitations to achieve a systematic, evidence-based *resolution* of much debated and unanswered questions in mainstream science, as also between science, religion, and philosophy. This is our avowed aim for which the writer has spared no pains, even at the expense of excessive pedantry at times, or labouring a point in order to underscore a vital matter.

What Central Message Does This Work Convey?

Moving on to the third question, the central message that this work seeks to convey, with concrete examples drawn from the *philosophia perennis* and the best of modern science, is that the so-called laws of nature are anything but blind or mechanical in character—rather, they are conscious principles (intelligently directed forces as Planck asserted) acting as the instrumental functions of Divine Consciousness. Hence, the universe is guided by intelligences at different levels of existence. This underlying, all-pervading, Divine Consciousness not only enables the exercise of the innumerable functions in the universe to happen, but also guides and co-ordinates the exercise of these functions in various spheres. This is why we find perfect co-ordination, harmony, symmetry, and *intelligent* direction and control everywhere in nature, and in the fine tuning of the constants of nature. Modern scientists fully admit this, but cannot explain why. The English physicist Stephen Hawking FRS (1942–2018), one of the leading modern-day theorists in cosmology, has calculated that at the time when the universe was one second old (and the temperature was then something like ten thousand million degrees), if it were not expanding at precisely the rate at which it was in order to produce the present universe (if in fact the rate of expansion had differed by one part in a million million), then either the whole expansion would have gone so rapidly that there would have been no opportunity for galaxies and stars to form or, alternatively, if the rate of expansion had been that tiny fraction slower, then the universe would have expanded and re-collapsed long before galaxies had a chance to form.[25]

Admittedly, the conventional scientist marvels at this spectacular phenomenon of nature but in attempting to seek an explanation, he resorts to some mechanistic theory to explain away what he cannot explain or hopes that one day science will find a physical explanation; or he thinks that by saying that these things are 'just natural' or 'just a coincidence' are sufficient answers. It does not seem to cross his mind that there is a correspondence with a higher Power, a relational connection between the Greater and the Lesser, or the Macrocosm and the Microcosm as, for example, in a power station where the electric current generated at a high voltage is then progressively stepped down to a lower level through transformer stations and supplied to users via a distribution network. By contrast, this correspondence between the Greater and the Lesser, otherwise known as the Hermetic Axiom, is a core teaching of the *philosophia perennis*. This recognizes the presence of Divine Consciousness presenting as Divine Intelligence ('universal Mind' in Eddington's terms) in the background of all natural processes. These processes are actuated under the direction of this Intelligence through the transforming agencies of Divine hierarchies of various grades acting along different pathways channelling the Divine Force. Each member of these hierarchies is an embodiment of a function, has a form and vehicle through which that function is performed, and has 'Divine electricity', namely, Consciousness and Power, as its guiding and propelling force.

Since time immemorial, sages and seers have all, without exception, unequivocally affirmed that the material arts and sciences are the mere shadows of Divine Wisdom. Moreover, they have maintained that only by penetrating the physical realm, to the innermost recesses of Nature in both her subjective and objective aspects, can man attain to reality and understanding and so achieve a true reformation of science, philosophy, and ethics. Therefore, one of the most important contributions of occultism in the study of deity, universe, nature, and man is the verifiable and demonstrable knowledge that, beside the visible and tangible world which we perceive through our physical senses, there are worlds of a subtler nature that can also be apprehended by means of subtler faculties which exist in an undeveloped state in the vast majority of people, but which have been refined to an extraordinary degree by those whom we call adepts and occultists. The methods and self-discipline required to unfold these latent faculties and contact these subtler realms have been laid down in detail in occult literature, but this is not the purpose of our work. However, the notion of such subtler worlds hidden within, above, and below the physical world is age-old. The so-called 'heavens' and 'hells' which the souls of men are supposed to inhabit eternally after death, depending on whether their earthly lives were virtuous or sinful, are nothing but popular versions of these subtler realms. Such distorted ideas are especially linked with orthodox notions of harsh judgement by a personal God involving punishment for the wicked in eternal damnation. Such things the writer regards as utterly nonsensical and pernicious, but since they are shrouded in vagueness, blind belief, and

Mind and intelligence exist at all levels

Character and inner life determine outer conditions and circumstances

superstition in popular mystical literature and conventional religious canons, it is not surprising that man nowadays, living as he does in an age of physical science, should regard mysticism and religion with deep suspicion.

Subtler realms exist in addition to the physical world

Be that as it may, it is the sure knowledge of the doctrines of the subtler and higher worlds, bequeathed to the modern world by the adepts of occult science, that have partly been corroborated by the discoveries of science. Moreover, this same knowledge has provided a reasonably clear idea about their nature, though much less detail about their content. We need to discriminate between nature and content. The former deals with the general meaning of the principles which underlie the character and dynamics of the subtler planes. This is easier to grasp than the latter, which concerns itself with detailed knowledge about the subtler realms, acquired by developing the inner faculties. As an extremely simplistic example of this distinction, it is much easier to describe the general principles of baking bread using flour, water, yeast, salt, and sugar than to detail the different proportions of these individual ingredients to make, say, a baguette, a bagel or a brioche.

What Then is the Particular Purpose of this Work?

Accordingly, this work is intended to fulfil a triple, interrelated purpose:

Restoring humanity to man is an urgent need in an age dominated by scientific technology

1. to point towards a deeper understanding of man's 'spiritual anatomy and physiology' (the physical aspects of which are, of course, marvellously served by medical science) in order to bring about a renaissance and restitution of what it means to be truly human;

2. to show how such insights into the subtle aspects of man provide an understanding of the constitution and functioning principles of the universe and nature because, as the legendary philosophers declared: 'Man is the Measure of All Things', meaning that man is the yardstick, or measuring rule, of the Universe;

3. to show that man and the universe, down to the minutest particle of matter, are imbued with consciousness, goal-orientated evolution, and purpose—all contrary to the dictate of scientific materialism, the irony of which was not lost on the British mathematician and philosopher Alfred North Whitehead FRS (1861–1947). In his Louis Clark Vanuxem Foundation lectures delivered at Princeton University in March 1929 he astutely observed:

> Scientists animated by the purpose of proving that they are purposeless constitute an interesting subject for study.[26]

Readership

This work is a trilogy aimed at the serious enquirer who genuinely appreciates the major contributions of science plus the immense worth of religions and philosophies in terms of our increasing knowledge of the world and advancement of human welfare. Such a seeker will primarily be driven by an unquenchable love of truth and the earnest desire to 'Know Thyself'. It is likely, but by no means a *sine qua non*, that he may belong to a university faculty or research department, say, in philosophy, the history and philosophy of science, or comparative and world religions; and he may also be affiliated to scientific, philosophical, or esoteric societies with an international outreach, such as the Scientific and Medical Network, the Institute of Noetic Sciences, the Temenos Academy or the Theosophical and Anthroposophical Societies. Such a seeker may already have undertaken considerable study and research, either personally or with an educational charity such as the ones mentioned above, on a wide range of topics embracing science and religion, philosophy and culture, but will eventually have realized that no single discipline has a monopoly on truth. Moreover, far from casting light on the intractable problems that beset humanity in an age of increasing mechanization, psychological distress, and uncertainty, partial truths and limited solutions tend to muddy the water. Having discerned such limitations the seeker may be frustrated that they do not offer an all-embracing philosophy of life or a moral compass to mitigate the difficulties of our age. For such reasons, he yearns for something overarching and eminently practical that integrates and synthesizes the tenets of science, religion, and philosophy. Furthermore, he looks for something which can be applied, rather like an algebraic formula of universal precepts, to respond to the most pressing needs of each individual. It is his belief that such precepts would resolve the interminable debates in science (our dominant paradigm) as also between science and religion on issues like evolution, purpose, destiny, the nature of consciousness, and what it truly means to be a human being as opposed to an animated robot or a biological machine.

Practical application of universal precepts must be sought

Such an earnest and intrepid seeker makes high demands, but they can be met in three stages corresponding to the three volumes of this work:

1. Volume I, appropriately designated *A Panoramic Survey – Science Contrasted with the Perennial Philosophy on Consciousness and Man*, provides an overall survey and appreciation of the field of enquiry. Whilst fully acknowledging the worth of science, its limits, and hence its limitations, the deeper questions of life and consciousness are recognized and laid bare. This then defines the legitimate boundaries of science and so establishes the need for invoking the perennial philosophy to provide the deficit that mainstream science, constrained by its philosophy of materialism, is unable to furnish.

   Outline of Volume I

   This entirely new way of looking at the world and human beings through the lens of the Mystery Teachings of diverse world cultures and epochs creates the hunger to probe still deeper into the nature of the human being and his consciousness beyond (but not excluding) the dictates of scientific materialism.

2. Volume II, *Peering Down the Microscope – Man's Internal Landscapes* will appease the seeker's appetite in large measure. But even for the most dedicated student of life, it is an overwhelming task to assimilate abstruse teachings on the inner governing principles of the human being derived from numerous weighty books from diverse cultures, religions, and philosophies. Accordingly, the mass of apparently contradictory, confusing and far flung doctrines, centuries old and modern, have been brought together in a comprehensive body of teaching that shows their overlap and unifying doctrine on such perennial issues as the subtle composition of the human being, the processes and dynamics of post-mortem existence and rebirth, and the infinite complexities of the human mind.

   Outline of Volume II

But this is not all. Encouraged by the hurdles that he has now crossed and therefore undaunted by the challenges lying ahead our seeker finally thirsts to be shown the entire spiritual and physical panorama: how the human being fits in to the grand scheme of the universe.

Outline of Volume III

3. Volume III, *Gazing Through the Telescope – Man is the Measure of All Things* will largely quench his thirst by explaining in a logical stepwise progression, the wider context of the human being in relation to the universe—the whole question of emanational emergence from the inner spiritual to the outer material. This will complement Volume II with insights drawn from symbolism and mysticism, supplemented by the deepest teachings of occultism on the nature of consciousness, how the human senses are the handiwork of Divine forces, and matters of human destiny, purpose, and immortality.

But we have yet to address the question as to why there should be an uproar about understanding ourselves in relation to the Divine and the universe. We have already alluded to the reasons; however, there is an especial and overriding motive as now explained.

Man, Know Thyself! But Why? What's the Point?

When we truly understand ourselves, we understand all our fellow human beings. Furthermore, we also understand the world and the universe, a statement which may seem ridiculous at first, but upon deeper examination will be shown to be true, since That which brought the universe into being also brought man into being. We are not talking of physical resemblances, but the laws, divine and physical, that underpin all realms of being. This will become plain as we proceed; however, this organic unity at the heart of the universe and man is the basis of the great Hermetic Axiom stated above, namely the correspondence between the Macrocosm, or the Greater, and the Microcosm, or the Lesser, which finds expression in sayings such as 'You are the world, and the world is you'.

As the great Canadian philosopher and occultist Manly P. Hall (1901–1990) avers, the oldest, most profound and most universal of all symbols is the human body. The Hindus, Egyptians, Persians, and Greeks considered a philosophical analysis of man's triune nature to be an indispensable part of ethical and religious training. The Mysteries (arcane teachings) of every nation since time immemorial teach that the laws, elements, and powers of

To know oneself is to know the world

the universe are epitomized in the human constitution; that everything which exists outside of man has its analogue within man. The universe, being immeasurable in its immensity and inconceivable in its profundity, is beyond mortal estimation.[27]

Consequently, recognizing the futility of attempting to cope purely intellectually with that which transcends the comprehension of the rational faculties, as Hall explains, the early philosophers turned their attention from the inconceivable divinity to man himself. It was within the apparently narrow confines of man's nature that they found manifested all the mysteries of the external spheres. As the natural outgrowth of this practice, a secret theological system was fabricated in which God was considered as the Grand MAN and, conversely, man as the little god. Continuing this analogy, the universe was regarded as a man and, conversely, man as a miniature universe. The greater universe was termed the

Macrocosm—the Great World or Body—and the Divine Life, or spiritual entity controlling its functions, was called the *Macroprosophus*. Man's body, or the individual human universe, was termed the *Microcosm*, and the Divine Life, or spiritual entity controlling its functions was called the *Microprosophus*.

Today mainstream science informs us that we humans are really quite insignificant creatures in the grand scheme of things. Albeit made of stardust, we are ultimately destined to become merely earthly dust in a purposeless universe.[28] That is certainly true of the mortal human body of each individual, but does such a forthright statement apply to the Human BEING?

This work argues and demonstrates that once the human state is understood, each human being will realize for himself his unique role in a purposeful universe guided by love and intelligence. Moreover, that the Human Being—a triumph of Nature—is a creature of supernal nobility and majesty whose future growth and splendour has no limits or limitations in terms of its own nature.

In her monumental work *Isis Unveiled*, H. P. Blavatsky summarizes the pagan concept of the *Human Being* thus:

> Man is a little world—a microcosm inside the great universe. Like a fœtus, he is suspended, by all his *three* spirits, in the matrix of the macrocosmos; and while his terrestrial body is in constant sympathy with its parent earth, his astral soul lives in unison with the sidereal *anima mundi*. He is in it, as it is in him, for the world-pervading element fills all space, and *is* space itself, only shoreless and infinite. As to his third spirit, the divine, what is it but an infinitesimal ray, one of the countless radiations proceeding directly from the Highest Cause—the Spiritual Light of the World. This is the trinity of organic and inorganic nature—the spiritual and the physical, which are three in one, and of which Proclus says that 'the first monad is the Eternal God; the second, eternity; the third, the paradigm, or pattern of the universe'; the three constituting the Intelligible Triad.[29]

Everything in the visible universe is the outflow of the Intelligible Triad

The truth of this tremendous maxim will gradually unfold as we proceed to unfold our story that man (like all other creatures) is the outcome of Divine Ideation and his body the product of Divine Forces sculpted by Divine Handicraft. This writer maintains that the plethora of health and social problems that currently beset individuals, societies, and nations would be greatly alleviated were this simple fact realized and acted upon, not from wishful thinking or hearsay, but through study and inner reflection.

I regard consciousness as fundamental. We cannot get behind consciousness. I regard matter as derivative from consciousness. Everything that we talk about, everything that we regard as existing, postulates consciousness. I regard matter as derivative from consciousness.

MAX PLANCK[30]

Endnote

Extracts from Jack Brown, 'Reminiscences – I Visit Professor Einstein' published in *Ojai Valley News*, Ojai, California in 1983.[31]

Jack Brown visited Albert Einstein in 1935 and records:

Einstein quotes from *The Secret Doctrine*

'I went upstairs to his study, and […] to my utter astonishment, a copy of Mme. Blavatsky's *The Secret Doctrine*, which sat at the far corner of the large desk.

"It's a very strange book [Einstein remarked] and I've even told prof. Heisenberg, my fellow physicist, to get a copy and keep it on his desk. I urged him to dip into it when he's handicapped by some problem. I'm astonished how much in keeping it is with modern Physics." He turned to a page with a paper slip in it. [Then, he said:] "I quote from *The Secret Doctrine* …

> This is sufficient to show how absurd are the simultaneous admissions of the non-divisibility and elasticity of the atom. The atom *is* elastic, *ergo*, the atom is divisible, and must consist of particles, or of *sub*-atoms. And these *sub*-atoms? They are either non-elastic, and in such case they represent no dynamic importance, or, they are *elastic* also; and in that case, they, too are subject to divisibility. And thus *ad infinitum*. But infinite divisibility of atoms resolves matter into simple centres of force, *i.e.*, precludes the possibility of conceiving matter as an *objective* substance. [32]

One thing I have learned in a long life, was that all our Science, measured against reality, is primitive and child-like—and yet it is the most precious thing we have."'

NOTES

1   'Ethical Culture' (Lulu Self-Publishing, 2017), 228, in Walt Martin and Magda Ott (eds), *Albert Schweitzer's Reverence for Life: The adventure of being true to yourself*, quoted from Albert Schweitzer, *Reverence for Life: The ethics of Albert Schweitzer for the twenty-first century* (New York: Philosophical Library Open Road, 2014). Reverence for Life is a translation of the German phrase *Ehrfurcht vor dem Leben*.

2   'The Nobel Prize' <https://www.nobelprize.org/nomination/redirector/?redir=archive/show_people.php&id=4397> accessed 24 October 2019.

3   Albert Schweitzer, *op. cit.*

4   I. Puente, 'Participation and Spirit: An interview with Jorge N. Ferrer', *Journal of Transpersonal Research*, 5/2 (2013), 97–111.

5   John Hinnells (ed.), *The Routledge Companion to the Study of Religion* (New York: Routledge, 2009).

6   'The Varieties of Mystical Experience: The theory of R. C. Zaehner', in Philip C. Almond, *Mystical Experience and Religious Doctrine: An investigation of the study of mysticism in world religions* (Berlin: Walter de Gruyter, 1982), 23–42.

7   R. C. Zaehner, in 'Mysticism', *The Stanford Encyclopedia of Philosophy* (31 July 2018), Section 4, 'Perennialism' <https://plato.stanford.edu/entries/mysticism> accessed 18 October 2020.

8   Erwin Schrödinger, 'What Is Life? On Determinism and Free Will' from The Tarner Lectures delivered at Trinity College Cambridge, 1956, in *What is Life?* with *Mind and Matter and Autobiographical Sketches*, foreword by Roger Penrose (Cambridge: Cambridge University Press, 1993), 87.

9   Edward Osborne Wilson, *Consilience: The unity of knowledge* (New York: Vintage Books, 1998), 7.

10 Marginally rewritten from P. D. Mehta, *The Heart of Religion* (UK: Compton Russell Element, 1976), 125.

11 The Happiness Movement, *Positive News*, 84 (first quarter 2016), 22–5.

12 *The Guardian*, 21 February 2012.

13 Leopold Infeld, *The World in Modern Science: Matter and quanta*, trans. Louis Infeld (Victor Gollancz, 1934), 231.

14 See: *The Week*, 20 March 2021, 15; 'NASA Finds Ancient Organic Material, Mysterious Methane on Mars' (7 June 2018) <https://www.nasa.gov/press-release/nasa-finds-ancient-organic-material-mysterious-methane-on-mars> accessed 24 March 2021; 'Mars 2020 Mission Perseverance Rover'

<https://mars.nasa.gov/mars2020/mission/overview> accessed 26 March 2021; 'Tianwen-1, China's Mars Rover and Orbiter Mission', *Planetary Society* <https://www.planetary.org/space-missions/tianwen-1> accessed 27 March 2021; Katyanna Quach, 'First UAE Interplanetary Probe now in Orbit around Mars – Two Craft from China, US near Red Planet, too', *Science* (10 February 2021) <https://www.theregister.com/2021/02/10/uas_mars_probe> accessed 27 March 2021.

15 James Jeans, *The Mysterious Universe* (Cambridge at the University Press, 1930), 37–8.

16 James Jeans, *op. cit.*, 1944 edn, 137.

17 'Reality', in Arthur Stanley Eddington, *The Nature of the Physical World* (1st edn, New York: The MacMillan Company and Cambridge: Cambridge University Press, 1928; repr. 1948), 273–92.

18 Max Planck: acceptance speech for 1918 Nobel prize in physics, quoted in Clifford Pickover, *Archimedes to Hawking: Laws of science and the great minds behind them* (New York: Oxford University Press, 2008), 417; *Das Wesen der Materie* [The Nature of Matter], a 1944 speech in Florence, Italy, Archiv zur Geschichte der Max-Planck-Gesellschaft, Abt. Va, Rep. 11 Planck, Nr. 1797.

19 Eugene Wigner, 'Remarks on the Mind-Body Question', in *Symmetries and Reflections: Scientific essays* (Bloomington: Indiana University Press, 1967), 172.

20 Erwin Schrödinger, 'General Scientific and Popular Papers', in Collected Papers, Vienna: Austrian Academy of Sciences, iv (Braunschweig/Wiesbaden, Friedr. Vieweg & Sohn, 1984), 334.

21 John Wheeler, *Some Strangeness in the Proportion: A centennial symposium to celebrate the achievements of Albert Einstein*, ed. Harry Woolf (Reading, Massachusetts: Addison-Wesley, 1980), 385–6.

22 *SD*-I, 'The Masks of Science', 519.

23 See Sylvia Cranston, *H.P.B.: The extraordinary life & influence of Helena Blavatsky, Founder of the Modern Theosophical Movement* (New York: G. P. Putnam's Sons, 1993), 605 n. 5. Whereas some senior members of the Theosophical Society have questioned the accuracy of this account of Einstein's possession of *The Secret Doctrine*, two more references are in: *The Journal of San Diego History* (San Diego Historical Society, summer 1974), 16, quoted in Sylvia Cranston (compiled and edited), *Reincarnation, The Phoenix Fire Mystery: An East–West dialogue on death and rebirth* (Pasadena: Theosophical University Press, 1994), 603 n. 56; Jack Brown, 'I Visit Professor Einstein', in *Ojai Valley News*, Ojai, California, 28 September 1983. Extracts from Professor Brown's conversation with Einstein in 1935 are shown in the Endnote. Brown expresses his amazement at witnessing *The Secret Doctrine* on Einstein's desk and records the conversation he had about it with Einstein, who also recommended the book to Werner Heisenberg.

24 Quoted in G. R. Jain, *Cosmology Old and New* (New Delhi: Bharatiya Jnanpith Publication, 1991), xxvi–xxvii.

25 'The Microcosm' and 'The Macrocosm', in Hugh Murdoch, 'The Universe, the Atom and You', *Theosophy in Australia*, 80/1 (March 2016), 15. Murdoch (1924–2015) was an Australian astrophysicist and reader in astronomy at the University of Sydney.

26 Alfred North Whitehead, *The Function of Reason* (Boston: Beacon Books, 1958), 16.

27 *STA*, 'The Human Body in Symbolism', LXIII.

28 Typically: Brian Cox and Andrew Cohen, *Human Universe & Forces of Nature* (London: William Collins, 2015); Peter Atkins, *On Being: A scientist's exploration of the great questions of existence* (New York: Oxford University Press, 2011).

29 *IU*-I, 'The Elements, Elementals, and Elementaries', 212.

30 *The Observer*, 25 January 1931.

31 Jack Brown, 'Reminiscences – I Visit Professor Einstein', *Ojai Valley News*, Ojai, California, 28 September 1983 <http://www.blavatskyarchives.com/brown/jackbrownoneinstein.htm> accessed 29 November 2019.

32 Quoted by Albert Einstein from *SD*-I, 'The Masks of Science', 519.

Introductory:
The Plan of the Contents and
Route Map

One thing I have learned in a long life: that all our Science, measured against reality, is primitive and childlike—and yet it is the most precious thing we have.

ALBERT EINSTEIN[1]

It is only a narrow passage of truth (no matter whether scientific or other truth) that passes between the Scylla of a blue fog of mysticism and the Charybdis of a sterile rationalism. This will always be full of pitfalls and one can fall down on both sides

WOLFGANG PAULI[2]

I maintain that Truth is a pathless land [...]. Truth cannot be brought down, rather the individual must make the effort to ascend to it. You cannot bring the mountain-top to the valley.... Again, you have the idea that only certain people hold the key to the Kingdom of Happiness. No one holds it. No one has the authority to hold that key. That key is your own self, and in the development and the purification and in the incorruptibility of that self alone is the Kingdom of Eternity...

JIDDU KRISHNAMURTI[3]

Having described in the Proem the justification for the work, what purpose it serves, and the intended readership, we now explain how we shall develop our theme and its contents. Given that we live in an age of science, it would be fitting to commence by enquiring into what success science has achieved in addressing the problems that we face in knowing about ourselves, referring of course to our inner nature, mind, and consciousness—the central theme of this work.

The Role of Science Today

It is something of a truism, but one that nevertheless bears repeating, that humanity owes a tremendous debt to modern science and technology. Sadly, this is something regarding which the fixated proponents of quasi spirituality do not accept. Such zealots indiscriminately denounce Western science and medicine wholesale on the one hand, and on the other hand, advocate their blanket version of unorthodox medicine and spirituality as the only viable alternative. Such people need to be reminded that it is science that has eradicated much disease through improvements in hygiene, sanitation, and drugs. Moreover, it is science that has enabled us to communicate with friends and family half way around the globe in a 'mouse-click' twinkling of an eye. Despite its sometimes poor press, Facebook has enabled literally millions of people all over the world to unite in endeavours like *Action for Happiness* and *Project Happiness*, see the Proem on page xlii. Science has not only illuminated the village street, but also illumined the village mind. Thanks to medical science, the dreaded smallpox, which ravaged human populations for millennia and claimed around 300 million lives in the twentieth century alone, was eliminated in the 1970s and is now virtually a forgotten disease. The Femtosecond Laser, which has a pulse duration in the femtosecond range (i.e., 10^{-15}, or one millionth of one billionth of a second) has recently brought micron level accuracy, needle-free and blade-free surgery to the public; it is hailed as one of the greatest advances in cataract surgery over the last quarter of a century. Furthermore, the scientific method of randomised controlled clinical trials has ensured that complicated surgical techniques and life-saving drugs administered can repeatedly be relied upon to perform exactly as required, hence avoiding any unpredictable results. In our lives, now so reliant upon technology and labour-saving gadgets, science has brought order and dependability, freeing up much time and energy that would otherwise be devoted exclusively to the daily chores needed to maintain our physical existence. This is a fact quite aside from the ethical questions which are synonymous with the observation, namely what are we now doing with the time that has been released to us and are we increasingly enslaved to technology?

It is also the case that whilst science and technology have solved many apparently unsolvable problems, both in modern times and in centuries gone by, the wisdom which should underpin their application has often been sadly lacking—thus, no sooner is one problem solved than another one is created in its wake. Hence today we see the future of our planet and its inhabitants weighing critically in the balance, on a veritable knife edge created by environmental degradation, pollution, and nuclear waste. The electricity that once brightened villages and cities is also used to power millions of television sets that provide fine programmes on current affairs, culture, and science for the discerning few, but in front of which millions (especially in the West) otherwise spend several hours a day escaping from life, hypnotized by facile, or even lewd, entertainment and a mind-numbing barrage of advertisements designed to fuel a consumerist, self-indulgent society. Computers, internet, and mobile phones have contributed enormously to our ability to retrieve vast amounts of information and share it with others anywhere on earth, but what we do with this information is governed by the richness, or otherwise, of our interior lives. We have already noted that Facebook has achieved tremendous success in uniting people of goodwill, but it has also been accused of hijacking private and personal data[4] or is used by unscrupulous subscribers to intimidate and incite teenagers and vulnerable people to commit crimes and violence. Moreover, there are 'diseases' associated with the computer as with the body. Like biological viruses affecting our bodies, the computer virus threatens our lives in numerous ways, viz. physical welfare, privacy, and financial security. Not a week passes without experiencing spam emails or media reports of serious cases of cybercrime involving hacking into the databases of international corporations or the records and private e-mails of public figures to steal personal information and financial data, or simply to cause mayhem. A comparatively recent case was the ransomware known as 'Wanna Decryptor', or 'WannaCry' that infected 200,000 machines in 150 countries in some three days and caused major disruption to National Health Service hospitals in England and Scotland.[5] It now seems that 'hacking towns' are springing up all over Eastern Europe. Some companies even have their own ' "customer service" departments.'[6] It is a matter of speculation whether antivirus software will become progressively ineffective in the elimination and quarantining of ever-smarter computer viruses and 'Trojans'. If so, this will mirror antibiotics that have been spectacularly successful in fighting infections for the last seventy years but are expected to be progressively ineffective in some twenty years' time due to super-bugs. The situation in this branch of medicine is now serious.

In a BBC programme, Dame Sally Davies FRS (*b.*1949), Chief Medical Officer for England said, 'The reason antibiotic resistance is such a worry now [...] is because we have an empty pipeline of new antibiotics, which is how we coped in the past.'[7] The BBC's Science Presenter added, 'It's conceivable that in 20 years, treatments such as chemotherapy and simple surgery will become impossible because they rely on antibiotics. We are facing a future where a cough or cut could kill once again.'[8] On 21 September 2016, the heads of state and leaders of delegations met to discuss the problem of antimicrobial resistance and together signed a United Nations declaration pledging to address 'the biggest threat to modern medicine'—the 'nightmare' and 'catastrophic threat' of resistance to antimicrobial (the agent, like an antibiotic, that kills microorganisms or inhibits their growth).[9] A 257-page report, published in April 2016 by the World Health Organization, concluded that 'alarming levels' of drug-resistant bacteria already exist in many parts of the world.[10]

Some drugs (such as penicillin) have achieved spectacular success in combatting sickness. But other kinds of drugs can produce side effects that outweigh their benefits—for example, the Type 2 diabetes drugs Avandia or Actos, which have caused patients to experience a deadly heart attack or stroke; or the psoriasis drug Raptiva, withdrawn from the market by the U.S. Food and Drug Administration after it received reports of brain infections and meningitis in patients taking it.[11] Much of this problem apparently stems from the overuse of antibiotics in the meat industry to sustain production, in turn driven by over consumption and consumerism.

In the mental health field the efficacy of drug treatment has also become questionable, as in the case of physical ailments. Here we tend to see more dramatic cases of side effects; and the drugs used to cope with depression, and similar ailments, seem to suppress symptoms rather than addressing the causes of problems. Mental health is now a serious issue. It is a sombre indictment of society, especially in the West, that a minister for suicide prevention has been appointed in England by the Prime Minister as the Government hosts the first ever global mental health summit.[12] But this is not surprising when we learn that a survey of 11,000 fourteen-year-olds, carried out in 2018 by The Children's Society, found that a quarter of girls, and one in ten boys, were self-harming.[13] Furthermore, a report in the British Medical Journal in 2017 found that self-harm among girls aged 13 to 16 in the UK has risen disproportionately by 68% in just over three years—and was three times more common among girls than boys; moreover, the same report concluded that those young people who self-harmed were at significantly increased risk of committing suicide. But under the strain of coping in the excessively pressurized times now prevailing, driven largely by social media and the attendant need to conform, life for them has become meaningless.[14] It does not take much reflection to be convinced about the impact of the COVID-19 pandemic on self-harm and suicide. Widely reported studies modelling the effect of the pandemic on suicide rates predicted increases ranging from 1% to 145%, largely reflecting variation in underlying assumptions.[15, 16] It is therefore clearly imperative that science policy-makers take action, as a matter of considerable urgency, to counteract the increasing dehumanization and spiritual starvation in society through excessive scientific materialism.

Can medical science cure all human ailments?

Why is mental ill health now on the increase despite advances in medical science?

Could Science Possibly be Missing Something?

In the light of the foregoing it becomes evident that there are invariably two sides to the scientific coin. Why is this? Could it be that:

1. Having now jettisoned religion, mainstream science by its own admission in addressing only the facts of the physical world, without any consideration of moral values, has no ethical signposts? Furthermore, could it be that it has no higher metaphysical understanding of the implications of its breakthroughs to guide its applications away from areas that are inimical to the human race when its discoveries fall into ruthless hands?

Do we hold that the universe and man are entirely physical, purely spiritual, or a compound of the two?

2. There is more to life than just the physical world and so by ignoring, or discarding, wider, deeper, and higher dimensions of existence, science is not understanding the whole picture? For example, if the mind were just another physical mechanism (as is commonly assumed), then why has orthodox medicine so far not been as effective in handling psychiatric issues as it has with addressing physical ailments?

3. If we accept the above, could the answer lie not in abandoning the fruits of science in the physical realm, but in raising science to a higher standpoint—a more profound vision where the physical/material world is seen as a phenomenon deriving from its noumenon (the true nature of being as distinguished from sense perceived objects) on the plane of causation?

4. Finally, if we agree that modern science concerns itself solely with the phenomenal and objective world, then it follows that it must have a limited, or partial, understanding of the totality of human nature, mind, and consciousness. Clearly, the corollary to this is that if we are merely our bodies, then our minds are just biological 'wet computers'—to use the current trendy phrase in neuroscience.

Perhaps all four factors apply in varying degrees depending on the context and circumstances in question. Nonetheless, given such a partial understanding of the wholeness of existence and the human being, science, in dealing with human problems, is bound to be incomplete in its approach and therefore prone to creating as many problems in the wake of those that it attempts to solve, as just exampled. This is not to deny the fact that unintended consequences in virtually all fields are universal. But they arise partly from not taking a systems approach, for example, in the case of mental health, where complex and multifaceted issues can be traced to systemic foundations.[17] This is because complex systems exhibit nonlinear and often unpredictable change. The so-called 'butterfly effect', the name coined by Edward Lorenz (1917–2008), the American mathematician and pioneer of chaos theory, is a good example. This suggests a sensitive dependence on initial conditions, such that a small change in one state of a deterministic, nonlinear system can result in large differences in a subsequent state of the system. In this wise, as the United States Army general, Stanley McChrystal (b.1954) states in his book about rules of engagement in a complex world:

A holistic, systems approach must complement reductionism

> Attempts to control complex systems by using the kind of mechanical, reductionist thinking […] tend to be pointless at best or destructive at worst.[18]

And it is precisely 'the kind of mechanical, reductionist thinking', whereby all nature and humans are reduced to mechanisms, that lies at the root of the *bête noire* and great annoyance to science—religion.

According to the profound humanist and physicist Max Planck:

> There can never be any real opposition between religion and science; for the one is the complement of the other. Every serious and reflective person realizes, I think, that the religious element in his nature must be recognized and cultivated if all the powers of the human soul are to act together in perfect balance and harmony. And indeed it was not by any accident that the greatest thinkers of all ages were also deeply religious souls, even though they made no public show of their religious feeling.[19]

How significant that a Nobel physicist and founder of modern science (quantum physics) should use the term 'deeply religious souls', reinforcing his point that 'it was not by any accident that the greatest thinkers of all ages' (Isaac Newton being another glowing example) were of such a predisposition.

Why have legendary scientists embraced religion?

Why, then, is it that having spurned religion in favour of its laudable aim of removing all beliefs, subjectivity, and personal bias, mainstream science has become its own religion, so to say? The writer means this in the sense of the exclusive focus modern science places on physical nature and objective facts, and its resistance to insights from all sources not strictly within the current scientific paradigm—pursued with a passion that is tantamount to religious zeal. Why has mainstream science in some ways turned into 'scientism'? Are scientists not 'serious and reflective' these days? Or is religion (in whatever guise) an indispensable component of the human soul, whether or not a scientist be a materialist and atheist?

The Nobel physicist Erwin Schrödinger, first mentioned in the Proem (page xl) and to whom we shall refer again, clearly understood the measure of what science cannot touch, without being anchored in a higher philosophy, when he declared:

> We do not belong to this material world that science constructs for us. Science sometimes pretends to answer questions in these [higher] domains, but the answers are very often so silly that we are not inclined to take them seriously.[20]

> The recognition ATHMAN = BRAHMAN [*sic*] (the personal self equals the omnipresent, all-comprehending eternal self) was in Indian thought [the Vedas and Vedānta] considered, far from being blasphemous, to represent the quintessence of deepest insight into the happenings of the world.[21]

The meeting of science and spirituality

> The unity and continuity of Vedānta are reflected in the unity and continuity of wave mechanics.[22]

Here we find the great scientist openly acknowledging the complement of Eastern wisdom to Western science, such that—

> … our present way of thinking does need to be amended, perhaps by a bit of blood-transfusion from Eastern thought.[23]

But along with this comes a warning:

> That will not be easy, we must beware of blunders—blood transfusion always needs great precaution to prevent clotting. We do not wish to lose the logical precision that our scientific thought has reached, and that is unparalleled anywhere at any epoch.[24]

A holistic enquiry must necessarily include man himself as part of the equation

So also did Max Planck realize the need to invoke higher domains when he explicitly stated:

> Science cannot [unaided] solve the ultimate mystery of nature.

Why?

> And that is because, in the last analysis, we ourselves are part of nature and therefore part
> of the mystery that we are trying to solve. Music and art are, to an extent, also attempts to
> solve or at least to express the mystery.[25]

This makes two points: first, that there are ways other than science 'to solve or at least to express the mystery'; second, and crucially, without knowing ourselves, i.e., the mysteries of consciousness, we cannot fathom the mysteries of nature of which we are a part. That is why the principal thrust of this work is concerned with that cardinal injunction of the sages: 'Man, Know Thyself'.

So What is the Underlying Message?

What is this telling us? Perhaps that there are three possible views of mankind:

1. that we humans are all biological machines, namely, animals, genetically pre-programmed with no free will in a deterministic, causally closed universe which is entirely purposeless;

2. that we are entirely spiritual beings;

3. that our essential nature is spiritual but presents some aspects that could be likened to a machine or behaviour that resembles that of the animal kingdom.

Readers who take the first view that our entire nature, our hopes and fears, aspirations and disappointments, genius and criminality, cruelty and compassion can all be explained perfectly by a linear extension to conventional physics and chemistry (i.e., by theories of matter in motion and the blind forces between particles), will in all probability have joined the ranks of several immensely powerful scientists on the international scene. These so called 'scientists' confidently pronounce that science will soon have the ultimate say-so on literally everything, such as proving beyond all doubt that there is no difference, in principle, between an animal, a computer, and a human being. Such influential boffins like the American inventor and futurist Ray Kurzweil (*b.*1948) working, predictably, for Google assuredly forecast that in just a few decades the technology that currently enables robots to simulate some mechanical functions of human beings will progress to engineer robots that match, or even surpass, human behaviour and characteristics in their totality.[26] Such readers had better close this work. Indeed, they may well have done so by now, quite advisedly, after reading Whitehead's witticism, quoted in the Proem, about the paradoxical situation of scientists obsessed with the purpose of proving that they are purposeless.

Readers must appreciate that science and spirituality complement one another

Other readers who believe that living the spiritual life is antipathetical to good science and the energizing of the reasoning and logical faculties, will be sadly disappointed by a work which is scientific as much as it is mystical, in the sense of seeking to explore the sufficient reasons for things. Spiritual aspirants are truly the most pragmatic of people.

But those who can perceive the indispensable need for both the spiritual and material realms of existence, invoking the mystical and intellectual faculties in their right proportion, will benefit from delving deeper into the subtler dimensions of the human being and the universe and their inter-relationship with the physical.

Layout and Content of this Work

Given the complexity of our subject and the density of material presented in this work, it would be useful to present a route map through its contents and outline the organization, purpose, and objective of the Chapters. This work comprises three Volumes, each addressing our theme from a particular angle and with a specific subject in mind.

Volume I: A Panoramic Survey – Science Contrasted with the Perennial Philosophy on Consciousness and Man

In line with Schrödinger's observations stated above, the overriding purpose of Volume I is to explain the scientific position on consciousness and the nature of the human mind; and then reveal the added insights to be gained from the *philosophia perennis*. This Volume also addresses reservations in the minds of readers about their persuasion: whom to 'vote for', so to speak, on questions about life, mind and consciousness. Should it be for mainstream science,[i] the *philosophia perennis*, or possibly both? It will soon become apparent that in making the case for embracing the *philosophia perennis*, what is needed is indeed an embrace, a true union of the *philosophia perennis* with science, not an either-or dichotomy or tussle between the two. Mainstream science and the *philosophia perennis* move in different orbits, but they have areas of overlap as well and it is important to recognize this. To this end, their respective paradigms, methodologies, and modes of thought are summarized, along with their attendant strengths and limitations, in the framework of their respective disciplines.

Justifying the case for the philosophia perennis

Volume I is written in two major sections, with two supporting Appendices. The first section, covering Chapters 1 to 6, constitutes the scientific portion with the principal objective of uncovering and exposing the shortcomings of mainstream science when faced with problems lying outside its legitimate bounds of expertise, notably on the nature of mind and consciousness; hence justifying the need for incorporating the *philosophia perennis* within the scientific ethos. The second section, comprising Chapters 7 to 9, explains the nature of the Mystery Teachings of the *philosophia perennis* and the insights that they provide as to the nature of the human being at all levels from the spiritual to the physical. The final Chapter is a recapitulation that provides the link with Volume II.

The subject matter of Volume I will now be outlined.

Abstract and sequential progression of Chapters of Volume I

The Chapters of this Volume have a natural sequential progression and interconnection. An abstract of each Chapter now follows.

Chapter 1 of the first section broadens the scope of the central theme, 'Who am I?' and the rejoinder 'Man, Know Thyself'. It invites the reader to set aside all that he has learnt

---

i 'Mainstream' as, for example, the science promoted by learned societies such as the Royal Society and international science journals like *Nature*. 'Science', also referred to as 'natural science', is, however, a term embodying a wide range of meanings. The Definitions in Volume IV provide an outline of the genesis of natural science, explaining its forerunner in natural philosophy, and the contrast between Western science and Eastern science in their respective philosophies and approaches to investigating nature.

over the years from books, discussions and lectures and, instead, to contemplate his own inner experience and what it means to be truly human. With notable and rare exceptions, mainstream scientists see human beings as sophisticated animals or biological machines and nothing more. On the other hand, artists, writers, and poets tend to acknowledge the spiritual, as well as corporeal nature, of the human being. Can science mature to embrace mysticism, religion, and art in a wider scope of enquiry, or has it become ossified—stuck within the confines of its own mechanistic approach? This exercise in self-reflection leads on logically to the next Chapter.

Chapter 2 presents the latest claims about the nature of mind and consciousness from science, and the arguments that neuroscience specifically puts forward to support its claims. Examples are given, from Nobel scientists, of diametrically opposed views about the role of the brain in regard to mind and consciousness. This dichotomy of views about the role of the brain from mainstream science provides the spur to a deeper enquiry into how a purely brain-based theory could account for the phenomenon of genius or child prodigy. Further examples are provided to show that robust evidence for phenomena, such as near-death experiences and the survival of consciousness after death, cannot be brushed aside on the grounds of hallucination or imperfect research data, nor explained based on purely mechanistic theories of the brain. This Chapter concludes with a summary of the principal flow of ideas that underpin the mainstream paradigm on mind and consciousness. Moreover it relates them to the perspective of renowned scientists and neurosurgeons who argue for and against the idea that neuronal activity is the only way of explaining the nature of mind and what it means to be human.

Chapter 3 is critical for the *raison d'être* of this work. It argues that it is not sufficient for science and neuroscience to make their categorical pronouncements regarding consciousness, mind, and brain without a full understanding of the paradigm upon which these assertions rest. Accordingly, terse accounts are given on the philosophy and metaphysical basis of materialism, and the requirement in science for causal closure associated with reductionism. This follows on to a discussion of the scientific basis of mind, and the promising trend nowadays to supplement quantitative science with a science of qualities. The historical basis and genesis of scientific materialism are summarized followed by their influence on the ontology and epistemology of science, and associated implications regarding a scientific theory of evolution. The natural fallout from the above arguments is the limits and limitations of science described in the following Chapter.

Chapter 4 concentrates on the limitations in the modern scientific outlook on mind and nature—phenomena that science cannot explain adequately. They include organizing fields, vitalism, and morphic resonance, along with phenomena like near-death experiences, remote viewing, and mediumship. It is explained how, and why, such phenomena have resulted in death-blows to materialism. Ironically, quantum science has cracked the hitherto exclusively materialistic paradigm of classical science, invoked the role of consciousness in an essentially non-material universe, and moved science close to the orbit of esoteric science. The paradigm shift has been such as to offer new vistas in subjects as wide-ranging as chemistry, telepathy, and the primacy of consciousness. Besides glimpsing the view through the cracks, its implications, in terms of what is meant by evidence and the pressing need for a science of qualities, are presented. The Chapter concludes by describing how the scientific establishment deals with anomalous evidence.

Not satisfied, however, with just a faint glimpse through the cracks of the exclusively materialistic philosophy, we need to strain our eyes to look further afield, as in the next Chapter.

Chapter 5 takes up the theme, set out at the close of the previous Chapter, about the dogma of scientism; then continues with a historical timeline showing the gradual breakdown of materialism. The question is posed whether brains are an indispensable necessity for intelligence. This leads on to a catalogue of the fatal flaws in a theory of mind and evolution based exclusively on Darwinism and thereby points towards the need for a broader science, not limited to the five physical senses. This 'enlightened science' is slowly coming to the realization that consciousness is not a fixed thing but has an elasticity, rather like a radio receiver that responds to a range of tuning frequencies. The far vistas that come into focus are summarized in terms of the various levels of consciousness. Given that there is the possibility of consciousness extending beyond the physical realm, the final Chapter in the first section of Volume I must obviously divulge the next step.

Chapter 6 opens the second section of Volume I. It depicts the brain processes of a person whose thinking is entirely materialistic, in contrast to someone who is able to explore the noumenal, as well as the phenomenal worlds. With respect to the latter, reference is made to Goethean Science in the West and *Jnana Yoga* (Yoga of the Mind) in the East. Both of these stress the need of a universal and holistic approach in contrast to the predominantly analytical thinking in mainstream science in the Western world. The seminal insights of psychology are shown to undermine the dogma that thought is solely a function of the brain.

This first section of Volume I has prepared the ground for the need of the Mystery Teachings of the *philosophia perennis* comprising the second major section in Chapters 7 to 9.

Chapter 7 presents an overview of the teachings imparted in the Mystery Schools that lie at the root of both Western and Eastern cultures. The location of these great centres of wisdom, and their emissaries, are also touched upon. A route map is provided to show how science, religion, philosophy, and culture are the tributaries fecundated by the stream of universal wisdom, or *philosophia perennis*.

A major portion of this Chapter comprises a necessarily meticulous explanation of terms such as esotericism, theosophy, and occult science. The reason is not difficult to fathom, since abstruse words conjure up meanings ranging from the absurd to the muddled and imprecise. More instructive than definitions, is insight into the origin of words. For this reason, and to counter foreign accretions which have grown up, like poisonous ivy, around their pristine essences, we elucidate the etymology of recondite words. This also furnishes a clue about their inner meaning at different levels and in different contexts. Having thus cleared the decks of prejudicial debris and clutter, we can proceed to the following Chapters to show the floodlight that occult science throws upon our understanding of man at all levels from the physical to the spiritual.

Chapter 8 commences with a careful description of the methods of science and occult science, emphasizing the fact that they are complementary and not antagonistic. Then follows an overview of occult science leading to summaries of key occult principles and essential characteristics. Particular stress is laid on the Hermetic Axiom—about the indissoluble relation and correspondences, at all levels, between the greater and the lesser, or the macrocosm and the microcosm. Three versions of the Emerald Tablet of Hermes are presented, including the translation by Sir Isaac Newton. A few examples of the operation of macro-microcosmic correspondences are outlined. What is further revealed in this light forms the context of the next Chapter.

Chapter 9 presents a condensed exposition on the nature of man from the Mystery Teachings of the West and the East, from archaic ages to the present century. These are the teachings of the Greeks and early Christians, the Egyptians, Persians, Indians, and the Americans of both continents. Contemporary Mystery Teachings are also included. The modern teachings of the Emerson era, namely, transcendentalism and the New Thought movement warrant a further section since these ideas were fermented during the early years of the Theosophical Society and resonate closely with the perennial wisdom that was disseminated through the latter. It is explained that from whatever corner of the globe these teachings emanate, their essential purpose is always to unfold the Inner nature of man, the various techniques, trials, and processes in the Mystery Schools all intended for that sole objective.

Having progressed this far, a *Recapitulation* should be welcomed. It is provided. Here we stress the need for a *science of consciousness*, not consciousness as a subject within mainstream science. Also explained is the meaning of soul and subtle bodies, in simple terms at this stage, thus providing a bridge for the full exposition in Volume II.

Volume I closes with two appendices. *Appendix A* provides a useful timeline showing principal milestones in the development of physics and cosmology in mainstream science from the middle of the nineteenth century (a time of extreme materialism) to the present age. This runs alongside what we have just referred to as 'enlightened science'. *Appendix B* provides a similar timeline for highlights in the parallel development in mainstream and enlightened life sciences, i.e. biology and evolution.

The overriding purpose and message of Volume I is to demonstrate that the realm of direct truth can be approached only by moving beyond, and rising above, the realm of intellect in which doubts and debates will always reign. The conclusions of science on matters that are not exclusively connected with the physical world are vitiated because they are based on the unjustifiable assumption that only the physical world exists. Consequently the experiments and mathematical inferences ensuing from this limited, and therefore limiting, perspective of science are tarred by the same brush.

Volume II: Peering Down the Microscope – Man's Internal Landscapes

Justifying the case for man's innate spirituality

Volume II is a microscopic exposition of man's complete constitution and nature—what is sometimes referred to in esoteric and occult literature as the 'Principles of Man'. As such, its purpose is to extend considerably the scope of Volume I on this subject. Here we progress well beyond general remarks about soul and spirit, or mind and consciousness, in favour of a detailed exposition of man's vehicles of consciousness (subtle bodies in modern parlance) on all levels from the spiritual to the physical.

Severely handicapped by a paradigm which confines itself to physical matter and, in consequence, the five physical senses which circumscribe what it 'knows' about matter, establishment science obviously has nothing to proclaim about the subtle, i.e., non-physical bodies—and so should desist from attempting to deny their validity. However, since time immemorial the sages, saints, prophets, and hierophants of the Mystery Schools of all cultures worldwide, have provided every possible evidence about the geography and contours of man's internal landscapes—his inner, subjective constitution and nature. This is something which has also been intuited by scientists possessed of an awakened mystical faculty. To this end, in order to show their commonality, we have drawn upon the profound occult doctrines, expressed in a modern scientific format, through the nexus with the modern Theosophical Society, and also from other great centres of learning. This has been supported by the pronouncements of legendary scientists who have progressed beyond the confines of physical science.

This Volume is written in three sections, with three supporting Appendices, and copiously illustrated. The *Preamble* sets the scene by briefly reviewing the message of Volume I focussing on the fundamental question of *who*, or *what* is man, and what is meant by mind and consciousness from the standpoints of science and occult science. The first section, covering Chapters 1 to 5, comprises major expositions from occult science on how man is constituted and how he functions. Such understanding provides the foundation for explaining death in terms of a change of state of consciousness, and not its extinction, as almost singularly promulgated by science. Accordingly, the dynamics of the cyclical transitional process—involving death, after-death states and rebirth—is explained and justified, along with the related phenomena of apparitions and phantoms. The second section, spanning Chapters 6 and 7, commences by clarifying common misconceptions that abound in a subject as abstruse as the occult sciences. This is followed by a comprehensive exposition on a major theme of this work, namely: justifying why the human being cannot be thought of merely as a bio-physical machine, nor the human mind equated with the brain, which in turn, cannot be regarded, even in principle, as 'just a computer'. The third section, comprising Chapter 8, draws together teachings from a wide range of sources, ancient and modern, from the West and the East, specifically to demonstrate their common origin in the *philosophia perennis*. Lastly, the *Coda* is a rather novel way of summarizing the contents of Volume II and the link with Volume III by way of two similes: the construction of a temple and man's structure and constitution; and the transmission of electricity and man's energies and nature.

The subject matter of Volume II will now be outlined.

Abstract and sequential progression of Chapters of Volume II

The Chapters of this Volume have a natural sequential progression and interconnection. An abstract of each Chapter now follows.

Chapter 1 of the first section is intended to dispel the confusion abounding in the vast literature on esoteric, philosophical, and religious matters on the composition of man. The main causes are differences in meaning between languages, thinking in dichotomies associated with literal interpretations without discerning nuances of meaning, errors of category, misperception of levels of meaning, and obscuring the content of a subject with its form of expression. These causes are individually discussed and are a necessary prerequisite to the following two Chapters dealing with man's constitution and nature—his occult 'anatomy' and 'physiology'.

Chapter 2 concerns man's constitution: man, as structure, that is, how he is constructed. We explain the significance of the basic twofold constitution of man into individuality (immortal Self) and personality (mortal self). We go on to discuss the rationale for their unfoldment into spirit and body, with soul as interface. Whilst it is acknowledged that man is a unity, we explore the fivefold and sevenfold constitution of man, ranging from the outer physical to the inner spiritual. This Chapter is supported by a detailed diagram and tabular summary.

Chapter 3 concerns man's nature: man, as process, that is, how he acts and is energized. 'Soul' is a word that is used so loosely in everyday speech that its meaning is distorted out of all proportion. For the avoidance of doubt, its meaning is defined at the outset. The unific nature of man is again stressed, but we continue to explore the dual, triple, quintuple, and septenary nature of man. Terminology is addressed so as to cleanse it from the modern accretions which have grown up around it. This Chapter also has a detailed diagram and tabular summary.

Chapter 4 deals with the three primary vehicles of consciousness through which man lives, functions, and has his being. These vehicles are described, first the two higher vehicles pertaining to the 'aura', a loose term whose meaning and function is explained; and then the brain consciousness. We discuss how and why the aura of a newly departed person can apparently materialize in the form of a seeming 'double' of the person during life. We note that in other cases, materializations appear to emanate from a higher source.

Chapters 2 to 4 provide a necessary foreground before detailing the process of death, and beyond, which now follows.

Chapter 5 presents an explanation about the three principal transitional stages involved in the cycle of reincarnation: physical death, post-mortem existence, and rebirth. It is demonstrated that contrary to the scientific dictum that death equals the extinction of consciousness, the *philosophia perennis* teaches that death is both transition and release from earthly bondage—not an extinguishment. The topic of apparitions is revisited with emphasis on how a strongly earth-bound nature can temporarily energize the post-mortem psychic vestures. The exposition draws on the occult doctrines presented earlier on the composition of man and his vehicles of consciousness. Further elucidation is provided from poetical and literary works of great stature, primarily the *Divine Comedy* by Dante Alighieri. Scientific and photographic evidence is adduced in support of some of the occult tenets. Post-mortem existence is commonly associated with 'heaven' and 'hell'. These terms are emotive; therefore no effort is spared in clarifying their meaning and significance. A major section is devoted to explaining how the fate of an incarnation depends on whether the connection between the personality and Higher Self is maintained and strengthened or weakened and severed. Since this is a complex Chapter, it is fully illustrated and closes with a summary and postlude.

Chapter 6 opens the second section of this Volume. It is concerned with clarifying numerous misconceptions that abound on topics such as the meaning of soul and the associated distinction between soul and spirit, the dual nature of mind, and whether man is just an animal, or whether he has some characteristics of mind unique to himself. The last topic is of such importance that the whole of the next Chapter is devoted to it.

Chapter 7 disperses the fog of mistaken ideas by shining a floodlight on the pivotal questions,'Who, or What Am I?' and relatedly, 'Does my Mind have Unique Characteristics that Distinguish it from an Animal or a Computer?' We ask whether the brain is just a 'wet computer' or a 'biological computer made of meat'—two commonly used colloquial phrases to convey the mainstream neuroscientific idea that there is fundamentally no difference between the way the brain and the computer operate. We approach this subject by describing what the brain-equals-computer analogy purports to show, and then unravel the philosophical weaknesses in this simile. Concrete cases are given to demonstrate the breakdown of the computationalist argumentation. Specific examples are cited of how scientists of impeccable standing are treated by their colleagues when the former dare to question the inviolability of materialistic theories about mind and consciousness, human life and evolution. We suggest a way forward to resolve the brain-versus-mind conundrum and close with the question of whether robots will eventually overtake humanity.

Chapter 8 opens the third section of Volume II. On the question of man's 'internal landscapes', we have consistently maintained that the *philosophia perennis*—whether from the West or the East, either ancient or modern—is essentially one Wisdom in essence. This is now demonstrated by summarizing major teachings that both complement and corroborate the detailed exposition in Chapters 2 and 3 on man's composition, based on the core occult doctrines disseminated through classical Theosophy.[ii] These supplementary teachings are: (*a*) the diverse expositions during the period of classical Theosophy, the post-classical era, and subsequent teachings based on the Theosophical tradition; then (*b*) from the East: the Buddhist, Vedānta, and Tarāka Raja-Yoga systems of India; and the Egyptian, Indian, and Zarathuśtrian (Zoroastrian) teachings; and (*c*) from the West: the Greek and Pauline traditions; the Fourth Way School; the twentieth century Anthroposophy of Rudolf Steiner; and modern transpersonal psychology from Ken Wilber, et al. The unity amongst these various doctrines should demonstrate forcefully that the composition of man is the distilled wisdom of the ages and no fanciful conjecture of any one individual or religion. The different approaches to the composition of man are celebrated and the recommendations of Gottfried Leibniz for establishing a framework to reconcile contrasting philosophical systems, while rejecting what is false, are examined.

The *Coda* to Volume II draws together the core precepts of the occult teaching on the complex and multifaceted features of man's complete makeup. The insights of three celebrated scientists are shown to lend support to the edifice of occult science on the composition of man and the nature of mind: from the English Nobel laureate in neurophysiology and President of the Royal Society, Sir Charles Sherrington OM (1857–1952); the Austrian Nobel physicist, Erwin Schrödinger (1887–1961); and the British philosopher, author, and educator, C. E. M. Joad (1891–1953) who openly declared his admiration for the trailblazing ideas of H. P. Blavatsky (1831–1891), the principal Founder of the Theosophical Society. We show how the conjoined function of desire and mind acts as the pivot linking the immortal and mortal parts of man.

The construction of a temple comprising the foundation, apex, and internal storeys is used as a simile for the physical, spiritual, and soul components of the constitution of

---

ii 'Theosophy' is capitalized to distinguish between theosophy—*theosophia*, or the *philosophia perennis*—and its modern expression through the Theosophical Society—see Volume I, Chapter 7.

man. The transmission of electricity from a power station to domestic houses, via trans-formers, is used as a simile to describe how the Divine Self energizes the physical body via the three soul components. This makes the case that the man of flesh becomes man *in toto* only when soul and spirit are conjoined in the same way. To draw a parallel, a building of bricks and mortar in vacant possession becomes a temple when it is occupied and energized by a living human being.

Volume II closes with three appendices:

Appendix A provides robust evidence from numerous academic, peer-reviewed scientific journals in support of the existence of an ether (the postulated medium required for the propagation of light waves through space, not considered possible in a vacuum)—a precept of occult science—the existence of which has supposedly been disproved for all time by mainstream science at large on the basis of the 1887 Michelson-Morley experiment.

Appendix B supplies more details about the function and role of the mysterious bridge that connects the two levels of the mind. If mainstream psychiatry were to take on board this important teaching of occult science, it would facilitate an understanding of the causes of problems of the split-personality type, typically the bizarre 'Jekyll and Hyde'[27] phenom-enon where the same person, virtually instantly and with little or no prior warning, displays vast and aberrant changes in moral character and behaviour from one situation to the next.[iii]

Appendix C explains the main contributory factors towards a conformist mindset in some sections of the Theosophical Society, and in other spiritual societies with similar aims and outlook. This tendency has, unfortunately, impeded insights from other sources especially on the subject of the occult composition of man.

This part of the work also makes our case cogently that occult science comprising, as it does, the wisdom of all ages, is unavoidably an enormous subject. Thus, it demands a holistic approach based on universality of enquiry, which clearly cannot be constrained to a single exposition, however erudite the latter may be. Hence, a one-track purist approach is neither sensible nor true to the spirit of the esoteric and occult tradition. This is our reason for stressing the importance of teachings from other great streams of learning not directly connected with the Theosophical Society, whilst showing their confluence and nuanced differences with the latter.

Volume III: Gazing Through the Telescope – Man is the Measure of All Things

Volume III is a telescopic exposition of the role of man in the overall scheme of the universe and nature. Written in three sections and fully illustrated, it explains how, and why, the wisdom and powers that have gone into the whole universe have gone into the making of man, including the human body. The core of this narrative is a detailed account of the derivation of the human senses: how a physical sensation can result in an internal experience.

---

iii The highly intuitive author displayed strong intimations of occult truths in his novel. This is fully explained in this Appendix and in Chapter 5.

The Preamble reviews the findings and implications of Volumes I and II; then elucidates the perceptive faculties that must be engaged in order to discover a new way of knowing and experiencing the subtle vistas of man and the universe that are hidden from ordinary sight.

The first section, covering Chapters 1 to 4, concerns one of the keys to wisdom—symbolism, the language of the Mysteries. Numerous demonstrations follow of the insights accruing from symbolic representations of the unity of Cosmos, Nature and man. The human body and its organs are also considered.

The second section, comprising Chapters 5 to 9, is of crucial importance and supplies the key to the adage, 'Man, the Measure of All Things'. We demonstrate this is by explaining the significance and operation of the Hermetic Axiom. This was described in general terms in Chapter 8 of Volume I, but here we deal in detail with the mirroring and correspondences between the macrocosm and microcosm, i.e., the greater and the lesser, or the divine and the human. This leads to a detailed treatment of the unfolding of consciousness, the derivation of the human senses, how external stimuli to the physical senses result in internal subjective experience, and the role of divine forces in the human body, especially in relation to the awakening of dormant faculties of consciousness.

The third section, comprising Chapter 10, commences with a major exposition on evolution that considerably extends the scientific viewpoint, constrained by materialistic concepts, into the realm of spiritual evolution, destiny, and purpose. Robust evidence is given on the origin and vast antiquity of man from findings (hitherto suppressed) in palæontology and archæology that corroborate the Vedic doctrine in contradistinction to Darwinian theory. The state of enlightenment is outlined and supplemented with a simple meditational technique based on the world-travelled English sage and philosopher, Paul Brunton (1898–1981)—that illimitable disciple of the peerless Indian saint, Ramana Maharshi (1879–1950).

Chapter 11 is a comprehensive summary of the complete work on the principal theme of consciousness and its unfoldment, as seen by science and the *philosophia perennis*. The vital role of science is contrasted with its shortcomings and an account given of what it truly means to think and work in the spirit of science. Thereafter, the attributes and precepts of the *philosophia perennis* are condensed and tabulated as a prelude to the assertion that Consciousness is the ultimate Element of existence.

The Epilogue briefly surveys the status of science and spirituality in contemporary society, then explains the obligation to choose between one of two paths in life in order to address the question uppermost in the mind of every human being—immortality, and how it may be attained. The Mathematical Codicil to this Volume amplifies the earlier expositions on how mathematics alludes to the fundamentally mental nature of the so-called physical world.

The subject matter of Volume III will now be outlined.

Abstract and sequential progression of Chapters of Volume III

The Chapters of this Volume have a natural sequential progression and interconnection. An abstract of each Chapter now follows.

Chapter 1 of the first section concerns symbolism—one of the universal keys to wisdom and the idiom of the Mystery Teachings. As this is a subject that abounds in misconceptions, we commence with a clear statement about the subtle differences of meaning in figurative language, such as: symbols, allegories, and similes. Thereafter, we show how universal symbols like the labyrinth, the forest, and the Philosopher's Stone, reveal the inner nature of man. This Chapter also includes a warning about the serious perils that ensue when symbols are interpreted literally or misinterpreted.

Chapter 2 concerns the unity of Cosmos, Nature, and Man, represented symbolically through the zodiac and the Bembine Table of Isis, which latter displays a system of occult symbols depicting the rites and ceremonies involved in evoking theurgic or (so-called) magical powers. Also described is how the Tablet symbolically depicts the Hermetic Axiom—Cosmos mirrored in man—and how the two great zodiacs—the fixed and the movable—are correlated to the physiology of the human body. All this begs the question as to whether astrology is a pseudoscience. After explaining exactly what is meant by pseudoscience, we justify why astrology (understood and applied in its rightful context) should be regarded as a royal science. This Chapter flows in a natural sense into the next one explaining the basis of the adage: 'Man, the Measure of All Things'.

Chapter 3 takes up the theme of the human body in symbolism in greater detail. We describe the anatomical symbolism of the organs and members of the body. The three main body centres of consciousness are summarized. Then, we show how the current dogma in mainstream neuroscience, which dictates that the brain is the sole organ of consciousness, is slowly being eroded by evidence from the budding science of neurocardiology. This points to the primacy of the heart, and not the head, as the seat of consciousness in the human body. The Chapter ends with symbolic representations of occult powers in man and discusses how the symbolism of the Great Pyramid unveils the mystery of man.

Chapter 4 refers back to Volume II regarding the composition of man, namely, his occult anatomy and physiology. Here we show their representation in terms of the universal symbolism found in the sacred literature of the West and the East. We touch upon the symbol of the Mythical Tree and the Rosicrucian Rose; then in more detail on Padma, the Lotus; the Sephirothic Tree of the Qabbalah; and the Cube, one of the Platonic solids, all of which beautifully illustrate the unfolding of man's sevenfold constitution.

Chapter 5 opens the second section and is pivotal to this Volume. It comprises an in-depth treatment of the Hermetic Axiom, and closely related matters of analogy, correspondence, and correlation that show how diversity is subsumed in organic unity. The different shades of meaning between the overlapping terms 'analogy', 'correspondence', and 'correlation' are clarified. Thereafter, the fundamental principles behind analogy and correspondence are reduced to terms of consciousness and described in three steps. How these abstract precepts are discernible in all life and existence is then shown by the relations between the human principles with cosmos, the chemical elements, phase states of matter, colours and sounds. The Chapter ends by explaining why in Indian classical music, the instrument, known as the *Veena*, mirrors the divinity within the human body. A summary prepares the reader for further insights from the *philosophia perennis* on how Divine Consciousness is reflected in human consciousness and how human principles are the correspondences of analogous principles in the cosmos.

Chapter 6 presents an overview of the principal stages in cosmogenesis: the overall process of kosmic unfoldment on the various planes of manifestation, but here with a specific focus on man as the mirror of kosmos. The Chapter opens with a clear definition of terms to distinguish between their everyday use and their distinctive meaning in an occult context. This particularly applies to the terms 'kosmos' (spelled with a k) and 'multiverse', a relatively modern concept to which the former alludes. By invoking the Hermetic Axiom, the correspondences between Divine Consciousness and human consciousness are shown to be equivalent to the correspondences between the different kosmic and human planes. The process of kosmic unfoldment on seven principal planes is summarized and followed by a related account of *Akasha*, the subtle primordial substance that underlies all things. This provides a clue about the nature of Universal memory and memory in man. The next three Chapters constitute the summit of our enquiry into the unfolding of consciousness in the universe, nature, and man.

Chapter 7 is concerned with the principal stages in anthropogenesis: the coming into being of man from the Divine Self resulting in the human body materialized on Earth. How the human senses are derived from the cascading of principles at higher levels is detailed. The exposition is in two major sections. The first is a description of the process from the sacred writings of the Sāṁkhya philosophy of ancient India, mirrored by equivalent precepts from the New Testament of Christianity. The second shows the same process according to occult science. The harmony and internal self-consistency between the Eastern and Western scriptures and the occult system are shown to be unmistakable.

Chapter 8 addresses the issue of the mind–sensation problem. We show how occult science alone is able to resolve the major conundrum that currently plagues neuroscience: to discover a neural correlate of consciousness—how external and objective input to the physical senses of, say, electromagnetic waves on the retina or air waves on the eardrum, can result in an internal and subjective *experience* of colour or sound. Overriding factors that cause confusion are first considered followed by an account of the overall process of emanation from Divine Consciousness to the human being on Earth. As per the Hermetic Axiom, the correspondences and resonances between Universal Mind and individual minds, and how perception results in sensation, are detailed. The clinching issue regarding the 'conversion' of neurology into experience is then laid bare. The resolution of the mind–sensation puzzle is taken a step further in the next Chapter.

Chapter 9 describes the three primary divine forces in the human being and their role in awakening latent faculties of consciousness. The role of one of the divine forces that trans-mutes external physical sensation into internal experience is described in more detail along with robust scientific corroboration of the occult tenets. We explain the two chief glands in the human body that act as neural transducers of consciousness. Related to this is the whole question of the means of attaining super-physical powers like clairvoyance. Three such techniques, and their attendant dangers, for awakening powers normally latent in man are outlined. This is followed by an outline of a simple method to attain higher states of consciousness in safety. Finally, two examples are given of mathematical geniuses who demonstrated the faculty of unerring intuition commensurate with heightened consciousness.

Have we reached the end of our journey? Most assuredly not. We can only claim to have taken a few faltering steps with difficulty towards the ever-receding summit of all human endeavour—to know ourselves and thereby to unveil and express, by way of love and active service, the divinity latent in each of us.

Chapter 10 opens the third section of Volume III. It describes the landscapes of our unfinished journey. This journey is of course, evolution, limitless and never-ending. But a word that has become common currency tends to attract a fixed meaning; and evolution is taken to be virtually synonymous with Darwinian theory in mainstream science and therefore in the public eye. Evolution, however, is not as simplistic as the one-sided meaning ascribed to it. Accordingly, this Chapter opens with a careful definition of terms. Thereafter, evolution is described from the standpoints of Darwinism and the *philosophia perennis*, followed by the origin of man contrasted with these two perspectives. Subsequent sections provide robust evidence, from meticulous findings in palæontology and archæology, about the enormous antiquity of man. The related question of intelligent design is then discussed. The final sections of this Chapter elucidate the indispensable complement of occult science on the evolution of man. We propose a simple meditational technique that may help in raising consciousness and show how such an exalted state has a direct bearing on the state of genius.

Chapter 11 comprises a summing up of the entire work in three sections. Starting with science, its role is highlighted in terms of its two sharply divergent facets: the first being its inestimable contribution in alleviating personal suffering and adding immeasurably to the quality of physical life and existence, plus our understanding of the universe, nature, and the miraculous workings of the human body; the second, concerning the hidden side of the universe, nature, and man that science struggles to understand, but provides no satisfactory answers, leaving modern man in search of a soul. This section closes with an exposition on the business of science, qualifying the reasons why the true scientific spirit is deemed a rare quality. The principal attributes of the *philosophia perennis* are highlighted, leading on to general precepts and fundamental propositions, the latter expressed in three ways: through the idiom of occult science, Western science, and esoteric philosophy. The Chapter closes with the resounding message of the work that answers the riddle of life: CONSCIOUSNESS is the primal ELEMENT; that all its manifestations are energetic forms on different planes of existence and so all our joys and sorrows are experienced, by, in, and through CONSCIOUSNESS. This understanding leads naturally to a brief mention of destiny and purpose.

The final *Epilogue* brings our ever-onward and upward journey temporarily to rest. Here we touch upon the subject of man's yearning for immortality. Drawing together the cardinal themes of the three Volumes, we review the whole question of the inroads of spirituality into the contemporary predominating materialistic paradigm. We explain that mankind is faced with a choice of just two paths regarding the unfolding of consciousness. He must choose one path exclusively: he cannot journey on both, or a part of each contemporaneously, or sequentially. The two paths have a major bearing on the question of immortality: either the scientific endeavour of enhancement and preservation of the body through transhumanism and cryonics, or the spiritual way of constant renewal and refinement of the vestures of consciousness.

Volume III concludes with Mathematical Codicil. It provides a general appreciation, philosophical postulates, and actual examples of the power of mathematics to reveal a recurrent theme of this Volume, indeed, the *philosophia perennis*—the quintessentially mental, or mind-based nature of the world.

Should this Volume, or indeed the whole work, unveil, in however small a measure, the unlimited splendour and flowering of the potential within the soul of each man, the writer will be amply rewarded.

What Unique Insights and Features will this Work Provide?

We suggested in the Proem that contrary to the viewpoint of orthodox science that each person is ultimately doomed to dust and extinction of consciousness, the perennial wisdom affirms that each individual is a being of untold magnificence with no limits put on his evolution and the flowering of his consciousness. Summarized below are the overarching themes, and the questions that need to be addressed in upholding this claim:

Overarching themes

❖ *Overall clarity of definition and meaning*: Words in common use (and overuse) like 'soul' and 'spirit' are unambiguously explained • Abstruse and non-English terms are kept to a minimum but where unavoidable, their etymology and meaning are clearly defined. This is particularly the case where Sanskrit words are employed.

❖ *Science (natural science, or Western science)*: Its indispensable role in understanding physical phenomena • limitations in responding to deeper questions of life and existence • underlying metaphysical basis and associated assumptions • Dangers from the exclusively materialistic viewpoint on biology, morality, ethics, existential matters, mind, and consciousness.

❖ *Occult science*: Its meaning carefully explained • Philosophy and methodology compared and contrasted with science • Indispensable role in understanding phenomena outside the legitimate boundaries of science • Dangers from misuse • How the understanding of the universe and man is immeasurably enriched by blending occult science with the finest discoveries of modern science.

❖ *The Hermetic Axiom*: Although hardly acknowledged by mainstream science, the reasons why legendary scientists like Newton, and occultists, without exception, resort to the principle of, 'As above, so below' in order to plumb the secrets of nature and man.

❖ *Analogies and symbolism*: Their power in unveiling the hidden meaning of that which is virtually indescribable in plain language (albeit irrelevant for science which deals with factual definitions) • Why this is so, and what otherwise unfathomable secrets are brought to light.

❖ *God*: If a delusional concept, as some powerful scientists resolutely maintain, then why, besides religious and spiritual people, do other legendary scientists like Newton, Einstein, Schrödinger, Heisenberg, and Eddington (to name but a few) explicitly speak of a transcendent power • Why Newton said, 'Opposition to godliness is atheism in profession and idolatry in practice. Atheism is so senseless and odious to mankind that it never had many professors'[28] • If God exists, then precisely what do we mean by 'God'?

❖ *The unity of the teachings of the universal wisdom tradition of all ages and all cultures*: Shown by way of detailed tabular comparisons of the diverse traditions, highlighting their common factors and overlap.

❖ *World religions*: Their unity when scriptures are understood allegorically and in their esoteric sense (stripped of orthodoxy, dogma, and priestcraft) • The basis whereby all scriptures admit that there is but one Goal.

❖ *The arts in culture*: How music, literature, and poetry can point to the divine origin of the universe, the human being and the universality of mind • Why mystics and artists are often better equipped than scientists to understand the human state and condition, though the former may know little about the mechanisms of the human brain and body.

❖ *Why science is an indispensable ally of occult science*: demonstrated with examples of how some tenets of occult science have been verified by the theories and experiments of modern science.

❖ *Why occult science resolves intractable problems in mainstream science*: demonstrated with cases of many intractable conundrums in mainstream science (such as the nature of consciousness) resolved by invoking occult science.

Key questions addressed

Volume I: A Panoramic Survey – Science Contrasted with the Perennial Philosophy on Consciousness and Man

❖ *The scientific world-view*: What did the Nobel physicist Erwin Schrödinger mean by: 'We do not belong to this material world that science constructs for us'; and 'Science cannot tell us a word about why music delights us, of why and how an old song can move us to tears'?[29] • What kind of world, then, do we belong to, if not a scientifically constructed material world?

❖ *The ultimate promise of science*: Why do some highly influential contemporary scientists claim that materialism will ultimately explain literally everything about the universe, nature, consciousness, and the human being in terms of physics and chemistry; that science will prove that the universe is purposeless, and that God is a delusional figment of human brains, which in turn are nothing but complex machines? • In contrast, why did the father of quantum physics, Max Planck say: 'Science cannot solve the ultimate mystery of nature'?[30] • Is there another way to solve this mystery?

❖ *The 'soft' and 'hard' problems of consciousness*: Why the current heated debate between those that hold that consciousness produced by the brain is an epiphenomenon versus others who maintain that consciousness is primal and the brain its filter and transducer? • How does objective stimulus to the human senses result in subjective experience, e.g. how do external acoustic waves on the eardrum produce an internal *experience* of music? • What is a neural correlate of consciousness?

❖ *A New continent of thought*: Is there a gateway through materialistic theories? • How has quantum science cracked the hitherto exclusively materialistic paradigm of classical science and invoked the role, and (arguably) the primacy of consciousness, in an essentially non-material universe? Moreover, how has it opened up new vistas on the nature of matter, and moved science closer to the orbit of esoteric science? • Why are the occult sciences an indispensable complement to the physical sciences?

❖ *Reincarnation research*: Is there robust evidence on phenomena like near-death and out-of-body experiences, or modern research into reincarnation and claimed memories of former lives from cultures around the world, to counter the fixed verdict of mainstream science that the death of the brain means the extinction of consciousness?

❖ *Timeline of advances in science*: Is it possible to delineate the historical basis of materialism by showing parallel developments from the late nineteenth century to the present in mainstream and avant-garde physical sciences (physics and cosmology); and similarly in the life sciences (molecular and developmental biology, and psychology)?

❖ *The ubiquity of life throughout the universe*: What are the implications of recent scientific discoveries that point to a cardinal teaching of the *philosophia perennis*—that there is no such thing as dead matter and the universe is teeming with life?

❖ *The Mystery Teachings of the perennial philosophy*: How do the teachings from the main Mystery-centres of the Occident and the Orient, ancient and modern, throw light on that most difficult of all things—'To Know Thyself'?

Volume II: Peering Down the Microscope – Man's Internal Landscapes

❖ *Subtle bodies*: Whereas mainstream science regards any mention of 'invisible' bodies as delusional, why do esoteric and spiritual traditions worldwide, since time immemorial, afford them, and their constitution and function, every credence? • What is the truth?

❖ *Death and after*: If brain death signals the extinction of consciousness as mainstream science adamantly maintains, then why do virtually all religious and spiritual traditions mention the dying process, post-mortem states of consciousness, and rebirth? • Where does the truth lie?

❖ *Apparitions*: Science maintains that there is no reliable evidence for them, yet why do countless, perfectly sane people report spectral occurrences? • If apparitions exist, what then are they 'made of', under what circumstances do they manifest, and what detailed processes and mechanisms underlie such phenomena?

❖ *'Wet computers' and computers*: Is the brain no different, in principle, from a computer? • Are human beings essentially the same as lumbering robots? • Will artificial intelligence soon equal and overtake human intelligence as international computer scientists confidently predict?

❖ *The Mystery Teachings on the body, soul, and spirit of man*: Why do we find that the esoteric systems from antiquity to the present day, from cultures, philosophies, and religions worldwide show an essential unity and self-consistency, despite their varying views as to man's composition?

Volume III: Gazing Through the Telescope – Man is the Measure of All Things

❖ *Man is said to be the measure of all things*: Why is this? • Are there correspondences between cosmos, man, and nature? • Is it the case that man is primarily a spiritual being expressing through an animal body; therefore, that man is not merely the most complicated form of animal although he displays characteristics that are animal-like?

❖ *Paranormal phenomena*: How do we account for the mounting evidence on near-death experiences, out-of-body experiences, telepathy, and a host of other phenomena for which science has no satisfactory physical explanations?

❖ *Powers latent in man*: What are they, how can they be awakened safely, and what are the dangers of premature arousal by abnormal practices or using psychedelic drugs?

❖ *The unfolding of consciousness*: What is the relationship of consciousness and mind to the physical world? • Is there an overall process showing the movement from the unseen worlds to the physical world? • Can a stepwise account be provided of the processes and mechanisms resulting in subjective experience derived from objective sense perception of the external world? • Why does mathematics allude to the world as mental (not physical) in essence?

❖ *Evolution*: Is there a deciding factor to settle the impasse between creationism and Darwinism? • Is there a spiritual evolution for humans, besides the physical? • Did humans evolve from apes?

❖ *The question of immortality*: Is it the scientific standpoint of transhumanism and cryonics? • Or is it the spiritual perspective of the limitless evolution of the soul?

Common Features Running through the Work

Given the scope and complexity of material covered, the following principal themes that are recurrent throughout the three Volumes provide coherence, serving to knit together topics, disparate in themselves, into an organic whole.

1. Maintaining a universal approach to our theme, by which we mean not becoming fixated upon any one authority, or to any one book, individual or teaching (a common failing in spiritual societies—as we shall comment shortly). Indeed, a measure of the mettle and calibre of a true researcher is his ability constantly to question his pet assumptions, his psychological dependence on familiar ideas and his belief systems, otherwise the universe all too obligingly reflects back to the unwary whatever beliefs he projects onto it, supplying him with proofs of his own conjectures in a closed feedback mechanism. Providence may indeed have an ironic sense of humour! For this reason, a non-partisan approach is not only desirable, but indispensable to guard against an excessive predisposition towards any one doctrine. But this is not to say that we have desisted from drawing upon the wisdom of leading protagonists in the spiritual field—quite the reverse.

2. Recognizing in all realms of existence the manifestation of the Hermetic Axiom as regards the correspondence between the macrocosm and the microcosm.

3. Demonstrating the consistency of the fundamental precepts of esotericism of all ages and cultures, religions and philosophies—from the West and the East—since time immemorial to the present. The *philosophia perennis* attracts very little disagreement over fundamentals, but much that can provoke it.

4. Drawing upon the complete spectrum of classical and modern science especially in the narratives on existence, evolution, mind, and consciousness.

5. Contrasting the insights from science and occult science regarding evolution, life, and consciousness and the value of blending physical science with occult science, especially to raise science to a higher standpoint and metaphysic.

6. Drawing attention to the candid pronouncements from legendary, modern, scientists like Einstein, Planck and, especially, Schrödinger, regarding the shortcomings of current

physical science; hence the need to extend and transcend current scientific theories to deal with issues that lie outside its legitimate boundaries and field of discourse.

7. Distinguishing provisional knowledge and facts from enduring wisdom; discerning between appearances and reality, the transitory and eternal.

Our Treasure Trove of Wisdom and Approach to the Theme

Given the range and depth of material covered, readers will naturally want to know about our source references. On the scientific front we have drawn upon the latest academic and scholarly books and papers on the paradigm of mainstream science together with its various theories and dicta on the nature of mind and consciousness. This same approach has been applied to the discoveries and avant-garde ideas of eminent scientists on the world stage who have perceived the need to step beyond pure materialism and invoke theories about life and mind that may not have a physical basis.

Regarding the *philosophia perennis*, readers will have gathered that we shall be drawing upon the universal wisdom of all ages, from the West and the East, from antiquity to modern times. This might seem like a well-nigh impossible task but for a pearl beyond price bequeathed to humanity across the globe over a century ago—the onset on the world stage of the Theosophical Society. Through the literature and work of this Society a lot of the spadework has been done for us—namely, that of gathering together and presenting a coherent body of knowledge, in English, about those portions of the archaic Mysteries that are relevant to our age. This knowledge of the unseen realms is the birthright of humanity and has always been scattered far and wide through the folklore, religion, and philosophy of all lands and ages, such as mystic Christianity, Qabbalah, and Rosicrucianism in the West, and Zoroastrianism, Buddhism, and the Vedas in the East; but it has been scattered in the form of abstruse doctrines, symbolism, and in archaic languages to which few have had access.

Importance of a plurality of sources

Where confusion reigned, Theosophy has provided clarity, order, systemic structure, and a rational outlook enabling the student of occultism to acquire a clearer understanding of the processes of manifestation and the laws which underlie the universe, both seen and unseen. But this does not in any way mean that Theosophy has revealed everything. Far from it—the majority of facts have been withheld from an as yet unprepared public— that is to say, unprepared in the vast majority, even intellectually, let alone intuitionally. However, that which has lawfully been revealed has provided a good measure of clarity and certainty—but at a price. The penalty is that many Theosophists regard the classical Theosophical literature as the last word. Thus, progress and research has been vitiated and Theosophy converted by some of its zealots into a new kind of religious dogma which is the last thing on earth that the Founders of this great movement intended. To counterbalance this trend towards fossilization of doctrine by way of a universal approach is one of the aims of this work, as mentioned above.

An Historical Digression

Since we shall be drawing extensively, but by no means exclusively, upon the Ancient Wisdom, or *philosophia perennis* in its modern scientific idiom as presented through

Theosophy (a word that we shall fully define later), an historical digression is needed in order to show the approach to the subject that this writer has upheld.

We owe a debt to Western scholars and orientalists in bringing these abstruse teachings to the notice of the world at large, mostly in the form of translations. For example, an enormous debt is owed to the German-born philologist, scholar, and orientalist Max Müller (1823–1900),[iv] who was one of the founders of the Western academic field of Indian studies and the discipline of comparative religion. Müller wrote both scholarly and popular works about Indology (the study of Indian culture). *The Sacred Books of the East* is a monumental fifty-volume set of English translations, prepared under his direction.[31] Whereas such scholarship may have lacked intuitive insights by virtue of treating the subject in relation to problems of scholastic research, and failing to appreciate the profound truths enshrined in the outer form,[v] yet they brought a measure of order and structure; and, most of all, stimulated interest in doctrines thitherto unknown.

Also, at this time in the nineteenth century, science was ultra-materialistic and its precepts completely at loggerheads with those of the Victorian spiritualism movement and new religion movements, like Christian Science. On the religious front, the Christian missionaries in India made it their vocation to proselytize their dogmatic concepts of Christianity to the 'heathen Hindus'. The atmosphere at that time is beautifully illustrated by this quote from one of the principal Adepts behind the Theosophical movement:

> Between degrading superstition [of religious orthodoxy], and still more degrading brutal [scientific] materialism, the white dove of truth has hardly room where to rest her weary unwelcome foot.[32]

This fertile, but unsettled, mental climate supplied propitious conditions for the intellectual and spiritual uplift that came from the genesis, and subsequent glorious flowering, of the modern Theosophical Society; the means for the 'white dove of truth' to steer well clear of the two prevailing evils—the *Scylla* of religious dogma and superstition, and the *Charybdis* of scientific materialism—by demonstrating forcefully and with evidence, three facts:

1. that nature is not simply a fortuitous compound of atoms that happened to self-assemble themselves according to blind, mechanical laws in the fullness of time;

Multiple sources of wisdom are needed

2. since there are invisible and unseen worlds all under the governance of divine Law that have barely been understood or approached by modern science;

3. moreover, there is an accumulated and uninterrupted wisdom that constitutes the archaic truths which are the basis of all religions and sciences since antiquity to the present day.

The contribution of Theosophy and its various offshoots, like the Anthroposophical Society founded by Rudolf Steiner (1861–1925) and the Arcane School of Alice Bailey (1880–1949), to the intellectual and spiritual advancement of the West and the East, and

---

iv Max Müller was the son of Wilhelm Müller, the lyric poet whose verses Franz Schubert had set to music in his immortal song-cycles *Die Schöne Müllerin* and *Winterreise*.

v A good case in point is the endeavour to prove the existence of the continent of Atlantis by way of a literal corroboration of Plato's dialogues in *Timaeus and Critias* with archaeological findings in Crete and the surrounding islands.

its parental role in spawning related organizations with similar sorts of aims, cannot be overestimated. That is why we have drawn heavily on the foundational, or classical, Theosophical teachings (by Blavatsky and her Teachers) and their subsequent clarification and elucidation, where appropriate, by later generations of Theosophists, because these doctrines constitute by far the most comprehensive and thorough expositions on Man and the Universe[vi] that have ever been made available to the public. Hitherto they had been revealed in secrecy to the deserving few in the sequestered environs of ancient monasteries, temples or Mystery schools as in India, Egypt, the Americas and Greece. Amongst these later generations of Theosophists, the British social reformer and philanthropist Annie Besant (1847–1933) and I. K. Taimni (1898–1978), professor of chemistry and scholar of Yoga and Indian Philosophy, deserve particular mention. Besant was a chosen, personal pupil of Blavatsky and the Second International President of the Theosophical Society. This fact, coupled with her phenomenal social and charity work in England and India, renders Besant's writings and teaching refreshingly simple and direct compared to the extremely recondite classical writings. Most significantly, they also demonstrate, in a practical way, how occultism and the wisdom tradition can illuminate the problems of everyday life. Taimni offers the triple benefit of being steeped in the Theosophical tradition, a practical occultist and exponent of yoga, and a professor of chemistry. In this way he is exceptionally equipped to present occult science, and its relation to mainstream science, with thoroughness and rigour.

Whereas the Theosophical teachings constitute the backbone of our exposition, especially in Volume II, we have also drawn heavily from other streams, all taking their rise in the *philosophia perennis*, but not all being tributaries of Theosophical literature and doctrine. To this end, a large golden nugget from our treasure trove is the wisdom bequeathed by the Canadian-born philosopher and occultist Manly P. Hall who deserves especial mention since his emphasis has been on the Mystery traditions of the West, thus countering the false notion that the Western tradition lacks the preeminence of the Eastern doctrines. Then also, from Paul Brunton who supplied that much needed practical dimension to the abstruse Eastern teachings in eloquent language tailored to the Western psyche.

The Role of Teachers and Organizations in Pursuit of Spirituality and Truth

We mentioned earlier the imperative need to maintain universality of enquiry. It would be instructive to examine why this should be so in matters of spiritual teachings and the search for truth, especially as regards organizations and societies set up for that purpose. Let us learn from history: hindsight is always invaluable.

The great British astronomer Sir Bernard Lovell FRS (1913–2012) said, 'A study of history shows that civilisations that abandon the quest for knowledge are doomed to disintegration.'[33] We may surmise that the same would also apply in equal measure to organizations set up for a specific purpose, especially if that purpose be the study and dissemination of spirituality and truth. A similar warning was sounded forcefully over half

---

vi 'Man' and 'Universe' here capitalized so as to underscore the noumenal and subjective aspects as against the phenomenal and objective—see the Definitions in Volume IV for further elucidation.

a century earlier by the 'Father of American psychology', William James (1842–1910) in the words, 'It is a matter unfortunately too often seen in history to call for much remark, that when a living want of mankind has got itself officially protected and organized in an institution, one of the things which the institution most surely tends to do is to stand in the way of the natural gratification of the want itself. We see this in laws and courts of justice; we see it in ecclesiasticisms; we see it in academies of the fine arts, in the medical and other professions, and we even see it in the universities themselves. Too often do the place-holders of such institutions frustrate the spiritual purpose to which they were appointed to minister, by the technical light which soon becomes the only light in which they seem able to see the purpose, and the narrow way which is the only way in which they can work in its service.'[34]

James's words were echoed with utter directness and clarity over a quarter of a century later by the Indian philosopher and international speaker Jiddu Krishnamurti (1895–1986) in his opening address, on 2 August 1929, to more than three thousand people assembled at the annual Ommen Camp in the Netherlands[vii] of the International Order of the Star in the East, and with many thousands of Dutch people listening on the radio: 'I maintain that Truth is a pathless land, and you cannot approach it by any path whatsoever, by any religion, by any sect [...]' This is tantamount to saying that an individual must make his own personal effort to ascend to Truth,[viii] for Truth can no more be brought down to the individual than the mountain-top can be lowered into the valley. Therefore, Krishnamurti maintained that no organization, or outer structures, can lead man to spirituality because any organization created for such purpose, soon becomes a crutch, or a bondage, and 'must cripple the individual, and prevent him from growing, from establishing his uniqueness, which lies in the discovery for himself of that absolute, unconditioned Truth.'[35] (Refer to the third epigraph for other excerpts from Krishnamurti's famous 1929 speech.)

So, having paid glowing tribute to the Theosophical Society, can it be said that this Society has consistently upheld the search for truth, unfettered by bondage to concepts and dogma? The answer is a variable one.

But first note carefully this direct, clear, and unequivocal statement from the Principal Founder, H. P. Blavatsky, about never investing any teacher, or book, with sole authority, but cultivating the capacity to think for oneself, whilst maintaining a comparative approach to all learning:

> In its capacity of an abstract body, the Society does not believe in anything, does not accept anything, and does not teach anything. The Society *per se* cannot and should not have any one religion. Cults, after all, are merely vehicles, more or less material forms, containing a lesser or greater degree of the essence of Truth, which is One and universal. Theosophy is in principle the spiritual as well as the physical science of that Truth, the very essence of deistic and philosophical research.[36]

Truth cannot be imprisoned in a straitjacket

---

vii Krishnamurti held dialogues and gave public lectures in the grounds of Eerde Castle—Eerde being a hamlet in the Dutch province of Overijssel, part of the municipality of Ommen. The site became a German concentration camp during World War II and was never used by Krishnamurti afterwards.

viii Capitalized here to accentuate its undefined and unqualified aspect—that which would truly, in Krishnamurti's closing words at the 1929 Ommen Camp speech, 'set men absolutely, unconditionally free'.

This obviously means that if the Theosophical Society were to establish any one teaching (including Blavatsky's) as exclusive and authoritative, the individual search for Truth, freedom and liberty, so extolled by Blavatsky, would necessarily be stifled. Accordingly, Blavatsky has issued precisely the same warning as William James, her contemporary, and Krishnamurti decades later. What is more, Blavatsky's statement was reinforced by her star disciple, Annie Besant, in the words, 'To proclaim one person as an infallible authority on a subject unknown to the proclaimer, is to show fanaticism rather than reason. The Theosophical Society […] may be injured by the blind zeal of those who pin their faith to any one investigator and denounce all the rest.'[37]

But alas, some injury has been done because, as more than one senior Theosophist has observed, the Theosophical Society has become a victim of its own success. For example, the scientist and occultist I. K. Taimni warns us that 'the Eternal Wisdom is a transcendent Reality which cannot be poured into a mould, preserved [in formaldehyde] and then worshipped as a fetish.'[38] To do so simply flies in the face of the spirit of constant questioning and freedom of enquiry that the Founders and pioneering leaders of the Theosophical movement strove so mightily to inculcate. Sadly, this, in no small measure, is what has happened. Instead of striving ever forwards and seeking new avenues of research and updated, modern terms of expressing the ageless wisdom corroborated by the latest science, it has rested on its laurels with the result that the vital and living message has become congealed into dead-letter modes of interpretation: the outer form of words has predominated over their inner meaning. Jeanine Miller (1929–2013), born to French parents in Shanghai, was a Vedic scholar and senior member of the Society. She spoke about the dangers of parrot-like imitation of others, saying that, 'this note of devotion to truth, not to any personalities or set of doctrines or concepts, sounded by Madame Blavatsky and taken up by our leaders, is far too often overlooked;' and that 'left-brain rehashing of what others have said or written simply will not do.' Most importantly, 'the fountainhead of spiritual truth is not contained in any one, single book. HPB [Blavatsky] herself told us that *The Secret Doctrine* [her magnum opus] lifts only a corner of the veil—that it must be drawn out and lived through the human soul.'[39] Large hearted enquiry can all too easily degenerate into narrow minded sectarianism. Of course Truth Itself is immutable and therefore cannot be affected by whatever 'spin' we may put on it, but the manner in which it is interpreted is necessarily crippled by small minds.

The Theosophical Society: its fundamental ethos

On this theme, the progression towards orthodoxy that has taken hold of some sections within the international corpus of the Theosophical Society will be delineated. Since such conformist attitudes pertain largely to the classical Theosophical expositions on this subject, this discussion is reserved for Appendix C to Volume II on the occult composition of man. Nonetheless, human nature being what it is, the general principles, obviously not the specific details, would apply to all societies that commence with an earnest commitment towards discovering and promulgating truth and unity, but then, as James observed, frustrate their original, founding purpose when internal schisms leading to power struggles start developing, resulting in polarized viewpoints and rigid ideas driven by the mind-sets of those who seem unable to embrace a plurality of viewpoints and can think only in terms of dichotomies.

Truth is ever living; its expressions must be contemporary

Meanwhile, we round off this section by asking: are organizations and societies devoted to spiritual study and practice of little or no value? Not at all, but with a major proviso. In his radical 1929 speech, Krishnamurti continues, 'the moment you *follow* someone you cease to follow Truth' [emphasis added]. So, it is the unquestioning and whole-hearted following of an assumed authority, be it a person or book regarded as a gold standard, instead of using them as guides to facilitate one's own thinking, that is the real bar to Truth. As we would expect, such attitudes are prevalent in spiritual societies that by their very nature attract members of devotional dispositions. But the solution to the problem lies in an organization that encourages networking amongst its members along with special interest groups, rather than hierarchical structures with an identifiable head, thereby placing no constraint upon individual freedom of enquiry. Such let it be said, is the Theosophical Society when true to its mission. Another fine example is the modern Scientific and Medical Network[40] which had several senior Theosophist–scientists amongst its ranks during the first decades of its inception, like D. M. A. (Peter) Leggett (1912–1994), the British Vice Chancellor of Surrey University and fellow of Trinity College, Cambridge, and the British professor Arthur Ellison (1920–2000), Head of Electrical and Electronic Engineering at City University and Visiting Professor at Massachusetts Institute of Technology. The Network Co-Founder, George Blaker (1912–2001), was a senior British civil servant and also a member of the Theosophical Society.

In the light of the above, this writer claims that he has strenuously avoided a one-sided approach and drawn on the teachings of Theosophy, as well as several other wisdom-streams, as mentioned in the source references above, being well aware that the *philosophia perennis*, even if it be sown in the soil of materialistic thought, must continually find newer and richer expressions, albeit in the realm of the intellect. Therefore, to reiterate, to treat any book, teacher or doctrine as a creed and absolute standard of authority is tantamount to a betrayal of the *philosophia perennis* which is larger than any one of its manifold expressions.

Both the Proem and this Introductory cite quotes, by legendary scientists, about the triumphs of physical science. However, they also sound a warning note about its incompleteness and hence, by implication, the urgent need to appeal to a higher wisdom—the *philosophia perennis*. On just this theme, it is fitting to close this prefatory with the beginning of a speech (transcribed verbatim) written for the United Jewish Appeal, and delivered during the darkest years of the Second World War, by a legendary scientist, philosopher, and humanitarian:

> *Ladies and gentlemen,*
>
> *Our age is proud of the progress it has made in men's intellectual development. The search and striving for truth and knowledge is one of the highest of men's qualities— though often the pride is most loudly voiced by those who strives [sic] the least, and certainly, we should take care not to make the intellect our goal. It has of course powerful muscles but no personality. It cannot lead, it can only serve, and it is not fastidious in its choice of a leader. This characteristic is reflected in the qualities of its priests, the intellectuals. The intellect has a sharp eye for methods and tools, but is blind to ends and values. So it is no wonder that this fatal blindness is handed on from old to young and today involves a whole generation.*
>
> Albert Einstein[41]

When authority becomes a crutch rather than an intelligent guide

NOTES

1 'Albert Einstein in Brief', *American Institute of Physics* <https://history.aip.org/exhibits/einstein/inbrief.htm> accessed 22 December 2020. Quoted also in Jack Brown, 'Reminiscences – I Visit Professor Einstein', *Ojai Valley News*, Ojai, California, 28 September 1983 <http://www.blavatsky-archives.com/brown/jackbrownoneinstein.htm> accessed 29 November 2019.

2 Maria Popova, 'Nobel-Winning Physicist Wolfgang Pauli on Science, Spirit, and Our Search for Meaning', *Brain Pickings* <https://www.brainpickings.org/2019/03/13/wolfgang-pauli-carl-jung-figuring> accessed 24 December 2019.

3 Brief excerpts from 'Truth is a Pathless Land' speech delivered on 3 August 1929 at the Ommen Camp, in Mary Lutyens, *Krishnamurti – The Years of Awakening* (London: Rider, 1984), 272–5.

4 'Facebook in the Dock', *The Week*, 31 March 2018, 4.

5 'Microsoft Warns Ransomware Cyber-attack is a Wake-up Call', 15 May 2017 <https://www.bbc.co.uk/news/technology-39915440> accessed 25 October 2019.

6 'Meet the Woman who Hacks the Hackers', *The Week*, 12 October 2019, 58, extracted from Kate Fazzini, *Kingdom of Lies: Unnerving adventures in the world of cybercrime* (New York: St. Martin's Press, 2019).

7 BBC iWonder, 'Human vs Superbug: Too late to turn the tide?' [video] (16 May 2014) <https://www.bbc.co.uk/programmes/p01z6wxd> accessed 25 October 2019.

8 *ibid.*

9 Julia Belluz, 'What to Expect from Today's UN Meeting on Antibiotic Resistance', *Vox* (21 September 2016) <http://www.vox.com/2016/9/20/12979968/antibiotic-resistance-superbugs-un> accessed 25 October 2019.

10 Esther Landhuis, 'Superbugs: A silent health emergency – bacteria are outsmarting antibiotics to an alarming degree', *Science News for Students* (10 July 2014) <https://www.sciencenewsforstudents.org/article/superbugs-silent-health-emergency> accessed 25 October 2019.

11 Terry Turner, 'Drug Side Effects and Medical Device Complications', *Drugwatch* (17 May 2019) <https://www.drugwatch.com/side-effects> accessed 25 October 2019.

12 'World Mental Health Day: PM appoints suicide prevention minister', BBC News, 10 October 2018 <https://www.bbc.co.uk/news/health-45804225> accessed 25 October 2019.

13 'The Guardian View on Self-harm: We live in uniquely pressurised times, and girls are suffering', *The Guardian* editorial, 29 August 2018.

14 'The Guardian View on Self-harm', *art. cit.*

15 Ann John, et al., 'Trends in Suicide during the Covid-19 Pandemic', *BMJ* 371:m4352 (12 November 2020) <http://dx.doi.org/10.1136/bmj.m4352> accessed 26 March 2021.

16 A. John, C. Okolie, E. Eyles, et al., 'The Impact of the COVID-19 Pandemic on Self-harm and Suicidal Behaviour: A living systematic review', *National Library of Medicine*, 9/1097 (4 September 2020) <https://pubmed.ncbi.nlm.nih.gov/33604025/> accessed 26 March 2021.

17 Matthew Taylor, 'We need Politicians to Understand Problems more Deeply', *RSA Journal*, 1 (2017), 5.

18 Ian Burbidge, 'Altered States', *RSA Journal*, 1 (2017), 12.

19 Max Planck, *Where is Science Going?* prologue by Albert Einstein, trans. James Murphy (New York: W. W. Norton & Company, 1932), 168–9.

20 Erwin Schrödinger, 'Nature and the Greeks' from The Shearman Lectures delivered at University College, London, 1948 in *Nature and the Greeks* and *Science and Humanism*, foreword by Roger Penrose (Cambridge: Cambridge University Press, 1961), 95. Quoted also in Ken Wilber (ed.), *Quantum Questions: Mystical writings of the world's great physicists* (Boston and London: Shambhala, 1985), 75–97.

21 —— 'Mind and Matter: On Determinism and Free Will' from The Tarner Lectures delivered at Trinity College Cambridge, 1956, in *What is Life?* with *Mind and Matter* and *Autobiographical Sketches*, foreword by Roger Penrose (Cambridge: Cambridge University Press, 1993), 87. Quoted also in Ken Wilber (ed.), *Quantum Questions: Mystical writings of the world's great physicists* (Boston and London: Shambhala, 1985), 92.

22 —— *My View of the World*, trans. Cecily Hastings (Cambridge: Cambridge University Press, 1964) [Ger. orig., *Meine Weltansicht* (Hamburg: Zsolnay, 1961)], cited in Walter J. Moore, *Schrödinger: Life and thought* (1989; Cambridge: Cambridge University Press, 1998), 173.

23 —— 'Mind and Matter: The Arithmetical Paradox – The Oneness of Mind' in *What is Life?* with *Mind and Matter*, 130.

24 *ibid.*

25 Max Planck, *Where is Science Going?* 217.

26 David Gelernter, 'The Closing of the Scientific Mind: Reflections on the zombie-scientist problem', *Commentary* (January 2014) <http://www.commentarymagazine.com/article/the-closing-of-the-scientific-mind> accessed 8 February 2020.

27 Robert Louis Stevenson, *Strange Case of Dr Jekyll and Mr Hyde* (New York: Charles Scribner's Sons, 1886).

28 'A short Schem [*sic*] of the true Religion', Keynes MS 7, King's College, Cambridge, UK.

29 Erwin Schrödinger, 'Nature and the Greeks', 95, 97.

30 Max Planck, *Where is Science Going?* 217.

31 Friedrich Max Müller (ed.), *The Sacred Books of the East*, An Anthology in Thirty Volumes (The Library of the World's Best Literature, New York: Warner Library Co., 1917).

32 C. Jinarâjadâsa (compiled), *Letters From the Masters of the Wisdom*, First Series, 'The Theosophical Society and Its Work: From the Mahâ-Chohan to A. P. Sinnett', Adyar Pamphlets XX, Letter 1 (Madras: Theosophical Publishing House, 1919).

33 *The Observer*, 14 May 1972.

34 William James, 'Human Immortality (1898)' [online] <https://www.uky.edu/~eushe2/Pajares/jimmortal.html> accessed 25 October 2019.

35 Mary Lutyens, *Krishnamurti: The years of awakening*, 272–5.

36 H. P. Blavatsky, 'The New Cycle', *La Revue Theosophique* 1/1 (Paris, 21 March 1889), 3–13; translated from the French original in 'Theosophical Study Paper 1', *Theosophical Society in Australia*, 2002.

37 Annie Besant, 'Investigations into the Super-Physical' (Theosophical Publishing House, December 1913), Adyar Pamphlet No. 36 <http://hpb.narod.ru/InvestigationsSuper-physicalAB.htm> accessed 25 October 2019.

38 I. K. Taimni, *Man, God and the Universe* (Adyar, Madras: Theosophical Publishing House, 1969), 379.

39 *Insight – Journal of the Foundation for Theosophical Studies* (UK, November–December 1999).

40 The Scientific & Medical Network <https://scientificandmedical.net> accessed 26 March 2021.

41 Opening of a speech by Albert Einstein for the United Jewish Appeal [video], recording by Radio Universidad Nacional de La Plata, Argentina, 11 April 1943 <https://upload.wikimedia.org/wikipedia/commons/4/46/03_ALBERT_EINSTEIN.ogg> accessed 11 March 2021. Einstein's own voice can be heard by accessing the above URL. Sound file length, 1 min. 30 sec.

1 Who, or What Am I?

I came out alone on my way to my tryst.
But who is this that follows me in the silent dark?
I move aside to avoid his presence but I escape him not.
He makes the dust rise from the earth with his swagger;
he adds his loud voice to every word that I utter.
He is my own little self, my lord, he knows no shame;
but I am ashamed to come to thy door in his company.

RABINDRANATH TAGORE, GITANJALI

SYNOPSIS

The first section of Volume I, comprising Chapters 1 to 6, prepares the ground for the need of the Mystery Teachings of the *philosophia perennis* comprising the second major section of Volume I in Chapters 7 to 10.

Chapter 1 takes up and broadens the scope of the central theme, 'Who Am I?' and the rejoinder, 'Know Thyself'. It invites the reader to set aside all that he has learnt over the years from books, courses, and lectures and instead to go within and contemplate his own inner experience and his understanding of the nature of mind and what it means to be truly human. With notable and rare exceptions, mainstream scientists seem to be quite certain about who, or what, a human being is—a sophisticated animal or biological machine and nothing more. However, interestingly, great writers and poets appear to recognize intuitively the threefold nature of man—spirit, soul, and body. Does it seem likely that mainstream science will ever provide all the answers to the infinite variety of human experience and the subtleties of mind? If not, then is there any justification for arbitrarily excluding insights from other sources? Why not also include mysticism, religion, and art, along with science, in a wider scope of enquiry into the complete nature of a human being? This exercise in self-reflection leads on logically to the next Chapter.

KEY WORDS: introspection, human body, human being, human 'robots', mechanization

The Proem opened with that most difficult of all, yet most important injunction that humanity must address: 'Know Thyself'—the aphorism inscribed in the pronaos of the Temple of Apollo at Delphi. In personal terms this equates to 'Who Am I?' or in more dispassionate terms, 'What Am I?' It is important first to undertake a preliminary exercise in order to avoid accepting from books statements that are contrary to, or are not corroborated by, experience. The pursuit of Truth, or the enquiry into the nature of reality, does not demand that we automatically reject what we do not know in experience, but that we distinguish clearly between concepts and information received on the one hand and experienced facts on the other.

Experience as against concepts

1

Before resorting to books, lectures, and other external sources, it might be profitable to give some thought to our personal experience of ourselves by asking 'What Am I?' or 'Who Am I?' In everyday experience we can recognize a distinction between subject and object, between the use of a tool and the tool that is used, between the writer and the pen, the pianist and the piano. With such introspection, is it also possible to distinguish the thought *producer* from the thought produced? That which can be produced, manipulated, and controlled cannot be exactly the same as the entity that produces, manipulates, and controls; the former must be other than—albeit related to—the latter. Thus, I know from personal experience that I am not just the body that I use. After all, I can make my body perform acts that it detests or likes doing. Who, or what, is the entity, the 'I', that is so acting on my body? Similarly, I know that by an act of will, I can change my emotional states, say managing and redirecting my anger, dispelling depression or calming my anxiety. Significantly, I also know that, despite the difficulties that I may have in my personal life, I can, as a deliberate act of will, select my thoughts and to some extent control them to create an optimistic outlook, rather than succumb to bleak pessimism. I also know that, more frequently than I would like to admit, I choose to do the wrong thing or speak hurtful words, even though I know in advance about the troubles that will ensue in the wake of such foolishness. At infrequent times, I can sense a sort of blurring of my subject–object awareness, in the sense that what I do, and the act of doing, seem to be fused—popularly known as being 'in the flow', or living 'in the present moment'. This brief introspection shows me that I am not the same as my body, or my emotions, and certainly not my thoughts. My instruments of expression physically, emotionally, and intellectually are at a lower level and therefore not the same as the 'I' who uses them.

In asking such questions about our essential nature, we can also look to numerous sources, such as science, medicine, psychology, and art. The English biologist Richard Dawkins FRS (*b*.1941) is quite certain, albeit still astonished, that we humans, 'are survival machines—robot vehicles blindly programmed to preserve the selfish molecules known as genes.'[1] He is quite entitled to his opinions as long as they are just opinions—especially regarding who, or what, the blind programmer happens to be. But we have yet to find a robot that can display a consciousness of itself, or ask self-reflective questions about the deep nature of itself and the world it inhabits, or express its thoughts in sublime poetry like the English Poet Laureate John Masefield (1878–1967) who wrote some remarkable sonnets about the search for the 'I' and the exploration of the 'me'. In one of them, the first line answers the question that it asks:

> What am I, Life? A thing of watery salt
> Held in cohesion by unresting cells.[2]

Now in the human body, sodium chloride makes up around 0.4 per cent of body weight at a concentration approximately equivalent to that in seawater. Consequently, a 50 kilogramme person would contain around 200 grammes of sodium chloride—comparable to around 40 teaspoons of common table salt.[3] So then, is 50 kilogrammes of seawater contained in a bucket the same thing as a human being? Yes, but only in one strictly limited aspect—of roughly equivalent salinity.

The same verse continues:

> Which work they know not why, which never halt,
> Myself unwitting where their Master dwells.

It seems that in the opinion of one person, human beings are 'blindly programmed', but directed by 'their Master' according to another. Let Masefield continue with the concluding lines of another sonnet about the inner inhabitant dwelling in the saline body:

> The god, the holy ghost, the atoning lord,
> Here in the flesh, the never yet explored.[4]

The line 'never yet explored' seems to encapsulate the view of mainstream science that equates the whole man to just his body and brain and neglects his soul and inner nature. But there are others—for instance, the English poet and playwright, Robert Browning (1812–1889), who come rather close to the truth. This is beautifully framed in his poem *A Death in the Desert*:

> How divers persons witness in each man.
> Three souls which make up one soul:
> What Does, what Knows, what Is; three souls, one man.[5]

Here we have an accurate, and tersely expressed, version of the perennial philosophy of the three natures which constitute man—spirit (*pneuma*, the enduring Self), soul (psyche, or the emotional-mental nature), and body—which will be the consistent subject of this work. (Of course, Browning uses the word 'soul' in a poetic sense rather than with strict precision of meaning, as we shall see later.) It would seem that poets gifted with mystical vision can express profound truths with a brevity that creates a striking impact out of all proportion to their profundity.

<aside>Distinguishing spiritual from physical</aside>

Reverting to science, its dictum that we humans are 'just animals' is practically a *sine qua non* amongst the vast majority of evolutionary biologists—the disarmingly simple word 'just' being of utmost importance, as it would be quite a different matter to state that humans have an animal component or can display animal-like propensities. What is the difference between the animal and human consciousness? The question is a vital one and will be explored in depth in Volume II. For the present, let us state what is self-evident. Some animals, like domestic pets, display great loyalty towards their owners; however, the animal is conscious of its environment and anything of interest to it. On the other hand, man is conscious not only of an objective world *outside himself*, but he possesses an awareness of himself *in it*, and his subjective reactions *to it*. How does Darwinian theory based on random mutations and natural selection explain this characteristic of *self-consciousness* in man, but not other animal species who inhabit the same environment?

<aside>Are human beings 'just animals'?</aside>

It is almost needless to stress that in asking, 'Who Am I?' we are enquiring primarily into the *content* of man's essential nature, rather than what form and shape it takes. Hence, our overriding concern is with consciousness and mind and not so much with man's physical form and structure, or physical mechanisms, important though they are. This is what Erwin Schrödinger realized with great force and clarity, as we showed in the Proem (page xlv) and the Introductory (page lxi), where we quoted key extracts from his writings arguing that man is more than just his physical body, because physical and sensory mechanisms of themselves cannot explain resulting feelings or experience. Let us develop these ideas a stage further.

<aside>Primacy of mind over body</aside>

Mainstream science has concentrated heavily on the outer, physical aspect of man to the virtual exclusion of his inner informing principles, namely his mind and spiritual nature. A physical mechanism can be investigated by systematically taking it apart and examining its systems, components, and subunits, down to the minutest detail. The whole is not greater than, but merely the sum of its component parts. So, the mechanistic outlook, with its associated methodology of reductionism, has turned out to be the 'machine paradigm' of science regarding the universe and man. Because this has become so entrenched in establishment science and taken on the role of an incontestable dogma, it would be useful to examine the philosophy and ensuing implications of science in order to identify the deficiencies in its exclusively materialistic worldview; hence to reinforce our case for the indispensable need for the psycho-spiritual and esoteric sciences to complete and complement (not replace) the picture of mainstream science.

<aside>Mechanistic paradigm of mainstream science</aside>

The excessive emphasis on science and technology, to the exclusion of human values, is neatly summed up by the following extract from a conversation between Matthew Taylor (*b.*1960), the former British Chief Executive of the Royal Society of Arts, and Steve Hilton (*b.*1969), the British visiting Professor at Stanford University and former senior adviser and Director of Strategy (2010–2016) to UK Prime Minister David Cameron (*b.*1966):[6]

> Matthew Taylor: 'We have done more to alleviate poverty in the past ten years than ever before in history, and people are living longer. So, do you think that the world is getting worse and that we need to do something about it? Or is it getting better and you are just encouraging us to go a little bit faster along that route?'
>
> Steve Hilton: 'The world is getting worse. There are things that we can all be happy about, in terms of people moving out of poverty and so on. But I think that generally speaking, daily experience is becoming dehumanised in different ways.'

<aside>'Machinization' of human beings</aside>

Hilton gives the example of systems and institutions that have become so large and bureaucratic that the human element is starved. He cites the case of Amazon where employees in the distribution centres are fitted with a personal GPS (Global Positioning System) in order to track their movements to make sure that they are operating as efficiently as possible. This tracking goes as far as ensuring that they use the correct toilet. If they use a toilet that is not optimal in terms of minimal walking distance they are reprimanded. A typical fifty-five hour working week at distribution centres like the one in Swansea in Wales, covering 800,000 square feet, involves ten and one-half hour shifts, including a paid half-hour break, and two, fifteen-minute unpaid breaks.[7] Workers are expected to collect orders every thirty-three seconds and have to walk some eleven miles during the course of their day or night shift.[8] Amazon's lowest paid US workers receive $15 an hour; and in the UK, pay will rise from £8.20 an hour in London to £10.50, while outside London the rate rises from £8 an hour to £9.50 (wages in 2018).[9] However, 60-hour weeks are now mandatory.[10] The benefit to the consumer of near instant 'mouse click' access to an enormous variety of goods and technical gadgets at economical prices thus comes at the cost of the unremitting ordeal of the workers.[11] Furthermore, there is the knock-on adverse effect on the livelihoods of those running high street shops and small industries driven out of business by retail giants like Amazon with their 'obsessive compulsive focus' on the customer.[12]

The above contentions are reinforced by some recent statistics on mental health in young people. These show that depression and self-harm is on the rise among younger millennials,[13] who are more likely to experience an existential crisis in their twenties than previous generations.[14] Moreover, this growing generation (especially amongst young women) is more stressed than any other age group.[15]

The reason for providing the above illustrations is to make our case that science cannot be divorced, on the one hand, from its underlying philosophical foundations, nor, on the other hand, from its overlying applications, as technology and the associated institutions and industries built around it, which, in turn, are strongly coupled with commercial, financial, and political structures. It cannot be argued in simplistic, blanket terms that science is 'making the world a better place' or that science is 'making the human being happier or more human'. In many areas we are immensely grateful to science—the alleviation of material poverty, and the health of the physical body, being but two of innumerable examples, as cited above. But there remains the overriding question that science, in the main, fails to address: 'Who, or What Am I?'—the foremost theme of this work.

Science is always underpinned by philosophy

Despite the phenomenal advances in science one sees a parallel, exponentially worsening, trend of *inner* poverty, one might say 'soul poverty'—a starvation not of the belly, but of the soul and spirit as evinced in all kinds of social disorders, such as drug taking, alcoholism, sexual violence, and barbaric or lewd entertainment, where the individual attempts to fill an inner vacuum with sensory distractions. As cogently argued in *The Metaphysics of Technology*, there are two phases of technological development and determinism: 'anthropogenic'—dependence without control; and 'autogenic'—when technology will become self-making and self-evolving.[16] The danger obviously lies with the latter— advances in technology (in some sectors, like computing, at an exponential rate), going hand-in-hand with a rapidly declining quality of life. How often do we go on our annual holiday nowadays and dare to remain off-line without fear of having to cope with a barrage of e-mails demanding instant replies upon our return? Of course, it is not technology *per se* that is the cause of the current malaise stemming from technological and psychological stress due to information overload, but human beings who have engineered the situation. So, the solution to the problems of excessive technology is not a technical one, but lies with the human being in terms of his ability to forge healthy relationships with his fellow beings, his role in society and in the world, his relationship to nature, and the fulfilment of his inner nature—all underpinned by understanding Himself.

Misuse or over- use of technology causes inner poverty

Let us continue along the journey of SELF-exploration.

Although the world is full of suffering, it is also full of the overcoming of it.
HELEN KELLER[17]

NOTES

1   Richard Dawkins, *The Selfish Gene* (Oxford: Oxford University Press 1976), xxi.
2   John Masefield, *Sonnets* (New York: Macmillan Company, 1916), Sonnet 2.
3   Len Fisher, 'How Much Salt is in a Human Body?' *Science Focus*
     <http://www.sciencefocus.com/qa/how-much-salt-human-body> accessed 27 October 2019.
4   John Masefield, *op. cit.*, Sonnet 6.
5   Robert Browning, *A Death in the Desert* (London: Swan Sonnenschein, 1904).
6   'Being Human', *Royal Society of Arts Journal*, 2 (2015), 19. See also Steve Hilton, *More Human: Designing a world where people come first* (UK: W. H. Allen, 2015).
7   BBC News, 'Amazon Workers Face "Increased Risk of Mental Illness"', 25 November 2013
     <http://www.bbc.co.uk/news/business-25034598> accessed 27 October 2019.

8   Vanessa Allen, 'Walk 11 miles a shift and pick up an order every 33 seconds: Revealed, how Amazon works staff "to the bone"', *Daily Mail*, 25 November 2013 <http://www.dailymail.co.uk/news/article-2512959> accessed 27 October 2019.

9   BBC News, 'Amazon Raises Wages Amid Criticism', 2 October 2018 <https://www.bbc.co.uk/news/business-45717768> accessed 20 November 2019. The wages in 2013 were £6.50 an hour on day shifts and £8.25 an hour on night shifts—see *Daily Mail*, 'Walk 11 miles a shift and pick up an order every 33 seconds', *art. cit.*

10 Áine Cain and Isobel Asher Hamilton, 'Amazon warehouse employees speak out about the "brutal" reality of working during the holidays, when 60-hour weeks are mandatory and ambulance calls are common', *Business Insider* (10 February 2019) <https://www.businessinsider.com/amazon-employees-describe-peak-2019-2?r=US&IR=T> accessed 26 November 2019.

11 Emily Guendelsberger, 'I worked at an Amazon fulfillment center; they treat workers like robots', *Time* (18 July 2019) <https://time.com/5629233/amazon-warehouse-employee-treatment-robots> accessed 26 November 2019.

12 'Jeff Bezos said the "secret sauce" to Amazon's success is an "obsessive compulsive focus" on customer over competitor', *Business Insider* (15 September 2018) <https://www.businessinsider.com/amazon-jeff-bezos-success-customer-obsession 2018-9?r=US&IR=T> accessed 30 November 2019.

13 'Changes in Millennial Adolescent Mental Health and Health-Related Behaviours Over 10 Years: A population cohort comparison study', *International Journal of Epidemiology*, 48/5 (October 2019).

14 O. C. Robinson and G. R. T. Wright, 'The Prevalence, Types and Perceived Outcomes of Crisis Episodes in Early Adulthood and Midlife: A structured retrospective-autobiographical study', *International Journal of Behavioral Development*, 37 (2013), 407–16.

15 A. A. Stone, J. E. Schwartz, J. E. Broderick, and A. Deaton, 'A Snapshot of the Age Distribution of Psychological Well-Being in the United States', *Proceedings of the National Academy of Sciences of the United States of America*, 107 (2010), 9985–90.

16 David Skrbina, *The Metaphysics of Technology* (UK: Ashgate Publishing, 2015). An excellent review of this book is by David Lorimer, 'Technology and the Future', *Journal of the Scientific and Medical Network*, 122 (2016), 38–9.

17 'Helen Keller' <https://www.brainyquote.com/quotes/helen_keller_109208> accessed 27 October 2919.

2 The Mind–Brain–Thought Problem: Even Nobel Scientists Disagree

I think, my Kepler, we will laugh at the extraordinary stupidity of the multitude. What do you say to the leading philosophers of the faculty here [University of Padua], to whom I have offered a thousand times of my own accord to show my studies, but who with the lazy obstinacy of a serpent who has eaten his fill have never consented to look at planets, nor moon, nor telescope?

Verily, just as serpents close their ears, so do these men close their eyes to the light of truth.

GALILEO'S LETTER (AUGUST, 1610) TO JOHANNES KEPLER[1]

SYNOPSIS

Chapter 2 presents the latest claims about the nature of mind and consciousness from science, and the arguments that neuroscience specifically puts forward to support its claims. Examples are given, from Nobel scientists, of diametrically opposed views about the role of the brain in regard to mind and consciousness; one camp dogmatically asserting that literally all our conscious experience is nothing more than the outcome of cerebral processes, and the other arguing that the diversity of human behaviour cannot be reduced to just a theory of molecular interactions. This dichotomy of views from mainstream science about the role of the brain, provides the spur to a deeper enquiry into how a purely brain-based theory could account for the phenomenon of genius or child prodigy, as for instance in science or music. Further examples, also from within the scientific camp itself, are provided to show that robust evidence for phenomena, such as near-death experiences and the survival of consciousness after death, cannot be brushed aside on the grounds of hallucination or imperfect research data, nor explained solely on purely mechanistic theories of the brain. This Chapter concludes with a summary of the principal flow of ideas that underpin the mainstream paradigm regarding mind and consciousness. Moreover it relates them to the perspective of renowned scientists and neurosurgeons who argue for and against the idea that neuronal activity is the sole explanatory mechanism to be employed in the attempt to understand the nature of mind and what it means to be human.

KEY WORDS: subjective experience, neuroscience on consciousness, molecular biology, genetics, genes, neurons, enigma of genius, scientific thinking, Occam's razor, *psi* evidence, Karl Vogt, Francis Crick, Gerald Edelman

As you read this, you are having a unique conscious experience. Nothing is more basic to our lives as thinking beings and nothing, it seems, is better known to us than our personal and individual experience. But the ever-expanding reach of mainstream science proposes that everything in our world is ultimately physical. Among the most intriguing explanatory problems in neuroscience of our times is the challenge

7

of fitting consciousness into the modern scientific worldview; of taking the subjective 'feel' of conscious experience and somehow showing that it is nothing but neural activity in the brain.

What follows is a taster for the arguments that will be further developed in this Chapter and fully in the next one. Our purpose is to show the disagreement not over details, but over matters of fundamental principles, between some of the most distinguished scientists on the nature of thought and how it is produced.

Arguably, the supreme modern exponents of the mainstream scientific theory about mind and consciousness are the English molecular biologist and neuroscientist Francis Crick FRS (1916–2004), who co-discovered the deoxyribonucleic acid (DNA) spiral with the American molecular biologist and geneticist James Watson KBE, ForMemRS (b.1928). Less well known is the contribution to understanding the structure of DNA (deoxyribonucleic acid) of the New Zealand-born British physicist and molecular biologist, Maurice Wilkins FRS (1916–2004). Wilkins was also awarded the 1962 Nobel prize in Physiology or Medicine along with Crick and Watson. Their joint work laid the foundations for molecular biology and genetics.

Mainstream
science
materializes
consciousness

Crick opens his book, *The Astonishing Hypothesis: The scientific search for the soul* with this manifesto: '"You", your joys and your sorrows, your memories and your ambitions, your sense of personal identity and free will, are in fact no more than the behaviour of a vast assembly of nerve cells and their associated molecules.'[2] Later in the book he continues along the same lines with, 'a person's mental activities are entirely due to the behaviour of nerve cells, glial cells, and the atoms, ions, and molecules that make them up and influence them.' Earlier in a scholarly paper he underlined his dictum that, 'our basic idea is that consciousness depends crucially on some form of rather short-term memory and also on some form of serial attentional mechanism. This attentional mechanism helps sets of the relevant neurons to fire in a coherent semi-oscillatory way, probably at a frequency in the 40–70 Hz range […].'[3]

Few amongst us, including the writer, would deny the role of neurobiology, but do neural mechanisms *of their own accord* supply the final answer to all our joys and sorrows, memories and sense of self? The American journalist, senior writer at *Scientific American,* and Director of the Stevens Institute of Technology John Horgan (b.1953) thinks that the 'Astonishing Hypothesis' should be renamed the 'The Depressing Hypothesis', since Crick's 'Search for the Soul' was more akin to a crushing of the soul out of existence.[4]

But let another Nobel laureate in Physiology or Medicine join the debate on consciousness and the soul.

Enlightened
science
understands parts
in the context of
the whole

In his book *Bright Air, Brilliant Fire,* the American biologist, neuroscientist, and philosopher of mind, Gerald Edelman (1929–2014), says: 'To reduce a theory of an individual's behaviour to a theory of molecular interactions is simply silly […] when one considers how many different levels of physical, biological, and social interactions must be put into place before higher order consciousness emerges.'[5]

Why does Edelman think the idea 'simply silly' and what are the grounds of his objection? In his own words, 'I hope to show that the kind of reductionism that doomed the thinkers of the Enlightenment is confuted by evidence that has emerged both from modern neuroscience and from modern physics […].'[6]

Here in a nutshell, the great scientist has hit upon the problem: the reductionist method of materialist science, where the whole must be understood by reducing it to its most elementary parts. Edelman has realized that when taken to absurd extremes, reductionism ceases to be a valuable technique in science and becomes an ideology upheld by faith rather than reason; and reason dictates that the whole is greater than the sum of its parts, something which clearly emerges from his later co-authored book, *A Universe of Consciousness*.[7]

Ideas similar to those of Edelman are related in a broad sense to panpsychism, which is the view that mentality is fundamental and ubiquitous in the natural world (the word 'panpsychism' meaning, literally, that everything has a mind[8]). The view has a long and esteemed history in mystically inclined philosophical traditions of both East and West and has recently been revived in analytic philosophy by the likes of the British analytic philosopher of mind, Galen Strawson (*b*.1952)[9] and the American neuroscientist, Christof Koch (*b*.1956),[10] who was Crick's collaborator.

Unfortunately, though, ideas like panpsychism, and the theories of scientists, like Edelman, in relation to the nature and production of thought, are still very much in the minority in modern day scientific thinking, which is entrenched in the completely materialistic, reductionist ideas of Crick, et al. However, other than details and technicalities, there is nothing new or original about what the vast majority of mainstream scientists are saying as this concept of theirs goes back a long way, in fact, well into the nineteenth century. It was the German scientist, philosopher, zoologist, and politician, Karl Christoph Vogt (1817–1895), who first mooted the idea that the brain generates consciousness. His well-known quote of 1846 was, 'The brain secretes thought as the stomach secretes gastric juice, the liver bile, and the kidneys urine.' Hence, Vogt continues, 'thoughts stand in about the same relationship to the brain as bile to the liver and urine to the kidneys.'[11]

Historical basis of mechanistic theory of consciousness

Notwithstanding the fact that the thoughts and language of large portions of human society (high ranking politicians included) are fit for the urinal, does the reader truly think that thoughts expressing nobility, sublime feelings, deepest love, universal compassion, scientific discovery, and artistic creation from the likes of Buddha and the Christ, or Plato (427–347 BC), Leonardo da Vinci (1452–1519), Shakespeare (1564–1616), Newton (1643–1727), and Mozart (1756–1791) can *all* be compared entirely to the brain equivalent of urine or bile production?

If not, then the writer of this work would like to invite his readers on a conversational journey with him, leaving aside all preconceptions, and ask some deep questions free from all conditioning. Let us look at the question of talent and genius, say in the world of music; although the same arguments would apply just as well to science or in any other field where there is exceptional performance. The BBC Young Musician of the Year competition is an annual musical highlight in England. Hyperboles would not do justice to the sheer dedication, accomplishments, and self-composure of these young performers, many of whom are in their early teens. Yes, we recognize and applaud their achievements, but let us now ask some questions. Two widely accepted theories that are virtually axiomatic in mainstream science concern evolution and consciousness. According to the Darwinian theory of evolution (simply put), we humans are the product of the interplay of chance mutations of genes and natural selection, which chooses the most favourable genes for our survival in the environment in question. Regarding consciousness, the accepted

Does the brain produce thought?

dictum in mainstream neuroscience is that our brain is the thought producer, or generator of our thoughts and that our consciousness is purely the result of brain neuronal activity and nothing else, as Crick and others have declared.

So now, looking squarely at these two theories—neither accepting, nor rejecting them, but just looking—we ask: how does such a combination of genes conspire to produce staggering talent at such an early age? Natural selection is decidedly a slow process over aeons, but somehow, inexplicable talent appears out of the blue in a family invariably of mediocre or no musical background. Why is this? Is there a gene, or combination of genes, that results in something so sudden and so specific as high musical talent? Next, there is the matter of the chosen instrument. From the very earliest age the performer is drawn to a specific genre of instrument, say piano, strings, woodwind or percussion. There is no wavering about the choice of instrument.[12] Furthermore, within a certain genre a specific instrument exerts a particularly magnetic fascination upon the player over all the others. Why is he drawn to one type, say the horn, but not to the trumpet in the brass section, or the violin rather than the cello in the string section? Is there a specific 'horn gene' or 'violin gene' that fires the individual to choose his instrument (often as early as age two)? As an interesting observation, many artists have attested that their chosen instrument seems to become part of the very fabric of their nature. And why does a performer, however catholic his tastes may be, still have a particular affinity for a certain composer? In modern times the affinity between the violin and the American-born Yehudi Menuhin OM KBE (1916–1999) or the piano and the Argentinian-born Daniel Barenboim KBE (*b*.1942), immediately springs to mind.

Let us take this a step further and consider the sudden onset of musical genius on the world stage. Arguably, the finest example is Wolfgang Amadeus Mozart. Granted his family were highly cultured and musical, but neither his ancestors nor his parents bore the hall-marks of genius. Why then suddenly, in 1756, was a towering genius born to this family? Is there not something totally inexplicable about a child prodigy unexpectedly appearing in their midst who was caught by his father composing a difficult harpsichord concerto when scarcely aged five? When Leopold Mozart remarked, 'it's so difficult that no one will be able to play it', young Wolfgang retorted, 'you have to practise till you master it.'[13] Add to that his first symphony composed when only eight years old, not to mention his prodigious output of concertos, symphonies, instrumental works, chamber music, operas, sacred music and much else, and it is truly surprising that he was able to achieve all this by the age of thirty-five, despite financial and health problems.[14] To this day, musicians are awestruck by Mozart's insights into human nature as dramatized in his operas such as *Così fan tutte* (usually translated into English as 'Women are like that'). Where did such profound insights into human behaviour come from? Did Mozart perform brain scans on people; or did he attend long lectures on psychology and psychiatry? If not, then *from where* did he receive his immortal gifts; and *from whom* were they bequeathed?

Turning to the world of science, in contrast to Mozart who was at least born into a musical family, Isaac Newton was born to a farming family 'wholly without distinction and wholly without learning.'[15] There were no scientists, mathematicians or scholars in his ancestry. Yet this diminutive and prematurely born child, given little chance of survival, whose yeoman father was totally illiterate—unable to sign his own name—and mother only barely educated, became one of the most celebrated scientists and a figure of universal significance for mankind, living to the ripe old age of eighty-five. A blazing meteor in the scientific

Is natural selection the sole evolutionary process?

Do genes alone explain genius?

firmament, his work changed science to its foundations. We all know that Newton went to Cambridge and obtained his Bachelor of Arts degree (Second Class Honours) in 1665. But innumerable people receive a fine university education in science and many more receive a higher degree than Newton did. So why did this particular university graduate amongst all others produce colossal tomes on mathematics, physics, optics, theology, alchemy, philosophy, chronology, economics, geography, plus voluminous correspondences and administrative papers, when he held high office as Warden, then Master, of the Royal Mint, and President of the Royal Society? Moreover, Newton was quite undistinguished at school and university and is reported to have disappointed his professor, the English Christian theologian and mathematician, Isaac Barrow FRS (1630–1677), by his lack of knowledge about Euclid.[16] Why then this sudden onrush of supernal genius when aged 22–24, especially during what is known as his *annus mirabilis* in 1666 when he made revolutionary discoveries in mathematics, mechanics, optics, and formulated the universal law of gravitation, that all heralded triumphs unequalled in the history of science?

Let us suggest (again, with no bias) that the answer lies entirely in our genes and neurons, in other words, that the essence of life, mind, and consciousness is solely material and physical. In that case we are forced to deny the existence of any non-physical creative agency in the universe and therefore in the final analysis, we must ascribe all creativity and genius to pure chance—to the fortuitous concurrence of genes that, in the case of Newton, were somehow 'switched on' in his early twenties.

If this be the case then, it is not unreasonable to ask: what ultimately is a gene? Surely just a physical chemical compound of atoms and molecules operating according to the well-known laws of physics and chemistry, however sophisticated and complex the arrangement may be. However, say in the case of a musician, can specific chemical compounds create or produce specificity of focus in the life of a performer, or cause distinctive characteristics of performance, or a unique relationship between the performer and his favourite composer? Then, how do such complex arrangements of chemical compounds translate what is entirely vibrations in the air of certain frequencies—pure sounds—into sensations that we experience as sublime music that can move us to tears? Do, or can, chemical compounds, of whatever arrangement and complexity, feel and experience sounds, colours, feelings, and emotions? Or perhaps they act as the physical medium of transmission for such experiences to occur in the same sort of way that a piano in itself does not feel music, nor does it play music on itself by itself; but is the physical medium for transmitting and communicating the experience and feelings of the pianist (via the composer) to his audience?

Are genes merely chemical compounds?

Is it the case that the brain and the mind are intimately correlated, or are they one and the same thing? If the answer is the latter, it would be no different in principle to asserting that the piano and the pianist are the same thing, to use the example above.

Let us then develop further what the latest mainstream science has to say, their approach and evaluation of evidence about this topic being much in vogue. There are innumerable books, learned papers and courses by international scientists and neuroscientists on the subject of brain and mind. Two of the best examples of modern expositions about the mind-brain problem in neuroscience are the joint courses by two American scientists: 'Your Deceptive Mind: A Scientific Guide to Critical Thinking Skills' by Steven Novella (*b*.1964), clinical and academic neurologist and assistant professor at Yale University

School of Medicine; and 'How to Think Like a Scientist' by Michael Shermer (*b.*1954), science writer, historian of science, and scientific adviser to the American Council on Science and Health. Both are available as a course on compact disc with accompanying manuals.[17] The ideas of Novella and Shermer are regarded as entirely typical of the standpoint of the vast majority of scientists and neuroscientists (apart from the technicalities and theoretical differences among the various scientific theories), so it would therefore be instructive to explore the implications of what they are proclaiming in terms of our consciousness and our humanity. What follows is a critique of their courses based on an examination of the source material aided by an excellent book review in the *Journal for the Society of Psychical Research* from which the quotes are extracted.[18]

Shermer does not propose, but asserts, that 'mind is just a word we use to describe neural activity in the brain', a rigid orthodox stance reinforced by Novella that, 'one of the premises of this course is that we are our brains', who further asserts, 'the left hemisphere has the ability to speak and understand language.' One would normally wish to avoid hairsplitting pedantry, preferring instead to exercise some context-dependent interpretative latitude in the face of any scientific propositions, but since Novella and Shermer state their case with such absolute certitude that brain = mind, we invite readers to pluck a leaf, or many leaves, out of their courses and accompanying manuals and apply some 'critical thinking skills' in order to 'think like a scientist'. This will not be in the least bit difficult.

Are mind and brain synonymous?

If 'we are our brains', presumably walking on two legs, to whom, or what, does that disarmingly simply pronoun 'we' refer? Just our brains? What about our consciousness? Do we not also have a heart, body, and organs of sensation, which are part of us? May all our feelings, sublime thoughts, pains, sorrows, and aspirations be airbrushed aside simply because they emanate from our 'deceptive minds'? Can the left hemisphere, unaided and on its own, understand language and speak? If we now propose that brain and mind can be correlated—like the piano and the pianist in the example above—does that make them both exactly the same? If so, then to assert that 'mind is just a word we use to describe 'neural activity in the brain' is no different in principle from declaring that the quivering strings of a piano are the same as the pianist. Whilst recognizing that the relation between mind and brain is not the same as that in the analogy between pianist and piano, does it not seem to be the case that this confusion between mind and brain is a confusion between the animating principle and its vehicle of expression? If we acknowledge the difference, whilst admitting the correlation between the two, we may legitimately rephrase Novella's left-brain assertion in terms such as, 'the ability to speak and understand language (the animating principle) can be correlated with the activity in the left hemisphere (the vehicle and medium of expression).'

Why ignore contradictory evidence?

Furthermore, how scientific is it to ignore the massive body of evidence from academic scientific, peer-reviewed journals that contradicts the dogma of brain = mind, and to regard any contradictory evidence as a case of 'deceptive mind'? If so deceptive, why does mind, in countless millions of humans, choose to be so deceptive? Has natural selection engineered deception as part of our survival mechanism? If so, why, and may we see the evidence? By contrast, considerable evidence will shortly be adduced from impeccable scientists (like Edelman mentioned earlier) who have seen through the misperceptions and resulting confusion caused by conflating an active principle with its medium of expression and therefore contest the brain = mind dogma.

Later in their courses and accompanying booklets Novella and Shermer flatly dismiss not just some but all the evidence from parapsychology and *psi* research. Readers are asked to consider whether turning a blind eye to whatever does not accord with one's preconceptions and refusing to examine robust evidence that flies in the face of one's opinions are the hallmark of 'critical thinking skills', or simply a case of prejudice and a myopic fixation of thought. Would a better title for the courses by Novella and Shermer perhaps be 'How to Think Like a Fundamentalist' or better still, 'How to Think Like a "Fundamaterialist"'?

Is it scientific to premise a course at the outset on an assumption that is merely stated without supporting evidence and simply taken for granted (namely, that we are our brains and no more)? Are we slowly beginning to realize that what is being promulgated as established and undisputed scientific fact is really an extreme form of materialism (a term that we have used previously and which we shall define fully later on, but for the moment it is best understood as the theory and belief that nothing exists in the universe except physical matter and its movements and modifications). This attitude is not one of science, but an ideology propped up by the 'church of scientism'—the equivalent of religious propaganda. Hence, if matter is taken as the only or fundamental reality, then all life, processes, and phenomena can be explained as manifestations or results of matter. On the grounds that nothing exists except physical matter, all things that can be measured are known only through the physical senses, which, in turn, are fully explainable in terms of the products of physical matter. From this it is obvious why materialists must deny the existence of spirit, or any kind of non-physical occurrences, and rely upon purely physical explanations for all phenomena, including the so-called paranormal.

Presuppositions and ideologies dominate materialism

But is it all so simple? Is it the mark of thinking like a scientist to resort to the minimalist principle of arbitrarily wielding Occam's razor[i] to slice off chunks of robust evidence that inconveniently run counter to expectations and beliefs, in this case about paranormal events? Let us touch on two of these chunks that will be developed as we proceed in this book.

Why arbitrarily cut out evidence?

By paranormal we mean occurrences and phenomena that are non-physical, being beyond the range and reach of ordinary human capabilities and not amenable to conventional scientific explanation.[19] A similar term is *psi*, the 'anomalous processes of information or energy transfer such as telepathy or other forms of extrasensory perception that are currently unexplained in terms of known physical or biological mechanisms.'[20] As we have just stated, although mainstream scientists remain highly sceptical about such claims, there is a typically high level of belief in the paranormal among the general population (which is neither so gullible nor credulous as some scientists would have us believe).[21] Novella claims that 'researchers have not been able to convincingly show that *psi* phenomena exist', furthermore, that '*psi* research […] has been going round in circles and not progressing at all. It has yet to develop a single repeatable demonstration of *psi*.' In the face of such sweeping statements, is there any hard evidence to refute them? Reproducibility has virtually assumed the status of a religious commandment in science and, according to Novella, the key flaw in *psi* literature is that 'initial impressive results tend to diminish over time as tighter controls are introduced'. We would add that this is also due to boredom induced

Paranormal phenomena derided by mainstream science

---

i This states that the fewest possible assumptions are to be made in explaining a thing, a principle attributed to the English philosopher William of Occam (*circa* 1287–1347).

14

by repetition, a fact which Novella seems to have conveniently misunderstood or disregarded. But is everything precisely reproducible? With physical experiments, if all parameters (initial conditions, boundary conditions, experimental protocols) are kept exactly the same, we can rightly mandate that the results must be exactly the same. But with *psi* experiments the parameters are vastly greater, subtler, and more sensitive to influence than physical experiments (the emotional state of the experimenter being one case in point).

Therefore, with such a proliferation of variables, it is more difficult to reproduce exactly the same results each time, and on demand. However, decades of painstaking *psi* research has addressed this very problem and come up with impressive demonstrations of *psi* from a variety of lines of study that have been independently corroborated and repeated to a high degree of statistical significance.[22] From the voluminous body of evidence we may cite such diverse lines of research as the investigations of direct mental interaction with living systems;[23] studies on pets that appear to know when their owners are returning home;[24] research into hypnotic telepathy conducted in Russia;[25] and studies on remote viewing.[26] The history of Ganzfeld studies[ii] provides strong evidence for *psi* with reproducibility in the sense of repeatedly positive results being obtained from different researchers working in different laboratories around the globe.[27] Furthermore, the statistical significance of *psi*, shown by the meta-analyses[iii] of the American parapsychologist Dean Radin (*b*.1952) and collaborators, is impressive.[28, 29] Once a concert violinist, Radin is Chief Scientist at the Institute of Noetic Science ('IONS') and Associated Distinguished Professor of Integral and Transpersonal Psychology at the California Institute of Integral Studies, having previously worked at AT&T Bell Laboratories and held appointments at Princeton University, and other academic and industrial facilities.

The second chunk to fall off at the behest of Occam's razor (renamed Occam's chainsaw[30] by some sceptics) concerns the whole field of survival after death. That consciousness is not extinguished at death is an unequivocal key tenet of the *philosophia perennis* of all ages since time immemorial, as we shall see later. But what does good science have to say on this topic which has never left the field of public interest? Of many examples that could be mentioned, the following are noteworthy: careful observations on near-death and end-of-life experiences conducted by the British husband and wife team Peter Fenwick (*b*.1935), neuropsychiatrist, neurophysiologist, and President Emeritus of the Scientific and Medical Network with Elizabeth Fenwick (*b*.1935), professional writer and counsellor on health and family matters;[31] experiences common in widowhood meticulously recorded in the British Medical Journal;[32] and the outstanding research, painstakingly recorded, by the Canadian-born American psychiatrist Ian Stevenson (1918–2007) on young children of different cultures, who were able to provide highly specific details on an apparent former lifetime.[33] (We describe Stevenson's work in detail in Chapter 4.) There is also considerable evidence to be found in extensive literature on the whole subject

Parameters of *psi* experiments more sensitive to influence than those of physical experiments

Reproducible evidence for *psi* from statistical analyses

Philosophia perennis takes as a given the continuity of consciousness after death

---

ii The Ganzfeld procedure is a mild sensory isolation technique that was first introduced into experimental psychology during the 1930s and subsequently adapted by parapsychologists to test for the existence of *psi*. Ganzfeld experiments are among the most recent in parapsychology for testing telepathy.

iii Meta-analysis is a statistical analysis that combines the results of multiple scientific studies, especially those with small sample size or conflicting results. The basic tenet is that there is a common truth behind all conceptually similar scientific studies, but it is recognised that this is measured with a certain error within individual studies. Statistical methods are used to derive a pooled estimate closest to the unknown common truth based on how this error is perceived.

of spiritualism, as in the annals of the British Society for Psychical Research in England, founded in 1882, and the first society to conduct organised scholarly research into human experiences that challenge contemporary scientific models.[34]

But what does Michael Shermer have to say about survival after death? In his manuals we are categorically informed that, 'either the soul survives death or it does not, and there is no scientific evidence that it does.' Granted that near-death experiences (NDEs) do not prove survival, they are indicative of the latter. We may cite two impressive instances of an NDE from eminent scientists, both of whom were sceptical about such things, before their actual experience of it.

Near-death experiences have a long history and are well documented—increasingly, these days, with rigour and insight from eminent doctors. One example is the American neuro-surgeon Dr Eben Alexander MD (*b*.1953) who taught at Duke University Medical Center, Brigham and Women's Hospital, Harvard Medical School, the University of Massachusetts Medical School, and the University of Virginia Medical School. He contracted a severe brain infection that left him in a coma close to death and in a vegetative state with no capacity to create thought since the neocortex (the part of the brain involved in higher functions, such as sensory perceptions, conscious thought, and in humans, language) had effectively shut down. Amazingly, he fully regained consciousness with a coherent and profound set of memories during the period of the coma. In his book *Proof of Heaven*, Alexander states, 'My experience showed me that the death of the body and brain is not the end of consciousness [...]. What happened to me while I was in a coma is the most important story I will ever tell. But it's a tricky story to tell because it is so foreign to ordinary understanding.'[35]

Of course, the diehard sceptics were quick to dismiss his book as proof of hallucination.[36] However, readers can see for themselves the biased skewing of the sceptical argument, which gives no clear idea of how a brain with the neocortex shut down can hallucinate.

Another instance of the separation of consciousness from the body is that of the Indian-American Dr Rajiv Parti MD (*b*.1957), who was a world-class practising cardiac anaes-thesiologist with a successful career as the Chief of Anaesthesiology at the Bakersfield Heart Hospital in California. He was the last man to believe in 'beyond the brain' states of consciousness—until his own near-death experience on the operating table, where he watched his own operation from the ceiling in accurate detail, even recalling a joke told by his doctors during his surgery (obviously during complete anaesthesia). His near-death experience led to a profound spiritual awakening that transformed his career, lifestyle, and most fundamental beliefs, as shown in his book *Dying to Wake Up*.[37]

Once more we ask the reader: is dismissing outright such a weight of evidence from the medical profession itself about NDEs, regarding the likely survival of consciousness following the clinical death of the brain, a scientific attitude or is it one of arrogance born of fear, ignorance, and prejudice? It seems, then, that the likes of Novella and Shermer (and they are by no means in the minority) are not putting forward any semblance of a careful scientific exposition *but promulgating their biases through a scientific façade*. How aptly did H. P. Blavatsky (whom we shall encounter in full measure later in this work) entitle one of the chapters of her monumental book, *The Secret Doctrine*, 'The Masks of Science'. We find the same phenomenon to this day. The distorted image that we see through the mask is an ideological abhorrence, tantamount to a cerebral knee-jerk reaction

Well documented evidence for near-death experiences

Scientism in contrast to science

to any evidence (experimental or theoretical), however rigorous, that contradicts the postulates or the assumptions of scientific materialism, or rather the fundamentalist *faith* of the materialist. The problem, and its resolution, would seem to be entirely with the conditioning and psychology of the scientist in question and have nothing to do with science as such. It is easy to confuse or conflate the practitioner with the practice.

> Refusal to believe until proof is given is a rational position; denial of all outside of our own limited experience is absurd.
>
> Annie Besant[38]

A Summary of What Modern Science and Neuroscience Proclaim about Consciousness

At this stage, a summary of the flow of ideas that underpin the position of mainstream science on consciousness, mind, and brain might be helpful. This view (presented step-wise for clarity) is typified by the latest scientific lectures and seminars on consciousness, for example, at the Royal Institution of Great Britain[iv] in London:

❖ brain = mind;
  …consequently…
  consciousness is an epiphenomenon (by-product) of brain activity;
  …which therefore…

Bottom-up, reductionist process

❖ can be discovered by experiments or scanning techniques like magnetic resonance imaging and positron emission tomography plus statistical data processing techniques;
  …to discover the big question of…

❖ neural correlates of consciousness along with mapping specific brain areas;
  …whilst all the while…

❖ keeping at bay philosophical conundrums plus the counter-assertions of leading dissenters in the field;
  …yet fully admitting that…

❖ our knowledge about consciousness spans the range from 'absolutely nothing to very little in just about every aspect of brain function'.[v]

Two points need to be stressed in relation to the above:

1. There are eminent scientists (like Edelman mentioned earlier) who are part of the mainstream culture even though their ideas do not accord with the extremely materialistic and reductionist approach taken by the majority of their colleagues. The summary shown above pertains to this extreme position—the majority ballot, so to speak—which is taught (with some exceptions) in the universities, colleges, and medical schools around the world.

---

iv Britain's premier scientific institution established over two hundred years ago, the Royal Institution of Great Britain has had fourteen of its resident scientists receive the Nobel Prize. Its heritage stretches back to scientists such as Humphry Davy and Michael Faraday, who are mentioned in H. P. Blavatsky's *The Secret Doctrine*.

v This frank admission was made by the neurosurgeon Henry Marsh CBE, FRCS at a lecture in the Royal Institution in 2004, which the writer attended.

2. Related to the above, the preceding narratives of this Chapter should make the writer's position clear that it is not materialism and reductionism *per se* that should be rebuffed or discarded; the rebuttal is warranted only when this approach is taken to extremes and used out of context as a universal explanatory elixir for every possible phenomenon, especially those relating to mind and consciousness.

Therefore, instead of a pro- or anti-materialism stance, as one invariably finds at philosophical conferences and debates, a helpful contribution to the philosophy of science, and the science of mind, would be to develop a clearer understanding of the legitimate boundaries of materialism, and those circumstances in which such an approach would not be viable or become absurd.

Materialism is valid in its context. It is not the same as scientism

A Brain Surgeon's Perspective on Mind and Consciousness

In 2015 the writer heard an insightful discussion between Henry Marsh (*b.*1950) and Jim Al-Khalili OBE FRS (*b.*1962):[39] the former, a leading English neurosurgeon, senior consultant neurosurgeon at the Atkinson Morley Wing of St George's Hospital, Tooting, one of the largest specialist brain surgery units in the country, Professor of Neurosurgery at the University of Washington, Seattle, USA, and a pioneer of neurosurgical advances in Ukraine; and the latter, the Iraq-born British Professor of Theoretical Physics and Chair in the Public Engagement in Science at the University of Surrey. Marsh's humility, gentleness, and deep commitment to the welfare of his patients, and the morale of the hospital staff, were outstanding. But what was striking was the statement that slicing through the jelly-like substance of the brain during surgery was 'slicing through our thoughts, hopes and memories'—strong echoes of Crick's dictum stated above. There was the unchallenged and automatic assumption amongst Marsh and Al-Khalili that consciousness is generated by the brain—no different from what Novella and Shermer have stated, but with far more modesty.

Consciousness generated by the brain?

So, we may ask: if, during the broadcast the writer of this work were to slice through the electronic components in his radio set, indeed he would be silencing the sound of Marsh's broadcasted words, but would he be slicing through Marsh's vocal chords or brain? By way of a wider outlook, if one were to smash a compact disc recording of—say Beethoven's Eroica Symphony—there could be no argument about ever being able to hear the music from that particular recording again, but would we be smashing the orchestral instruments, the score and ultimately, the composer? So, does the brain generate consciousness, or is it a transmission mechanism or transducer of consciousness? And what about NDEs where there is a mounting wealth of scientific evidence about detailed memory recall despite the subject being clinically brain-dead (as was the case with Eben Alexander described earlier)?

We remind ourselves of the philosopher Paul Brunton's wise words:

> Are the physicians and surgeons not already worthy to be called dead who know so little of their own selves, and so much of the bodies in which they are lodged?[40]

If a hesitant reader feels that the words of one of the world's greatest modern philosophers, mystics, and sages do not quite suffice for querying the assumption of brain = mind and that the thoughts of scientists would offer more convincing proof, then just two of several examples may be cited. Firstly, we quote Peter Leggett, a British mathematician by profession, who was a Fellow of Trinity College, Cambridge, Vice-Chancellor of Surrey University, and a Founding member of the Scientific and Medical Network. In his distinguished Leggett Lectures, we find:

> By analogy with a pianist and a piano, the mind corresponds to the pianist and the brain to the piano. If either pianist or piano is inadequate, so will be the music. If either mind or brain is inadequate, so will be the person.[41]

But if a tenacious reader would still complain that these are the thoughts of a highly distinguished scientist, but not a practising neuroscientist or neurosurgeon, then perhaps we must rest our case with two conclusive examples.

First, the mature reflections of a pioneering neurosurgeon, one of the few to whom Brunton's quip quoted above would certainly not apply—the American–Canadian Wilder Penfield FRS (1891–1976), once dubbed 'the greatest living Canadian':

> The problem of neurology is to understand man himself.[42]

> Although the content of consciousness depends in large measure on neuronal activity, awareness itself does not. To me, it seems more and more reasonable to suggest that the mind may be a distinct and different essence.[43]

Next, the thoughts of a British knight of neuroscience, Sir Francis Walshe FRS (1885–1973) who, like Leggett, puts his finger on the root cause of the conundrum—that of identifying the mechanism with its informing principle:

Distinguishing 'performer' from 'instrument'

> From sheer psychological and philosophical necessity [there is the] existence in man of an essential immaterial element […] psyche, entelechy, anima or soul […] setting him above the merely animal.

> It has also to be recognized that for the soul's functioning as an essential element in the hylomorphic human person, it needs some data, of which the brain is the collecting, integrating and distributing mechanism. Yet it would be quite childish to identify the instrument with its user, even though the user be dependent upon the instrument for operating. [44]

We will revert to Walshe and Leggett in a substantial Chapter reserved for Volume II of this work which explores whether the brain is just a 'wet computer'—the dominant neuroscientific viewpoint of our age. But for now, we may sum up by pointing out that the scientific viewpoint is just a viewpoint held by some scientists who believe it to be such and tell us so. That does not make it a fact. Such belief and viewpoint are underpinned by the paradigm of science which will be explained in detail in the following Chapter. It is important to grasp this in order to understand why, for mainstream science, the universe is thought to be constituted of just physical matter; and nature and all humans are bio-physical mechanisms and nothing else; for which the natural corollary is that the brain is the *generator* of thoughts and consciousness, which have a purely physical basis as summarized in the preceding section.

Viewpoints are merely viewpoints

To close this Chapter, reverting to the standpoints of Shermer and Novella about the allegedly 'deceptive mind' that needs to be honed into 'critical thinking skills' in order to 'think like a scientist', we are entitled to ask: 'is it more important to think like a scientist or to think, feel, and act as a human being?'

The Indian sage and philosopher Jiddu Krishnamurti (1895–1986) constantly admonished those who argued dogmatically from a particular point of view—whether as a scientist, a religious leader, politician, or in any other role, by reminding them that we are all first and foremost human beings, not the labels and concepts we accumulate about ourselves. This self-evident, but little recognized fact, was reinforced by The Russell–Einstein Manifesto in London on 9 July 1955 during the height of the Cold War—see Figure I-1. The signatories included eleven pre-eminent intellectuals and scientists, ten of whom were Nobel laureates, including, of course, the British philosopher and mathematician Bertrand Russell FRS (1872–1970) and Albert Einstein (1879–1955).

Human beings must come first

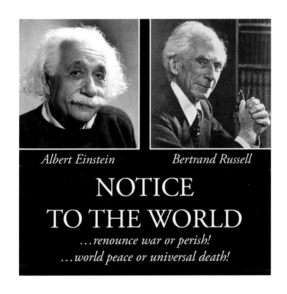

Figure I-1   The Original Russell–Einstein Manifesto
Image credited to https://commons.wikimedia.org,
montage by Artefact Design

One especially poignant phrase quoted often is:

Remember your humanity, and forget the rest. If you can do so, the way lies open to a new paradise; if you cannot, there lies before you the risk of universal death.[45]

NOTES

1   Isis, University of Chicago Press (Chicago, Illinois: University of Chicago), on behalf of The History of Science Society, University of Florida. See also 'Galileo's Letter to Kepler', posted 15 October 2010 <https://onefortyfirst.wordpress.com/2010/10/15/101310-galileos-letter-to-kepler> accessed 27 October 2019.

2   Francis Crick, *The Astonishing Hypothesis: The scientific search for the soul* (New York: Charles Scribner's Sons, 1994), 3.

3   Francis Crick and Christof Koch, 'Towards a Neurobiological Theory of Consciousness', *The Neuroscience*, 2 (1990), 263.

4   John Horgan, 'We Have No Souls' <https://www.edge.org/response-detail/10879> accessed 27 October 2019.

5   Gerald Edelman, *Bright Air, Brilliant Fire: On the Matter of the Mind – A Nobel laureate's revolutionary vision of how the mind originates in the brain* (New York: Basic Books, 1992), 166.

6   *ibid.*

7   Gerald Edelman and Giulio Tononi, *A Universe of Consciousness: How matter becomes imagination* (New York: Basic Books), 2001.

8   Philip Goff, William Seager, and Sean Allen-Hermanson, 'Panpsychism', *The Stanford Encyclopedia of Philosophy* (18 July 2017) <https://plato.stanford.edu/entries/panpsychism> accessed 19 October 2020.

9   Galen Strawson, *Mental Reality* (Cambridge, Massachussets and London: MIT Press, 1994).

10 Tononi Giulio and Christof Koch, 'Consciousness: Here, there and everywhere?' *Philosophical Transactions of the Royal Society London B: Biological Sciences* (2015).

11 Carl Vogt, *Physiologische Briefe für Gebildete aller Stände* [Physiological Letters for Educated People of all Classes] (4th edn, rev. and enl, Gießen, Germany: J. Ricker, 1874), 354. See also one of the best historical studies of materialism currently available in English by Frederick Gregory, *Scientific Materialism in Nineteenth Century Germany* (Dordrecht: Springer, 1977). The writer is grateful to Dr Andreas Sommer, University of Cambridge, for supplying this reference.

12 Paul Robertson, *Soundscapes: A musician's journey through life and death* (London: Faber & Faber, 2016).

13 H. C. Robbins Landon, *Mozart: The golden years* (London: Thames and Hudson, 1990), 14.

14 *ibid.*

15 Richard Westfall, *Never At Rest: A biography of Isaac Newton* (Cambridge: Cambridge University Press, 1995).

16 Rob Iliffe, *Priest of Nature: The religious worlds of Isaac Newton* (Oxford: Oxford University Press, 2017).

17 Steven Novella, *Your Deceptive Mind: A scientific guide to critical thinking skills*, 2012; and Michael Shermer, *Skepticism 101: How to think like a scientist*, 2013. Two CD courses with accompanying manuals from 'The Great Courses' <www.thegreatcourses.co.uk> accessed 30 November 2019.

18 Arthur P. K. John, *Journal of the Society for Psychical Research*, 80/2 (April 2016), 90–2.

19 Refer to M. A. Thalbourne, *A Glossary of Terms Used in Parapsychology* (London: William Heinemann, 1982).

20 Daryl J. Bem and Charles Honorton, 'Does *Psi* Exist? Replicable Evidence for an Anomalous Process of Information Transfer', *Psychological Bulletin*, 115/1 (1994), 4–18.

21 See for example M. Castro, R. Burrows, and R. Wooffitt, 'The Paranormal is (Still) Normal: The sociological implications of a survey of paranormal experiences in Great Britain', *Sociological Research Online*, 19/3 (2014), 16 <http://www.socresonline.org.uk/19/3/16.html> accessed 27 October 2019.

22 See for example K. Dalton, 'Exploring the Links: Creativity and *psi* in the Ganzfeld', *Proceedings of Presented Papers, The Parapsychological Association 40th Annual Convention* (Durham, North Carolina: The Parapsychological Association, 1997), 119–34.

23 W. Braud, *Distant Mental Influence* (Charlottesville, Virginia: Hampton Roads Publishing, 2003).

24 R. Sheldrake and P. Smart, 'A Dog that Seems to Know When Its Owner is Coming Home: Videotaped experiments and observations', *Journal of Scientific Exploration*, 14 (2000), 233–55.

25 L. L. Vasiliev, *Experiments in Mental Suggestion (Studies in Consciousness)* (Charlottesville, Virginia: Hampton Roads Publishing, 2002).

26 J. Utts, 'An Assessment of the Evidence for Psychic Functioning', *Journal of Scientific Exploration*, 10/1 (1996), 3–30.

27 Daryl J. Bem, 'Ganzfeld Phenomena', in G. Stein (ed.), *Encyclopedia of the Paranormal* (Buffalo, New York: Prometheus Books, 1996), 291–6.

28 Dean Radin and Diane Ferrari, 'Effects of Consciousness on the Fall of Dice: A Meta-analysis', *Journal of Scientific Exploration*, 5/1 (1991), 61–83.

29 Dean Radin, *The Conscious Universe: The scientific truth of psychic phenomena* (New York: HarperOne, 2009).

30 See Bryan Caplan, *The Myth of the Rational Voter* (Princeton and Oxford: Princeton University Press, 2007).

31 Peter Fenwick and Elizabeth Fenwick, *The Art of Dying* (London: Continuum, 2008).

32 W. D. Rees, 'The Hallucinations of Widowhood', *British Medical Journal*, 4 (1971), 37–41.

33 Ian Stevenson, *Children Who Remember Previous Lives: A question of reincarnation* (rev. edn, North Carolina: McFarland & Company, 2001).

34 Impressive literature also exists in the Scottish Society for Psychical Research
    <https://www.spr.ac.uk/link/scottish-society-psychical-research> accessed 24 December 2019; and
    the American Society for Psychical Research <http://www.aspr.com> accessed 24 December 2019.

35 Dr Eben Alexander, *Proof of Heaven: A neurosurgeon's journey into the afterlife* (Great Britain: Piatkus,
    US: Simon & Schuster, 2012), 10.

36 Esther Zuckerman, 'The "Proof of Heaven" Author Has Now Been Thoroughly Debunked by
    Science', (2 July 2013) <http://www.theatlantic.com/entertainment/archive/2013/07/proof-
    heaven-author-debunked/313681> accessed 28 October 2019.

37 Rajiv Parti (with Paul Perry), *Dying to Wake Up: A doctor's voyage into the afterlife and the wisdom he
    brought back* (UK: Hay House 2016); reviewed by David Lorimer, 'Deep Transformation', *Journal of
    the Scientific and Medical Network*, 122 (2016), 52–3.

38 Carolyn Warner (selected and introduced), *The Words of Extraordinary Women* (New York:
    Newmarket Press, 2010).

39 BBC Radio 4, 'The Life Scientific' (30 June 2015).

40 *NPB-5*, Part 2: *The Intellect*, 'When Science Stands Alone', 62, 123.

41 D. M. A. Leggett, *The Implications of the Paranormal* (First 'Leggett' lecture, University of Surrey,
    April 1977), in D. M. A. Leggett, *The Sacred Quest – By Experiment and Experience: The next step*
    (Norwich, UK: Pilgrim Books, 1987), 51.

42 'Wilder Penfield (1891–1976)', McGill University <https://www.mcgill.ca/about/history/penfield>
    accessed 30 November 2019.

43 Wilder Penfield, *The Mystery of the Mind: A critical study of consciousness and the human brain*
    (Princeton: Princeton University Press, 1975). See also in this context David Lorimer, *Survival?
    Death as a Transition* (Hove, UK: White Crow Books), 2017.

44 Sir Francis Walshe, 'Thoughts Upon the Equation of Mind with Brain', *Brain: A Journal of Neurology*,
    76/1 (March 1953), 1–18.

45 'Statement: The Russell–Einstein Manifesto', *Pugwash Conferences on Science and World Affairs*, 9 July
    1955 <https://pugwash.org/1955/07/09/statement-manifesto> accessed 28 October 2019.

3 The Paradigm of Science – its Ideology, Assumptions, and Beliefs

I am very astonished that the scientific picture of the real world around me is very deficient. It gives a lot of factual information, puts all our experience in a magnificently consistent order, but it is ghastly silent about all and sundry that is really near to our heart, that really matters to us. It cannot tell us a word about red and blue, bitter and sweet, physical pain and physical delight; it knows nothing of beautiful and ugly, good or bad, God and eternity.

So, in brief, we do not belong to this material world that science constructs for us. We are not in it, we are outside. We are only spectators. The reason why we believe that we are in it, that we belong to the picture, is that our bodies are in the picture. Our bodies belong to it.

ERWIN SCHRÖDINGER[1]

SYNOPSIS

Chapter 3 is critical for the *raison d'être* of this work. It argues that it is not sufficient for science and neuroscience to make their categorical pronouncements regarding consciousness, mind, and brain without a full understanding of the paradigm upon which these assertions rest. In other words, the philosophy, assumptions, and beliefs that frame the scientific world-view need to be thoroughly grasped. Accordingly, terse accounts are given on the philosophy and metaphysical basis of materialism and the requirement in science for causal closure associated with reductionism. The Chapter continues by exploring the scientific basis of mind, and the promising trend nowadays to supplement quantitative science with a science of qualities. Since this is a complex subject, the historical basis and genesis of scientific materialism are summarized followed by their joint influence on the ontology and epistemology of science, and associated implications regarding a scientific theory of evolution. From these arguments the natural corollary is the limits and limitations of science described in the following Chapter.

KEY WORDS: materialism and physicalism, logical positivism, paradigm of materialism, metaphysical foundations of materialism, causal closure, primary and secondary qualities, scientific basis of mind, science on evolution, ontology of science, epistemology of science, transcending materialism, Karl Popper, John Eccles, Arthur Eddington, James Jeans

Is reality just the physical world?

In effect, the epigraph underpins the essential content of this Chapter. Why? Notwithstanding the tremendous insights proffered by quantum physics, most notably that reality may not be equated with just the physical world devoid of consciousness, the modern scientific paradigm is almost exclusively based upon the assumptions of classical physics, namely, materialism: that matter is the fundamental and only kind of substance in nature, and that the emergence of life and all phenomena, including mental phenomena and consciousness, are the result of matter acting upon matter according to the immutable laws of physics and chemistry. This is what Erwin

Schrödinger so clearly realized when he said: 'We do not belong to this material world that science constructs for us', as quoted in the epigraph above.

In recent years, materialism has been modified and re-named 'physicalism'. This 'ism' is slowly creeping into the modern philosophy of materialism to replace the closely related earlier concept of materialism. This term was first coined in the early twentieth century by Otto Neurath (1882–1945), the Austrian philosopher of science, sociologist, and political economist who was a leading member of the Vienna School of Logical Positivism (also known as the Vienna Circle of Logical Empiricism).[2] He argued that the enormous strides in the physical sciences—for example, particle-wave duality, non-locality, the exchange of matter into energy, and non-material forces produced by particles—involved a more sophisticated identification of the most basic substance that exists than the rudimentary concept of matter, which has no fixed meaning. Physicalism can also be considered a variety of naturalism—the belief (and it is no more than an unsubstantiated belief) that physical nature is all that exists, and that all things supernatural therefore do not exist.

Physicalism an outgrowth of materialism

David Lorimer (b.1952) a Scottish writer, lecturer, former Chairman and current International Programme Director of the Scientific and Medical Network neatly captures the ethos of establishment scientists thus:

> Scientists do not always recognize that science is based on a number of key philosophical assumptions that underpin, define and even restrict the scope of its thinking. When scientists define science in exclusively mechanistic and materialistic terms and refuse to acknowledge the validity of other ways of knowing, they transform it into a dogmatic [ideology of] scientism.[3]

Metaphysical foundations of science

Accordingly, the overall objective of this Chapter is to unfold the hidden layers of meaning embedded in the above terse quotation. In the forthcoming sections we deal with the philosophy and metaphysical basis of natural science (a branch of science that deals with the physical world), and what it regards as matter, or physicalism, to use the term in vogue. In addition to the physical sciences such as physics, chemistry, astronomy, and geology, natural science also includes the life sciences such as biology, marine science, and zoology. Environmental science is also a branch of natural science—one that has naturally become increasingly important as our planet swings from one ecological crisis to the next. Mechanisms such as peer review and the replication of findings are generally employed in order to ensure the validity of scientific advances. Given the preoccupation in the West with the objective nature of science and the consequent emphasis placed on the systematizing and categorizing of knowledge, as well as the discovery and exploration of the laws governing each domain, the term 'Western science' is frequently used as a virtual synonym for 'natural science'. The distinction is, however, a fine one, as explained in the Definitions provided in Volume IV, which further outlines the genesis of natural science, explains its forerunner in natural philosophy, and describes the contrast between Western science and Eastern science in their respective philosophies and approaches to investigating nature.

We then move on to discuss the various versions of physicalism and how they underlie the scientific paradigm of mind. Concluding observations deal with weaknesses in the theories about nature and man when viewed through an exclusively mechanistic lens. Finally, we present an overview of the approach and governing assumptions of natural science and show how its ideas about evolution are consistent with its paradigm. The route map overleaf presented in tabular format should assist readers to navigate through what is necessarily a complex subject.

Major section heading	Subject matter	Intended purpose
The Philosophical and Metaphysical Basis of Materialism – Causal Closure	• Sets out the contention of natural science that the universe, nature, man, and all that exists, are entirely physical and governed by physical laws. • Establishes the arguments for the weak and strong version of causal closure, which asserts that all physical phenomena can be traced back to their antecedent physical causes.	To highlight the metaphysical basis of natural science regarding its view that physical matter is all that exists and therefore all phenomena and events will (ultimately) be explained by the known laws of physics and chemistry concerning the properties and interactions of matter.
Rationale for Physicalism	• Sets out the logic and justification of physicalism.	To set the scene for the descriptions of the various versions of physicalism in the next section.
Versions of Physicalism	• Explains the two principal versions of physicalism: reductive and non-reductive, along with the arguments used to uphold them. • Summarizes the objections raised from within science itself about physicalism, especially concerning the empirical evidence used to uphold the theory. • Outlines the problem of explaining mind, based on physicalism.	To show how the various versions of physicalism are reflected in, and can be correlated with, the 'soft' and 'hard' problem of consciousness.
Primary and Secondary Qualities – Their Distinction	• Summarizes the distinction between primary and secondary qualities (what is quantifiable and measurable, and what is sense-experienced). • Summarizes the objections to such watertight distinctions from philosophers, scientists, and physiologists from the Age of Enlightenment to the present. • Explains why materialism has transcended itself.	• To show the default position in science that mind can ultimately be reduced to, and then explained by physicalism. • To show the reasons why modern physics itself has produced the most important arguments against classical materialism.

Major section heading	Subject matter	Intended purpose
The Ensuing Scientific Basis of Mind	• Summarizes the mainstream scientific position on mind based on primary qualities. • Summarizes the objections to the mainstream standpoint from within the scientific camp itself. • Describes a modified version of materialism that takes in formative causation. • Describes the contribution of the new science of qualities. • Outlines the role of Goethean science and quantum science as complementary, holistic influences beyond the purely mechanistic paradigm.	To show how modified materialism and the science of qualities have emerged as complementary propositions due to the limitations of primary qualities to account for qualia (inner experience and sensations).
Concluding Observations on the Materialistic Paradigm	• To acknowledge the strengths, but also point out the weaknesses in the philosophy and metaphysics of materialism. • To demonstrate how the notion of causal closure has overspilled into an attitude in natural science of a closed mind regarding any avenues of exploration not within mechanistic confines.	To act as the rationalization and springboard for the further exploration and understanding of man as revealed through the Perennial Wisdom.
Materialism – Its Historical Basis and Genesis	• To outline the historical basis of the dominant paradigm of science. • To show the reasons for the progressive movement away from spirit towards matter.	To centre the scientific paradigm within its historical context in order to view the former as part of the ongoing stream of evolution and progression of scientific thought.
Summary of the Ontology and Epistemology of Natural Science	To summarize, in seven steps, the overall approach of science, highlighting its underlining assumptions.	To show that however we view the scientific paradigm, there is a circular and closed argument used to uphold its theories on nature and man.
Natural Science on Human Evolution	To show that the now virtually universally accepted evolutionary theory is a logical outcome of, and consistent with, the scientific (naturalistic) paradigm.	To point out the major weaknesses in the neo-Darwinian theory to justify and spur further explorations into the non-physical dimensions of man and the nature of consciousness.

The Philosophical and Metaphysical Basis of Materialism – Causal Closure

The obvious philosophical corollary to the position that physical nature is all that exists, or can exist, is that:

Metaphysical basis of physicalism

1. Physical laws, and nothing else, govern all objects, phenomena, and events in space and time.
2. Hence, the properties identified by physics form the fundamental nature of the universe and all its inhabitants.
3. So every physical event has a physical cause that brings it about in accordance with the known laws of physics. This is known as *causal closure* (sometime referred to as the completeness of physics) and constitutes the axis around which the entire philosophical basis of materialism, or physicalism revolves.

Causal closure

By claiming that not only is all substance physical, but that the very fundamental nature of the universe is physical—including all its properties and occurrences—causal closure has built into it the metaphysical position of physicalism (materialism). Simply stated, causal closure maintains that 'every physical phenomenon has a physical cause'.[4] It comes in three forms: weak, strong, and extreme. It is a matter of speculation whether strong and weak causal closure can be correlated to the strong and weak versions of the anthropic principle (explained in Volume III, Chapter 10). Nonetheless, it is important to note that the causation referred to is entirely of the type investigated meticulously by physics, namely, energetic in terms of fields and different forms of energy like mechanical, electrical or thermal.

Three examples of the weak formulations of the theory extracted from modern scholarly publications are:

Weak causal closure

1. 'Every physical effect (that is, caused event) has physical sufficient causes.'[5]
2. 'If we trace the causal ancestry of a physical event we need never go outside the physical domain.'[6]
3. 'Every physical phenomenon that has a sufficient cause has a sufficient physical cause.'[7] And, in the same paper, the author clarifies that 'in order to stave off the objection that a sufficient physical cause still allows for the cause to go through a chain of causes, one link being nonphysical, "sufficient physical cause" should be taken to mean "physical through and through".'

These formulations are held by philosophers of mind like the Korean–American Jaegwon Kim (*b*.1934) and the Spanish Agustín Vicente (*b*.1970).

But what constitutes 'a sufficient physical cause' is still ill defined, as will become apparent. Therefore, even at this stage, the term invokes an element of subjectivity.

All these formulations are implying that there may be other kinds of causes for physical events, in addition to the purely physical causes, as for example, the notion that, 'every physical effect that has a sufficient cause has a sufficient *physical* cause.'[8] However, 'the true theory of physics will not include mental (or, in general, dubious) concepts in its repertoire.'[9]

Two examples of the strong formulations of causal closure are:

1. 'Physical effects have only physical causes.'[10]
2. 'Physical effects have only physical causes'; moreover, 'the conclusion is that dubious events are physical events.'[11] Dubious events are those events that are assumed to occur from physical causes on a priori grounds, even when such events cannot be traced entirely to physical causes.

Strong causal closure

The strong formulations, then, assert that for physical events, any causes, other than physical causes, simply do not exist (and by metaphysical implication, are not allowed to exist). Another version asserts that 'physical events that are not causally determined may be said to have their objective chances of occurrence determined by physical causes.'[12] Alternatively stated, it means that even if we do not fully understand the cause of anything, we can still be entirely certain that such cause is physical. Needless to say, to enquire about even the possibility of non-physical causes or graded states of substance, or to question the understanding of what give rise to causes, is ruled out on a priori grounds.

An extreme version of causal closure is known as 'two-way closure'. Two examples are:

1. 'No causal chain will ever cross the boundary between the physical and the non-physical.'[13]
2. 'There is no causal interaction between the physical and the nonphysical',[14] which also happens to be the problem posed by the French mathematician and philosopher René Descartes (1596–1650), as many philosophers and scientists assert.

Extreme causal closure

This position argues that physical phenomena can have only physical causes and only physical effects. This therefore denies any causal transaction or interaction between body and mind and so the mental equivalent of two-way causal closure would be that mental phenomena can have only physical causes and only physical effects. Both these quotations do not deny explicitly the existence of the non-physical, but explicitly deny any communication or contact between it and the physical. However, it would appear that for Kim the non-physical, even as a possibility, does not exist since the mind-body problem is 'finding a place for the mind in a world that is *fundamentally physical*' [emphasis added].[15]

Sufficiency of physical causes

The paper 'Varieties of Causal Closure' by the contemporary American philosopher of mind, Barbara Montero (published in 2003 and subsequently summarized by its editors), presents a weak closure, allowing the possibility of non-physical causes of physical effects, requiring only that the physical cause be sufficient (for example, as long as there is a sufficient physical cause of bodily movement, the possibility of this movement also being caused by non-physical effects is not excluded).[16] By contrast, strong closure entirely excludes any non-physical causes of physical effects, 'thus not only guarantees the presence of physical causes but also the *absence of non-physical causes*: every physical effect with a sufficient cause has a sufficient physical cause, and it has *only* this cause.'[17] Finally, the extreme version imposes a two-way restraint on causal closure which is generally expressed as a one-way restraint, which denies any causal interaction between body and mind whatsoever: 'Physical events can have only physical causes and only physical effects (likewise for mental events).'[18] So, regarding bodily movement in the example just stated, there is no question that the movement of say, the hand is a physical act; however, any mental decision to move the hand would also be a purely physical act: the mind, like the soul (if it exists) are both entirely physical.

As clearly shown above, even within the materialist camp there are several hair-splitting differences of opinion, especially regarding theories of mind and consciousness. This work is not about the overall philosophy of scientific materialism: we are concerned with the latter only insofar as it bears upon our central theme of mind and consciousness. So, to avoid putting the reader through a 'cerebral gymnasium' of quibbling taxonomies, we break down an immense subject into three manageable facets: first, an outline of the various versions of materialism, followed by the principal strands of philosophical arguments put forward to support these various contentions; finally, the methodology ensuing as a logical consequence of the underlying philosophy.

Rationale for Physicalism

Physicalism of various types (see below) has become the dominant theory in the mind-body argument. Also referred to as *materialistic monism*, it holds the logical position that the only existing substance is physical, hence everything which exists is nothing other than its physical properties. Therefore, mind is a purely physical construct, and will eventually be explained entirely by the enormous advances that are occurring in physical theory, such as fundamental particle theory, complexity theory, evolutionary models, neuroscience, and computer technology associated with neural networks.

This sounds straightforward and simple, so why then does the mind-body problem generate innumerable (and interminable) arguments and sharp differences of opinion, not to mention a plethora of learned academic papers full of jargon and 'isms', attempting to uphold a particular point of view and falsify other ideas? We shall withhold the answer to this as it will become only too apparent during the course of Volume I of this work, especially in Chapter 4, where we summarize the deficiencies in the modern scientific worldview. Meanwhile let us move on to consider the two principal versions of physicalism, as stated above.

Versions of Physicalism

There are two cardinal versions of physicalism that are more or less mutually exclusive: reductive and non-reductive. They can be framed, as explained below, in terms of what the Australian philosopher of mind and cognitive scientist David Chalmers (*b*.1966) refers to as the 'soft problem' and the 'hard problem' of consciousness:[19]

1. The 'soft' problem is closely related to reductive physicalism, which argues that a mental state is well defined by physical processes. This is very much in line with Crick's hypothesis quoted in Chapter 2.
2. By contrast, the 'hard' problem is associated with non-reductive physicalism and posits that mental states cannot be fully accounted for by reduction to the explanations of physical sciences. This is in accord with Edelman's rejoinder to the Crick dogma, also quoted in Chapter 2.

We now outline the arguments for and against these various theories of physicalism and touch upon their philosophical basis and underlying assumptions.

Reductive Physicalism

Reductive physicalism argues that because physical processes are fully sufficient to under-stand mental states, the latter will be completely understood, and fully defined, when further scientific research results in a greater understanding of all the physical details and processes—but not the underlying philosophical basis, which is now regarded as well established. (This line of thinking has been called 'promissory materialism' by the philoso-pher of science Karl Popper, as expounded later in this Chapter.) Reductive physicalism is of four main types, shown below from contemporary academic sources, including well known proponents of psychology and philosophy of mind like the American philosopher David Lewis (1941–2001), the American behavioural psychologist John Watson (1878–1958), and David Chalmers:

1. Physicalism (Type Identity Theory, or Identity Theory), is a family of views on the relationship between mind and body.[20, 21] It holds that specific mental states are literally identical to specific physical internal states of the brain. This again is akin to Crick's hypothesis.
2. Behaviourism, which holds that mental states are just descriptions of observable behav-iour and that such behaviours can be described scientifically without recourse either to internal physiological events or to hypothetical constructs, such as the mind.[22, 23] It avers that psychology should have only concerned itself with observable events.
3. Functionalism, which holds that mental states (beliefs, desires, being in pain, etc.) are constituted solely by their functional role (the causal relations of mental states to other mental states, sensory inputs, and behavioural outputs), and can be char-acterized in terms of non-mental functional properties.[24, 25, 26] It further asserts that mental states can be sufficiently explained without taking into account the underlying physical medium (e.g. the brain, neurons, etc.) so that the former can be realized in multiple ways, including, theoretically at least, within non-biological systems, such as computers.
4. Revisionary physicalism (materialism), is a somewhat intermediate position between reductive and non-reductive (eliminative) physicalism (explained below), but closer to the former.[27, 28] It proposes that the mental state in question will prove to be somewhat reducible to physical phenomena provided that common sense concepts are suitably altered. However, the terms 'common sense', 'somewhat', and 'suitably' are not defined clearly, if at all.

> Can mental states be fully explained by physical processes?

Non-Reductive Physicalism

Non-reductive physicalism is a philosophical stance that maintains that complex structures or concepts can have irreducibly non-physical properties, such as consciousness and will. However, that does not mean it upholds any notion of non-physical or higher dimensional states of matter; it posits that there is simply nothing to the mind other than the brain, but the bases and language used in mental descriptions and explanations cannot be reduced to the language and lower-level explanations of physical science. Thus, mental states supervene (depend) on physical states, and, without some change in the physical, there can be no change in the mental, but the mental cannot be reduced to the physical at a lower level—hence this type of physicalism is non-reductive. A closely related concept is *supervenience* (see below).

There are four main categories of non-reductive physicalism:

1. *Anomalous monism*, which states that mental states or events are identical with physical events; however, the mental state is anomalous, meaning that although not regulated by strict physical laws, nevertheless, these mental states are real and identical with physical matter. Therefore, all mental things are physical, but not all physical things are necessarily mental. This hypothesis was first proposed by the American philosopher Donald Davidson (1917–2003) in the 1970s.[29, 30]

2. *Emergentism*, which involves a hierarchically layered view of nature, with the layers arranged in terms of increasing complexity, each corresponding to its own special science.[31, 32, 33, 34]

3. *Eliminative materialism* is another important category of non-reductive physicalism. It is a new position that took root in the 1960s in philosophy of mind. It declares that our ordinary, or common-sense understanding of the mind (so-called 'folk psychology'), is false and utterly flawed, and will eventually be replaced (i.e., eliminated) by an alternative, usually taken to be neuroscience. This is akin to Michael Shermer's views on the illusions caused by what he calls the 'deceptive mind'—refer to Chapter 2.

    On this basis, certain classes of mental states that most people accept unquestioningly, such as beliefs, desires, and the subjective sensation of pain, do not actually exist in practice. In this sense, it lies in opposition to reductive materialism. Some versions of eliminative materialism go as far as to assert that conscious mental states, such as pain and visual perceptions, are non-existent. Other eliminativists argue that because many everyday psychological concepts, such as belief or desire, are poorly defined, no coherent neural basis will be found for them. Instead, psychological concepts of behaviour and experience should be evaluated on the basis of how well they can be reduced to the biological level. The principal proponents of *eliminativism* about propositional attitudes (i.e., a mental concept regarding a proposition) are the Canadian and Canadian–American philosophers Paul (*b.*1942) and Patricia (*b.*1943) Churchland.[35, 36] As regards *qualia*[i] (properties of sensory experiences, or 'the way things seem and feel to us'), the leading proponents are the American philosophers Daniel Dennett (*b.*1942)[37] and Georges Rey (*b. circa.* 1950s).[38] According to these philosophers, introspection is an illusion.

4. *Supervenience* is an important concept within non-reductive physicalism. It is an ontological relation that is used to describe cases where the lower-level properties of a system determine its higher level properties. The argument for this is that whereas all physicalist theories of the mind are agreed that the mind is not a separate substance, they disagree on whether mental properties are physical properties, namely, mental states and events are merely physical states and events. This then invokes the question of reduction, and not all physicalists are reductionists. Those who are not, propose that the relation between mental and physical properties is supervenience, the idea that higher levels of existence are dependent on lower levels, such that there can only be a change in the higher level if there is also a change in the lower level (hence, the higher level supervenes on the lower level). But according to Kim, the 'mind-body supervenience itself is not an explanatory theory; it merely states a pattern of property

---

i The term 'qualia' derives from the Latin neuter plural form of the Latin adjective *quālis* meaning 'of what sort', or 'of what kind'.

covariation between the mental and the physical and points to the existence of a dependency relation between the two. Yet supervenience is silent on the nature of the dependence relation that might explain why the mental supervenes on the physical.'[39]

Philosophers who subscribe to supervenience, however, hold that the world is structured into a kind of hierarchy of properties, where the higher-level properties supervene on the lower level properties. So, according to them, social properties supervene on psychological properties, psychological properties supervene on biological properties, biological properties supervene on chemical properties, and chemical properties supervene on atomic properties. Reversing the argument, atomic properties therefore determine the nature of chemical properties, which then determine a distribution of biological properties, which determine a distribution of psychological properties, which ultimately determine the distribution of social properties. For example, mind-body supervenience holds that, 'every mental phenomenon must be grounded in, or anchored to, some underlying physical base (presumably, a neural state). This means that mental states can occur only in systems that can have physical properties; namely physical systems.'[40]

As a hypothesis, however, this is clearly falsifiable and indeed has been falsified by one of the greatest philosophers of science of the twentieth century—the Austrian-born British philosopher Sir Karl Popper FRS (1902–1994). Popper is especially known for his rejection of the exclusive adoption of the classical scientific method of induction[ii] in favour of empirical[iii] falsification. In other words, a theory in the empirical sciences can never be proven, but it can be falsified in that it can be scrutinized by appropriate experiments.[41]

Falsifiability by experiment

Objections to Physicalism from Science

Overall objections to physicalism concern the apparent contradiction of the existence of inner, subjective experiences (qualia) in an entirely physical world (also known as the *knowledge argument*). 'Hempel's Dilemma', propounded by the German philosopher Carl Hempel (1905–1977), attacks how physicalism is defined: if, for instance, one defines physicalism as the belief that the universe is composed of everything known by physics, one can point out that physics cannot describe how the mind functions; if physicalism is defined as anything which may be described by physics in the future, then one is really saying nothing.[42] Against this, it can be argued by the proponents of physicalism that many examples of previously dualistic concepts are being eroded by continuous scientific progress, and that the physical basis of the mind will almost certainly be known sometime in the future—again, a case of promissory materialism (see Karl Popper's critique of this kind of reasoning below).

In a paper published in the *Journal of Philosophy* the authors state that whether or not non-reductive physicalism is tenable depends on the empirical characteristics of each causal system in question. For systems exhibiting some instances of downward (top-down) exclusion, non-reductive physicalism is vindicated, at least minimally. Conversely, for systems

Problem of subjective experience and the physical world

---

ii Inductive methods are based on developing theories and systems by generalizing from meticulously analysed data.

iii Empirical methods are concerned with, or verifiable by, observation or experience, rather than theory or pure logic.

exhibiting only instances of upward (bottom-up) exclusion, and no instances of higher-level causes compatible with lower-level ones, non-reductive physicalism is false.[43]

Another insightful scholarly paper *Non-Reductive Physicalism and the Mind Problem* argues that non-reductive physicalism is false because it cannot completely uphold the concept that all substances are physical or are exhaustively composed of physical substance. And the reason is that non-reductive physicalism faces the thorny mind problem because its commitment to property irreducibility prevents what bears the mental properties, namely, the mind (otherwise stated as the self, or person) from being a physical thing. As succinctly put by the contemporary American philosopher and cognitive scientist Susan Schneider: 'As things stand, NRP [non-reductive physicalism] cannot deliver the most commonly agreed upon element of the physicalist platform: the view that all particulars are ultimately physical. Embarrassingly enough, minds outrun these.'[44]

The Problem of Mind

Causal closure, which was described earlier as a logical outcome of the paradigm of science, has significant ramifications in the study of metaphysics and the mind from the scientific standpoint. Given the view (rather, the belief) that everything that exists is entirely physical, or depends upon something that is physical, the essential properties of which can therefore be identified and described by the laws of physics (and chemistry), the overall stance of materialism regarding mind is obviously a natural corollary of materialism or physicalism: that mind is nothing more than the physical activity of the brain; therefore, adopting Karl Vogt's metaphor (see Chapter 2), *our thoughts cannot have any effects upon our brains and bodies, or other minds and the physical world any more than bile production can affect the liver*. Logically, then, the concept of reductionism supplements causal closure by claiming that all events can ultimately be reduced to physical events. As declared by Kim, this also applies to mental events that are not primary, but secondary; in other words, a subset of physical events and caused by them, hence reducible to them.[45] We therefore need to explain, carefully, what we mean by primary and secondary qualities.

Reductionism and causal closure applied to mind

Primary and Secondary Qualities – Their Distinction

The difference between primary and secondary qualities is a conceptual distinction in epistemology and metaphysics concerning the nature of reality. In short, primary qualities are measurable aspects of physical reality, whereas secondary qualities are subjective and dependent upon the observer. This distinction was most clearly articulated by the English philosopher John Locke FRS (1632–1704)[46] in his essay concerning the foundation of human knowledge and understanding;[iv] however, earlier thinkers, such as the Italian astronomer and physicist Galileo Galilei (1564–1642) and Descartes (1596–1650), made similar distinctions. Primary qualities are regarded as being the properties of objects that are independent of any observer, such as solidity, extension in space, and mass. Being measurable and quantifiable, these characteristics are supposed to convey just the facts that can be determined with certainty, since they inhere in the thing itself without any

Primary qualities independent of observer

---

iv According to Locke, the mind at birth is a blank slate gradually filled in through life experience.

reliance upon subjective judgments. For example, if a foot rule is straight, everyone would be in agreement and no one would really argue that it is circular.

By contrast, secondary qualities are those properties that result in internal experience (qualia) or produce sensations in observers, like sound, colour, taste, smell, and touch (corresponding to the physical senses). They are seen as the effect that things have on people and the nature of the effect varies with the person concerned. There is no agreed benchmark for evaluating the experience or sensation. For example, what is loud to one person may be soft to another person with less sensitive hearing; hence knowledge acquired through secondary qualities does not provide objective and independently verifiable facts and figures about things.

Secondary qualities: how things affect people

This brings up the difference between knowledge and opinion in science. The former is based on the primary qualities about which there can be no reasonable dispute as they are based on measurement and quantification; the latter is in the nature of knowledge that is vitiated by the secondary qualities of internal experience, hence it is prone to a variety of interpretations and disagreements. The distinction between knowledge and opinion, or rationalism and empiricism, actually goes back to Plato where opinion is identified with the senses, i.e., experience acquired through the senses.[47] Plato (428–348 BC) argued that because the information we get by relying on sense experience is constantly changing, it is therefore unreliable, so cannot provide any guarantee of truth. It can be corrected and evaluated for dependability only by appealing to unchanging principles, or 'Forms' that themselves do not change. However, unlike the materialist philosophers, Plato argues that such Forms cannot be restricted to the physical realm of quantitative measurements. On the contrary, the ever-changing flux of the physical world has to be transcended in order to grasp an order that will demonstrate the universal in the particular, a permanent rational order behind the flux of worldly events and experience. The whole question of the impermanence of the physical world is central to the overall theme of this work and will be expanded in Volume III. Meanwhile, we move on to explain why rigid distinctions between primary and secondary qualities have attracted the criticism of some of the greatest minds in philosophy and science.

Knowledge as against opinion

Quantitative versus qualitative

Criticisms about Rigid Distinctions

Legendary philosophers and scientists from the Age of Enlightenment until the present time have criticized the idea of hard-and-fast distinctions between obtaining knowledge through primary qualities as opposed to holding opinions based on secondary qualities.

Criticisms During the Age of Enlightenment

In his 'Discourse on Metaphysics', the polymath, mathematician, and philosopher Gottfried Wilhelm von Leibniz (1646–1716) argued, 'that the conception of the extension of a body is in a way imaginary and does not constitute the substance of the body,' stating further that, 'it is even possible to demonstrate that the ideas of size, figure and motion are not so distinctive as is imagined, and that they stand for something imaginary relative to our perceptions as do, although to a greater extent, the ideas of colour, heat, and the other similar qualities in regard to which we may doubt whether they are actually to be found in the nature of the things outside of us. This is why these latter qualities are

Metaphysics of Gottfried Leibniz

unable to constitute "substance", and if there is no other principle of identity in bodies than that which has just been referred to[,] a body would not subsist more than for a moment.'48

Another criticism came from the English philosopher George Berkeley (1685–1753), who argued that the ideas created by sensations are all that people can know for sure. As a result, what is perceived as real consists only of ideas in the mind. All we can know of the world is our reaction to it. Therefore, he made mind the yardstick of the reality of our universe and hence placed (immaterial) mind as the first and fundamental reality: 'All the choir of heaven and furniture of the earth, in a word all those bodies which compose the mighty frame of the world, have not any subsistence without a mind.'49 His theory which he called 'immaterialism' therefore denies the existence of material substance and instead contends that familiar objects, like tables and chairs, are only ideas in the minds of perceivers, and as a result, cannot exist without being perceived. So once an object is stripped of all its secondary qualities, it is not possible to assign any acceptable meaning to the idea that there is some tangible, identifiable object that is independent of the observer. This movement from the corporeality of material objects to the reality of ideas in the mind was a tremendous intuitional leap that presaged a central tenet of quantum physics two centuries later.v

In §13 Remark II of *Prolegomena*, the German philosopher Immanuel Kant (1724–1804) wrote, 'long before Locke's time, but assuredly since him, it has been generally assumed and granted without detriment to the actual existence of external things that many of their predicates may be said to belong, not to the things in themselves, but to their appearances, and to have no proper existence outside our representation. Heat, colour, and taste, for instance, are of this kind. Now, if I go further, and for weighty reasons, rank as mere appearances also the remaining qualities of bodies, which are called primary—such as extension, place, and, in general, space, with all that which belongs to it (impenetrability or materiality, space, etc.)—no one in the least can adduce the reason of its being inadmissible [...]. I find that more, nay, *all the properties which constitute the intuition of a body belong merely to its appearance* [italics by Kant].'50 This is clearly saying that primary and secondary qualities are both subjective; both are appearances in the mind of an observer. For example, the foot rule that appears in front of one to be straight is an internal sensation: no physical foot rule exists inside our eyes or our brain.

Finally, in the range of criticisms during the Age of Enlightenment, the great Newton famously cautioned in his *Opticks*: 'For the rays to speak properly are not coloured. In them there is nothing else than a certain Power and Disposition to stir up a Sensation of this or that Colour. For as Sound in a Bell or musical String, or other sounding Body, is nothing but a trembling Motion, and in the Air nothing but that Motion propagated from the Object, and in the Sensoriumvi 'tis a Sense of that Motion under the Form of Sound; so Colours in the Object are nothing but a Disposition to reflect this or that sort of Rays more copiously than the rest; in the Rays they are nothing but their Dispositions to propagate this or that Motion into the Sensorium, and in the Sensorium they are Sensations

---

v In the sense of the 'Schrödinger's Cat' paradox in one interpretation of quantum physics, which proposes that an object is a probability wave (in a superposition of states) until a perceiving consciousness collapses the wave function into an object, such as a cat.

vi *Sensorium* means the seat of sensation, or the sensory apparatus and faculties considered as a whole.

of those Motions under the Forms of Colours.'[51] For example, the colour red has a frequency of around 430 trillion vibrations a second, but the eye cannot discern trillions of vibrations a second, so how do we *experience* red as a colour?

Orthodox science has no answer or solution to this if it insists in restricting its purview solely to primary qualities and ignoring secondary qualities (qualia), as Schrödinger realized and as stated earlier. Moreover, the materialist's hope that the problem will eventually be solved by piling more knowledge upon knowledge, and amassing further mountains of data, is a forlorn hope and doomed to failure, for as Schrödinger further points out concerning the experience of colour:

> The sensation of colour cannot be accounted for by the physicist's objective picture of light-waves. Could the physiologist account for it, if he had fuller knowledge than he has of the processes in the retina and the nervous processes set up by them in the optical nerve bundles and in the brain? *I do not think so* [emphasis added]. We could at best attain to an objective knowledge of what nerve fibres are excited and in what proportion, perhaps even to know exactly the processes they produce in certain brain cells—whenever your mind registers the sensation of [say] yellow in a particular direction [...]. But even such intimate knowledge would not tell us anything about the sensation of colour [...].[52]

Erwin Schrödinger on physics and sensation of colour

Later on, we show how the equal importance of secondary qualities is steadily making inroads into the scientific corpus by way of the burgeoning science of qualities. Meanwhile, we remark how closely the thoughts of the likes of Leibniz, Berkeley, Kant, and Newton have approached the Eastern doctrine of *māyā*—the illusory appearances of real things—fully explained in Volume III.

Modern Criticisms – 'Materialism Transcends Itself'

That part of the above title in inverted commas is the same title as Chapter P1 of the seminal book *The Self and Its Brain*, aptly subtitled *An argument for interactionism*, by Sir Karl Popper, co-authored with the Australian neurophysiologist and philosopher Sir John Eccles FRS (1903–1997), who received the Nobel Prize in medicine or physiology. This large scholarly book (touchingly dedicated 'to our wives') is in three Parts: Part I by Karl Popper, Part II by John Eccles, and Part III comprising dialogues between the two authors.

Karl Popper and John Eccles on the fate of materialism

In Part I Popper argues that in 'thus *explaining matter* [original italics] and its properties modern physics transcended the original programme of materialism.' Ironically, 'in fact it was physics itself which produced by far the most important arguments against classical materialism'. He counters the argument of a modern physicist that physical things, like bodies or matter, have an atomic structure by pointing out that whereas atoms do indeed have a structure, that structure 'can hardly be described as "material", and certainly not "substantial".' Thus, the 'whole development beyond materialism was a result of research into the structure of matter, into atoms, and thus a result of the materialist programme itself.' For this reason, Popper posits that 'materialism has thus transcended itself'[53]—clearly realized decades earlier by Max Planck, who argued that matter originates and exists only by virtue of a force, which therefore precludes the possibility of conceiving matter as an objective substance (see the Proem, page xlv for further details).

Popper therefore points out that what he calls 'promissory materialism' is essentially an act of faith. In other words, if we adopt it, we are accepting a promissory note on the future

Promissory
materialism is
merely faith
of materialism. It is the contention of the writer that promissory materialism has been highly influential in the sciences because any doubt about materialism—no matter what the abundance, or lack of evidence—can be brushed aside and explained away as being 'anti-science' or 'unscientific in principle'.

In addition to objections to classical materialism accrued from the disciplines of philosophy of science and neurophysiology, similar criticisms regarding the notion of a fundamental reality attaching to physical matter as the primary quality have been raised from the scientific branches of mathematics and astronomy. Three great figures stand out, all Fellows of Trinity College, Cambridge and Fellows of the Royal Society.

Alfred North
Whitehead on
matter and waves
Alfred North Whitehead reasoned that just as 'a steadily sounding note is explained as the outcome of vibrations in the air […] if we explain the steady endurance of matter on the same principle, we shall conceive each primordial element as a vibratory ebb and flow of an underlying energy, or activity. Suppose we keep to the physical idea of energy: then each primordial element will be an organized system of vibratory streaming energy.'[54] Whitehead has thus reduced matter to a mode of vibratory motion (which can, in principle, be mathematically expressed)—a fact of pivotal importance to our further exposition on consciousness, mind, and matter in Volume III.

Arthur Eddington
on universe and
mind
The physicist and Astronomer Royal Sir Arthur Eddington pictured the universe not as a machine, but as an idea, or a great thought, in the mind of God.[55] To expand now on what was briefly stated in the Proem (page xlv), in the Introduction to his famous book, *The Nature of the Physical World*, he declares: 'The external world of physics has thus become a world of shadows. In removing our illusions, we have removed the substance, for indeed we have seen that substance [i.e. physical matter] is one of the greatest of our illusions. The frank realisation that physical science is concerned with a world of shadows is one of the most significant of recent advances.'[56] Then in Chapter 13, entitled 'Reality' in the same work, comes his outright assertion, *based on solid science*, that, 'the universe is of the nature of a thought or sensation in a universal Mind. To put the conclusion crudely—**the stuff of the world is mind-stuff** [Eddington's emphasis]. As is often the way with crude statements, I shall have to explain that by "mind" I do not exactly mean mind [meaning, not brain] and by "stuff" I do not at all mean stuff [i.e., not physical, ponderable matter].' What then of consciousness? Again, in Chapter 13 he asserts: 'Consciousness is not sharply defined, but fades into sub-consciousness; and beyond that we must postulate something indefinite but yet continuous with our mental nature. This I take to be the world-stuff.' In other words, the very 'stuff of the world' according to Eddington is of the nature of mind—something that finds unequivocal confirmation from literally every great esoteric and mystical tradition the world over since time immemorial. As summarized in Chapter 9, this has also been affirmed in recent times by the American artist, musician, and natural philosopher Walter Russell. However, Eddington fully admits that, 'It is difficult for the matter-of-fact physicist to accept the view that the substratum of everything is of mental character. But no one can deny that mind is the first and most direct thing in our experience, and all else is remote inference—inference either intuitive or deliberate.'

Primacy of mind
Where then does the answer lie? Not in the illusory phenomena of the seen world, but in the reality of the *unseen world*, its noumenon, as described in his book bearing that name in part.[57] Reaffirming the evanescent nature of matter with two bold statements:

'Materialism in its literal sense is long since dead. It is [...] belief in the universal dominance of scientific law which is nowadays generally meant by materialism'[58] and 'Matter and all else that is in the physical world have been reduced to a shadowy symbolism',[59] he affirms:

> The scientific answer is relevant so far as concerns the sense-impressions [...]. For the rest the human spirit must turn to the unseen world to which it itself belongs.[60]

This is a major theme of our work which will become apparent especially in Volume III where we explain the alluring power of *māyā*, popularly translated as 'illusion', in our perception of the world.

Then, using physical sight as a metaphor to make his point about the crippling limitations of the reports of the sense-impressions to which scientific materialism is wedded, Eddington adds:

> If in a community of the blind one man suddenly received the gift of sight, he would have much to tell which would not be at all scientific.[61]

Analogy with eyesight

To which we may perhaps add the oft repeated anonymous observation:

> We live in a conceptually enclosed, definition-based reality, held in place by peer review.

The astronomer, physicist, mathematician, and professor of applied mathematics at Princeton University Sir James Jeans, gives a very similar message to Eddington—again, on the basis of scientific facts, not hypothesis or conjecture. The last paragraph from Chapter III of *The Mysterious Universe* was quoted in the Proem, but bears repeating because of its crucial significance:

> The tendency of modern physics [speaking in the 1930s] is to resolve the whole material universe into waves, and nothing but waves. These waves are of two kinds: bottled-up waves, which we call matter, and unbottled waves, which we call radiation or light. If annihilation of matter occurs, the process is merely that of unbottling imprisoned wave-energy and setting it free to travel through space. These concepts reduce the whole universe to a world of light, potential or existent, so that the whole story of its creation can be told with perfect accuracy and completeness in the six words: 'God said, Let there be light'.[62]

James Jeans on matter and waves (light)

The Mysterious Universe opens with a full-page citation of the famous passage in Plato's *Republic*, Book VII, laying out the allegory of the cave about distinguishing appearances from realities (described in outline in Volume III, Endnote III-6).

It is too easy nowadays to dismiss the above with a condescending remark like 'of course we all know about $E=mc^2$'. However, the tremendous import of this seminal scientific discovery that there is nothing in existence other than mind (consciousness) and energy has barely scratched the cerebral surface of mainstream science, which is still wedded to materialism as the sole explanatory paradigm of reality and mind.

However, a deep irony remains. That which on the one hand seems so objective and real to our everyday sensate experience dissolves upon deeper consideration. No one could have expressed this paradox more wittily than Phiroz Mehta (1902–1994), the Indian-born Cambridge scientist, concert pianist, philosopher, and writer:

Paradox of immaterial materiality

> Despite all the findings of modern science, shake the branches of an apple tree when you feel like it and delicious but indubitably *material* apples will rain down on your head. You can be rest assured of that fact.

But equally true is the fact that every single apple will be composed of countless insubstantial subatomic particles![63]

This surely alludes to the fact that our very notion of materiality pertains to our sense perceptions, as Eddington fully realized; hence, in the deepest sense, this notion is a subjective experience, which we conceptualize and externalize as being objective.

After this necessary detour about primary and secondary qualities we will shortly explain why natural science is slowly realizing that it needs a science of qualities as an essential complement to the well ingrained science of quantities. Meanwhile, we revert to mainstream science and explain the basis of mind that emerges as a logical consequence of the virtually exclusive emphasis placed on materialism and primary qualities.

The Ensuing Scientific Basis of Mind

Given the weight of the foregoing, it is not hard to understand why, despite the pronouncements of luminaries of science such as Eddington and Jeans, mainstream science much prefers the illusory safety and security of primary qualities characterized by the measurable, ponderable, and quantifiable; and is therefore determined to explain consciousness in terms of primary qualities, i.e., the various brain states that can be mapped and quantified by experimental techniques. Accordingly, with respect to our thoughts, the orthodox scientific dictum is very much in line with Karl Vogt's 1846 contention, previously stated and worth restating: 'The brain secretes thought as the stomach secretes gastric juice, the liver bile, and the kidneys urine;' hence, 'thoughts stand in about the same relationship to the brain as bile to the liver and urine to the kidneys.' Accordingly then, mainstream science declares that in the same sense that the liver secretes bile, so bile cannot produce a liver; therefore our brains produce (secrete) thought and so our thoughts cannot possibly have any effect upon our brains, bodies, the physical world, and our actions.

Dominance of
mechanistic
theories

However, we have been at pains to point out, in some detail, that there have been robust criticisms of the sharp distinctions between primary and secondary qualities from the highest sources in science and philosophy; hence, science has no overriding basis or justification whatsoever in downgrading the significance of secondary qualities and adopting a one-sided stance that happens to be usefully compatible with its paradigm of materialism. Moreover, the enormous price tag attached to this philosophical position is the relegation of secondary qualities to literally 'second place' or not 'worth bothering about', unless they can be explained (away) in terms of primary qualities. Whereas, to reiterate, it cannot be assumed that observation is independent of the observer. The greatest of philosophers and thinkers have known that primary and secondary qualities are both subjective. And indeed, in this respect, examples from the Age of Enlightenment and modern times were cited above. Moreover, we will show, later, how some significant interpretations of modern science (quantum physics) have corroborated their findings in reinstating the central role of consciousness *per se*.

Predominance of
primary qualities
in science

Thus, to revert to the main theme of this section on the scientific basis of mind, in attempting to explain consciousness on a purely physical (neurological) basis, another powerful driving force must be noted. It is the phenomenal advances in natural science itself over the last century. It would be difficult to identify any other realm of human endeavour that has progressed by such leaps and bounds over this period as science and associated technology. This has unfortunately engendered a hubristic attitude of omniscience in the scientific community at large. And the technological issue is an important one, as it tends to be confused or conflated with science, for technology is the application of science but, because of their close coupling, it is argued on the analogy of hardware and software in computers, that there ought to be an equivalent technological basis to mind.[vii] The contemporary American philosopher Josh Weisberg takes on one of the most intriguing explanatory problems of our times: the challenge of fitting consciousness into our modern scientific worldview, of taking the subjective feel of conscious experience and showing that it is just neural activity in the brain. His book *Consciousness: Key problems in philosophy* concerns the complexity of current debates on consciousness.[64] He presents the range of contemporary responses to the philosophical problem of consciousness and also systematically deals with philosophical theories of consciousness. The extreme points of view are held by the dualist and other non-reductive theorists who hold that our basic physical ontology must be enlarged to include the intrinsic features of consciousness. Conversely, identity theorists and functionalist theorists hold that consciousness can be accommodated into the standard (i.e., materialistic) scientific picture provided that the philosophical platform is suitably modified. But as before with reversionary physicalism, the term 'suitably', is not defined. Moreover, it would seem that modifying the philosophical platform to accommodate the scientific picture is tantamount to moving the goal posts to achieve the intended end result.

Science a victim of its own success

In an earlier, but no less seminal work, previously referred to on the brain and the notion of self, Sir Karl Popper and Sir John Eccles admit with a refreshing humility (a rare quality indeed amongst top philosophers of science or neurophysiologists) their fallibility and the difficulty of the problem: the relation between body and mind, especially of the connection between brain states (anatomical structures and functional processes) on the one hand, and mental dispositions and inner experience on the other hand. Whilst fully upholding the notion of the intrinsic value of all endeavour to deepen the understanding of the human being and of the world we live in, both authors think it improbable that the problem will ever be solved, in the sense that the body-mind relation will never be really understood.[viii] As Popper says, 'The physicalist principle of closedness of the physical [...] is of decisive importance and I take it as the characteristic principle of physicalism or materialism.'[65] In that case, given the denial a priori of the existence of any kind of non-physical (or non-material) agency (i.e., the compulsory causal closure of the physical world), internal and subjective experiences that act upon, and affect, the physical body, are regarded as being either illusory or a subset of the physical, meaning material (physical) states of the brain. (In passing, we are entitled to ask, 'illusory to whom; who is the perceiver of the illusion?')

Popper and Eccles on body-mind problem

There are two possible ways out of the closedness, still within the realm of natural science: the theory of modified materialism; and a science of qualities.

---

vii   This issue is expounded in depth is Volume II, Chapter 7 where we enquire into the question of whether the brain is merely a 'wet computer'.

viii   Ample evidence is adduced in Volume III that the mind–body relation—intractable for natural science—has been understood and resolved by occult science.

Modified Materialism

Modified materialism is one possibility stated by the English biologist Rupert Sheldrake (*b*.1942). It is an elaboration of materialism (or physicalism).[66] Whereas conventional materialism (physicalism) avers that brain states are determined by a combination of energetic causation and chance events, modified materialism proposes that they are, in addition, determined by formative causation, namely, the morphogenetic (biological) fields that play a causal role in the development and maintenance of the forms of systems at all levels of complexity. (Sheldrake's ground-breaking ideas on biology and morphogenesis are discussed in Chapter 4.) For the present, it is important to note that morphogenetic fields are not energetic in themselves and so can bring about their effects only in conjunction with energetic processes. In order to illustrate the fact that not all causation need be energetic, Sheldrake uses the analogy of the plan of a house and its actual construction with bricks. The plan would be the 'formative cause' of the house, for it does not have any energy of its own or weigh anything; but it works in conjunction with the energy of the builders and the weight of the bricks. Morphic fields are the fields that organize the shape or form of living organisms—the invisible 'plans' that shape them, just as the architect's plan determines the shape of the house. The causal relationship can be traced back to Aristotle's Four Causes[67]—four kinds of things that can be given in answer to a why-question: material, formal, efficient, and final.[ix] According to modified materialism, then, conscious experience could be regarded as an aspect of morphic field(s) acting on the brain.

Formative and conscious causation must also figure with energetic causation

There is also the matter of conscious causation, if it can be acknowledged that the conscious self has a reality that may be dependent upon, but not derived from physical matter, using the simile that a pianist is dependent upon his piano but is not himself made up of wood, strings, ivory, and metal. However, any notion of conscious causation, with its obvious teleologic implications, is a complete anathema to mainstream physical science, which currently has enough difficulty in coming to terms with formative causation. We reserve full treatment about the conscious self to Volumes II and III.

A Cloud with a Silver Lining

Notwithstanding its preoccupation with primary qualities, our intention in the preceding sections has not been to convey an overly pessimistic or one-sided account of natural science: only, to reiterate, to underline its strengths and highlight its deficiencies when wedded to its own mechanistic paradigm. One of the greatest strengths of science is its unimpeachable adherence to discovering truth and its painstaking rigour in doing so. Within the scientific camp itself, and as a result of its own labours, has emerged a new light: the science of qualities which, in the spirit of Goethean science, puts the emphasis on the *whole system* of the organism rather than the component parts. This new science, along with other developments in the field, like quantum theory and the theory of morphogenesis (considered later), is slowly but inexorably uplifting the corpus of natural science towards a higher metaphysic and a wider perspective.

Systems approach is needed

---

ix The four causes are: the properties out of which a thing is made; the form, structure and design; the agency, or primary source, of the change; the end, or purpose, that for the sake of which a thing is done.

Background

Since antiquity, philosophers and scientists have realized that all natural processes have an aspect that is rational and quantifiable. But it was Galileo's crowning achievement to delineate a methodology of natural science in quantitative terms, i.e., in terms of a systematic study of number and measure. Ever since then, mainstream science has focussed almost exclusively on the measurable, mathematically expressed—mass, velocity, momentum, etc.—and ignored (or explained away) the domain of experience referred to earlier as 'qualia', such as beauty of form and texture, since they could not be quantified with certainty or precision. (The assumption here is that understanding the properties of the reacting molecules is sufficient to provide an explanation of the reaction and the molecules which are produced from it.) This resolve towards the quantification as a characteristic of our times has resulted in a science well adapted to the machine-like aspects of the world. The French metaphysician René Guénon, also known as Abd al-Wāḥid Yaḥyá (1886–1951), has explored, in depth, the contemporary influence of the reign of quantification from the perspectives of both Western and Eastern philosophy, metaphysics, and esotericism.[68]

Role of science of qualities and complexity theory

But since this very science has admitted, from within its own camp, that it is not at all adequate in answering to the active becoming, the contextual relatedness, and the living wholeness we discover in natural phenomena, its escape route has been to relegate secondary qualities to second place. But at the same time, despite the ever-mounting number of scholarly papers attempting to explain (away) secondary qualities in terms of primary qualities, there really is no escaping from qualities *per se*. We have just cited objections from such giants as Kant, Newton, and Eddington, to the sharp distinction between primary and secondary qualities. Referring to the epigraph, we see how Schrödinger hit the qualitative nail squarely on the head when he pithily remarked that understanding the mechanical constructs does not explain the living experience.

In modern times, another weakness of the science of quantities is its failure to provide satisfactory predictions for complex systems. Weather patterns, and an organized cloud of migrating starlings, are two of many such examples that resist solutions from a science with a strongly deterministic and reductionist methodology. Why? Because, in *every* sense, the whole is greater than the sum of its parts.

The science of qualities and complexity theory are the butterflies that have emerged from the chrysalis of the science of quantities.

Healing the Split

The recent discovery of deterministic chaos in dynamical systems (e.g. weather patterns) allows a reconciliation of the two, apparently contradictory aspects, of certain categories of natural processes that are intelligible, but apparently unpredictable. With this discovery, scientific knowledge, originally seen to make possible the prediction and manipulation of nature, appears now to point towards a new relationship with the natural world based on sensitive observation and participation, rather than control. This requires the cultivation of a new type of science, a science of qualities, albeit with its roots in the past. It is inspired by the scientific work of the German poet, playwright, novelist, and natural philosopher Johann Wolfgang von Goethe (1749–1832).[69] He grasped the unity of

Participation rather than control

wholes as dynamic transformations and the context-sensitive generative processes within the living organism, which he described as 'the real Proteus', necessarily producing diversity of form since context is continuously changing in the developing organism. Goethe's thoughts have influenced intelligentsia in the fields of medicine and natural science such as the English neurophysiologist, Nobel laureate in medicine and President of the Royal Society (in the 1920s) Sir Charles Sherrington (1857–1952),[70] the German Nobel physicist Werner Heisenberg FRS (1901–1976),[71] and Henri Bortoft (1938–2012),[72] the British researcher and writer on physics and the philosophy of science.

Goethe's Science

Goethe formulated his science more than two hundred years ago, but his contemporaries offered little in the way of fertile ground for his ideas to take root. Moreover, it is doubtful whether Goethean science would have taken off, even to the limited extent that it has, without the sterling contribution of the great Austrian philosopher, social reformer, and esotericist Rudolf Steiner (1861–1925), who recognized the significance of Goetheanism for the future development not only of science, but of human culture in general, and who developed Goethe's work in modern times. In fact, Steiner was the editor of the first ever edition of Goethe's scientific expositions; also, editor of the complete edition of Goethe's output ('The Weimar edition')[73]. Given Steiner's own profound understanding and research into science, esotericism, drama, and poetry, he was uniquely qualified to highlight and disseminate similar thought currents pertaining to the scientific-cum-spiritual basis of Goethe's thoughts and works. Moreover, he was able to reveal the esoteric wisdom hidden in Goethe's science as well as in his drama and poetry.[74] Steiner maintained that the source of the anthroposophical conception[x] that he taught was synonymous with the wellspring from which Germany's great poet and thinker had derived his creative power. That, 'it was with such a conception that Goethe approached the animal, mineral and vegetable kingdoms to grasp the hidden spiritual unity in the manifest multiplicity of sense-perceptible phenomena. It is in this sense that he speaks of *primeval plant, primeval animal*. And it was for him Intuition which stood behind these conceptions as the active spiritual force.'[75] So in essence, Goethe thought of the phenomena of nature as exhibited in plants, clouds, geology, etc., as a 'book of Nature' that could be read to illuminate processes that must be occurring in the inner life of each person. Up until the mid-nineteenth century, before becoming mesmerized by technology, the imagination of humanity was still learning from, and enamoured by, nature.

Steiner elevates contribution of Goethean science

Goethean science, therefore, deserves far more exposure nowadays when mass extinctions of species and alarming predictions about climate change, caused largely by human activity, are becoming daily news items.[76] Whereas there have been five mass extinctions in the past 450 million years, triggered by natural events like volcanic eruptions and asteroid strikes, the current extinction, however, is the first man-made event driven mainly by population growth, climate change, pollution and excessive hunting that are destroying habitats and damaging ecosystems more rapidly than the time needed for them to recover

---

x 'Anthroposophy', meaning 'wisdom of the human being' is Steiner's modern 'science of spirit' based on his work on direct knowledge and perception of spiritual dimensions, accessible with the precision and clarity attained by the natural sciences in their investigations of the physical world to anyone with the right training and willing to exercise clear and unprejudiced thinking.

naturally. A fine anthology of Goethe's science has been compiled by the contemporary British philosopher, cultural historian, and gardener Jeremy Naydler who is also a Fellow of the Temenos Academy.[77] The extracts in his book are essential reading to understand, in Goethe's own words, his key ideas on nature and science; and his qualitative approach to science and the scientific method, where he advocates the study of our world and nature as humans at home in it, rather than detachedly as mere onlookers.

Goethe and Steiner

Man or Matter is a classic book that combines Goethean science with the added insights of Rudolf Steiner.[78] Written by the German anthroposophist, Waldorf teacher,[xi] lecturer, and writer, Ernst Lehrs (1894–1979), it provides a step-by-step, scientific–spiritual method of investigating nature by means of which scientific understanding can be carried across the boundaries of the physical–material to the metaphysical origins and supersensible sources of all natural events, and thereby into the realm where is rooted the true being of man. This is a pioneering new method of training both the mind and eye, as well as other human senses, leading to a transformation from the conventional modern, third person perspective consciousness (detached and 'onlooking') to a new kind of 'participative' consciousness. Some quantum physicists have come to a similar understanding of the need for participative consciousness, although it is doubtful whether this has been influenced by Goethean science. For example, the American theoretical physicist John Wheeler FRS (1911–2008) prefers the term 'participator' to 'observer', stating, '"participator" is the incontrovertible new concept given by quantum mechanics. It strikes down the term "observer" of classical theory, the man who stands safely behind the thick glass wall and watches what goes on without taking part.'[79] Wheeler thus introduced a holistic element allied to a systems approach into the world-view of classical science which undermines the rigid distinction between object and subject (and between primary and secondary qualities) and invokes the central role of mind in the genesis of the universe. Notwithstanding that, quantum science does not appear to have undertaken any steps towards developing a practical or structured methodology based on this insight in the manner of Goethean science as taught in the Waldorf schools.

Participating with nature

Towards a Science of Qualities

The consequence of this new way of looking at nature and complex systems is a movement beyond mechanism and reductionism. The action of a machine can be fully described in terms of the forces acting between separate parts, which are coupled to one another in unique and specific ways to achieve a particular function. But when this type of mechanical explanation gets extended or extrapolated to the action of dynamical systems and living processes, such as molecular reactions, the results are unsatisfactory because of the unwarranted assumption that understanding the properties of the individual reacting molecules is sufficient to provide an explanation of the overall reaction and the new molecules or biological tissues that are produced from it.[80] This is something that the Canadian mathematician, biologist, and philosopher Brian Goodwin (1931–2009) realized.[81] He was a modern pioneer in the emerging science of qualities, the implications of which have yet

---

xi Education based on anthroposophy, or the philosophy of Rudolf Steiner.

to be understood and absorbed by the scientific establishment. He was also one of the leading dissenters of the ideology of modern evolutionary, genetic, and developmental biology.[82] Goodwin maintained that natural selection was a 'too weak force' to explain evolution fully and only operated as a sort of filter mechanism. Accordingly, he challenged the exclusively neo-Darwinist reductionism which saw organisms simply as carriers of selfish genes, and instead emphasised the importance of their self-organising power, complexity, and creativity, having grasped that a whole organism is always greater than the sum of its individual components.[83] This led him to develop a culture shift in science away from its emphasis on control towards participation with nature, by healing the split between facts and values, and, quantities and qualities. In this way he attempted a healing of the split between the communal left and right brain of the scientific corpus considered as a whole. Goodwin's vision and work are embodied to great effect in the courses (like the Master of Science course in holistic science) offered at Schumacher College, an international centre for ecological studies.[84]

Brian Goodwin pioneers science of qualities

The science of qualities is still within the confines of matter but may be regarded as a refined form of materialism and therefore an effective bridge towards newer and deeper ways of viewing our world and ourselves. It is still at an early stage (if not quite in its infancy) and much headway and paradigmatic ground clearing needs to be done before it gains a firm footing in, and acceptance by, mainstream natural science.[85]

Syntropy

The same sort of remarks apply to *syntropy*, a relatively new concept that is slowly gaining currency amongst a few scientists, even though the term was coined by the Italian mathematician Luigi Fantappiè (1901–1956) as early as 1942.[86] Interestingly, but not altogether surprisingly, this was during the same time that Einstein coined the term *ubercausalitat* (supercausality) to stress the need to extend the scientific paradigm of his time (largely the same even now in the mainstream).[87] The equations which combine special relativity and quantum physics show that in addition to causality, governed by the law of entropy indicative of a diverging tendency of the system in question, there is also retrocausality governed by a symmetrical law signifying a converging tendency characterized by an increase of differentiation, complexity, and structures. Hence, by combining the two Greek terms, *syn* 'converging', and *tropos* 'tendency', Fantappiè coined the term 'syntropy' to describe the retrocausal action of attractors and the converging tendency of evolution towards a final, unifying cause, which he termed love.

Retrocausality as against causality

Syntropy is the complementary principle to entropy, both being fundamental features of our universe. Syntropy, however, is not the same as negentropy, which is the opposite of entropy. Entropy, associated with the Second Law of Thermodynamics, is a quantitative measure of the dissipative process that indicates the degree of disorder or uncertainty in a closed physical system (hence a tendency towards divergence, as stated above). It is unidirectional and always moves forward in time. It has had spectacular success in scientific processes that are strictly deterministic and mechanistic; but singularly fails to account for many scientific paradoxes, such as life itself. By contrast, as proposed by Fantappiè: 'Syntropy produces a continuous increase in complexity through the action of "attractors" that emanate from the future and provide systems with their purpose and design. Rather than generating disorder via increasing differentiation, syntropy draws individuals and

Syntropy and entropy contrasted

systems together based on their similarities. In a certain sense, syntropy can be regarded as the action of love.'[88] And what is 'love' in this context? Powerfully articulated by the French Nobel quantum physicist Louis de Broglie (1892–1987) it is: 'that force which directs all of our delights and all of our pursuits. Indissolubly linked with thought and action, love is their common mainspring and, hence, their common bond.'[89]

The above strongly suggests that the activity of syntropy is teleological—the *bête noire, par excellence* of orthodox science—as expounded in the next Chapter.

Synchronicity

As the complement of entropy, syntropic information flows opposite to the entropic arrow of time, i.e., from the future, a good example being the experiments of Dean Radin showing causality from the future (also described in the next Chapter). Converse to generating disorder, syntropy draws individuals and systems together by their common characteristics and goals. Therefore, in this sense, *syntropy can be regarded as the ordering life force that emanates from the unifying action of love.* Similar concepts were developed by the Swiss psychiatrist and psychoanalyst Carl Jung (1875–1961) jointly with the Austrian physicist and Nobel laureate Wolfgang Pauli FRS (1900–1958), which they called *synchronicity*; and by the French philosopher and Jesuit priest Pierre Teilhard de Chardin (1881–1955) named *Omega Point*. (Teilhard de Chardin also trained as a palæontologist and geologist and is known for his theory that man is evolving, mentally and socially, toward a final spiritual unity.)

It is quite startling to find the word 'love' used in a strictly scientific context, but this is indeed the case. Furthermore, it is immensely reassuring to find that even a handful of top scientists are waking up to the fact that human beings are not complex machines programmed by a wet computer, otherwise known as the brain, but on the contrary, spiritual beings animated by the exhaustible force of love, so eloquently expressed by Louis de Broglie. The implications of this are inestimable, not just for science, but our whole culture. However, it is important to appreciate that there is no suggestion that syntropy will be the ascending star on the scientific firmament eventually to replace entropy. Entropy and syntropy are the complementary, balancing agencies in nature rather like yang and yin. In this sense, when taken together, the entropy–syntropy couplet could, arguably, be seen as an aspect of the *Śiva* (*Shiva*) principle of Vedic mythology: *Maheśa* (Mahesha), or *Śiva* the Regenerator and the complementary *Rudra Śiva*, the so-called Destroyer, for the breaking up of old and outworn structures in order that new, more complex forms may emerge to express better the indwelling life and the informing consciousness.

'Love' in a scientific context

Concluding Observations on the Materialistic Paradigm

The above exposition on the philosophy and metaphysics of materialism is necessarily only a representative cross section through an enormous subject where practically no overall agreement has been reached by the pundits over the course of quite literally hundreds of scholarly books and academic papers. Be that as it may, one cannot but notice the twists and turns of materialist philosophers and scientists in their resolute attempts to avoid invoking any notion of non-physical causes or mind and consciousness transcending the brain, which would obviously imply higher states of matter and being—let alone any question of divinity. We have just explained that 'physicalism' is the fashionable term used to replace materialism. But in reality, surely this is all just a game of semantics, as implied above, as both terms denote essentially the same thing: that all that exists, including mind, is ultimately physical and therefore can be traced back and reduced to the most elementary physical building blocks.

The central weaknesses in the materialist position are twofold:

Circumventing non-physicality at all costs

1. The unwarranted assumption about the primacy of matter. Re-labelling 'materialism' as 'physicalism' does nothing other than move the 'hot potato' from one hand to the other. Mixing metaphors, a rose is a rose by any name.
2. The corollary to this is the assumption that the physical senses are the only senses that a human being possesses. The vast corpus of mystical and esoteric literature (which terms will be fully defined later) the world over since time immemorial attests to the fact of faculties transcending the physical, which therefore enable man to explore higher dimensions of being and states of consciousness.

The main problem about evaluating evidence in natural science and Western (allopathic) medicine is the dominance of theory over observation and actual experience; in other words, theory driving experience, which is totally alien to the spirit of science where theory must continually be modified to align with observation and experience. The reason for this is that metaphysical and scientific questions are frequently confused and conflated because of the close connection between the metaphysical theory of materialism (or physicalism) and the mechanistic theory of life, a connection that Sheldrake[90] explains and which is also traced by the American philosopher Edwin Arthur Burtt, usually cited as E. A. Burtt (1892–1989).[91]

Theory dominates experience

Innumerable conundrums therefore exist. We list five chief ones relevant to the theme of this work:

1. The hardest nut to crack is the causal closure of the physical world. It is one thing for natural science to declare that by using the known laws of physics any event can be predicted with complete accuracy, if we know the initial boundary and starting conditions (i.e., conditions in space and time), as its cause; this supposition, incidentally, now refuted by complexity theory—weather patterns, for example, cannot be predicted with one hundred per cent accuracy. But who 'gave' scientists the laws of physics in the first place? This is the gaping hole in the causal closure of the physical world. As the American ethnobotanist Terence McKenna (1946–2000) perspicaciously puts it, 'What orthodoxy teaches about time is that the universe sprang from utter nothingness in a single moment […]. It's almost as if science said, "Give me one free miracle, and from there the entire thing will proceed with a seamless, causal explanation." '[92] The 'one free miracle' was, of course, the sudden and unexpected appearance of all the matter and energy in the universe, with all the laws that govern it from nothing, at a single instant—the alleged 'Big Bang'. Alas! the cause and manner of the bequeathing (not the use) of that 'free miracle' transcends physical science.
2. What do revisionary materialists mean about mental states being reducible to physical phenomena provided that common sense concepts are suitably altered? Is

Sciece has faith in miracles

common sense something that can be tailored to suit the physical phenomenon that is intended? What is common sense? Given the enormous diversity of human experience and culture, is there an agreed basis, or a common benchmark, or an independent repeatable experiment, for evaluating the common sense of humanity according to social groups or at large? How does one deal with the perennial problem of common sense, i.e. what is common sense to one person is invariably nonsense to another?

Mind-body conundrum

The answer surely lies in dialectics, or reasoning according to first principles. A premiss is agreed by all parties and sequential steps are followed, each step being assented to before passing on to the next step. If the process is followed assiduously, truth becomes self-evident. The practice is exemplified in Plato's dialogues which demonstrate the 'Socratic Method' whereby truth is educed from the interlocutor through question and answer. Such a process enables the participants to transcend any personality differences. Psychotherapeutically, when differences arise, it is helpful to remember that we cannot fully understand another person until we have 'walked a mile in their moccasins.' Again, the parable of the blind men and the elephant is helpful in reminding us that whilst our neighbour may insist that the trunk of the elephant is the truth and we may insist that the leg of the elephant is the truth, it is one elephant—one truth, greater than the sum of its parts.

Role of dialectics

3. What degree of downward causation vindicates non-reductive physicalism; and what kind of upward exclusion to a higher-level would render it false? The partial vindication of non-reductive physicalism by systems exhibiting downward exclusion is really a circular argument because non-reductive physicalism has been defined in the first instance as, *systems that cannot be adequately explained by reduction to the lower-level explanations of physical science.*

Circular arguments

4. Then, according to materialism, modified or otherwise, human beings go about their everyday business and adopt their belief system—including belief in materialism—as a result of physical necessities and all this is ultimately the outcome of chance events in their brains (quantum processes notwithstanding, and in any case not accepted by many scientists as a satisfactory explanation). Hence, life, and all experience, are determined by a combination of three factors: energetic causation—the domain of physics; formative causation—the domain of some versions of biology; and statistical improbabilities. The obvious corollary, then, is that other than satisfying biological and social needs, human life has no other purpose; neither does the universe, nor the evolution of life on Earth, have any intrinsic purpose and their destiny is ultimately at the mercy of chance events, otherwise dressed up in terms of statistics. But we ask, if human behaviour is ultimately geared towards satisfying biological and social needs, then who, or what, is the '*experiencer*' of these needs? Needs cannot be satisfied without a subject wanting to achieve such satisfaction. How do energetic causation, formative causation, and chance determine what a person's needs are and what criteria govern the satisfaction of them, given that at rock bottom all humans, including materialists and atheists, have virtually the same needs of food, shelter, companionship, and love?

Three ingredients of life

5. If mind embarrassingly outruns physicalist arguments, as proposed by the American professor of philosophy and cognitive science Susan Schneider (*b.*1968), then is it

not sensible to suggest an alternative, or rather a complementary argument to supervene? Erwin Schrödinger seems to think so, declaring in his famous Tarner Lectures at Cambridge that:

Weakness of
physicalist
argument

> By this [i.e. objectivization] I mean the thing that is so frequently called the 'hypothesis of the real world' around us. I maintain that it amounts to certain simplifications which we adopt in order to master the infinitely intricate problem of nature. Without being aware of it and without being rigorously systematic about it, we exclude the Subject of Cognizance from the domain of nature that we endeavour to understand. We step with our own person back into the part of an onlooker who does not belong to this world, which by this very procedure becomes an objective world.[93]

In passing, this vital insight accounts for the partial success, at best, of much of psychiatry that is centred on brain states, or on outward behaviour, and can only deal with the subjective problem by way of symptom suppression, using drugs.

The Serbian–American philosopher and Professor of Philosophy and Law Emeritus at New York University, Thomas Nagel (*b.*1937) educated at Cornell, Oxford, and Harvard, says much the same thing, whilst reinforcing the limitations of Darwinian theory:

Supervenience
points towards
esotericism

> I shall assume that the attribution of knowledge to a computer is a metaphor, and that the higher-level cognitive capacities can be possessed only by a being that also has consciousness […]. That already implies that those capacities cannot be understood through physical science alone, and that their existence cannot be explained by a version of evolutionary theory that is physically reductive.[94]

It is important to note that neither Schrödinger nor Nagel were arguing through a religious window. (We revert to Nagel in Volume II.)

If some of the greatest scientific philosophers admit the improbability of resolving the body-mind problem under the current scientific paradigm, is it not reasonable to look to a higher order of science and philosophy?

We propose, then, (in line with the thoughts of Nagel, Schrödinger, and several others) that supervenience, properly understood, is not within different strata of physicalism but a higher level of philosophy that supervenes or subsumes the physical philosophy. This higher philosophy is, of course, the esoteric and occult philosophies of the great mystery traditions of the East and the West that deal with subtle states of matter and with regard to man, his subtle bodies and higher dimensions of consciousness.

It is this higher philosophy that answers the candid admission by Popper and Eccles about the inability of contemporary natural science to resolve the body-mind problem. Before dealing with that we round off this section with some thoughts about the methodology of materialism.

From Physical Causal Closure to 'Mental Closure'

Maintaining
status quo at all
costs

Earlier we mentioned Karl Popper's observation about the decisive characteristic principle of physicalism, or materialism, being the 'closedness of the physical'. This closedness of the physical has had a major, not to say devastating, impact on the progress of the scientific investigation of mind; for it has resulted in the 'closedness of the mind' by limiting science (including, of course, medicine and psychiatry) just to the physical domain, and scientific research in general to highly vested interest groups—vested not only in the sense of acquiring funding or research grants, but the phobic attempt to uphold materialism and defend the paradigmatic fortress of scientific materialism against all other complementary viewpoints. This is no exaggeration.

It is indeed a matter of common experience and observation that those scientists who are solely wedded to the materialistic paradigm will protect the notion of physical causal closure at all costs and overtly display a 'closure of mind' in regard to new evidence that seems to violate their fixed position. Such new evidence could be, for example, authenticated cases of non-drug based cures for cancer, clear evidence of near-death experiences entailing vivid recall of specific events (i.e., veridical experience) despite the patient being clinically 'brain dead', and authentic cases of telepathy. The list could go on, but the common feature about the response of the scientists[xii] is this: their fearful and defensive attempts to maintain status quo and 'close the argument', i.e., leave no unanswered questions, and when normal physical facts fail, they will frantically attempt to explain *away* the evidence by any means possible, such as using statistical artefacts, or coming up with all manner of irrelevant (physical) counter-arguments or resorting to the usual overriding accusations of poorly designed experiments, experimental error, and fraud.[95] Recall Schrödinger's insight quoted in the Introductory: 'Science sometimes pretends to answer questions in these [higher] domains, but the answers are very often so silly that we are not inclined to take them seriously.'

Materialism cripples scientific progress

But when all else fails, the final resort is to overbearing authority. Indeed, several of the 'paradigm police' are immensely powerful authority figures in the world of mainstream science—Sir John Maddox FRS (1925–2009), the British chemist and editor of the prestigious science journal *Nature* to cite just one example—who would think nothing of crushing the career of anyone who dared to oppose his ideological beliefs, if such opposition were to result in new ways of viewing the universe or holistic forms of medical care, for the simple reason that immense sums of money and vested interests are involved, for example in allopathic medicine, which would be threatened by public perception of non-drug based forms of treatment like acupuncture or homœopathy. Maddox's intemperate remarks about Sheldrake's first book *A New Science of Life*, now in its third edition, are mentioned in Volume II, Chapter 7 of this work and his ruthless behaviour towards Jacques Benveniste (1935–2004), the French immunologist and head of NSERM Unit 200 (directed at immunology, allergy, and inflammation) is well known.[96] Strong and powerful egos are behind much of mainstream science and medicine in large multi-national corporations, especially the pharmaceutical industry, where massive finances and prestige are involved, more than the proponents are prepared to admit or are even aware of. *Deadly Medicines* and *Organised Crime* and *Bad Pharma* are authoritative and well-researched books painting a similar picture of systemic corruption in the pharmaceutical industry which has effectively 'bought out' the health system: meaning journals, medical education, doctors and psychiatrists, patient groups, governments, and regulators.[97] A more covert, but no less ruthless, operation of the paradigm police is to be found on Wikipedia. Scientists whose ideas are perceived as posing a threat to mainstream practices, and the funding that goes into them,

Policing the materialistic paradigm

---

xii We emphasize 'the scientists' for it is no fault of science *per se*. The practitioner and the practice have to be clearly distinguished.

have had major portions of their web pages slanted or eradicated. A classic instance is Rupert Sheldrake's talk 'The Science Delusion', at TEDx Whitechapel in 2013, which was removed from circulation by the TED community after being aired in response to protests from two hardcore materialists in the US.[98] Ironically, before the banning the video had a modest 35,000 views. Since then its clones have been watched over five million times and it has also been dubbed in Russian and has subtitles in over twenty languages.[99]

A matter of humility

What do we think these scientists should be saying when faced with unknown territory and anomalous evidence? Why not start with humility and the simple words: 'I simply do not know, but how interesting. Therefore, I will listen first and try to find out in the true spirit of scientific enquiry, without any prejudice or preconceived theories.' Alas! such thoughts hardly enter their minds, or equivalent words pass through their lips. How can the new be discovered from the standpoint of the old? When personal ego and pride obstruct the way, what room is there for dispassionate enquiry?

Freeing the spirit of science

So, what has happened, in effect, is that causal closure of the physical world has spilled over into an attitude of 'mind closure', or 'explanatory closure'.[xiii] Open-ended questioning is rarely welcomed in *orthodox* scientific or medical circles. Nonetheless, an international organization like the Scientific and Medical Network is a fine example of eminent scientists who champion the rigour and impartial attitude of science but seek to free scientific enquiry from militants who use scepticism as a weapon to defend an ideology or belief system, hence inhibiting the spirit of enquiry. The Network 'takes the view that the materialistic explanation for the nature of Reality is only one perspective [and] follows the guidelines of respect and open mindedness within a framework of academic rigour.'[100] Another such body is Skeptical About Skeptics organized by The Association for Skeptical Investigation and supported in part by The Moez Masoud Foundation for the Advancement of Science and Education.[101] It 'looks at ways in which scientific objectivity is compromised by vested interests, fraud, experimenter effects, and merchants of doubt who use scepticism as a weapon to further corporate interest.' Both of these organizations passionately uphold science, but not scientific fundamentalism. They recognize that healthy doubt and scepticism are important parts of scientific enquiry, but maintain that dogmatic, ill-informed attacks, levelled by self-styled sceptics (especially those who court the popular media), seriously obstruct pioneering scientific research, researchers, and the public understanding of science. They both have eminent scientists on their advisory boards.

In summary, given the scientific assumption about the primacy of matter, concepts like mind, spirit or even just ideas in themselves, are regarded as secondary, as products of material interactions. This is, frankly, an affront to the scientific method, which is a strictly unbiased and non-dogmatic approach to investigating nature through observation, hypothesis, then experimental testing and theoretical predictions and explanations about the phenomena in question, without prior commitment to particular ideologies or beliefs.

What, then, is the true spirit of science? Tersely stated by the Welsh judge and scientist Sir William Grove FRS FRSE (1811–1896):

> SCIENCE SHOULD HAVE NEITHER DESIRES NOR PREJUDICES. TRUTH SHOULD BE HER SOLE AIM.[102]

---

xiii 'Explanatory closure' is the term coined by Anthony Judge, a senior member of the Scientific and Medical Network, to connote the completeness of an explanation..

Materialism – Its Historical Basis and Genesis

> The second half of the nineteenth century […] was a period of enormous explosion-like development of science, and along with it of a fabulous, explosion-like development of industry and engineering which had such a tremendous influence on the material features of human life that most people forgot any other connections. Nay, worse than that! The fabulous *material* development led to a *materialistic* outlook, allegedly derived from the new scientific discoveries.
>
> Erwin Schrödinger[103]

The assumptions and methods of scientific materialism are a valid part of natural science insofar as they apply within the legitimate framework of physical science and materialistic enquiry; but they are not to be confused with, and are not synonymous with, the overall methodology of science in its wider scope. Having just expounded what materialism (or physicalism) proclaims as the basis of our world and our minds, it would be instructive now to position this viewpoint in a wider context—there are historical reasons for the current prevalence of the mechanistic paradigm of science. Accordingly, we explain the reasons behind what mainstream science takes as given facts, but which, upon deeper consideration, are its assumptions and beliefs that all follow in the wake of its dominant metaphor of the machine.

Beliefs taken for facts. Assumptions harden into dogmas

The predominant fashionable belief in the world-view of natural science has historical roots, which are important to appreciate. Materialism, or physicalism, represents one side of the Cartesian worldview that splits off matter from spirit (or mind). From the seventeenth century until now, the scientific worldview has prejudicially ignored the spirit aspect. Such materialistic assumptions (and they are no more than assumptions) progressively hardened, by degrees, into dogmas during the nineteenth century and fused into an ideological belief system that became known as 'scientific materialism' or 'scientism'. This is neatly encapsulated by Schrödinger shown in the above quote. It is also well explained by E. A. Burtt as constituting part of the revolutionary shift from the earlier philosophy of the Middle Ages where man was regarded as the focus of creation, to the later view about the less central role of humanity in the overall scheme of things.[104] Burtt has also described and conducted an in-depth analysis of the profound changes which have taken place in the philosophy of the Middle Ages to modern times, considering the works of philosopher–scientists, such as the Polish Nicolaus Copernicus (1473–1543), and the German Johannes Kepler (1571–1630); the English philosophers Thomas Hobbes (1588–1679) and Gilbert Ryle (1900–1976); the Anglo-Irish philosopher and chemist Robert Boyle FRS (1627–1691); and of course, Descartes, Galileo, and Newton.[105] His work is both a history and a critique of the changes that made possible the ascent and supremacy of modern natural science. In addition to establishing the reasons for the triumph of the modern scientific perspective, he explains the limitations in this view that continue to characterize contemporary scientific philosophy and thought.[xiv] At this juncture however, it would be instructive to touch upon the ideas of three leading thinkers of the nineteenth century, who were instrumental in advancing a scientific theory of evolution, even though their contributions were somewhat overshadowed by the theories of the English naturalist, geologist, and biologist Charles Darwin FRS (1809–1882).

Scienticism is the dogma of materialism

E. A. Burtt on the metaphysical foundations of science

---

xiv   It is ironic that Burtt's book was published just when behaviourism was on the rise.

Alfred Russel Wallace

Alfred Wallace on materialism in its proper context

The British naturalist, explorer, and anthropologist Alfred Russel Wallace FRS (1823–1913) was a younger contemporary of Darwin and the co-founder of the theory of natural selection.[106] He argued that a theory of evolution based entirely on natural selection could not explain the development of consciousness; moreover, that materialism could not explain how consciousness could exist at all (a problem that still confronts materialists to this day). In rejecting materialism as the sole explanatory framework, Wallace claimed that there is more in the universe than matter, but nothing that is beyond the scope of natural science when considered from a wider outlook.[107] (His ideas are expanded in Volume III, Chapter 10.) This is surely placing materialism in its rightful context: not as the ultimate paradigm but an indispensable component and aspect of a total natural science to embrace physical as well as spiritual realms. It is high time that natural science was released from its relentless association with purely mechanistic theories.

Julian Huxley

Julian Huxley on importance of teleology and synthesis

Another proponent of natural selection of the time was the British evolutionary biologist Sir Julian Huxley FRS (1887–1975). He remains an important transitional biologist in redressing evolution in that he also combined evolutionary theory with broader ideas about spirituality and the progress of humanity. Even more, much of Huxley's writings (like Wallace's) have a teleological aspect.[108] Therefore, he was not hidebound to materialism although he recognized its important contribution. Julian Huxley felt that evolutionary humanism was necessary for the betterment of our species. (See Volume III, Chapter 10 for more details.) So, it is not surprising that he became interested in writings that attempted to synthesize these differing views. This becomes apparent in his writing of the introduction to the translation of Teilhard de Chardin's *The Phenomenon of Man*, which alarmed his orthodox fellow biologists.[109]

(Incidentally, Julian Huxley's brother was Aldous Huxley who immortalized the term 'Perennial Philosophy', suggesting that this represented the highest common factor of all theologies; his book of the same name being an assemblage of key passages from the writings of those saints and prophets who have attained direct spiritual knowledge through union with divine existence, or transcendence.[110])

Alister Hardy

Alister Hardy on group mind and cosmic mind

Mention must also be made of the English marine biologist and expert on marine ecosystems, Sir Alister Hardy FRS (1896–1985), who was a close contemporary of Julian Huxley. Like Huxley, Hardy approached evolution from a broad perspective. Although he referred to himself as a Darwinian, and went so far as to deny the Lamarckian inheritance of acquired characteristics, he was a proponent of organic selection (known as the Baldwin effect, being the result of the interaction of evolution with learning by individual animals over their lifetime) and held the view that behavioural changes can be important for evolution.[111] However, Hardy did not restrict his evolutionary ideas purely to mechanistic biology and evolution. He suggested that certain animals share a 'group mind', which he described as 'a sort of psychic blueprint between members of a species'. He also considered that all species might be linked in a 'cosmic mind' capable of carrying evolutionary information through space and time.[112] His views on evolution could arguably be regarded as a form of vitalism[113] (see later regarding vitalism).

Hardy's concern about the relation between evolution, religion, and spirituality found its fullest expression when he gave the Gifford Lectures at Aberdeen University during the academic sessions on the evolution of religion presented in the years 1963–64 and 1964–65. These sessions were later published as *The Living Stream*[114] and *The Divine Flame*,[115] the former containing a chapter titled 'Biology and Telepathy' where he explained that 'something akin to telepathy might possibly influence the process of evolution.'

Value afforded to religious experience

The Gifford Lectures gave Hardy the spur to his founding of the Religious Experience Research Unit in Manchester College, Oxford in 1969 (moved to Lampeter University in 2000) with the objective of scientifically compiling and researching the accounts of people from across the world who claim to have had a spiritual or religious experience. Active to this day, the Research Unit reflects his deep interest in natural theology and the integration of his scientific worldview with his spiritual and religious impulse by developing a 'science of natural theology'.[116]

Summary – From Rational Materialism to Dogma

Thus, the late nineteenth and early twentieth centuries were promising times for a rapprochement between science and spirituality. Thereafter, materialism as a legitimate element of scientific thought gradually hardened into an ideology and then into a dogma. Despite the findings of quantum physics, this ideology became so dominant in academia, and learned societies in the twentieth century, that the majority of scientists unquestioningly believed that it was based on empirical evidence and therefore represented the one and only credible view of the world. This, in a nutshell, is the historical *raison d'être* for the present mechanistic and mechanical thinking in science where the whole must be explained by the motion and properties of its physical parts, exactly like a clock or a machine. The ensuing assumptions and associated methodology for investigating nature from this stance is, as we have just seen, reductionism which says that the best way to understand complex things and organisms is to reduce them to their constituent parts and in the ultimate degree, to the interactions between fundamental particles. Whilst giving full credit to the tremendous advances in technology and attendant benefits that materialistic philosophy has bestowed on our increased understanding and investigation of physical nature, our contention is that the near-total dominance of the philosophy and methodology of materialism in academia and industry, medical science and social values has seriously fettered the scientific investigation of mind, consciousness, and spirituality. Such ignoring or brushing aside of the inner and subjective dimension of human experience has led to a highly impoverished, distorted, and one-sided understanding of ourselves, our place in society, and how we relate to the overall scheme of nature. In this regard, earlier in Chapter 1, we mentioned the observations of the British political adviser Steve Hilton, supported by independent statistical evidence, that the world is not getting any better due to the degree of dehumanization in society through excessive reliance on technology-driven consumerism.

Excessive materialism stultifies scientific enquiry

Reductionism, then, represents the triumph of the Cartesian worldview. It is taken to extremes in the study of mind and consciousness. However, the situation is not entirely bleak. Heisenberg perspicaciously argued that by reducing things to ever smaller units we

Ultimate particle of matter is a figment of imagination

do not reach a final 'fundamental particle' but reach a stage where division has no meaning;[117] but it is doubtful whether the scientific community at large (especially at CERN, the European Organization for Nuclear Research) has taken on board this remarkable insight from one of the most metaphysically minded Nobel physicists of the twentieth century quantum era—see, for example, the proposal to build another hadron collider at CERN, summarized in the final Epilogue to this work.

Willis Harman on values and integration

Encouragingly however, as we have just seen, the science of qualities is a movement away from pure reductionism. Another positive step comes from Willis Harman (1918–1997), a Founding President of the Institute of Noetic Sciences.[118] Widely recognized as one of the practical visionary thinkers of our time, he was deeply committed to the integration of the spiritual and the intellectual plus the concomitant global transformation that he regarded as evidently part of our immediate future. Harman enquires whether the nature and belief of the observer, i.e., his consciousness, conditions what is observed, and he provides a wide-ranging examination of the role of causality in our understanding of what constitutes reality, and how things happen. Similar questions were posed by those who had reservations about the sharp distinction between primary and secondary qualities. We therefore propose that the fundamental assumptions embedded in the establishment scientific paradigm place blinders, or at least boundaries, on what contemporary science is free to discover. The obvious corollary to the materialistic philosophy that consciousness is either 'just an illusion' or 'merely an epiphenomenon (by-product) of brain activity' is discussed in depth in Chapter 7 of Volume II where we address, in detail, the popular notion that the brain is just a 'wet computer'.

Summary of the Ontology and Epistemology of Natural Science

The assumptions and beliefs of mainstream (establishment) science are part and parcel of its ontology (metaphysics of the nature of being) and epistemology (theory of knowledge and methodology of validation, i.e., way of knowing). Broadly speaking then, we can depict this ontology and epistemology in two ways: top-down and bottom-up. That is not to say that science is advocating a top-down approach: its approach is primarily bottom-up. (One of the few neuroscientists who advocated a top-down approach in order to place the emphasis on the overall system rather than the individual components was the Nobel

Top-down and bottom-up methods

laureate Roger Sperry.[119]) The idea here is to demonstrate that however we view the paradigm of science, whether from a bird's eye or a worm's eye perspective (i.e., from the 'top' or the 'bottom'), we see an essentially circular and causally closed nature of the arguments used to support its contentions about the universe and nature, mind and man.

The top-down approach is as follows:

God is irrelevant

1. God, or a transcendent power, by whatever name, is an unproven hypothesis.
2. Since there is no God, there obviously cannot be any transcendent purpose or meaning to our lives. (Nevertheless, we are entitled to wonder why the rabid atheists and diehard materialists are so passionate and vociferous in dogmatizing their beliefs about purposelessness, whilst attacking all those who politely disagree with them with robust evidence to the contrary.)
3. Both the universe and the life of the universe came into existence by chance events.

4. The universe is physical and so, logically, consists of purely physical matter, which, at any level down to the sub-atomic, is both inanimate and 'dead'.
5. So, evolution can be explained perfectly adequately by Darwinian theory.
6. Consciousness is an epiphenomenon, or by-product, of the physical brain and therefore beliefs and concepts of a non-material soul that survives the physical body are irrelevant.
7. Therefore, there can be no survival of consciousness after death because the death of the brain, which is physical, signals the termination of consciousness.

Compare this with the bottom-up approach which leads to the same conclusions:

1. Inert, consciousness-less physical matter is the primary property of the universe, hence observable, quantifiable, and real—presenting objective and repeatable facts to a detached observer.
2. That being so, the universe and nature are physical systems, so science is the best way to understand them applying mechanical laws by reductionism to elementary building blocks.
3. In which case, chance and necessity are sufficient explanations for the origin and evolution of (purposeless) life and so-called consciousness, which are both explainable by invoking mechanical and physical mechanisms based solely on the processes of physics and chemistry.
4. Since physical matter and its interactions are primary, physical processes in the brain give rise to consciousness/awareness/experience, otherwise known as mind—as an epiphenomenon.

Physical matter is the primary reality

5. Naturally then, brain equals mind and consciousness dies with the brain.
6. Therefore, it is taken for granted that all experiences—mystical/religious/spiritual—are secondary qualities, non-observable, unquantifiable and therefore, merely subjective opinions.
7. It goes without saying that beliefs about God, soul or spirit are unnecessary hypotheses at best, and at worst, immature superstitions.

QED

In essence then, the mainstream scientific view of the causation of life and mind is strictly one-way upwards: matter → life → brain = mind; i.e., inorganic matter is the primary; life therefore emerges from matter; and brain, which is synonymous with mind, emerges as the product of life. In this view, the death of the brain means the extinction of the life of the person. There is no question of after-death states or the survival of consciousness beyond the brain. The English chemist, Fellow of Lincoln College and professor of chemistry at the University of Oxford Peter Atkins (*b*.1940), perfectly encapsulates the materialistic view of life taken to extremes and inevitably associated with a total lack of any intrinsic purpose ascribed to the universe or to our existence:

Materialistic science on purpose and life after death

> We are the children of chaos, and the deep structure of change is decay. At root, there is only corruption and the unstemmable tide of chaos. Gone is purpose; all that is left is direction. This is the bleakness we have to accept as we peer deeply and dispassionately into the heart of the Universe.[120]

As David Lorimer astutely observes, this kind of ultra-materialistic creed, and any notion of a reconciliation between science and religion, is 'still popular in the [controversy driven] media as it generates the maximum heat and the minimum light.'[121]

Media prefer controversy to compromise

Despite the present predominance of the machine paradigm there are encouraging signs ahead. International initiatives towards a post-materialist paradigm, including the Manifesto for an Integral Science of Consciousness and the *Galileo Commission Report: Beyond a Materialist Worldview – Towards an Expanded Science*, are outlined in Chapter 5 and with more details in the Epilogue in Volume III.

Natural Science on Human Evolution

Notwithstanding the few notable objectors to the sovereignty of Darwinism (like Brian Goodwin and Thomas Nagel), the vast majority of scientists accept unquestioningly Darwin's theory on human evolution, as stated in *The Origin of Species*:

> Can we doubt (remembering that many more individuals are born than can possibly survive) that individuals having any advantage, however slight, over others, would have the best chance of surviving and of procreating their kind?
>
> On the other hand, we may be sure that any variation in the least degree injurious would be rigidly destroyed.
>
> This preservation of favourable variations and the rejection of injurious variations, I call Natural Selection.[122]

The two components of Darwinian theory are:

1. Natural selection, which is the process that maintains or promotes adaptation; it was proposed by Darwin to account for the adaptive organization of living beings. It works to ensure the survival of the most effective competitors in the competition for limited resources, and also in their response to changing environments.

Darwinism

2. Mutations, which are the accidental changes in the structure of genes. They are individually unpredictable, in every sense, because they depend on probabilistic (as opposed to deterministic) events, namely, the probability of such changes occurring.

The neo-Darwinian (mechanistic) synthetic theory states the above with a slight change of emphasis in that the driving force behind evolution has these two, coupled aspects:

1. Gene frequency changes caused by spontaneous (meaning accidental, or chance) mutations and hereditary variations which provide the gene pool with a continuous supply of new genes.

Neo-Darwinism

2. Natural selection which directs that the gene frequencies change so that favourable, or advantageous genes occur and are preserved in increasing proportions.

The logical implications of Darwinism for human beings are that:

1. Humans have evolved from common ancestors with the apes, rather than made in the image of God or according to a Platonic archetype—see below.

Humans share a common ancestry with the apes

2. Hence the argument for a God (or transcendent power, by whatever name) from the fact of design is rendered irrelevant, since there can now be design of the utmost sophistication, intelligence and complexity, beauty and self-consistency—but without a designer.

3. By the same token, notions about a soul are irrational if we evolved by tiny increments from prokaryotic bacteria[xv] and after that from the australopithecines.[xvi]

4. For the same reason the idea of an afterlife becomes an inference that does not follow from the premises, i.e. it is a *non sequitur*.

Concerning 1. above, the renowned American palæontologist, evolutionary biologist and historian of science Stephen Jay Gould (1941–2002) states in several of his books that he finds no documents of human thought more exciting than the notebooks the young Darwin wrote in London, just after returning from five years aboard the HMS Beagle. In *The Flamingo's Smile*, Gould asks us to consider this one pithy statement from Darwin's notebooks:

> Plato says in *Phaedo* [in which one of the main themes is the idea of the immortality of the soul] that our 'imaginary ideas' arise from the pre-existence of the soul, are not derivable from experience—read monkeys for pre-existence.[123]

Darwin and Stephen Jay Gould on Plato

In the same book Gould declares that 'science has no gods', but virtually every page of his copious books conveys the clear impression that, for him, Darwin is the god of evolutionary science.[124] But it is interesting to note the 'religious disputes' between Gould and his arch-rival Richard Dawkins on fundamental issues about evolution.[125] For Gould, then, this note of Darwin to himself stands as a glowing symbol of Darwin's achievement and key to a new view of life whereby Darwin transformed the entire intellectual world by cutting through two thousand years of Western philosophy with his theory of natural selection, which impinged on a whole panoply of issues ranging from biology and psychology, morality, literature, philosophy and, of course, the evolution of humans, plants, insects, and animals. Readers are at liberty to make up their own minds about the worth of a such a statement by Gould. But two facts are noteworthy.

Gould's rivalry with Richard Dawkins

Objections to the Restrictedness of Darwinism

Firstly, as the American essayist, lecturer, philosopher, and poet Ralph Waldo Emerson (1803–1882) wrote in *The Poet*, by confining its speculations just to physical matter, natural science is purely sensual (i.e., physical sense-based and materialistic) and therefore superficial.[126] The true scientist must consider the whole picture and deal not only with forms but also with the inner life (spirit) if he hopes to fathom the secrets of evolution and nature. This is also very much a Goethean concept of science. (We shall revert to Emerson's thoughts later in Chapter 9.) Secondly, as the astronomer Gustaf Strömberg (1882–1962) points out, Darwin stated in his later years that the accidental nature of the variation *may be only apparent*, possibly implying, without saying it in so many words, that in the end, the score is always settled by a higher power.[127]

This suggestion of a higher power, by whatever name, is also alluded to by the Gaia theory (Gaia hypothesis, or Gaia principle), advanced in the 1970s by the English scientist,

---

xv *Prokaryote* is a single-celled organism that lacks a membrane-bound nucleus (karyon), mitochondria, or any other membrane-bound organelles.

xvi *Australopithecines* is a group of higher primates whose bones were first excavated in the Kalahari Desert (South Africa) in 1924 and later in east and central Africa.

environmentalist, and futurist James Lovelock FRS (*b*.1919) and the American evolutionary theorist and biologist Lynn Margulis (1938–2011). It proposes that organisms interact with their inorganic surroundings on Earth to form a self-regulating, complex system that helps to maintain the conditions for life on the planet.[128, 129] Another similar concept was introduced in 1972 by the Chilean biologist, philosopher, and neuroscientist Francisco Varela (1946–2001) who, together with his teacher, the Chilean biologist Humberto Maturana (*b*.1928) is best known for introducing the concept of autopoiesis. The term is derived from the Greek αὐτο- (auto), meaning 'self', and ποίησις (poiesis), meaning 'creation', or 'production'. It was introduced in 1972 by the two Chilean biologists to define the self-maintaining chemistry of living cells, such that a system is capable of reproducing and maintaining itself.

However, the teleological implications of Gaia theory and autopoiesis have, unsurprisingly, attracted criticism from scientists who uphold the ideas of chance and necessity central to the theory of natural selection—a classic demonstration of the 'map driving the territory', namely, the refusal to look at any new evidence or ideas that contradict an established theory now become a dogma. Interestingly though, later in life Darwin's suspicions about the apparently accidental nature of variations were echoed by his contemporary Alfred Russel Wallace. As stated earlier, Wallace independently conceived the theory of evolution through natural selection and published a paper in 1858 on the subject jointly with some of Darwin's writings, which spurred Darwin to publish his own ideas in *On the Origin of Species* a year later.[130] Wallace's especial contribution was to combine evolutionism with spiritualism and to understand human evolution and evolutionary ethics within a spiritualistic teleology.[131, 132] Unsurprisingly then, Wallace was also a staunch supporter of spiritualism and thought that 'naturalists are now beginning to look beyond this, and to see that there must be some other principle regulating the infinitely varied forms of animal life.'[133] But it is singularly unfortunate, however, that neither Darwin's later premonitions, nor Wallace's further speculations on evolution, have ever gained the same foothold as Darwin's central theories. Had that been so, evolution, as understood by mainstream science, might not have suffered from the stranglehold of mechanistic and materialistic concepts, as is the case today.

The neo-Darwinists ardently maintain that their explanation of human evolution (as summarized above) in no way detracts from human dignity or the majesty of the world. Of course, if all this were true, then a human being would be entirely synonymous with his physical body and all talk of subtle bodies would be mere conjecture. The next Chapter elucidates the main reasons why such a claim is to be doubted; and Chapter 10 of Volume III includes further details about Darwinism set alongside a detailed exposition on evolution from the standpoint of the *philosophia perennis*.

Having expounded the scientific paradigm, its metaphysical underpinnings and assumptions, the next Chapter explains how these factors have limited science in its investigation of the wider vistas of nature and mind.

Meanwhile, we close with another pithy saying by Schrödinger who again puts his finger neatly on the problematic pulse by addressing that most fundamental of all questions with which we opened the Proem, and in response to the deficiencies of the exclusively scientific world-view stated in the epigraph to this Chapter:

> *It seems plain and self-evident, yet it needs to be said: the isolated knowledge obtained by a group of specialists in a narrow field has in itself no value whatsoever, but only in its synthesis with all the rest of knowledge and only inasmuch as it really contributes in this synthesis toward answering the demand τίνες δέ ήμείς ('who are we?').*

ERWIN SCHRÖDINGER[134]

NOTES

1   Erwin Schrödinger, 'Nature and the Greeks' from the Shearman Lectures delivered at University College, London, 1948, in *Nature and the Greeks and Science and Humanism*, foreword by Roger Penrose (Cambridge: Cambridge University Press, 1961), 95, 96. See also Ken Wilber (ed.) *Quantum Questions: Mystical writings of the world's great physicists* (Boston and London: Shambhala, 1985), 75–97.

2   Otto Neurath, 'Radical Physicalism and the "Real World"', in *Philosophical Papers 1913–1946* (Dodrecht, Holland: D. Reidel Publishing Company, 1983), 100–14.

3   David Lorimer, *Radical Prince: The practical vision of the Prince of Wales* (Edinburgh: Floris Books, 2003), 389.

4   Barbara Montero, 'Varieties of Causal Closure', in Sven Walter and Heinz-Dieter Heckmann (eds.), *Physicalism and Mental Causation: The metaphysics of mind and action* (Charlottesville, Va.: Imprint Academic, 2003), 177.

5   Agustin Vicente, 'On the Causal Completeness of Physics', *International Studies in the Philosophy of Science*, 20/2 (2006), 150.

6   Jaegwon Kim, *Supervenience and Mind: Selected philosophical essays*, ed. Ernest Sosa, Cambridge Studies in Philosophy (Cambridge: Cambridge University Press, 1993; repr 1999), 280.

7   Barbara Montero, 'Varieties of Causal Closure', 177.

8   Sahotra Sarkar and Jessica Pfeifer (eds), 'Physicalism: The causal impact argument', in *The Philosophy of Science: An encyclopedia* (New York: Routledge Taylor & Francis Group, 2006), 566.

9   Agustin Vicente, 'On the Causal Completeness of Physics', 168 n. 5.

10 Barbara Montero, 'Varieties of Causal Closure', 178.

11 Agustin Vicente, 'On the Causal Completeness of Physics', 150.

12 Sahotra Sarkar and Jessica Pfeifer, 'Physicalism', 566.

13 Jaegwon Kim, the 1996 Townsend Lectures, in *Mind in a Physical World. An essay on the mind-body problem and mental causation* (Cambridge, Massachusetts: MIT Press, 1998), 40.

14 Barbara Montero, 'Varieties of Causal Closure', 178.

15 Jaegwon Kim, *Supervenience and Mind*, 2.

16 Barbara Montero, 'Varieties of Causal Closure', 178.

17 Introd. to Part II: 'Overdetermination and the Causal Closure of the Physical', in Sven Walter and Heinz-Dieter Heckmann (eds), *Physicalism and Mental Causation: The metaphysics of mind and action* (Charlottesville, Va.: Imprint Academic, 2003), 138.

18 *ibid.*

19 David J. Chalmers, 'Facing Up to the Problem of Consciousness', *Journal of Consciousness Studies*, 2/3 (1995), 200–19.

20 David Lewis, 'An Argument for the Identity Theory', *Journal of Philosophy*, 63 (1966), 17–25.

21 John Jamieson Carswell Smart, 'The Mind/Brain Identity Theory', *The Stanford Encyclopedia of Philosophy* (18 May 2007) <https://plato.stanford.edu/archives/spr2017/entries/mind-identity> accessed 18 October 2020.

22 John B. Watson, 'Psychology as the Behaviorist Views It', *Psychological Review*, 20 (1913), 158–77.

23 John A. Mills, *Control: A history of behavioral psychology* (New York University Press, 2000).

24 Ned Block, 'What is Functionalism?' a revised version of the entry on functionalism in *The Encyclopedia of Philosophy Supplement* (Macmillan, 1996).

25 David J. Chalmers, *The Conscious Mind* (Oxford: Oxford University Press, 1996).

26 Janet Levin, 'Functionalism', *The Stanford Encyclopedia of Philosophy* (20 July 2018) <https://plato.stanford.edu/entries/functionalism> accessed 18 October 2020.

27 John Bickle, 'Revisionary Physicalism', *Biology and Philosophy*, 7/4 (1992), 411–30.

28 William Ramsey, 'Eliminative Materialism', *The Stanford Encyclopedia of Philosophy* (11 March 2019) <https://plato.stanford.edu/entries/materialism-eliminative> accessed 18 October 2020.

29 Donald Davidson, 'Mental Events', in *Essays on Actions and Events* (Oxford: Clarendon Press, 1980), 207–24.

30 Steven Yalowitz, 'Anomalous Monism', *The Stanford Encyclopedia of Philosophy* (6 September 2019) <https://plato.stanford.edu/entries/anomalous-monism> accessed 19 October 2020.

31 J. J. Clarke, *The Self-Creating Universe: The making of a worldview* (Xlibris publishing, 2013).

32 S. Kauffman, *At Home in the Universe: The search for the laws of self-organization and complexity* (New York: Oxford University Press, 1993).

33 A. Beckermann, H. Flohr and J. Kim (eds), *Emergence or Reduction?* (Berlin: Walter de Gruyter, 1992).

34 Timothy O'Connor, 'Emergent Properties', *The Stanford Encyclopedia of Philosophy* (10 August 2020) <https://plato.stanford.edu/entries/properties-emergent> accessed 19 October 2020.

35 Patricia Churchland, 'Eliminative Materialism and the Propositional Attitudes', *Journal of Philosophy*, 78 (1981), 67–90.

36 Patricia Churchland and Paul Churchland, 'Recent Work on Consciousness: Philosophical, empirical and theoretical', *Seminars in Neurology*, 17 (1997), 101–8.

37 Daniel Dennett, 'Why You Can't Make a Computer that Feels Pain', in *Brainstorms* (Cambridge, Mass.: MIT Press, 1978), 190–229.
—— 'Quining Qualia', in A. Marcel and E. Bisiach (eds), *Consciousness in Contemporary Science* (New York: Oxford University Press, 1988), 42–77.

38 Georges Rey, 'A Reason for Doubting the Existence of Consciousness', in R. Davidson, G. Schwartz, and D. Shapiro (eds), *Consciousness and Self-Regulation* (New York: Plenum, 1983), 1–39.

39 Jaegwon Kim, *Mind in a Physical World*, 40.

40 Brian McLaughlin, Ansgar Beckermann, and Sven Walter (eds), 'Mental Causation', in *The Oxford Handbook of Philosophy of Mind* (Oxford: University Press, 2009), 40.

41 Karl Popper, *The Logic of Scientific Discovery* (Abingdon, Oxon and New York: Routledge Classics, 2002). See especially Part I: 'Falsifiability as a Criterion of Demarcation', 17; and Part II: 'Falsifiability', 57.

42 Carl Gustav Hempel, 'Reduction: Ontological and linguistic facets', in S. Morgenbesser, P. Suppes, and M. White (eds), *Philosophy, Science, and Method: Essays in honor of Ernest Nagel* (New York: St. Martins Press, 1969), 179–99.

43 Christian List and Peter Menzies, 'Non-reductive Physicalism and the Limits of the Exclusion Principle', *Journal of Philosophy*, 106/9 (2009), 475–502.

44 Susan Schneider, 'Non-Reductive Physicalism and the Mind Problem' (University of Pennsylvania, Wiley Periodicals, 2011), 1–22.

45 Jaegwon Kim, 'The Myth of Non-Reductive Materialism', *Proceedings and Addresses of the American Philosophical Association*, 63/3 (2003), 31–47.

46 John Locke, 'An Essay Concerning Human Understanding (1690)' (University of Adelaide Library, Adelaide, South Australia).

47 See for example Plato, *Phaedo* (Createspace, 2013), Section 73c.

48 G. W. Leibnitz, *Discourse on Metaphysics, XII*, 1686 (Open Court Publishing Company, 1902). See also D. S. Clarke (ed.), *Panpsychism: Past and recent selected readings* (New York: State University of New York Press, 2004), 48–9.

49 'The Distinction between Primary and Secondary Qualities', in George Berkeley, *A Treatise Concerning the Principles of Human Knowledge*, ed. Jonathan Dancy (Oxford: Oxford University Press, 1998), §6.

50 Immanuel Kant, *Prolegomena zu einer jeden künftigen Metaphysik, die als Wissenschaft wird auftreten können* [Prolegomena to Any Future Metaphysics That Will Be Able to Present Itself as a Science], in *Prolegomena to Any Future Metaphysics that Will Be Able to Come forward as Science with Kant's Letter to*

Marcus Herz, February 27, 1772, trans. Paul Carus, rev. and introd. James W. Ellington (Indianapolis: Hackett Publishing Company, 1977), 30.

51 Isaac Newton, *Opticks, Or, A Treatise of the Reflections, Refractions, Inflections & Colours of Light* (London, 1730; 4th edn, New York: Dover Publications, 1979), 124–5.

52 Erwin Schrödinger, 'Mind and Matter: The Mystery of the Sensual Qualities' from the Tarner Lectures delivered at Trinity College Cambridge, 1956, in *What is Life?* with *Mind and Matter* and *Autobiographical Sketches*, foreword by Roger Penrose (Cambridge: Cambridge University Press, 1993), 154–5.

53 Karl R. Popper and John C. Eccles, *The Self and Its Brain: An argument for interactionism* (New York: Springer-Verlag, 1977), 5–8.

54 Alfred North Whitehead, 'Science and the Modern World', in *An Anthology*, eds F. S. C. Northrop and Mason W. Gross (Cambridge: Cambridge University Press, 1953), 396.

55 Arthur Stanley Eddington, *Why I believe in God: Science and religion, as a scientist sees it* (US: Haldeman–Julius Publications, 1930).

56 Arthur Stanley Eddington, *The Nature of the Physical World* (Cambridge, at the University Press, 1948), xi, xii.

57 Arthur Stanley Eddington, Swarthmore Lecture at Friends' House, London, in *Science and the Unseen World* (London: George Allen & Unwin, 1929).

58 —— *op. cit.*, 50–1.

59 —— *op. cit.*, 33.

60 —— *op. cit.*, 43.

61 —— *op. cit.*, 79.

62 James Jeans, *The Mysterious Universe* (Cambridge: Cambridge University Press, 1930), 37–8. The book opens with a full-page citation of the famous passage in Plato's *Republic*, Book VII, laying out the allegory of the cave.

63 Phiroz Mehta, *Holistic Consciousness: Reflections on the destiny of humanity*, ed. John Snelling (UK: Element Books, 1989), 32.

64 Josh Weisberg, *Consciousness: Key problems in philosophy* (Cambridge, UK: Polity Press, 2014).

65 Karl R. Popper and John C. Eccles, *The Self and Its Brain*, 51.

66 Rupert Sheldrake, *Morphic Resonance: The nature of formative causation* (US: Park Street Press, 2009), 193. Note that Sheldrake is not advocating this idea singularly: it is one of four possible conclusions to the conundrum of life and consciousness—see pp. 192–9.

67 Refer to Aristotle's *Physics* II 3 and *Metaphysics* V 2.

68 René Guénon, 'The Reign of Quantity and the Signs of the Times', in *Collected Works of René Guénon*, trans. Lord Northbourne (1945; US: Sophia Perennis et Universalis, 2004).

69 An excellent source reference is Jeremy Naydler (ed.), *Goethe on Science: An Anthology of Goethe's scientific writings* (Edinburgh: Floris Books, 1996). Other useful sources are shown in notes 70, 72, 73, 74, and 75 below.

70 Sir Charles Sherrington, *Goethe on Nature and on Science* (New York: Cambridge University Press, 1949).

71 Werner Heisenberg, 'On the History of the Physical Interpretation of Nature', in *Philosophic Problems of Nuclear Science* (University of California: Faber and Faber, 1952).

72 Henri Bortoft, *The Wholeness of Nature: Goethe's way of science* (Edinburgh: Floris Books, 1996).

73 Works of Johann Wolfgang von Goethe, Rudolf Steiner Archives <https://wn.rsarchive.org/RelAuthors/GoetheJW/Goethe_index.html> accessed 17 November 2019.

74 Adrian Anderson, 'Encountering the Sacred: Rudolf Steiner's discovery of spiritual wisdom in Goethe's poem 'Elegy' <http://www.rudolfsteinerstudies.com/free-ebooks/Spirituality.pdf> accessed 28 Oct. 2019.

75 Rudolf Steiner, *The Spiritual–Scientific Basis of Goethe's Work*. Address given in July 1906. The German text is published under the title *Die okkulte Grundlage in Goethes Schaffen*, Bibl. No. 35, by the Rudolf Steiner-Nachlassverwaltung, Dornach, Switzerland. The translation online since 5th May 2004 in <http://wn.rsarchive.org/Articles/SSBoGW_index.html> accessed 28 Oct. 2019, has been authorized for the Western Hemisphere by agreement with the Rudolf Steiner Nachlassverwaltung, Dornach, Switzerland.

76 See 'Why Mass Extinctions Matter', *National Geographic*, cited in *The Week*, 21 October 2017, 44.

77 Jeremy Naydler (ed.), *Goethe on Science*.

78 Ernst Lehrs, *Man or Matter: An introduction to a spiritual understanding of nature on the basis of Goethe's method of training observation and thought*, ed. Nick Thomas and Peter Bortoft (3rd edn, Forest Row, UK: Rudolf Steiner Press, 1985).

79 J. A. Wheeler, K. S. Thorne, and C. Misner, *Gravitation* (San Francisco: W. H. Freeman and Co., 1973), quoted in Yvonna S. Lincoln and Egon G. Guba, *Naturalistic Inquiry* (US, UK, India: Sage Publications, 1985), 87. Quoted also in Gary Zukav, *The Dancing Wu Li Masters: Overview of the new physics* (New York: William Morrow and Company, 1979), 29.

80 B. C. Goodwin, 'A Cognitive View of Biological Process', *J. Soc. Biol. Structures*, 1 (1978), 117–25.

81 What follows is an abstract from Brain Goodwin, 'From Control to Participation Via a Science of Qualities', *ReVision* (1999), repr. Schumacher College <https://www.schumachercollege.org.uk/learning-resources/from-control-to-participation-via-a-science-of-qualities> accessed 5 May 2020.

82 David B. Wake, 'How the Leopard Changed Its Spots: The evolution of complexity by Brian Goodwin', *American Scientist* 84/3 (1996), 300–1.

83 Brian Goodwin, 'Meaning in Evolution', *J. Biol. Phys. Chem.* 5 (2005), 51–6.

84 'Schumacher College' <https://www.schumachercollege.org.uk/about> accessed 29 Oct. 2019.

85 'In the Shadow of Culture', in John Brockman (ed.), *The Next Fifty Years: Science in the first half of the twenty-first century* (London: Weidenfeld & Nicolson, 2002).

86 Ulisse di Corpo and Antonella Vannini, *Syntropy: The spirit of love* (ICRL Press, 2015). For a comprehensive review of this book see *Journal of the Scientific and Medical Network*, 116 (2015), 41–2.

87 For an analysis of Einstein's concept of causality see Yemima Ben-Menahem, 'Struggling with Causality: Einstein's case', *Science in Context* 6/1 (1993), 291–310, online by Cambridge University Press (26 September 2008) doi: https://doi.org/10.1017/S0269889700001393.

88 Ulisse di Corpo and Antonella Vannini, *Syntropy*, 87–8.

89 Louis de Broglie, 'The Role of the Engineer in the Age of Science', in *New Perspectives in Physics*, trans. A. J. Pomerans (New York: Basic Books, 1962), 213.

90 Rupert Sheldrake, *Morphic Resonance* (US: Park Street Press, 2009), 192.

91 Edwin Arthur Burtt, *The Metaphysical Foundations of Modern Physical Science* (Doubleday & Company, 1955).

92 Rupert Sheldrake, Terence McKenna, and Ralph Abraham, *The Evolutionary Mind: Conversations on science, imagination and spirit* (New York: Monkfish Book Publishing, 2005), in Rupert Sheldrake, *The Science Delusion: Freeing the Spirit of Enquiry* (UK: Coronet, 2012), 65.

93 Erwin Schrödinger, 'Mind and Matter: The Principle of objectivation' from the Tarner Lectures delivered at Trinity College Cambridge, 1956, in *What is Life?* with *Mind and Matter* and *Autobiographical Sketches*, foreword by Roger Penrose (Cambridge: Cambridge University Press, 1993), 118.

94 Thomas Nagel, *Mind and Cosmos: Why the materialist neo-Darwinian conception of nature is almost certainly false* (New York: Oxford University Press), 71.

95 Representative examples over the past half-century are: C. E. M. Hansel, *ESP: A scientific evaluation* (New York: Charles Scribner's Sons, 1966), rev. edn, *ESP and Parapsychology: A critical re-evaluation* (Buffalo, New York: Prometheus Books), 1980; W. G. Roll and J. Beloff (eds), *Research in Parapsychology* (Metuchen, NJ: Scarecrow Press, 1980); Arthur S. Reber and James E. Alcock, 'Searching for the Impossible: Parapsychology's elusive quest', *American Psychologist* (13 June 2019) <http://dx.doi.org/10.1037/amp0000486> accessed 18 November 2019.

96 See also Edi D. Bilimoria, *The Snake and the Rope: Problems in Western science resolved by occult science* (Adyar, Madras: Theosophical Publishing House, 2006), 261–3.

97 Peter C. Gøtzsche, *Deadly Medicines and Organised Crime: How big pharma has corrupted healthcare* (CRC Press, Boca Raton, Florida: Taylor & Francis Group, 2017); and Ben Goldacre, *Bad Pharma: how medicine is broken, and how we can fix it* (London: Fourth Estate, 2012). Both books were reviewed by David Lorimer, *Journal of the Scientific and Medical Network*, 114 (2014).

98 Joe Martino, 'Banned TED Talk: Rupert Sheldrake – The Science Delusion', *Collective Evolution* (10 February 2017) <https://www.collective-evolution.com/2017/02/10/banned-ted-talk-the-science-delusion-by-rupert-sheldrake-10-dogmas-that-exist-within-mainstream-science/> accessed 31 July 2020.

99 Rupert Sheldrake, 'TED "Bans" the Science Delusion' <https://www.sheldrake.org/reactions/

tedx-whitechapel-the-banned-talk> accessed 31 July 2020. The complete talk can be accessed from the URL cited.

100 The Scientific and Medical Network <https://scimednet.org> accessed 17 November 2019.

101 The Scientific and Medical Network <http://www.scepticalaboutsceptics.org> accessed 29 October 2019.

102 *SD*-I, 'The Masks of Science', 509. Quoted also in I. M. Oderberg, *Sunrise* (August/September 2000) <https://www.theosociety.org/pasadena/sunrise/49-99-0/sc-imo11.htm> accessed 3 February 2020, in book review of Robert Nadeau and Menas Kafatos, *The Non-Local Universe: The new physics and matters of the mind* (Oxford: Oxford University Press, 1999).

103 Erwin Schrödinger, 'Science and Humanism: Physics in Our Time' from lectures delivered at University College Dublin in 1950, in *Nature and the Greeks* and *Science and Humanism*, foreword by Roger Penrose (Cambridge: Cambridge University Press, 1961), 114.

104 Edwin Arthur Burtt, *The Metaphysical Foundations of Modern Physical Science*.

105 —— *op. cit.*

106 Alfred Russel Wallace, *Contributions to the Theory of Natural Selection* (London: Macmillan and Company, 1870).

107 Helena Cronin, *The Ant and the Peacock: Altruism and sexual selection from Darwin to today*, foreword by John Maynard Smith (Cambridge: Cambridge University Press, 1994).

108 Julian Huxley: *Evolution in Action* (New American Library: Mentor Books, 1957); *Religion without Revelation* (New American Library: Mentor Books, 1958); *Evolution: The modern synthesis* (New York: John Wiley & Sons, 1963); *Evolutionary Humanism* (Buffalo, New York: Prometheus Books, 1992).

109 Pierre Teilhard De Chardin, *The Phenomenon of Man; with an introduction by Julian Huxley*, trans. Bernard Wall (London: Collins, 1963).

110 Aldous Huxley, *The Perennial Philosophy: An interpretation of the great mystics, East and West* (New York: Harper & Brothers, 1945).

111 J. S. Wyles, J. G. Kunkel, and A. C. Wilson, 'Birds, Behavior and Anatomical Evolution', *Proc. Natl. Acad. Sci.*, 80/14 (1983), 4394–7.

112 Sylvia Fraser, *The Book of Strange: A thinking person's guide to psychic phenomena* (Canada: Doubleday, 1993), 60.

113 Ernst Mayr, *Toward a New Philosophy of Biology: Observations of an evolutionist* (Cambridge, Mass. and London: Harvard University Press, 1988), 13.

114 Alister Hardy, *The Living Stream: A restatement of evolution theory and its relationship to the spirit of man* (New York: Harper and Row, 1965).

115 Alister Hardy, *The Divine Flame: An essay towards a natural history of religion* (The Religious Experience Research Unit, Manchester College, Oxford, 1978).

116 Alister Hardy, *The Spiritual Nature of Man: Study of contemporary religious experience* (Oxford: Clarendon Press, 1979).

117 The deeper significance of this is developed by Edi Bilimoria, *The Snake and the Rope*, 217–19.

118 Willis Harman and Jane Clarke (eds), *New Metaphysical Foundations of Modern Science* (Sausalito, California: Institute of Noetic Sciences, 1994).

119 See Willem B. Drees, *Religion, Science and Naturalism* (Cambridge: Cambridge University Press, 1996), 102.

120 See Peter W. Atkins, *The Second Law* (New York: Scientific American Library, 1984), quoted in Laurence Foss, *The End of Modern Medicine: Biomedical science under a microscope* (Albany: State University of New York Press, 2002), 199.

121 David Lorimer, *Radical Prince*, 393.

122 Charles Darwin, *The Origin of Species* (London: Penguin Books, 1985), 130–1.

123 Stephen Jay Gould, *The Flamingo's Smile: Reflections in natural history* (New York: W. W. Norton & Company, 1987), 346.

124 —— *op. cit.*, 347.

125 Kim Sterelny, *Dawkins Vs. Gould: Survival of the fittest* (UK: Icon Books, 2007).

126 Ralph Waldo Emerson, *Essays, Second Series (1844)* (London: Routledge, 1900).

127 Gustaf Strömberg, *The Soul of the Universe* (1940; 2nd edn, Philadelphia: David McKay Company, 1948), 136, 232.

128 James Lovelock and Lynn Margulis, 'The *Gaia* Hypothesis' <http://www.mountainman.com.au/gaia_jim.html> accessed 5 May 2020.

129 'Atmospheric Homeostasis By and For the Biosphere: The Gaia hypothesis', *The International Metereological Institute in Stockholm*, 26 (1974).

130 Alfred Russel Wallace, 'On the Tendency of Varieties to Depart Indefinitely from the Original Type (S43: 1858)' <http://people.wku.edu/charles.smith/wallace/S043.htm> accessed 31 October 2019.

131 Alfred Russel Wallace, *Man's Place in the Universe* (London: Chapman & Hall, 1904).

132 Li Liu, 'Evolutionism Combined with Spiritualism: A. R. Wallace's approach', Peking University, *Journal of Cambridge Studies*, 5/4 (January, 2010).

133 'Wallace (1853)', quoted in Martin Fichman, *An Elusive Victorian: The evolution of Alfred Russel Wallace* (Chicago: Chicago University Press, 2004), 28.

134 Erwin Schrödinger 'Science and Humanism: Physics in Our Time', 109.

4 Limitations in the Modern Scientific Picture

Science cannot tell us a word about why music delights us, of why and how an old song can move us to tears.

Science, we believe, can, in principle, describe in full detail all that happens in the latter case in our sensorium and 'motorium' from the moment the waves of compression and dilation reach our ear to the moment when certain glands secrete a salty fluid that emerges from our eyes. But of the feelings of delight and sorrow that accompany the process science is completely ignorant—and therefore reticent.

In particular, and most importantly, this is the reason why the scientific world-view contains of itself no ethical values, no aesthetical values, not a word about our own ultimate scope or destination, and no God, if you please. Whence came I, wither go I? That is the great unfathomable question, the same for every one of us. Science has no answer to it.

ERWIN SCHRÖDINGER[1]

SYNOPSIS

Chapter 4 concentrates on the limited approach of contemporary science to the arenas of mind and nature—phenomena that science cannot explain adequately. They include organizing fields, vitalism, and morphic resonance, along with the whole gamut of paranormal phenomena like near-death experiences, remote viewing, and mediumship. It is explained how, and why, such phenomena, unaccountable or only partially explained by science, have resulted in deathblows to materialism, previously confidently assumed to be the exclusive basis of reality. Ironically, quantum science has cracked the hitherto exclusively materialistic paradigm of classical science, invoked the role of consciousness in an essentially non-material universe, and moved science close to the orbit of esoteric science. The paradigm shift has been such as to offer new vistas in subjects as wide-ranging as chemistry, telepathy, and the primacy of consciousness. Besides glimpsing the view through the cracks, its implications, in terms of what is meant by evidence and the pressing need for a science of qualities (explained in Chapter 3), are presented. The Chapter concludes by describing how the scientific establishment deals with anomalous evidence, not on the basis of its validity, but by way of 'knowledge filtration'. Not satisfied however, with just a faint glimpse through the cracks of the exclusively materialistic philosophy, we need to extend our vision to look further afield, as in the next Chapter.

KEY WORDS: scientific methodology, scientific conundrums, vitalism, morphogenesis, organizing fields, evidence for paranormal phenomena, materialism undermined, quantum physics insights, knowledge filtration in science, scientism, Rupert Sheldrake, Karl Popper, John Eccles, Gustaf Strömberg, Marie and Pierre Curie

The purpose of this Chapter is to highlight the shortcomings in mainstream science; hence, to make the case for the *philosophia perennis*, not as an alternative, but as its indispensable complement.

To Explain Away is Not to Explain

In the epigraph, the mystically inclined Nobel physicist, Erwin Schrödinger, succinctly states what science cannot explain and therefore tries to explain away, namely, that science can, in principle, explain the minutiae of the dynamics of sound and the ensuing acoustic and neurological processes in the human brain, but 'science is completely ignorant—therefore reticent' about why, and how, music should move us to joy or tears along with the accompanying feeling of delight or sorrow. Still less can science pronounce on the purpose and destiny of humanity and its relation to divinity (other than a bleak nihilism).

Of course, Schrödinger is referring specifically to secondary qualities and experience ('the feelings of delight and sorrow') that natural science disdains to address. But are we now any closer to the answer, through establishment science, than over fifty years ago when Schrödinger made this observation? If he were alive today he might have quipped why there should be such a hullabaloo about extracting the personal details of over eighty seven million Facebook users by the British political consulting firm Cambridge Analytica.[2] After all, are not the 'feelings' of outrage at having one's privacy invaded merely a matter of secondary qualities? Least of all, then, can all talk of primary qualities, or brain electro-chemistry and neural correlates of consciousness, in themselves, explain the genius of a Newton, born to virtually illiterate parents, or a Mozart, who composed a harpsichord concerto at age five and his first symphony at the age of eight years, by which time, he was already notable in Europe as a *wunderkind* performer[3] (see Chapter 2 for more details).

The situation is no better with academic philosophers of science who are trapped in their own manufactured self-locking language and circular arguments. Reality is apprehended less in itself and more in terms of physical, sense-perceived logical concepts. The whole is considered in the light of limited and partial data, and the all-inclusive qualitative succumbs to the fragmented quantitative. Moreover, statistical data hold sway over direct personal experience as orated, typically, by Richard Dawkins who states, 'the essence of life is statistical improbability on a colossal scale' but then to his credit, he admits that, 'whatever is the explanation for life, therefore, it cannot be by chance. The true explanation for the existence of life must embody the very antithesis of chance.'[4]

These predominantly left-brained academicians seem unwilling (or unable) to grasp the fact that one cannot experience higher dimensions of consciousness without the necessary altered states of consciousness. One might as well try to view the world from the top of Mount Everest by standing at the foot of the mountain. Essentially, we are blind to that which we are not ready to perceive.

In one sense, the ultra-materialistic stance of science finds its justification amongst those who only look to the outward appearance of nature and choose to deny or ignore her inner working principles. Such outward appearances, however, are always illusory on the physical plane and, as we saw in the previous Chapter, there is no central, organizing principle

Explaining versus explaining away

Can life and experience be reduced to numbers and statistics?

to synthesize the myriads of theories and conjectures that are put forward in the attempt to explain the nature of the world or to account for mind and consciousness.

So, with all this confusion and hair-splitting taxonomy of scientific materialism (see Chapter 3) is it not reasonable to seek a way out of the impasse? We intend to accomplish this by drawing upon Einstein's counsel: 'We cannot solve our problems with the same level of thinking that created them.'[5] We therefore seek a resolution at a higher level than what purely materialistic science can provide; and that way out is onwards and upwards through the gateway of the eternal wisdom that goes well beyond, but never denies, the physical realm.

Seeking a resolution needs a higher standpoint

Phenomena Science Cannot Explain Satisfactorily – Justifying the Need for a Wider Paradigm

There is no question about the success of the materialistic philosophy in bringing about greater understanding of the physical world and our physical bodies and brains, as well as bequeathing freedom through advances in technology, whilst also admitting the attendant penalty of enslavement to the latter (see Chapter 1). But it needs to be acknowledged that the assumptions of classical science of the nineteenth century have hardened into dogmas that have congealed into a belief system known as *scientific materialism*. Such ideology has become so dominant in academia and industry that the vast majority of scientists unquestioningly believe that it is grounded in established empirical evidence and therefore represents the one and only rational account of the world, as we observed above. Blind faith in this 'religion of scientific materialism' otherwise known as 'scientism', as an exclusive explanatory framework for understanding reality, has seriously hindered investigation into the subjective and spiritual dimensions of the universe and human experience, thereby diminishing our understanding of our place in nature and of ourselves—who, or what we *truly* are.

Presuppostions, dogmas, and ideologies skew progress in science

So whilst sincerely applauding the scientific ethos for its ideals of rigour and integrity, its open-mindedness and commitment to independent and objective verification, it must also be pointed out that such diametrically opposed views from Nobel laureates like Francis Crick and Gerald Edelman about consciousness, that we cited in Chapter 2, and the several instances that will shortly be presented below of phenomena that science cannot satisfactorily explain, all rest upon the 'take-it-for-granted' paradigm and associated beliefs and assumptions detailed in the previous Chapter. It is to be expected, of course, that there are some invincibly materialistic scientists who refuse to see, let alone acknowledge, hard evidence and data that do not fit their favoured theories and beliefs or their rigid concepts of the world. Actually, only in exceptional cases are facts and observations seen in themselves. In most cases they are distorted through the prism of preconceived concepts, beliefs, expectations, and presumptions—how we would like them to be, or not to be, as opposed to how they actually are. Here, a short detour is needed in order to describe an experiment that reinforces this point about how strongly held preconceptions about nature can unconsciously influence a scientist from observing facts right before his eyes.

We See What we Believe we shall See, Expect to See, and Want to See

'Turning a blind eye' is an idiom familiar to most of us. We conveniently ignore information that is not compatible with the way we believe things should be, in other words, information that is not sympathetic to our mindset. But there is a yet more profound blindness whereby we do not choose to turn a blind eye, but literally do not (and cannot) see a truth—it is outside our experience because we have not yet developed faculties by which to see it. There are numerous instances of the former, but an anecdote which illustrates the latter is the so called 'missing ships' phenomenon. The story has been cited in various forms and its interpretation is controversial but, in a nutshell, when the British explorer Captain James Cook FRS (1728–1779) arrived in Australia in 1770 aboard HMS *Endeavour*, it was reported that the natives of that land were oblivious of its presence. It has been conjectured that they did not see the ship because their eyes were closed to the possibility of its existence. But however much one may debate the apocryphal implications of this story, there is no argument about the following scientific experiment that proves the point.

Beliefs and expectations distort clear vision

Arthur Ellison (1920–2000) was Emeritus Professor of Electrical and Electronic Engineering at The City University, London. A distinguished voice in paranormal research, he was twice President of The British Society for Psychical Research (a scientific body for studying paranormal phenomena) and the author of a comprehensive and lucid book, *The Reality of the Paranormal*.[6] In the early 1970s, during a talk on paranormal topics as part of a University Conversazione, Ellison suggested to the audience that they try to levitate a bowl of flowers placed on the lecture table. This was to be done by imagination and concentration, and also by chanting the word 'OM' believed in the East to be a sacred sound. After a minute or so of such concentration and chanting the bowl of flowers wobbled, levitated about twenty millimetres into the air, remained there for a few seconds and then crashed down again. There was a gasp from the audience that was virtually primeval as they rushed forward to examine the table and bowl of flowers. They could find no normal means or explanation for what they had just witnessed. However, one lady said she noticed a 'greyish substance under the bowl lifting it and the same greyish substance under the legs of the table lifting that.' Then a professor of physics in the audience standing on the edge of the crowd listening to this 'silly woman' could stand it no longer. So, he pronounced, 'Well, I saw nothing!', turned on his heel and left the room. Nobody, least of all the lady and the physics professor, were aware that the actual levitation was caused by a purely physical arrangement of an electromagnetic levitator artfully concealed in the drawer of the table and a disc of aluminium stuck to the bottom of the very light plastic flower bowl. The OM chant (amplified through two loudspeakers) was suggested purely in order to hide the 100 Hz humming sound from the levitator.[7]

The Message – Seeing and Hearing are Not Necessarily Looking and Listening

Neither the lady nor the physics professor observed the true, objective fact of the actual levitation of the flower bowl, but rather 'saw' what they both *believed* and *expected* (and therefore in a sense *wanted*) to see according to their own subjective states, conditioned by their own cultural make-up and belief systems, i.e., according to their own conceptual models. The lady was presumably a Spiritualist and therefore saw the greyish 'ectoplasm' lifting both the bowl and the table—conforming to her mental model; whereas in fact only the bowl levitated, the table having been screwed to the duct in the floor. By contrast, the physics professor saw nothing at all since his materialistic outlook—his mental model—admitted of no 'silly nonsense' like levitation by imagination, concentration, and chanting OM.

The ability to observe without bias is rare

The flower-bowl experiment thus shows that, despite the laudable intention in science to strip out extraneous influences that could bias the results, what happens in practice is that the latter invariably hold sway; for both the lady and the physics professor were seeing according to their subjective states and neither were truly looking. Only the general public, presumably having no particular persuasions (towards either spiritualism or materialism), were able to look objectively and truly, therefore saw the actual (physical) levitation.

All this demonstrates that disarmingly simple phrases like 'physically observed' and 'independent repeatable experiments' have deeper implications. Observation cannot always be relied upon for the 'real test' of a scientific theory. We see only what we expect to see; and overlook what does not accord with our mental model. Perhaps it also shows that there is no sharp dividing line between the Cartesian notion of *res extensa* (what we fondly believe to be corporeal matter) and *res cogitans* (mind substance). The corollary to this is that we also hear what we want, and expect to hear, but remain oblivious to what we do not wish to hear—a statement too obvious to warrant comment, as the chairman of any disorganized committee would willingly testify.

Reverting now to the main theme of this Chapter about the need for a wider paradigm than that of mainstream science, an impressive account of recent developments in biology that have eroded the conventional views upheld by the public through journalists and scientific commentators, is the work of one of the leading British philosophers of science, John Dupré (*b*.1952).[8] He highlights the limitations of the mainstream viewpoint with a wealth of evidence to show that biology cannot be explained solely by a reductionist approach using the laws of physics and chemistry. Notwithstanding the fact that Dupré does not profess to have any religious or spiritual proclivities, his arguments make a good case for highlighting the shortcomings of the orthodox position as being the sole account of reality. For example, by default, reductionism would ignore bacteria that could be essential to the functioning of one part of the human body but could cause serious issues in another part of the same body.

Biology vitiated by exclusive reductionism

In consequence, we now cite the chief obstacles that mainstream science tries, unsatisfactorily, to side-step. They are all related, either directly or indirectly, to our overall theme of self-enquiry, consciousness, and non-physical (hence subtle) states of matter and being that are not amenable to detection by physical instruments; therefore, outside the purview of natural science. In just the same sense, our subtle bodies are, by definition, non-physical and so cannot be commented upon—or denied—by mainstream science. Of course, it must be admitted that those who most need to wake up to such things hardly ever do. The psychological defences to their paradigms are well-nigh impregnable. Informational inertia, i.e., the aversion to ambiguity and new ideas is becoming a serious problem!

Vitalist and Organismic Theories

Particularly challenging to modern mainstream biology is Rupert Sheldrake's theory of morphogenesis,[i] which cannot be banished simply by piling every possible statistical artifice against it. This is the biological process that causes an organism to develop its shape

---

i Morphogenesis can, arguably, be regarded as an aspect of the esoteric doctrine on the Akashic Chronicle (see later) expressed in a modern scientific idiom.

and is one of three fundamental aspects of developmental biology along with the control of cell growth and cellular differentiation. Before précising this theory, it would be instructive to outline the background to earlier, related, ideas of vitalism and organicism, as depicted in the notion of entelechy.

Vitalist and organismic theories argue that evolutionary innovations cannot be explained entirely in terms of chance occurrences or random influences, but must invoke an inner organizing, non-mechanistic creative principle, still unrecognized by science. These ideas are completely alien to modern science as they imply teleology, namely, purpose-driven design in the material world, such that phenomena are explainable by the overriding purpose that they serve, rather than by postulated causes progressing to their logical end results according to the known laws of science. By this premiss, evolution does not take place solely on account of spontaneous mutation and natural selection, but rather it is based on the outcome of the purpose towards which the organism is intended to live and function.

Vitalism and the Notion of Entelechy

One of the best modern vitalist theories was provided by the German biologist, philosopher, and embryologist Hans Driesch (1867–1941).[9] He considered that the facts of regulation, reproduction, and regeneration showed that there was some aspect of living organisms that remained whole even though parts of the physical whole could be damaged, mutilated or removed. He postulated the existence of what he called entelechy—a non-physical causal factor, which acts on the physical system, but is not itself a part of it, somewhat like the action of a catalyst in chemical processes.

Entelechy concerns the essential nature or inner guiding principle of a living organism that enables the latter to realize its true potential. It is a goal-orientated factor that directs the system under its control towards its intended aim.[ii] Hence, if the normal line of development be disturbed by environmental or any other factors, entelechy re-directs the system towards its internalized purpose along different pathways. But if entelechy is non-physical, then how can it bring about physical results?

Entelechy, Memory, and Brain

According to mechanistic theories, memories are stored within the brain cells acting rather like the silicon-chip memory banks of a computer. But there is persuasive evidence to demonstrate that this simplistic outlook is far from the whole truth; that, in fact, memories are not stored physically within the brain and furthermore, that no satisfactory mechanistic explanation of memory, in terms of physical phenomena, is possible, even in principle. Near-death and out-of-the-body experiences point to veridical experience (i.e., coinciding with reality) by the subject, involving the retention of the memory of specific events, times, and locations, despite the clinical death of the brain (through accident, stroke or

---

ii It would not be too far-fetched to suggest that there is ample evidence about goal orientation, or entelechy, in great music. By way of just two examples, the closing bars and two final definitive chords of the third, rondo, movement of Beethoven's Violin concerto, and the final resolving chords of the slow movement of Mozart's clarinet concerto, convey a feeling of utter inevitability towards its ending—that it could not be otherwise; that the first note of each piece moves inexorably towards the last.

other causes). Therefore, mind and conscious awareness need not be restricted just to a functioning brain and may even transcend the brain.[iii] This being so, certain kinds of memory need not necessarily be confined to individual minds, and memories could therefore pass from person to person, or many individuals could inherit a pooled memory from countless individuals in the past. Jung's theory of a collective unconscious refers to structures of the unconscious mind that are not shaped by personal experience but comprise archetypal forms which are shared among beings of the same species. These archetypal forms could then be regarded as a kind of collective memory pool.

But if memories are not stored within the brain, then how do we remember? If the brain is the physical means for accessing information that is actually 'stored' in what Jung referred to as the collective unconscious, or, more accurately, what wisdom philosophers, most notably the Hungarian philosopher of science Ervin László (b.1932) refer to as the 'Akashic Record' (also called the 'Akashic Chronicle'),[10] then perhaps the 'biological chips' in the brain act in this way more like transducers, rather like the record/playback heads (the 'brains') of a video or tape recorder for retrieving and transmitting data that are actually stored on the tape and certainly not in the heads. Rupert Sheldrake, whose pioneering ideas in biology will shortly be outlined, discusses the whole question of memory in *The Presence of the Past*.[11]

Akashic Record— the universal memory of nature

Organicism, the Chreode, Attractors, and the Concept of Organizing Fields

The description of organismic theories of morphogenesis given by Sheldrake in *A New Science of Life*[12] (now in its third edition in the UK, renamed *Morphic Resonance* in the US) may be summarized as follows.[13]

Organismic theories of morphogenesis have evolved under a variety of influences, including philosophy, modern physics, psychology and, of course, vitalism. These theories represent a more modern approach to the same problems of regulation, regeneration, and reproduction that vitalism claimed were insoluble in purely mechanistic terms. Organismic theories, such as were propounded by the Russian biologist and medical scientist Alexander Gurwitsch (1874–1954)[14] and, independently, by the Austrian biologist Paul Weiss (1898–1989)[15], account for the wholeness and goal orientation of organisms in terms of morphogenetic fields, instead of the non-physical entelechy of Driesch. This field is supposed to account for the wholeness of detached parts of organisms, which can subsequently grow into new organisms, rather like a bar magnet, which, when cut in half, results in two whole magnets with their respective magnetic fields.

Organizing fields account for wholeness

The British developmental biologist Conrad Waddington FRS (1905–1975), who was Brian Goodwin's supervisor, has extended the idea of the morphogenetic field by way of a new concept which he called the chreode to make explicit the temporal aspect of development, which is only implicit within the idea of morphogenetic fields. The chreode represents the channelled, or guided pathway of change towards a definite goal, or endpoint, over the developmental history for a biological system or entity, say an embryo.[16]

The chreode

---

iii The Scientific and Medical Network hold biennial conferences on the themes *Beyond the Brain* and *Body and Beyond*. World renowned academics and professionals are invited to lecture on the wider aspects of consciousness.

The French mathematician René Thom (1923–2002) attempted to produce mathematical models to correspond as closely as possible to the developmental processes in biology. He incorporated the concepts of chreodes and morphogenetic fields, developing them in topological models, qualitative rather than quantitative, where he referred to the end points as 'morphogenetic attractors.'[17] His models were dynamic in the sense that dynamic systems move toward attractors, the latter being explicitly Waddington's concept of chreodes.

Mathematical models

Dilemmas Posed by Vitalist and Organismic Theories

Viewed as a whole, Driesch's entelechy, Waddington's chreode, and Thom's attractors all share the common concept of development that is guided or canalized in space and time by some factor that cannot itself be regarded as confined to a particular place and time. This common feature of a guided end, or goal, of the developmental process is a wonderful example of substantiation by modern science of a principal tenet of the perennial wisdom: that the whole order of nature demonstrates a progressive advance towards a higher order of life; and that there is universal intelligence (consciousness), and hence design,[iv] in the action of the seemingly blind forces of nature. We shall revert to this theme in due course.

However, we need to outline three chief dilemmas posed by these new theories:

1. The main problem with vitalist theories is the irresolvable dualism between the non-physical entelechy and the physical organism, such that either one cannot be explained in terms of the other.
2. Organismic theories suffer a similar drawback. Although Waddington's chreode and Thom's attractors, like Driesch's entelechy, incorporate the idea of canalized development, this idea is essentially descriptive and lacking in explanatory rigour.
3. Chance failure of genes, 'mistakes' or mutations, genetic drift, entelechy, and the chreode are all descriptions that cannot be accounted for without invoking metaphysical ideas to explain the operation of invisible causative influences. This problem has been recognized by a few biologists. One such metaphysically inclined biologist was indeed Waddington who has written: 'So biologists uninterested in metaphysics do not notice what lies behind—though they usually react as though they feel obscurely uneasy.'[18] Another example is the mathematician and theoretical biologist Brian Goodwin, who regards morphogenetic fields and chreodes as aspects of eternal Platonic forms in the sense of given archetypes that are necessary and changeless.[19]

The need for a metaphysical complement

By invoking the concept of extended mind, these limitations have, to a great extent, been resolved by arguably the best example of a contemporary metaphysically inclined biologist, Rupert Sheldrake, who has developed the idea of morphogenetic fields to a high degree of sophistication as we will show presently.

———

iv By 'design' we emphatically do not mean the naïve and literal notion of 'intelligent design by a Creator-God' as proselytized by Christian creationist–fundamentalists.

Morphogenesis and Morphic Resonance

The word 'morphic' in the above title comes from the Greek *morphé*, 'form'. Hence morphogenesis is concerned with the question of formative causation: what causes simple organisms to develop in space and over time into complex structures having a shape and pattern that uniquely characterizes them, for example, an oak tree that grows from an acorn seed.

The difference between molecular and developmental biology must be clarified. The former is mechanistic and is concerned mainly with understanding the interactions between the various systems of a cell as well as learning how these interactions are regulated. By contrast, developmental biology is holistic since it is the study of the processes by which plants and animals grow and develop; it is synonymous with ontogeny or morphogenesis. But there is no question of superiority of one over the other, as both are entirely meaningful in their rightful context.

The English cryptanalyst Alan Turing FRS (1912–1954) is honoured for his pivotal role in cracking intercepted coded messages (the 'Enigma' code) that enabled the Allies to defeat the Nazis in many crucial engagements during the Second World War. He is also highly esteemed as a mathematician and pioneering computer scientist. Less well known is his advancement of the mathematical basis of pattern formation in biology.[20] Turing was one of the first to offer a molecular explanation of morphogenesis through chemistry. He theorized that identical biological cells differentiate, change shape, and create patterns through a process called intercellular reaction–diffusion. In this model, a system of chemicals called morphogens, react with each other and diffuse across a space, for example, between cells in an embryo. Although such a system may originally be quite homogeneous, it may later develop a pattern or structure, triggered by random disturbances, due to an inherent instability of the initially homogeneous equilibrium. These chemical reactions need a dynamic balance between an excitatory agent to activate the reaction, and an inhibitory agent to suppress the reaction. This chemical reaction, diffused across an embryo, will create patterns of chemically different cells. Turing predicted six different patterns that could arise from this theory which has served as a basic model in theoretical biology.[21]

Alan Turing's model in theoretical molecular biology

Although a significant step in the right direction, the reaction–diffusion theory of morphogenesis is based on molecular biology and lacks the organismic approach provided by later theories of developmental biology to explain the spatiotemporal development of highly complex structures from relatively simple ones. However, it must be stressed that both molecular and developmental biologists agree that all cells come from other cells, that all cells inherit fields of organization, and that genes are an essential part of this organization. But the problem for molecular biology is that genes do not explain the organization itself. What genes do is enable organisms to make particular proteins. Other genes are involved in the control of protein synthesis. But just making the right proteins at the right times cannot explain the pattern or form of complex structures without other influences coming into play, including the organizing activity of cell membranes and microtubules (tubular structures constructed from globular proteins called tubulins), any more than assembling all the right components of a motor car would produce the car in the absence of a master organizing plan. The missing explanation comes from developmental biology.

The missing complement of developmental biology

The theories of the Scottish biologist, mathematician, and classics scholar Sir D'Arcy Wentworth Thompson FRS (1860–1948) laid much of the preparatory groundwork. In his master work *On Growth and Form*[22] he advanced his main thesis that biological form can reflect physical and mathematical principles. For instance, the spicules (needle-like anatomical structures) of sponges adopt several characteristic shapes. D'Arcy argued that these were the consequence of slight differences in the 'starting conditions' such as ionic concentrations and other physical parameters. Thus, the initial conditions might well reflect some aspect of natural selection, but the resulting morphology of the spicules did not.

We have previously referred to the work of the Cambridge biologist, and one-time Rosenheim Research Fellow of the Royal Society, Rupert Sheldrake. We now describe what could arguably be considered as his crowning achievement: his innovative and modernized version of morphogenesis that has greatly contributed towards resolving the shortcomings in the molecular theory. Central to his hypothesis is the idea of morphogenetic fields and morphic resonance.[23]

A 'field' is defined as regions of influence that stretch out beyond the entity from which it radiates. Familiar examples are magnetic, electric or gravitational fields. However, morphic fields differ from the known fields of physics in some important respects. The latter are local to the entity from which they emanate (like the magnetic field surrounding a bar magnet) and extend and connect things in local space. Morphic fields extend and connect things in both space and time, as well as displaying a universal characteristic, in that they seem to involve not just living systems (biological entities) but also non-biological entities like chemicals and minerals. Furthermore, morphic fields are thought to be non-local—an important characteristic that has a significant bearing on explaining the nature of instinct and memory, and accounting for such phenomena as telepathy.

Morphic resonance is the hypothesis that there is a kind of inherent memory in nature. For example, within each species (or self-organising system), each individual draws upon a collective memory pool and in turn contributes to it. Just as a magnetic field will attract iron filings within its domain of influence, so a morphic attractor will attract developing systems towards it. The hypothesis, backed by experimental evidence (see below), predicts that, for example, new chemicals should get easier to crystallize as time goes on because the crystal forms become increasingly habitual, sustained by morphic resonance from increasing numbers of previous crystals of that type. Likewise, if animals, such as rats, learn a new trick in one place, rats all over the world should be able to learn it more quickly.[24]

The hypothesis of formative causation is supported by impressive evidence for phenomena in minerals, plants, animals and humans, hitherto unexplained by mainstream science. In support of this assertion, a list of new tests that involve morphic fields (connecting morphic units in *space*) and morphic resonance (cumulative influence of morphic units in *time*), plus a selection of peer-reviewed papers in support of the above, is provided in Endnote I-1.

Morphic Resonance Upholds the Perennial Philosophy

The explanatory power of morphogenesis in biology needs to be underscored. There is no denying the spectacular success of the reductionist approach to life, for example, the discovery of the double-stranded structure of DNA ('cracking' of the genetic code), the

Non-local
characteristic of
morphic fields

Morphic
resonance and
habits of nature

interactions between the different types of DNA, RNA, and protein biosynthesis. But to reiterate, despite its success at the molecular level, the mechanistic approach has not been able to explain satisfactorily some of the central problems in biology, such as the development of form, i.e., pattern, shape, and spatiotemporal order in the mineral and plant, the animal and in man. The mechanistic–reductionist approach assumes that these must somehow be fully explainable in terms of the complex physico-chemical interactions (based obviously on the known laws of physics and chemistry) between the component parts. But this has not adequately explained the characteristics of the macroscopic entity whereby an increasingly complex structure can grow from less complex ones, for example, an embryo develops from a relatively simple egg cell into a living entity displaying great structural form and complexity. The development of complex structures progressively in space and time cannot be satisfactorily explained by an exclusively micro-level focus upon interactions between its basic constituent chemicals. It is important to stress that morphogenesis in its modern version, as developed by Sheldrake, operates in addition, not as a postulated alternative, to molecular biology. It provides the holistic, or organismic complement, to the mechanistic and reductionist theory, which partially explains the development of form in space, but not in time.

Molecular biology requires developmental biology to account for growth of complex forms

Inheritance of Acquired Characteristics

The inheritance of acquired characteristics means that, on average, anything that is learnt, or new skills acquired, will be progressively easier for succeeding generations of the same species to learn than was possible for their ancestors. Such improved learning is not necessarily dependent upon specifically modified genes being passed on from trained parents to their offspring. This was shown by experiments on rats conducted by the British psychologist William McDougall FRS (1871–1938) in 1920, which showed the same improvement in a specific learning skill displayed by successive generations of rats, descended from both trained and untrained ancestors, i.e. from the trained lines and the control line in the experiment. This robust evidence in favour of Lamarckian inheritance palpably repudiates the orthodox theory of inheritance based exclusively on Mendelian genetics founded upon a materialist philosophy, which denies, even to this day, that such a thing can happen. This is not meant to imply that Mendelian genetics is 'wrong' and Lamarckian inheritance is 'right'; both are complementary, depending upon the context and circumstances. From the standpoint of this work, the evidence for Lamarckian inheritance coming from the strictly scientific discipline of developmental biology strongly alludes to the *philosophia perennis*, which explicitly pronounces on processes and mechanisms in nature that are non-local and non-physical, complementing the familiar local and physical.[v]

Lamarckian inheritance and Mendelian inheritance are complementary

The Nature of Instinct and Memory, Mind and Brain

Memory and instinct are thorny problems that modern science cannot fully explain in solely mechanistic terms. The established contemporary view, strongly upheld in

---

v Lamarckian inheritance, or the inheritance of acquired characteristics, is the theory that an organism can pass on to its offspring physical characteristics that the parent organism acquired, through use or disuse, during its lifetime. This is in contrast to Mendelian inheritance which is the transmission of characteristics in a predictable way by factors (genes) which remain intact and independent between generations and do not blend.

mainstream neuroscience, is that memory is stored in the brain in specific 'memory banks' rather like on the hard disk of a computer; and that mind and brain are equivalent terms. The primary evidence proposed in favour of this theory is that brain damage causes loss of memory (analogous to crashing the computer hard disk); and electrical stimulation of the temporal lobes of the brain[25] causes buried memories to be evoked (analogous to powering up a computer to retrieve the data on the hard disk). However, attempts to localize memory traces (engrams) within the brain, as the presumed encoding in neural tissue that provides a physical basis for the persistence of memory, have been singularly unsuccessful.

The American psychologist and behaviourist Karl Lashley FRS (1890–1958) is well remembered for his influential contributions to the study of learning and memory. Based on years of research he failed to find the biological locus of memory. In fact, he was one of the first to claim that memories are not localized in one part of the brain but are widely distributed throughout the cortex. Summing up the results of numerous experiments conducted on trained animals, he said:

> It is not possible to demonstrate the isolated localization of a memory trace anywhere within the nervous system. Limited regions may be essential for learning or retention of a particular activity, but within such regions the parts are functionally independent.[26]

Lack of evidence for memory storage within brain

Invertebrates also display the same phenomenon. Observations on the survival of learned habits in an octopus, after the destruction of various parts of the vertical lobe of the brain, led the English biologist and neuroscientist Brian Boycott FRS (1924–2000) to conclude that 'memory is both everywhere and nowhere'.[27]

In attempting to explain matters, still within a materialist framework, the Austrian psychiatrist and neurosurgeon Karl Pribram (1919–2015) has suggested that memory traces are somehow distributed within the brain in an analogous manner to the storage of information in the form of optical interference patterns in a hologram.[28] But according to Sheldrake, this is just a vague speculation.[29]

Would the same conclusions from animal and invertebrate studies apply to human brains? Lashley's conclusions based on animal experiments were later corroborated by the discoveries of the distinguished brain surgeon Wilder Penfield, mentioned in Chapter 2, who once held the conventional view that the mind and brain are simply different aspects of one and the same thing. But after a long career involving much pioneering research on the brain, along with brain surgery for the relief of epilepsy and other conditions resulting from brain damage, he was compelled to realize, unwillingly at first, that the mind is a separate and *superior non-material* entity that directs the brain and body for its own purposes. Penfield likened the brain to a computer and the mind to an *intelligent human programmer* who uses the computer as a tool. Penfield had the courage of his conviction to write a superbly concise book *The Mysteries of the Mind* in which he charts the many episodes that led to his complete transformation in outlook in relation to an interactive view of brain and mind.[30]

Wilder Penfield realizes that mind is superior to brain

Wilder Penfield's conviction that the mind cannot be reduced to the brain, and therefore presupposes the soul, is shared by two Nobel Prize-winning neuroscientists. The first is Sir Charles Sherrington mentioned in Chapter 3, described in the obituary notice of the *British Medical Journal* for March 1952 as the 'genius who laid the foundations of our knowledge of the functioning of the brain and spinal cord.' 'For me now the only reality is the human soul,'[31] was his passionate statement, nine days before his death, to his former student—the second Nobel laureate, Sir John C. Eccles.

In Chapter 3 we also mentioned the influential book *The Self and its Brain* that Eccles wrote jointly with the philosopher Sir Karl Popper. In Volume III, as the authors conclude their dialogue, Eccles says:

> So I am constrained to believe that there is what we might call a supernatural origin of my unique self-conscious mind or my unique selfhood or soul; and that gives rise of course to a whole new set of problems. How does my soul come to be in liaison with my brain that has an evolutionary origin? By this kind of supernatural creation, I escape from the incredible improbability that the uniqueness of my own self is genetically determined.[32]

John Eccles admits the need for soul

Is it not of especial significance that a highly distinguished, modern neuroscientist uses the words 'soul' and 'supernatural' not just once, but twice in the same breath? Furthermore, Eccles again resorts to a supernatural and soul explanation of selfhood in his subsequent book *Mind and Brain*:

> It is my thesis that we have to recognise that the unique selfhood is the result of a super-natural creation of what in the religious sense is called a soul.[33]

The clear message that resounds is the consistent pronouncements coming from such celebrated scientists, philosophers, and neurosurgeons, as cited above, who were in the most favourable of circumstances to discover the truth about the mind-brain problem at first hand. Moreover, each had the courage to admit to their former erroneously held views and formulate new conclusions in line with their convictions. Therefore, for some famous scientists (like Michael Shermer quoted in Chapter 2) to proclaim that there is no scientific evidence to disprove that 'mind is just a word we use to describe neural activity in the brain' and that 'we are our brains' is utter nonsense—scientifically demonstrable.

Famous scientists tend to lie in thrall to ideology and prejudice: great scientists are wedded to a discovery of truth, at all costs, and go wherever it may lead. The distinction between famous scientists and great ones (many of whom are unknown to the world at large because of their self-effacing nature) must always be borne in mind.

Modern research has shown that the brain functions in an all-inclusive, or holistic manner, such that severe damage to one region, as in a stroke, is gradually compensated by complementary functioning of other regions of the brain.[34, 35] Known as brain plasticity, or neuroplasticity, the brain is now regarded as a plastic, living organ that can actually change its own structure and function, even into old age. This recent discovery is a formidable addition to the mounting arsenal of evidence that promises to overthrow the centuries-old notion that the brain is fixed and unchanging, along with the long-held canon of neuroscience that the brain is like a machine or 'hardwired' like a computer, so damage to, or removal of, a component means the permanent impairment or loss of that specific function. A lot of meditation research also points towards brain neuroplasticity.[36]

The brain functions holistically

The whole question of whether the brain is essentially like a computer—currently the strongly prevalent conventional view—will be explored in depth in Chapter 7 of Volume II. For now, we again need to underline a principal contention of this work: that there is mounting evidence from impeccable scientists working with utmost rigour within the field of science itself, to show that the mechanistic–reductionist method, associated with the materialist philosophy, is unable to provide the sole explanatory framework about life and the nature of memory. The need for a fundamentally new approach is obvious and the answer from the perspective of modern science comes mainly from Sheldrake's theory of morphic resonance.

Memory and Biological Inheritance

According to Sheldrake, the hypothesis of morphic resonance leads to a radically new concept regarding the notion of memory storage in the brain and of biological inheritance. Memory need not be stored in material traces inside brains (as would be required in the mechanistic molecular theory), since in this new understanding, brains are more like television receivers than video recorders, tuning into influences from the past. And biological inheritance need not all be coded in the genes, or in epigenetic modifications of the genes; much of it depends on morphic resonance from previous members of the species. Genes therefore act more like transformers and transducers—to continue the simile—rather than being the originators of inheritance and species memory. Thus, everyone inherits a collective memory from the experiences of past members of the species, and also contributes to the collective memory, affecting other members of the species in the future. Therefore, in the understanding that the brain acts more in the nature of a transceiver/transducer than a storage device, as just suggested, there is no need to assume that all memories are stored inside the brain in 'memory banks' like the hard disk of a computer. The habits of nature depend on non-local similarity reinforcement. Through morphic resonance, the patterns of activity in self-organizing systems are influenced by similar patterns in the past, giving each species, and each kind of self-organizing system, a collective memory.[37]

How morphic resonance explains memory

Animals inherit the successful habits of their species as instincts because the more often they are repeated, the more probable they become, other things being equal, so the reinforcement of habits will play an essential part in any integrated theory of evolution, including not just biological evolution, but also physical, chemical, social, mental and cultural evolution. Humans inherit bodily, emotional, mental, and cultural habits, including the habits of language.[38]

Group Memory

Social groups are likewise organized by fields, as in schools of fish and flocks of birds. Human societies have memories that are transmitted through the culture of the group and are most explicitly communicated through the ritual re-enactment of a founding story or myth. This is especially noticeable in aboriginal and tribal societies characterized by a group memory which individual members tune into. Scientists and anthropologists are beginning to unearth a wellspring of knowledge buried in the ancient stories of Australia's Aboriginal peoples[39] in 'Dream Time', a commonly used term for describing important features of Aboriginal spiritual beliefs and existence that is not generally well understood by non-indigenous people.[40] Such group memory is also evident in mob violence, racial riots or gang hooliganism where the people involved behave in ways that would be unlikely when on their own and not part of the crowd. Note that the morphic fields of social groups

Evidence of group memory in aboriginal societies, gangs, and racial riots connect together members of the group even when they are many miles apart and provide channels of communication through which organisms can stay in touch at a distance. They help provide an explanation for telepathy.

Animal Telepathy

There is now good evidence that many species of animals are telepathic, and telepathy seems to be a normal means of animal communication, as discussed in the book *Dogs That Know When Their Owners are Coming Home*.[41] Telepathy is normal, not paranormal, natural not supernatural, and is also common between people, especially people who know each other well. It is easy to dismiss the evidence with the retort that one often thinks of someone, but there is no sign of communication from that person. However, controlled experiments have given repeatable positive results that are statistically significant.[42]

Mounting scientific studies show animal telepathy

Scientific Breakthroughs

Another area in which the hypothesis of morphic resonance might cast some light is the revolutionary developments in science. There are a number of historical accounts which seem to demonstrate that 'an idea whose time has come' is 'received', almost out of the ether, by several individuals simultaneously. Moreover, it can also be seen that an idea or discovery is brought to its full maturity by several individuals all working at different times, perhaps even spanning different centuries. The mathematical calculus is a good case in point. The pioneers of the calculus stretch far back to the time of the Babylonians, the Egyptians, and the Greeks.[43] During the Age of Enlightenment (Age of Reason) several mathematicians in England and Europe were fervently working on mathematical problems of this genre. However, the complete formulation of the calculus was the supreme achievement of Sir Issac Newton and Gottfried Leibniz, independently and practically contemporaneously.[44] It was more in the nature of a scientific breakthrough than a linear advancement on previously held theories. 'It is clear that calculus was on the doorstep, and that it only took some great minds to bring it in[to] the open.'[45]

Could morphic resonance partly explain scientific revolutions?

Refer again to Endnote I-1 for a representative selection of peer-reviewed papers and latest tests conducted in support of the hypothesis of formative causation involving morphic fields and morphic resonance.

Organizing Fields

A closely similar concept to morphogenetic fields is 'organizing fields'. Both these concepts are far more than mere theories: they are scientifically testable, and they can explain phenomena that are baffling to science, such as telepathy.

Gustaf Strömberg was a Swedish–American astronomer who was a member of the Staff at Mount Wilson Observatory from 1916 to 1937. He was distinguished for his investigations into the movements and luminosities of the stars and the structure of the universe; but his interests included other scientific fields (his remarks on Darwin's mature reflections on hereditary variations were mentioned in Chapter 3).

Gustaf Strömberg's entirely scientific work points to the eternal wisdom on matters of immortality and soul

His main work *The Soul of the Universe* is a purely scientific work which in numerous respects alludes to the later discoveries of quantum science, while also supporting the fundamental tenets of esotericism.[46] Strömberg presents an array of facts from the latest science of his day, i.e., late 1930s; nevertheless, his book is highly instructive and relevant to modern readers because he touches upon the perennial wisdom which belongs to every age. We find the mature thought of a scientist fully informed in the latest trends of modern research, who, by applying the principles of relativity and quantum theory to the field of biology and the relationship between mind and matter, has discovered, in his own words, 'that the individual memory is probably indestructible and that the essence of all living elements is probably immortal. The study leads to the inevitable conclusion that there exists a World Soul or God.'[47]

The culmination of his search for the Soul of the Universe was the sublimities of Cosmic Space which he declares to be a fullness, a plenum—not a blank or empty vacuum but the Origin and inner World of Life. In clarifying our ideas about Space, he shows that it is not just 'an empty place to put things in'—an advanced concept in the 1930s—but that it has an objective reality, properties, and definite rules for its activities. He found our familiar world of space and time, the training school of souls, to be different from the more real 'world' of life and consciousness. There are elements, both material and 'immaterial', which connect these worlds and provide a rational foundation for the existence of the soul and its survival after bodily death. All this is in perfect harmony with the perennial wisdom teaching that no single point in the universe is devoid of life and consciousness of some order. We then learn something about matter, a very mysterious substance, which leads to gravitational and electrical fields and the nature of the atom, about which Strömberg has much to share of special interest.

Then comes the most important factor in Strömberg's argument, the so-called 'immaterial wave-structure' in the cosmos, the nature of which the most advanced physicists of his generation (mid-twentieth century) were studying, for example, the 'hidden variables' theory[vi] proposed by the deeply philosophical and metaphysical American physicist David Bohm FRS (1917–1992).[48]

The immaterial (i.e., non-physical) waves represent one half of the duality in nature. The other half is the particles *controlled and organized by the immaterial waves*. As Strömberg states in the same work:

> Immaterial structures help solve the nature of forgotten memory and survival after death

> We shall regard the two aspects as belonging to two different 'worlds', which we designate by the terms *material* and *immaterial*. An electron will be regarded as belonging to the material world; electrical fields, radio waves and pilot waves will be regarded as belonging to the immaterial world. The earth is material, its gravitational field is immaterial. An atom consists of *particles*, neutrons, positrons, electrons (perhaps also photons and neutrinos), which are cemented together into a unit by an *immaterial wave-structure* with certain space and time properties. It is this structure which 'organizes' and 'inflates' atoms, molecules, crystals, and solid bodies in general […]. The mysterious *forces* of classical physics can be regarded as manifestations of such immaterial structures.[49]

---

vi The hidden variables theory posits that the behaviour of a quantum entity is determined by an unobservable, non-local field or 'pilot wave', the hidden variations of which guide the behaviour of its associated particles.

To illustrate the guidance, or control by the 'immaterial structure' and its 'pilot' waves, Strömberg cites the development of the living cell, a most elaborate process and an unexplained 'miracle' to biology. He shows that material, physical, or even electrical forces, fail to explain these mysterious processes, but that 'a living immaterial structure or wave system' can do so. Biologists have vaguely called the power which inspires the visible marshalling of the particles of the developing cell an 'organizing field', but Strömberg adopts the term 'genie', a word which, he says, 'suggests a relation with genes', but 'also suggests a wisdom far beyond our comprehension'. He speaks of many grades or hierarchies of genies, and the 'Supreme Genie' may be called the Soul of the World or of the Cosmos, the wellspring of all sensations, ideas, thoughts, and aspirations. The immaterial wave-structure of space greatly helps to solve the problem of memory, and therefore of survival after death. The matter in our brains is constantly being replaced, yet memories are accumulated and preserved during a long lifetime. Even long-forgotten events may suddenly flash into vivid consciousness when some inner contact is made. These long-forgotten events also erupt into the mind when there is some pressing *need*, perhaps prompted by external circumstances—as if the urgency triggers the memory which provides just what is needed. How could this be unless an immaterial living structure subsists, in which memory inheres independent of the physical atoms? Furthermore, there seems to be no valid reason why this immaterial structure should not continue without impairment after death, regardless of the dissolution of the physical structure. Strömberg devotes many pages to the logical working out of these points and provides a well-supported position from which the existence of the soul is scientifically demonstrable.

In relation to *The Soul of the Universe* Albert Einstein wrote: 'What especially impressed me was the successful attempt to isolate the essential facts from the bewildering array of discovered data and the presentation of them in such a way that the problem of the unity of our knowledge becomes a rational one.' Einstein continues, 'Very few men could of their own knowledge present the material as clearly and concisely as he has succeeded in doing.' Einstein's verdict is one of a series of twenty-two statements written by scientists in the April 18, 1948 edition of *The American Weekly*.[50] Strömberg's own statement, 'My Faith' was republished as Appendix Six in the second edition (1948) of *The Soul of the Universe*. In the opening paragraph he states:

> I believe that behind the physical world we see with our eyes and study in our microscopes and telescopes, and measure with instruments of various kinds, is another, more fundamental realm which can not [*sic*] be described in physical terms. In this non-physical realm lies the ultimate origin of all things, of energy, matter, organization and life, and even of consciousness itself.[51]

Regarding consciousness, Strömberg has this to say:

> I am convinced that our consciousness is rooted in a world not built of atoms, and that our mind in its many facets reflects some of the fundamental characteristics of its own origin. All our mental characteristics and faculties have their origin in the non-physical world.[52]

In the same work, the second edition of which sheds new light on the scientific evidence of human immortality, Strömberg describes fields of organization as the intelligent and 'highly organized activity' of nature that determines the structure of a living body, its disorganization, and its reorganization, maintaining that 'all living organisms are imbedded in

Strömberg argues that consciousness, the ultimate origin of all things, is rooted in the non-physical realm complex electric fields, and these fields disappear at death.' Furthermore, Strömberg cites Harold Saxton Burr (1889–1973) professor of anatomy at Yale Medical School and researcher into neuroanatomy and bioelectrodynamics involving fields of organization, who concluded that 'it is hard to escape the conclusion that these fields are independent of the matter involved and by their innate properties determine the structure and functions of the living organism.'[53]

> It is reasonable to infer that in his commendation of *The Soul of the Universe,* Einstein's own thoughts must have been in harmony with three key precepts that pervade Strömberg's work: (*a*) the existence of non-physical worlds; (*b*) scientific evidence of human immortality; and (*c*) the non-material root of consciousness.

Strömberg's work was taken up by the Polish priest, healer, and physicist Andrew Glazewski (1905–1973), who was a strong influence on the founders of the Scientific and Medical Network.[54] Like Strömberg, he used the language of science to speak about spiritual matters because he sensed the urgent need of bringing together scientists interested in discussing the spiritual side of science. Glazewski asserted that not only are living and non-living[vii] entities surrounded by sonic, electric, and infrared fields, but that there is another field that controls the others and determines the growth of the entity and its functioning. This master field he called 'soul' in the Aristotelian sense of an organizing field (based on Gustaf Strömberg's work as outlined above), which operates beyond our ordinary realm of space and time;[55] hence, by implication, outside the bounds of science since it cannot be detected by physical apparatus but is amenable to investigation by a sensitive person. Nonetheless, it is this organizing field which provides the (non-material) template around which the body is organized in rather the same way as the field surrounding, say, a bar magnet organizes the pattern of iron filings surrounding it. According to Glazewski, the process of psychological and spiritual unfoldment involves an increasing awareness of one's own field, that of other people, and of other entities.

> Andrew Glazewski argues for a master organizing field unamenable to investigation by physical science

Chapters 2 and 3 of Volume II describe in detail the function of fields of organization, and the role of electricity in the human body is further taken up in Chapter 9 of Volume III.

The Limitations of Establishment Biology and the Implications for Subtle Bodies

In conclusion then, morphogenesis, organizing fields, and immaterial wave-structures collectively show the indispensable non-physical, non-local functioning of mind in addition to the working of the physical body and brain. Such advanced ideas underpinned by the work of eminent scientists, as we have just seen, cannot be belittled by purely materialistic theories backed by statistical ammunition. There is a strong allusion, therefore, to subtle bodies and subtle energies that, in addition to the familiar physical body, constitute our whole being.

---

vii 'Non-living' meaning non-biological, for example minerals, for there is no such thing as dead matter *per se.* The esoteric philosophy unequivocally declares that there is no single point or particle in the universe devoid of life and consciousness at its own level and grade.

Paranormal Phenomena

It would be entirely out of place here to attempt a summary of the vast literature on paranormal phenomena. However, we can draw attention to a few areas that are especially well researched and proven.

We have already touched upon telepathy, a human and animal faculty that is now virtually proven and cannot be accounted for, or rationalized mechanistically, or put down to coincidence. Like other paranormal phenomena, it cannot be explained away by a materialistic paradigm which equates mind with brain.

Psychology and Parapsychology

Psychological studies have confirmed what is popularly known as 'mind over matter', namely that mental activity can causally influence behaviour, the more conscious and focussed the attention, the more pronounced are the results. It means that mental events can significantly influence the activity of the brain. In *Science and Moral Priority* the neuropsychologist, neurobiologist, and Nobel laureate Roger Sperry (1913–1994) describes how after separating the two hemispheres of the brain by cutting the corpus callosum connecting them, he found that each remained 'a conscious system in its own right, perceiving, thinking, remembering, reasoning, willing, and emoting, all at a characteristically human level, and [...] both the left and the right hemisphere may be conscious simultaneously in different, even in mutually conflicting, mental experiences that run along in parallel.'[56] (This seems to agree with the experience of the American neuroanatomist Jill Bolte Taylor (*b.*1959) who, after a massive stroke, discovered that what we take for granted as 'objective reality' is in fact highly influenced by the brain hemisphere in question—see Chapter 6 for more details). Sperry states that this demonstrates a radical departure from the prevalent view from about 1920 to 1970 (and largely still to this day), 'when the most influential thinkers in the behavioural sciences argued that the human mind is an illusion or, at best, a powerless by-product of physical brain processes.'[57] However, the movement is not purely one way, as Sperry also shows.

Put simplistically, mind affects matter, but matter also affects mind: the mental affects the brain but the brain also affects the mental. We see here a perfect instance of the operation of the universal Hermetic Axiom: *As is the greater, so is the lesser.* The 'greater' has a stronger influence on the 'lesser', albeit the lesser can also influence the greater, to some extent.[viii] However the primary causation according to Sperry is downward. He distinguished conscious events from their neural correlates; and his latest concept of the mind as a causal, functional emergent distinguishes the causal efficacy of consciousness from its neural correlates.

Further evidence accrues from psychotherapy, neuroimaging studies, and psychoneuroimmunology, which collectively show that our thoughts and emotions, expressed in such things as our expectations, beliefs, and wishes, can bring about changes in our external environment as well as markedly affecting the activity of our physiological

Roger Sperry shows brain hemispheres and mental experiences affect each other

---

viii We discern this primary downward and secondary upward causation in all walks of life, like parents and children, government and citizens, managers and workers.

systems connected with our brain (such as the cardiovascular, endocrine, and immune systems).[58]

The 'experimenter effect' and 'confirmation bias' are two sides of the same coin. The former, otherwise known as 'subject–expectancy effect', is a well-known occurrence in parapsychology as well as in scientific experiments or medical treatments. It is a phenomenon that occurs when a researcher expects a given result, otherwise known as cognitive bias (recognized or unknown preconceptions and assumptions) and therefore unconsciously affects the outcome or reports the expected result.[59] The effect is most commonly found in medicine when a patient is administered a harmless substance but experiences the placebo reaction or nocebo (i.e., negative) reaction, depending on the state of mind of the patient or the expectation of the doctor. Because this effect can significantly bias the results of experiments (especially on human subjects), double-blind methodology is used in an attempt to eliminate the bias effect. Nonetheless, there are higher than statistical average data showing that the latter are biased according to the experimenter even when all possible unconscious clues and means of communication are eliminated. There is a vast body of scientific, peer-reviewed material on this fascinating subject.[60]

This is closely associated with 'confirmation bias', also known as 'confirmatory bias', which *is an irrational tendency to search for, interpret or recall information in a way that supposedly confirms preconceptions, prior assumptions or hypotheses*, while giving disproportionately less consideration to alternative possibilities.[61] The effect is stronger for emotionally charged issues, and for emotional people, especially regarding deeply entrenched beliefs (invariably of a scientific or religious nature). As a result, the experimenter can interpret ambiguous evidence as supporting his existing position because of the tendency to look for information that conforms to his preconceptions and overlook information that argues against it.

There is another kind of experimenter effect whereby a person's psychic nature, his personal psychological signature, so to speak, can influence the outcome of experiments. This will be described in the following section. A well-known case is the great Nobel quantum physicist Wolfgang Pauli, who formulated the 'Exclusion Principle' in quantum physics.[ix] The English theoretical physicist and cosmologist Stephen Hawking FRS (1942–2018) was no enthusiast of parapsychology or *psi*, but he had the integrity to state, 'it was said of him that even his presence in the same town would make experiments go wrong!'[62] Unfortunately, Hawking did not take up the implications of this admission of Pauli's *psi*[x] proclivities.

Paranormal and 'Psi' Phenomena – Robust and Repeatable Evidence?

Research into *psi* phenomena indicates that living organisms (including human beings) and physical apparatus can be influenced mentally. Possibly, the most astonishing evidence

Perceived outcome influenced by personal subjective factors (expectations, beliefs, emotions, etc.)

The psychic nature of the person can also influence results

---

ix The exclusion principle helps explain a wide variety of physical phenomena and the variety of chemical elements, and their combinations, in terms of the electron shell structure of atoms and the way atoms share electrons.

x *Psi* is a collective and generalizing term for the aggregate of parapsychological functions of the mind including extrasensory perception, precognition, and psychokinesis (the psychic ability to influence a physical system without physical interaction).

of psychokinesis ('PK'), the power of the human mind to exert non-physical control over inanimate objects, comes from the American plasma physicist Robert Jahn (1930–2017) and colleagues of the Princeton Engineering Anomalies Research project (PEAR) at the School of Engineering and Applied Sciences—an Ivy League university, no less (where Einstein worked after emigrating to the United States from Germany).[63] A variety of experiments were performed: electronic, mechanical, optical, acoustic, and fluidic. All these devices produced strictly random outputs when unattended and were calibrated precisely to establish their unattended statistical output distributions. Millions of experiments were carried out over almost a quarter of a century to reveal incontrovertible evidence of the power of 'mind over matter'. The human subjects proved capable of 'mind-altering' the output of the devices, such that the chances of obtaining such a bias by coincidence alone was calculated to be less than one in one thousand billion. Furthermore, the Princeton experiments have shown some astonishing (to Western science, that is) facts that have been admitted even in 'hard' science journals. First, that distance and time do not figure in the results; people thousands of miles away seem able to affect the machines as if they were in the same room. Then, operators do not even have to apply their thoughts whilst the device is operating. Another characteristic is that each individual seems to have a unique effect on the machines, producing in effect his personal 'signature', i.e., his own particular bias in the unattended Gaussian distribution of the output from the machines.[xi]

Psychokinesis proven by rigorous experiments at PEAR by Robert Jahn

However, predictably, the fact that this daring research was conducted using the utmost rigour of science did not feature in the backlash against Jahn and the PEAR team because, as neatly stated in 2003 by Adrian Berry, Science Correspondent of the British national newspaper *The Daily Telegraph*: 'Few subjects more infuriate scientists than claims of paranormal phenomena, because if confirmed, the whole fabric of science would be threatened.' It would have been more accurate to have stated that the whole fabric of scientific materialism would be threatened.

Unfortunately, though, the irritating evidence for such 'infuriation' is mounting exponentially, as we now describe. We start by wondering how diehard sceptics would react to robust evidence that the war-hero and mathematical prodigy, Alan Turing (see earlier), believed in extrasensory perception.[64, 65, 66]

The international professional organization for scientists and scholars interested in *psi* phenomena is the Parapsychological Association. It is an elected affiliate (since 1969) of the American Association for the Advancement of Science, which is the largest general scientific organization in the world. In Great Britain, the Society for Psychical Research, mentioned earlier, is another such scientific body having highly distinguished professors and academics on its editorial board. Another eminent reference source containing links to scholarly articles on *psi* and parapsychology is the blog of the contemporary American Carlos S. Alvarado, Research Fellow at the Parapsychology Foundation.

Dean Radin is one of the foremost researchers of *psi* phenomena at the Institute of Noetic Sciences (IONS). There will always be ripostes of flawed methodology and confirmation

---

xi Also known as *normal distribution*, it is a bell-shaped curve, and it is assumed that during any measurement, unbiased values will follow a normal distribution with an equal number of measurements above and below the mean value.

Dean Radin
provides robust
evidence for *psi*
phenomena
bias amongst invincible materialists who, as it so happens, only display their own biases in their one-sided criticisms; however, the weight and volume of facts speak for themselves. Using meta-analysis, Radin has demonstrated once and for all the experimentally repeatable existence of a range of *psi* phenomena and abilities. It is important to understand the statistical power of meta-analysis in the investigation of *psi*. It is a structured method of statistical analysis that combines thousands of results over hundreds of experiments to obtain high levels of confidence about the existence of the *psi* phenomena being investigated. Put another way, when the results of many similar studies are combined to form the equivalent of a single, grand experiment conducted by many experimenters from many locations and over many years, the confidence in the outcome is substantially increased. In a single experiment, the raw data points are typically the individual responses of *psi* participants; but in meta-analysis, the raw data points are the results of *separate experiments* involving *numerous participants*. By combining the results from multiple studies over individual studies, an improved pooled estimate of the size of the effect can be obtained and uncertainties better resolved when reports disagree. The virtue of this

Sophisticated
statistics used to
validate evidence
for *psi*
phenomena
approach is that it circumvents the 'file draw effect'; otherwise known as 'publication bias'—the bias introduced into scientific literature by selective publication, primarily by a tendency to publish positive results but not to publish negative, or non-confirmatory, results. Publishing only results that show a significant finding disturbs the balance of findings.[67]

Using the statistical technique of meta-analysis, then, Radin methodically and rigorously examined the results from nearly a century of increasingly sophisticated experiments. Notwithstanding the possibility of many hundreds of researchers committing fraud in a massive, decades-long conspiracy, or a complete misapplication and misunderstanding of meta-analysis by eminent scientists and statisticians, the existence of telepathy (mind-to-mind perception), clairvoyance (perception at distance), precognition (perception through time), psychokinesis (mind-matter interaction), and other *psi* phenomena (e.g. mental interactions with living organisms) are all shown to be incontrovertible. This work definitively lays to rest any doubts as to the experimentally demonstrated existence of at least some psychic (or *psi*) phenomena. Similar robust evidence for *psi* has been obtained by many other researchers, like the Swedish psychologist Etzel Cardeña (*b*.1957),[68] but Radin's work is arguably one of the most outstanding contributions in terms of withstanding scientific scrutiny.

In response to outright sceptics, like Michael Shermer (see Chapter 2), who orate the usual three objections: that there is no valid scientific evidence for *psi*; or such phenomena are impossible, by definition; or the results are all entirely due to fraud, Radin has developed a 'Show Me the Evidence' page, periodically updated, of selected peer-reviewed publications on *psi* research containing downloadable articles on *psi* and *psi*-related topics, all published in peer-reviewed journals.[69] Most of these papers were published in the twenty-first century; however there are also some important papers of historical interest

Massive database
of peer-reviewed
papers confirming
psi
and other resources. (A full comprehensive list would run into several thousands of articles.) The majority of papers report experimental studies, or meta-analyses, of classes of experiments. They appear as the *Selected Peer-Reviewed Journal Publications on Psi Research* on the IONS website along with books, journals, and videos. Major topics addressed are: Healing at a Distance, Causality from the Future, Physiological Correlations at a Distance, Telepathy & ESP, General Overviews & Critiques, Survival of Consciousness,

Precognition & Presentiment, Theory, Mind-Matter Interaction, and Potential Applications. Besides Radin himself, the galaxy of other contemporary scientists, psychologists, and researchers listed on the site includes Marilyn Schlitz, Russell Targ, Harold E. Puthoff, Pim van Lommel, Bruce Greyson, Brian Josephson, Robert G. Jahn, Brenda J. Dunne, Charles Tart, Stephan Schwartz, Rupert Sheldrake, Amit Goswami, and Larry Dossey.

These sources show that objections to *psi* have been soundly rebutted for decades, using facts and figures which serve to support this phenomena. As Radin states, active research now focusses not on demonstrating *psi* abilities, but on advances in methodology, issues about effect, size, heterogeneity, robustness of replication, development of adequate theoretical explanations, and finding the 'source' of *psi*.[70] As we shall see in Volumes II and III, the esoteric and occult sciences provide every aspect of this explanatory framework, plus a great deal more.

Journeys Out of the Body

Under this heading are included the near-death experience (NDE), out-of-body experience (OBE), and lucid dreaming experience. There are subtle distinctions as well as considerable overlap between these three experiences; so even though they are described under separate headings for the sake of clarity, it is completely futile to attempt a hard and fast demarcation line between them since they all involve altered states of consciousness not confined just to the physical body. We stress that this is an enormous subject; hence what is shown below is by no means comprehensive but in the nature of a taster, supported by references, to satisfy any unbiased reader about how scientific evidence on these altered states of consciousness undermines the limitations of the purely materialistic scientific paradigm on mind and consciousness, and therefore points to different realms of consciousness expressing through appropriate subtle bodies. Representative literature, in addition to the references provided, is suggested in Endnote I-2 and Endnote I-3.

Near-Death Experiences

Advances in medical science have demonstrated that a person pronounced clinically dead (no breathing, no heartbeat, no electrical brain activity registered on the electrodes of the electroencephalograph machine for a few minutes or sometimes even longer) may be revived and can sometimes describe in vivid and accurate detail the phenomenon known as an NDE. This has shown that conscious mental activity and memory can be experienced even when there are no vital signs of physical life during a critical accident or cardiac arrest. It is important to note that the electrical activity of the brain ceases within a few seconds following a cardiac arrest. Several of these experiences have been proven to be veridical, namely, to coincide with reality. It is noteworthy that in the near-death experience (as in the out-of-body experience), the recollection is extremely clear with no confusion, jumbled perceptions or phantasies, as could well be the case if the experience were drug induced.

Proof about consciousness not limited to brain

The Self Does Not Die: Verified paranormal phenomena from near-death experiences by Titus Rivas, Anny Dirven, et al. is an important book providing robust evidence in favour of veridical perception during NDEs when the brain, according to the accepted dicta of

Veridical NDE
perceptions
unexplained by
neuroscience
modern neuroscience, is incapable of supporting such conscious experiences.[71] A fine review of this book is by no lesser an authority than Eben Alexander, whose own remarkable NDE experience, added to his impeccable qualifications as a Harvard neurosurgeon, uniquely qualifies him to have written his own book, *Proof of Heaven* (mentioned in Chapter 2). In his review, Alexander states that the authors have gone to great lengths to make an objective analysis of over one hundred cases. Moreover, the quality of empirical data and objective assessment, and refutation of possible materialist interpretations, makes this an important and timely book that offers significant empirical support to the emerging scientific view that consciousness is fundamental to the universe; moreover that the soul exists and does *not* depend solely on the physical brain for its conscious expression.[72]

The veridical trait of NDEs is supported by robust empirical evidence from science. But despite the numerous interpretations of doctors, based on their own various disciplines and personal paradigms, there seems to be no satisfactory explanatory mechanism based on ordinary physiological, biochemical or psychological lines; and least so regarding what many, but not all, NDE subjects discover—that they seem to have a second body, just like their physical body, or that they possess no body at all but appear to themselves as a cloud of mist. In Volume II we shall see how occult science supplies the overwhelming theoretical framework and practical psycho-spiritual explanations that render the phenomenon,
NDEs show need
to transcend
materialistic
theories
and much else related to it, incontrovertible. Reverting to Alexander's review of *The Self Does Not Die*, he concludes by stating that as one studies the mounting scientific evidence in this book and other recent works on the mind-brain relationship, 'it becomes clear that to reach a deeper understanding we must reject the materialist position. These empirical data refute the production model, which states that the brain produces consciousness out of physical matter. Rather, the filter model (i.e., that the brain serves as a receiver of primordial consciousness) is far more reasonable in accounting for all the available evidence. Sooner or later, *the sheer frustration with the ongoing inadequacies of materialist pseudo-explanations* [emphasis added] will nudge the prevailing western paradigm towards the deeper truth, as it is objectively presented in this remarkable book.'

Two further points are noteworthy. First, a valiant attempt 'to nudge the prevailing western paradigm towards the deeper truth' was one of the primary aims of the modern Theosophical Society. Secondly, that the 'filter model' in science and psychology is not something new; it was advocated as far back as the late nineteenth century by several enlightened thinkers and philosophers, like the Father of American psychology, a fitting epithet for the American philosopher and psychologist William James (1842–1910)— see Chapter 6 for the seminal import of his ideas.

A litmus test of the genuineness of an experience is the long-lasting effects it has on the affected person. Whereas some NDEs are not pleasant and can sometimes be terrifying,
Means to assess
the genuineness
of an NDE
numerous NDE subjects report profound spiritual experiences during the actual NDE. Furthermore, upon recovery, their lives, entire sense of values, and outlook have changed dramatically. For example, selfish and grasping tendencies seem to melt in favour of compassionate and philanthropic behaviour. Above all, the fear of death is relinquished as the subject inwardly realises that physical death is but a transition to a new and fuller mode of consciousness, untrammelled by the limitations of the physical body and senses. A fine example from another classic of recent NDE literature is the experiences of Rajiv Parti recorded in his book *Dying to Wake Up* mentioned in Chapter 2.[73] Before his

life-changing experience, he was selfish and steeped in materialistic values, living in a large mansion, running expensive cars, and adopting a high-pressure lifestyle as a successful cardiac anaesthetist—not to mention his callous attitude to many of his patients and abusive pressure meted out to his eldest son. Near-death proved to be a dramatic awakening for him, completely re-orientating his life towards spiritual values, whilst losing interest in material things which resulted in downsizing his house and getting rid of his expensive cars. He resorted to meditation to gain access to inner guidance and practised immense kindness and love towards his wife, son, and his friends. There is a wealth of information on the life transforming and soul-affirming nature of numerous NDEs from modern scientific studies of NDEs, for example by the world-renowned authority Peter Fenwick (see again Chapter 2).[74] All these books and personal accounts convey a common, essential, message which we can all apply to our lives without having to undergo an NDE for ourselves.

What does the *philosophia perennis* have to say about NDEs? The *Bardo Thödol* whose actual title is *The Great Liberation upon Hearing in the Intermediate State* is known in the West as the *Tibetan Book of the Dead*,[75] traditionally believed to be the work in the eighth century AD of the legendary Padma Sambhava, regarded in Tibetan Buddhism as an emanation of Amitābha, the celestial buddha. It is intended as a guide through the experiences of consciousness after death so that the dying person may recognize the nature of his mind in the bardo, the interval between death and the next rebirth. The Tibetan book has a major bearing on the NDE because it teaches that once awareness is freed from the body, it creates its own reality as one would experience in a dream.[76] This dream occurs in various phases, or 'bardos', in ways that are wonderful or terrifying, with peaceful or wrathful visions occurring, since the awareness of the near-deceased is in a state of confusion because it is no longer connected to a physical body. This shows a similar pattern of events to the NDE, as just outlined, except that, of course, in an NDE such disconnection with the physical body is temporary as the experience is one of near-death and not death *per se*.

NDEs upheld by the perennial philosophy

The journey of consciousness after death, and in the afterlife, is also described in detail in the *Egyptian Book of the Dead*[77] and in the legend of the 'Myth of Er' that concludes Plato's *Republic*,[78] from which many details can be correlated to the transitions of consciousness during an NDE.

'Death is sleep' is an old adage, meaning that the key to understanding death as transition, and the associated post-mortem states of consciousness, is by analogy with the sleeping and dreaming states during earthly life. This is all explained in detail in Volume II.

Near death experiences bear out the perennial wisdom that, although death destroys form, death can never destroy life and consciousness which is ever renewed through newer forms.

Out-of-Body Experiences

An 'OBE' is closely allied to the near-death experience, which in turn can sometimes, but not always, result in an OBE from the point of view of the subject. OBE is a modern term for 'astral projection' used in the occult literature mainly of the East.

OBE subjects state that they seem to possess what may generally be described as a 'second body' having an idioplastic nature: in other words, a second body moulded by the influence of thought, so much so that thought and action seem to be much more closely coupled than in normal life. Subjects also identify different kinds of space in which they find themselves. For example, Robert Monroe (1915–1995), a businessman in the United States, and qualified in communication engineering, found himself in three kinds of space.[79] He referred to 'Locale I'—the 'here now' space—as the space just like the physical world. 'Locale II' is apparently a very much larger space of the traditional heavens and hells and is a region that people appear to occupy soon after death. 'Locale III' is the space in which people are living their lives in very much the same way as they were on Earth, only at what seems to be at some quite different time of history.

Subtle body and three different kinds of space

Sceptics should note carefully that it is entirely possible to train oneself to have an OBE. (This is not without its dangers but scaling the heights of consciousness can hardly be expected to be without its pitfalls any more than climbing a mountain would be without risk of falling into a ravine.) Such training has been well documented from personal experience by eminent scientists such as Robert Monroe[80] and Arthur Ellison mentioned earlier in this Chapter. Ellison reported OBEs by following, for one month, the methods prescribed by the American esotericist Sylvan Muldoon (1903–1969) and British-born American investigator of psychic phenomena Hereward Carrington (1880–1958).[81] The writer attended a one-week course on parapsychology by Ellison at Leicester University in 1998. Ellison described the discipline he undertook to induce an OBE. To test the authenticity of his OBE vision he visited his local chemist shop in the OBE state and noted the labels on the bottles in the shop window. The next day he visited the same shop to verify whether his OBE sight corresponded to physical reality. Indeed, it did, and this is the hallmark of an impeccable scientist who, despite his rigorous scientific training, is not hidebound by a materialistic paradigm but is always open to new modes of enquiry and discovery. Unfortunately, the writer cannot recall whether Ellison stated that he took the additional step of writing down the bottle labels in advance of visiting the chemist shop to verify his OBE.

Arthur Ellison shows OBEs achievable through suitable training

The essential message from OBEs is that quite clearly, there can be more than one stream of consciousness operating at one time (which matter will be addressed in detail in Volume III in relation to the mind-sensation problem). Given that consciousness needs an appropriate vehicle through which to manifest and express, this implies that there can be more than one 'body' used at one time—bodies other than the physical, namely, the subtle bodies. It is especially noteworthy that Monroe's three Locales correspond closely to the physical and the two principal after-death states of consciousness (as will be explained fully in Chapter 5 of Volume II dealing with the after-death states of consciousness).

Lucid Dreaming

The lucid dreaming experience is closely linked to the OBE. It can be induced using various techniques or it can occur during sleep. The eminent British scientist, horticulturist, and Theosophist E. Lester Smith FRS (1904–1992) suggests that our dreams can loosely be grouped into four categories that are by no means watertight.[82] The common dream is one where we see the various scenes and episodes as passive observers. In other types, we ourselves seem to play a role, but one that is imposed on us as if we were actors in a play written by another playwright. In the third type of dream we seem to play a more active role. Whereas the dream scenery is invariably imposed, we can choose what we do

E. Lester Smith describes four kinds of dreams

in it. This is the so-called lucid dream in which we are aware that we are dreaming and can deliberately take control over the course of the dream events.[xii] There is also a fourth kind of dream where a few people have been able to pre-programme their dreams and decide in advance to visit some place or a particular person.

Laboratory work on lucid dreams has produced interesting results. Of course, it is not possible for a dreamer to indicate when he is lucidly dreaming since the body is virtually paralysed during dream episodes and electroencephalogram, or other records, provide no clue. Fortunately, however, the onset of lucid dreams is indicated by two bodily functions that escape this paralysis, namely, breathing and eye movements. For example, deliberate left-to-right eye movements can signal the onset of lucid dreams, also, the onset and ending of flying episodes. The end of the lucid dream is usually marked by the subject waking up and describing the dream.

Physiological indicators of a lucid dream

Ellison has reported several lucid dreams by following the stepwise techniques laid down in the book by the American writer on cultural and social issues Howard Rheingold (*b.*1947), co-authored with the American psychophysiologist Stephen LaBerge (*b.*1947), whose work is based on extensive laboratory research at Stanford University mapping mind/body relationships during the dream state, the teachings of Tibetan dream yogis, and the work of other scientists.[83]

Mediumship

> I shall not commit the fashionable stupidity of regarding everything I cannot explain as a fraud.
>
> C.G. Jung[84]

Mediumship is generally understood to be the ability of a person to communicate with someone who has physically died. On what level such communication occurs is another highly complex matter that will not be considered here. Nonetheless there is documented evidence from controlled laboratory experiments that skilled research mediums can sometimes obtain specific and detailed information about deceased persons.

Arthur Ellison participated in numerous séances, and meticulously investigated dozens of mediums, all through his life. He stresses that, contrary to public perception, mediums are amongst the most honest and genuine people he has known; that one very rarely meets a fraudulent medium. This testimonial, coming from an impeccable scientist and lifelong psychic investigator, flies in the face of unsubstantiated, throwaway opinions from scientists who have never bothered to investigate such phenomena and merely air their own prejudices and materialistic presuppositions—for example, the Oxford professor of chemistry Peter Atkins (mentioned in Chapter 3) who opines: 'Without exception, all spiritualists are sharks feeding on the gullibility of the weak, distressed, and hopeful who inhabit the oceans of the world.'[85]

Controlled laboratory experiments show genuiness of mediumistic phenomena and honesty of most mediums

However, and this is important, unless mediums happen to be trained scientists, they are unlikely to be aware of the dramatizing machinery of their minds, or the shortcomings of

---

xii It is the writer's experience that thought and action in the dream state seem to be closely coupled. For example, to think oneself weightless and flying is to be weightless and flying. Moreover, it is possible consciously to awake oneself from a dream that is unpleasant.

their rather literal interpretation of the experiences that they genuinely do have.[86] What might be the prime advantage of a scientific training bestowed upon a medium or on someone who seriously researches mediumship? We would say that undoubtedly the quality of discernment is the most notable advantage since it enables the practitioner to 'see through' to the truth in all its bare simplicity, devoid of the dramatic and fictitious imagery about people and events which is created by the undisciplined phantasizing mind and which is gullibly taken as fact.[xiii]

Endnote I-2 gives details of learned scientific bodies that have investigated psychical phenomena and mediumship, along with references to representative books and scholarly papers on the subject.

In essence, then, mediumship, like all the other phenomena described, provides further evidence about consciousness not necessarily restricted to the physical brain—in other words, that mind can exist apart and separate from the brain.

Remote Viewing and Remote Dowsing

Obtaining an image of a distant place existing in the present by focussing the attention on it is known as 'remote viewing'. It uses the same core faculty as dowsing, but in different ways. The distant location need not necessarily be on planet Earth. For example the English engineer and consciousness researcher Peter Stewart FREng (1928–2018) used remote dowsing on a map of the lunar surface when he carried out a feasibility study for the Hawker Siddeley Aeronautics Group for 'A Programme for the surface exploration of the Moon'.[87] Another good example is the remote viewing of the planet Jupiter by the American psychic Ingo Swann (1933–2013), years before the planet was explored by the NASA/JPL space probe, which confirmed the accuracy of the viewing.[88]

Remote viewing of the Moon and Jupiter

Unsurprisingly, the major research effort into remote viewing has been for military intelligence, such as the remote viewing at Stanford Research Institute initiated by the US Central Intelligence Agency (Stargate Project).[89] Jessica Utts (*b.*1952) is an American parapsychologist and statistics professor at the University of California, Irvine who recently served as the President of the American Statistical Association. In her presidential address to approximately six thousand members of that society from sixty-two countries, published in 2016, she commented on her work that confirmed the statistical likelihood of remote viewing and precognition as being real effects: 'I can provide a more concrete example based on the research I have done in parapsychology […]. For many years I have worked with researchers doing very careful work in this area, including a year I spent working on a classified project for the United States government, to see if we could use these abilities for intelligence gathering during the Cold War. This 20-year project is described in the recent book *ESP Wars East and West* by physicist Edwin May, the lead scientist on the project, with input from his Soviet counterparts.[90] At the end of that project I wrote a report for Congress, stating what I still think is true. The data in support of precognition and possibly other related phenomena are quite strong statistically, and would be widely accepted if they pertained to something more mundane.'[91]

Remote viewing by the CIA for espionage

---

xiii Ellison in his lectures frequently made reference to H. P. Blavatsky's warning about unconscious *kriyāśakti*, i.e. the image-making, or phantasizing, propensity of the mind.

Remote viewing can also be done in time so that, intriguingly, information can be obtained about a distant place in the past, but no longer existing; or about a place or event that will materialize in the future. The most outstanding example of the use of this faculty was when one of the United States Army remote viewers, Joe McMoneagle (*b*.1946) who co-authored the book with Edwin May, remote-viewed a new Soviet nuclear-powered submarine of the 'Kursk' class and was then able to 'fast forward' into the future to ascertain the launch date. The US 'KH9' spy satellite was positioned over the Soviet shipyard and recorded the launch of the submarine on the date predicted by McMoneagle.xiv

Remote viewing can access the present, past, and future

Remote viewing, then, is not the province of the gullible or overly credulous, albeit such types abound in this as in other areas involving altered states of consciousness. More substantiation about this fascinating subject is given in Endnote I-3 where other key scientific researchers are mentioned along with their reference material for the serious enquirer.

This is not the place to delve into the protocols for remote viewing which are detailed and able to be learned by those who have the appropriate mental aptitude for it.[92] One of the main difficulties to surmount is to discern parallel realities involving spatial and temporal anomalies from the familiar physical reality. Hence the attempt to remote view in space and time can involve spatial shifts, or time slips, into the past or the future. In view of the fact that this faculty engages the inner and subtle strata of consciousness, the dangers are considerable, especially so if the know-how acquired is used for anything other than the highest ethical and moral purposes. Suffice it to say that any researcher can verify for himself that the information gained from remote viewing is detailed and verifiable.

Dangers of remote viewing

In essence, remote viewing has shown the non-local, non-temporal nature of mind plus its ability to access past and future events in our ordinary space–time world. From the standpoint of this work, remote viewing clearly shows that consciousness is not limited to the brain and extends far beyond it.

Implications of the Above – Two Deathblows to Materialism

The objective of the above sections has been specifically to demonstrate—with facts and evidence—the limits and limitations of the exclusively materialistic paradigm as the sole explanatory basis of life and consciousness, hence to open up the case for the perennial wisdom teachings to complete our understanding (described further in Chapter 9). However, the disbanding of this paradigm of science was foreseen by H. P. Blavatsky (mentioned in the Proem, page xlvii) over one hundred years ago. With remarkable prevision she states:

> It is at the close of great Cycles, in connection with racial development, that such events generally take place. We are at the very close of the cycle of 5,000 years of the present Āryan Kaliyuga; and […] there will be a large rent made in the Veil of Nature, and materialistic science will receive a deathblow.[93]

Very significantly both these deathblows have come at the turn of centuries when –

---

xiv Abridged from the course notes of the Centre for the Study of Extended Human Consciousness by Professor Peter Stewart, DSc, FREng.

Paradigm shifts
and new
revelations about
nature occur at
the close of major
cycles of racial
development

one by one facts and processes in Nature's workshops are permitted to find their way into the exact Sciences, while mysterious help is given to rare individuals in unravelling its arcana.[94]

Deathblow No. 1 came from quantum physics which cracked the backbone of materialism by dragging into the scientific arena such considerations as non-locality, and the linking between the observer and the observed, with its naturally corollary of the importance of consciousness. Consider these two explicit statements about the central role of consciousness: the first one quoted earlier in the Proem, but repeated below to reinforce our case, and the second by the Hungarian–American theoretical physicist and mathematician Eugene Wigner FRS (1902–1995):

> As a man who has devoted his whole life to the most clearheaded science, to the study of matter, I can tell you as a result of my research about atoms this much: There is no matter as such. All matter originates and exists only by virtue of a force which brings the particles of an atom to vibration and holds this most minute solar system of the atom together. We must assume behind this force the existence of a conscious and intelligent mind. This mind is the matrix of all matter.
>
> Nobel physicist, Max Planck[95]

The central role of
consciousness in
quantum
phenomena

> When the province of physical theory was extended to encompass microscopic phenomena, through the creation of quantum mechanics, the concept of consciousness came to the fore again: it was not possible to formulate the laws of quantum mechanics in a fully consistent way without reference to the consciousness. […]. It will remain remarkable, in whatever way our future concepts may develop, that the very study of the external world led to the conclusion that the content of the consciousness is an ultimate reality.
>
> Nobel physicist, Eugene Wigner[96]

These forthright assertions coming from none other than the founder of quantum mechanics (physics) and an early pioneer in the field, respectively, cut right across the paradigm of materialism and expose science to the perennial wisdom which upholds the supremacy of consciousness, as we shall clearly see later on. Consciousness has been forced into the maelstrom of science implicitly, so to say, but restricted mainly to quantum physics; it has certainly not figured to any extent in other disciplines like biology and medicine.

Deathblow No. 2—occurring nowadays with mounting intensity—comprises the rapid breaking of the hitherto cracked backbone of materialism and this has come, ironically, from consciousness as a primary and explicit subject in its own right. In avant-garde science of the late twentieth and the present century, spurred by increasing results from quantum physics, we do not have consciousness as a component within science, as with the quantum physics of the early part of the twentieth century, but are slowly moving on to realize a science within consciousness, rather than consciousness within (existing) science. (The well-established methodology of natural science and its contrast with the method of occult science is explained in Chapter 8.)

In this regard, the ever-increasing proliferation of scholarly books and articles that are seriously and fundamentally questioning the roots of scientific materialism by transferring the focus on consciousness and mind, is evidence of this shift of emphasis. To provide even a comprehensive, let alone an exhaustive, list on it of such scholarly reference material would be out of place here. Nevertheless, a representative cross-section of learned papers and books, in both the physical sciences and the life sciences from the nineteenth century (an age of extreme materialism) to the present, is proffered in the next Chapter. A slow, but progressive movement from matter to mind, so to say, and the increasingly important role of consciousness, can be discerned in scientific research and enquiry.

Quantum Physics Cracks the Backbone of Materialistic Science

The onset of quantum physics was indeed a unique and spectacular event in the annals of science. It may for good reason be regarded as the crown jewel of science, for it, above all other scientific disciplines, has cracked the hitherto exclusively materialistic paradigm of science, and implied a non-material universe where consciousness need not be regarded as the product of solely material processes (although not all quantum physicists would agree). From the perspective of this work it is instructive to summarize the evidence for the radical paradigm shift in philosophy and science that it has engendered.[97]

It will come as no surprise to intuitive readers that some of the greatest discoveries about nature have come through investigating the nature of light. Towards the close of the nineteenth century, science was secure in its understanding of electromagnetic radiation, or light. However, the nature of the spectrum of radiation (light) emitted by a hot body still needed to be resolved. In 1900, Max Planck realized that this radiation could be explained if bodies were considered to emit and absorb radiation only in specific amounts, not smoothly and continuously—ever since Newton, physicists had assumed radiation to flow continuously. Planck however considered radiation to be emitted in 'spurts', or non-continuous, discrete energy packets, which he called *quanta*.[xv] (For example, the photon is the quantum of the electromagnetic field, i.e., a photon is a particle of light.) His famous equation directly related the energy of each quantum of radiation to its frequency. This was the main discovery that ushered in the era of quantum physics. But for completeness it must be stated that the process of scientific awakening that was to undermine the materialistic foundation of classical physics was occasioned by five events around the turn of the twentieth century: (*1*) 1897—the discovery of the electron by J. J. Thomson (1856–1940); (*2*) 1898—the discovery of radium by Marie (1867–1934) and Pierre (1859–1906) Curie; (*3*) 1900—Planck's discovery of quanta as described above; (*4*) 1905—Einstein's famous equation showing that energy and matter are convertible; and (*5*) 1911—the discovery by Ernest Rutherford (1871–1937) that atoms are practically 'empty space'.

Historical roots of quantum physics

Paradigm Shift Caused by Quantum Physics

Quantum physics has necessitated five key changes in outlook which, in their totality, have amounted to an overall paradigm shift in the notion of order and measure over those prevailing in classical physics:

1. *Indivisibility of quantum action*: in that a system changing from one state to another does so in discrete transitions ('quantum leaps'), and not in a smoothly continuous series of intermediate states, as believed in classical physics.

---

xv *Quanta* is the plural of the Latin *quantum* 'how much'. The equivalent word in Sanskrit is *katama*.

2. *Probabilities rather than actualities*: such that every physical situation is characterized by statistically formulated potentialities, rather than actual properties as held by classical physics. Thus, at the subatomic level, matter does not exist with certainty at a specific location but shows a 'tendency to exist'; similarly, atomic events do not occur at definite times and in a precise way but show 'tendencies to occur'. These 'tendencies' are the potentialities within the physical situation.

3. *Principle of indeterminacy (uncertainty principle)*: as formulated by Werner Heisenberg, in that the properties of conjugate (paired) observables[xvi] (such as position and momentum or energy and time) cannot be determined with equal accuracy *both simultaneously*. For example, accurate determination of the position of a particle alters its momentum with consequent uncertainty in the value of momentum. Conversely, accurate determination of momentum alters its position, with consequent uncertainty in the latter. This is because any measurement of any property of a system disturbs the dynamics of the system under investigation (by virtue of interaction with the measuring device) resulting in lesser accuracy in the measurement of any other property. It is vital to appreciate that such uncertainty is a principle in physical nature, having nothing to do with the errors inherent in any measurement technique. Furthermore, such uncertainty is a general phenomenon in physical nature and is not restricted to microscopic particles. However, for macroscopic objects the uncertainty is extremely small.

How quantum physics undermined the notion of strict causality in classical physics

This scientifically proven principle of indeterminacy has shattered the notion of strict determinism and causality that prevailed in classical physics. (Refer to the importance of causal closure in science described in Chapter 3.)

4. *Non-causal correlations associated with non-locality (instantaneous action-at-a-distance)*: such that paired particles apparently disconnected in space can communicate instantaneously. Any cause at one location produces immediate effects at distant (and disconnected) locations. However, this fact is not compatible with Einstein's dictum on relativity theory which requires that the speed of light is a constant and cannot be exceeded; hence, nothing can link two particles *instantaneously* across space—because such communication requires a signal to travel from one place to another, and no signal can travel faster than light (more on that later). But in quantum physics, such apparently disconnected particles (whatever may be the distance between them) can communicate instantaneously. Non-locality has been proven to occur by a series of carefully controlled real experiments (not merely 'thought experiments') that are consistent with quantum theoretical predictions.[98] There is, however, more to relativity than even Einstein might possibly have realized, given his disagreement with quantum theory and its implications—see later.[99] Nonetheless, even to this day there has been no satisfactory resolution of the incompatibility between Einstein's relativity theory, on the macro-scale, with quantum theory, on the micro-scale.

5. *Particle ~ Wave Duality*: whereby the early 1920s saw a resolution of the dichotomy posed by the dual nature of light, which had occupied the first two decades of the century. The French Nobel physicist Louis de Broglie FRS (1892–1987) proposed that every particle in motion is associated with the propagation of a wave, and that

---

xvi By 'observable' we mean an experimentally measurable property of a physical system.

it is impossible to separate the two. His celebrated equation related the momentum of a quantum entity to its wavelength. This equation, together with Planck's equation, resulted in a fusion of the particle and wave theories of light. Finally, Schrödinger's wave mechanics installed the particle–wave duality as a fundamental characteristic of all physical reality. He formulated a fundamental differential equation governing the evolution of the wave-like characteristics of physical systems. It is now universally acknowledged in modern science that waves and particles are two aspects of one reality; furthermore, that every entity in nature presents dual wave and particle characteristics.

Besides supplying a rich store of clues for the *philosophia perennis*, the above changes all have an important bearing on the study of light—hence on the prevailing consciousness of the acme of the scientific community, especially in cosmology and physics, but unfortunately not as yet, with rare exceptions, in biology, molecular science, and medicine.

Given the above considerations it is not surprising to witness the following views through the cracks in the walls of the materialistic fortress.

The Distant Views Through the Cracks

Our primary objective now is to justify the central role of mind and consciousness by citing a wealth of evidence from biology, psychology, parapsychology, and quantum science concerning phenomena that cannot be accounted for fully on the basis of purely materialistic science—hence demanding a wider paradigm. The distant views through the cracks of materialism are more cases that furnish stronger evidence of the primacy of mind.

Central Role of Consciousness Shown in Quantum Physics

We have sketched how quantum physics has undermined the material basis of our worldview with evidence from refined theory, backed by sophisticated experiments, that subatomic particles and atoms (hence by implication, all of nature and ourselves constituted of these particles) are not solid entities existing with absolute certainty at a precise spatial location and a definite time. Crucially, mind has entered the picture, such that for many quantum physicists the consciousness of the observer is a vital component to making sense of the physical events being observed. These results strongly imply that the world of physical matter is neither the fundamental nor the sole component of reality and indeed (as unequivocally affirmed in the *philosophia perennis*) that mind is primary and matter its effects, that is, the form taken by mind—its appearance.

A step in this direction is, arguably, the quantum hybrid model, a biological philosophy of mind proposed by the English Nobel physicist and philosopher of science Sir Roger Penrose OM FRS (*b.*1931) and the American anesthesiologist Stuart Hameroff (*b.*1947). Their multidisciplinary hypothesis, first published in 1996, draws on molecular biology, neuroscience, quantum physics, pharmacology, philosophy, quantum information theory, and quantum gravity.[100, 101, 102] The contention is that the act of observation causes a system to collapse from a wave-state of a range of probabilities into one type of unpredictable particle state, known as 'subjective reduction' (subjective, because it requires an

The observer cannot be left out of the equation

external observer); however, in the brain there is no outside observer, hence suitable conditions might prevail under which quantum events are not downgraded subjectively, but instead occur spontaneously, without anyone 'watching'—a phenomenon they call 'orchestrated objective reduction'. Moreover, and crucially, the *medium* for such an orchestration of neurons is posited as the minute, fluid-filled microtubules, which are present in every cell of the body. However, this novel hypothesis is not without its critics both by neuroscientists[103] and physicists[104, 105] who consider it to be a poor model of brain physiology.

But in any case, we need to be quite clear that because it is not possible to formulate the laws of quantum mechanics in a fully consistent way without reference to consciousness, as many physicists like Eugene Wigner would maintain, this does not mean that quantum theory, on its own, provides an explanatory framework for consciousness. A scientific model of consciousness must necessarily transcend quantum theory (and of course, relativity theory). Nevertheless, by proposing that consciousness originates at the quantum level in neurons, the quantum hybrid model alludes to the *philosophia perennis* and represents a radical departure from the conventional view that consciousness emerges as a by-product of connections between neurons.

Occult Chemistry and Sacred Geometry

Occult chemistry refers to a book by that name about a special case of remote viewing, or clairvoyance, namely, that of subatomic particles. Experiments were conducted at intervals over a period of nearly forty years from 1895 to 1933 by two pioneering British Theosophists, Charles Webster Leadbeater (1854–1934) and Annie Besant using a form of extrasensory perception virtually unknown to parapsychologists, although long known in India as a yogic *siddhi* (psychic faculty) having the Sanskrit name of 'anima'. What was observed, and meticulously recorded by them in *Occult Chemistry*, has demonstrable consistency with the established facts of nuclear physics quarks and superstring theories,[xvii] with the qualification that not all their interpretations can be taken at face value because of the 'observer effect', namely, the disturbance of the quantum dynamics of particles by the act of clairvoyant observation (a possible manifestation of Heisenberg's Uncertainly Principle).[106] Nonetheless this is the only recorded example of a whole series of extrasensory perception (ESP) observations where one can have cast-iron certainty that any charge of fraud, or the unconscious use of sensory clues, can be excluded a priori by the total absence of any scientific information on what they foresaw and verified, which was only discovered decades later. For example, after the first edition of *Occult Chemistry* in 1908, the British Nobel physicist Ernest Rutherford OM FRS (1871–1937) confirmed the nuclear model of the atom two years later; the neon-22 isotope—clairvoyantly detected in 1908 and referred to as 'meta-neon'—was discovered four years later using the mass spectrograph constructed by the English chemist and physicist Francis Aston FRS (1877–1945); the Danish Nobel physicist Niels Bohr FRS (1885–1962) presented his theory of the hydrogen atom five years later; the British Nobel physicist Sir James Chadwick FRS (1891–1974) discovered the neutron twenty-four years later; and the first

Clairvoyant observations of atoms and particles confirmed by scientific discoveries decades later

---

xvii Quarks are any of a number of types of subatomic particles and a fundamental constituent of matter. Superstring theory attempts to explain all of the particles and fundamental forces of nature in one theory by modelling them as vibrations of tiny supersymmetric strings.

quark model was proposed fifty-six years later in 1964 by the American Nobel physicist Murray Gell-Mann FRS (1929–2019) and the Russian–American physicist George Zweig (*b.*1937).

But even more than showing the consistency of the findings in *Occult Chemistry* with the facts of modern science—a feat in itself—the Cambridge-trained English physicist Stephen Phillips (*b.*1946) further proves that these descriptions (to reiterate, provided well over a century ago from the remote viewing of atoms and their constituent particles) confirm the proposition that the Pythagorean Tetractys,[xviii] the Qabbalistic Tree of Life,[xix] and other forms of sacred geometry not only express the multidimensional nature of space–time, but also embody the dynamics and structure of superstrings.[107]

In summary, after making appropriate adjustments for the observer effect, the numerous diagrams, figures, and descriptions of the chemical elements in *Occult Chemistry* have shown the clairvoyant viewing of atomic particles to be largely corroborated by modern particle physics. Accordingly, and again from the standpoint of this work, it shows the power of consciousness to access information in subatomic realms. This makes a substantial case for extended mind, hence consciousness not being generated by, or the product of, material processes in the brain.

Reincarnation

By 'reincarnation' we mean 'reinfleshment', the coming again into a human body of an excarnate human soul, or in other words, the repetitive re-embodiment of the reincarnating Human Soul in bodies that are physical, spiritual, and intermediate between the two, i.e., ethereal or subtle. The meaning of the term 'Human Soul' will become clear in subsequent Chapters (and in any case will be explained in detail in Volume II), but for now suffice it to say that it is the 'individuality' of man—immortal in essence, as distinct from his mortal personality, which includes body and brain. It cannot be emphasized too strongly that the personality, body, and brain permanently disintegrate upon physical death and do not reincarnate. It is man's higher principles, referred to above as the individuality, that 'reinfleshes' by assimilating a new personality conditioned by karmic law (the law operating on all levels—physical and moral) whereby a man reaps what he has sowed, whether the sowing was done in this life or previous lives.

Reincarnation and karma are inextricably bound

Belief in reincarnation is universal amongst many ancient philosophies and religions of both East and West. It was taught in the esoteric schools of India, Egypt, Greece, and elsewhere. The doctrine is universally propounded by enlightened philosophers, sages, and saints of all ages, ancient, like Jesus and Buddha, or modern, like the Indian saints Ramana Maharshi and Śrī Aurobindo (1872–1950), and philosophers like Paul Brunton and the Indian philosopher, academic, and statesman Sir Sarvepalli Radhakrishnan (1888–1975), nominated fifteen times for the Nobel Prize in literature and eleven times for the Nobel Peace Prize—to name but a very few. However, this is no place to venture into the colossal

---

xviii The Tetractys is a triangular figure consisting of ten points arranged in four rows. For the Pythagoreans it is the symbol of the musical, arithmetic, and geometric ratios upon which the universe is built.

xix The Quabbalistic Tree of Life is a diagram comprising ten nodes symbolizing different archetypes and twenty-two lines connecting the nodes. The nodes are arranged into three columns to denote that they belong to a common category.

Reincarnation is a ubiquitous belief, disseminated through a wealth of literature worldwide

reincarnation literature from science, medicine, parapsychology, spiritualism and, above all, occult science in its finest and most digestible form through the aegis of the modern Theosophical Society.

Representative literature from Western and Eastern sources is cited in Endnote I-4. A reader who desires just one volume as a standard reference can do no better than to peruse *Reincarnation: The Phoenix Fire Mystery* by the American Theosophical author Sylvia Cranston, AKA Anita Atkins (1915–2000).[108] This fabulous work is an anthology in the true sense of the term, meaning a symphony of ideas, about death and rebirth garnered from the worlds of science, religion, philosophy, and psychology; also from history, mythology, art, and literature. Suffice it to say that this vast body of material and cited evidence allude strongly to realms of existence that are not based solely on physical matter; they also fly in the face of a purely materialistic science that equates the extinction of life with the death of the brain. (This theme is developed in detail in Chapter 5 of Volume II, which delineates the post-mortem transitional states of consciousness before reincarnation.) It is a *sine qua non* that an understanding of reincarnation requires an understanding of the spectrum of consciousness and it is because mainstream science has not the slightest idea about consciousness *per se* (only its correlates in terms of neuronal correlates in the brain[xx]) that our science-dominated Western culture has, on the whole, jettisoned any notion of reincarnation, pronouncing such ideas as 'unscientific' or 'pseudoscience'. But

Transition—not extinction—of consciousness central to reincarnation

such is not the case with other cultures, especially in ancient Asia, including of course, India. It is the arcane sciences of both the West, and especially the East, that have provided chapter and verse on a science of the subjective which recognizes the primacy of consciousness. In the West, there is now a slow but inescapable recognition of a totally new science of consciousness, not consciousness as a subject within pre-existing science as just stated. Leaving such weighty issues aside for Chapter 5 of Volume II, what evidence can we adduce from academia, peer reviewed journals, and scientific bodies in support of reincarnation?

When we look for evidence the general tendency these days is to turn to science, which concerns itself with matters of proof. But although science in its current state is self-limited by its materialistic paradigm that brain death means extinction because the brain generates personal consciousness, yet, despite such limitations, the rigorous methodology of science can still be an invaluable asset. For it can rigorously evaluate the quality of evidence, namely, the numerous personal experiences of claimed memories of previous lives, and eliminate any extraneous influences from such claims that would otherwise make a physical explanation perfectly plausible without any need to invoke former lives. A classic book

Scientific support for reincarnation

on this subject is *Past Lives* by Peter and Elizabeth Fenwick.[109] Other eminent researchers in the West include the American esotericist Sylvan Muldoon (1903–1969), Sylvia Cranston, the Swiss–American psychiatrist and pioneer in near-death studies Elisabeth Kübler-Ross-Ross (1926–2004), and scientists in The Society for Psychical Research.

Arguably, the finest and most scientific contribution to scientific reincarnation research in the West was done by the Canadian-born U.S. psychiatrist Ian Stevenson (1918–2007) of the University of Virginia. He became internationally recognized for his research into reincarnation (from a non-religious perspective) by discovering evidence from children

---

xx For example, science cannot as yet explain how the particular set of neurons activated by a wavelength in the range 577×10^{-9} to 492×10^{-9} metres would result in a person experiencing the colour green.

suggesting that memories and physical injuries can be transferred from one lifetime to another. His meticulous research presented evidence that such children had unusual abilities, illnesses, phobias, and philias (affections, the opposite of phobias), which could not be explained by the environment or heredity. The relation between reincarnation and biology is meticulously recorded in a two-part monograph (of 2,268 pages).[110] He travelled extensively over a period of some forty years, investigating three thousand cases of children around the world who recalled having past lives. His investigations outside of Western culture have been recorded in four volumes of his work bearing the overall title of *Cases of the Reincarnation Type*.[111] Other cases in Europe and America are documented in various books, for example, *European Cases of the Reincarnation Type*[112] plus the references shown in Endnote I-5.

Ian Stevenson's meticulous scientific research into reincarnation

Full details about his methods of investigation and results are published in two of his books.[113, 114] Essentially, they include interviews, often repeated, with the subject and with many other informants, for all families concerned. With rare exceptions, only first-hand informants were interviewed. All pertinent written records that existed, particularly death certificates and post-mortem reports, were sought and examined. He made every effort to exclude all possibility that some information might nevertheless have been passed normally to the child, perhaps through a half-forgotten mutual acquaintance of their own or any other related or unrelated families.

Stevenson placed much emphasis on children exhibiting birth marks whose location coincided with the recollected site of a claimed past-life lethal injury. This has opened up a fascinating area of recent scientific research by the contemporary Australian physicist Richard Silberstein who was head of the Department of Physics at Swinburne University of Technology in Australia and subsequently Director of the Brain Sciences Institute, having over forty years in neuroscience research to his credit. In October 2019 the writer attended Silberstein's talk 'Bioelectric Fields: Where Biology and Reincarnation Intersect' where he outlined recent findings on the nature of bioelectric fields and their crucial role in developmental biology and health.[115] This was used as a stepping-stone to postulate the role of bioelectric fields as one of the mechanisms mediating the appearance of birthmarks at the site(s) of past-life lethal injury. Silberstein also explained the role of such fields in the modification of foetal and early-life brain development, permitting in turn the recollection of past-life first-person memories.

Promising pointers from bioelectric fields

Loss of past-life memories is often used as an argument against reincarnation. Research on mice shows that in infancy the hippocampus (the area of the brain involved in the formation of new memories) undergoes rapid neurogenesis (the process by which new neurons are formed in the brain when an embryo is developing, continuing in certain brain regions after birth and throughout the lifespan) with new synaptic connections replacing older ones indicating loss of memories previously established. In humans this could explain the phenomenon of *neonatal amnesia* whereby past-life memories in children are more difficult to access after five to seven years of age, a time invariably concurrent with the rapid onset of neurogenesis. Further research shows that such memories may be forgotten but not eliminated and may manifest in later-life behaviour. These preserved memories might be unconscious and remain in what Silberstein called 'implicit memory'. Examples may be skills in children who manifest incredible talent at an unusually young age, as with musical child prodigies or mathematical geniuses, or in sport, as in the case

The contention about loss of memory

of 'Hunter' a young golf prodigy in the US who was born after 2000 and recalled a past life as Bobby Jones, a golfing superstar of the 1920s.

In the Preface to the revised edition of *Children Who Remember Previous Lives*, Stevenson, who was Chair of the Department of Psychiatry at the University of Virginia School of Medicine for fifty years, states his reservations about neuroscience in these words:

> I have not failed to follow developments in this important field [neuroscience], which has greatly advanced with the infusion of funds it received during the 'decade of the brain'. I remain sceptical, however, that the reductionist approach of nearly all neuroscientists will contribute to understanding the mind-body problem. I believe that only the recognition of the experiences now called paranormal will do that. I look forward eagerly to the 'decade of the mind'.[116]

Bioelectric fields in their interaction with biology may well provide the spur to the 'decade of the mind'.

Much evidence about reincarnation also comes from spiritualism and it is not all a case of smoke and mirrors, delusion and gullibility. Certainly, this area has attracted its fair share of charlatanry, but there is also testimony from the best side of spiritualism that has attracted serious attention from eminent scientists in the nineteenth century and in modern times, such as Arthur Ellison, Lester Smith, and the British professor of mathematics and astronomy at Queen Mary University of London, Bernard Carr (*b.*1949), former Fellow of Trinity College, Cambridge, past President of the Society for Psychical Research, past Chairman and current President (2021) of the Scientific and Medical Network. Note our earlier mention of Alfred Russel Wallace, the co-founder of the theory of natural selection and a solid supporter of Darwin, who combined evolutionism with spiritualism and tried to understand human evolution and evolutionary ethics with a spiritualistic teleology. Spiritualism, then, demonstrated to the smug materialistic society of the nineteenth century Western world the existence of another world beyond that of our five physical senses, and the fact of survival. Many spectacular séances were conducted at which, beyond reasonable doubt, discarnate entities were brought back into communication with the sitters. The New Zealander Dr Jackson Crawford DSc (1881–1920), a lecturer in mechanical engineering at Belfast Technical Institute proved conclusively that any weight gained by materialized spirit entities was equal to the weight lost by the medium plus small losses suffered by the sitters.[117, 118, 119] Obviously, the die-hard sceptics will attribute all this to fraud; however, qualified scientists made rigorous unbiased observations and were totally convinced about the genuine nature of the phenomena they observed, albeit at a loss to explain the mechanisms. We again stress what Arthur Ellison found over the course of a lifetime of research (see earlier): that most mediums are sincere, the instances of fraud being rare. *Fraud only points a finger at the fraudster and says nothing about the phenomenon in genuine hands.* The finest aspect of spiritualism is arguably the rescue circle, which brings in other interesting facets of life after physical death, such as earth-bound souls, apparitions seen by several people, premonitions and phenomena of rapport.[120] All of these cases undermine a purely materialistic basis of life, which is why we place such emphasis upon them.

Spiritualism then, was helpful in countering the deeply materialistic thinking of the time and the existence of normally unseen worlds came to be recognized and accepted by science. But as is the nature of things, the spiritualist movement gradually lost its scientific

Neuroscience must include mind in addition to brain

Spiritualism supplies convincing evidence on reincarnation

investigative spirit and took on by degrees the tenor of religiosity. (This is, arguably, the metaphysical equivalent, loosely speaking, of the Second Law of Thermodynamics whereby a closed system increases in disorder unless there is energy input to restore it to its original state.) But this downturn need not concern us further in this work.

In summary, Carl Jung stated in his book on archtypes that rebirth (reincarnation) must be counted among the primordial affirmations of mankind. The 'primordial affirmations of mankind' are more powerful than the ill-researched and unsubstantiated assertions of any number of sceptics who doggedly refuse to look at the weight of evidence before their eyes. However stated, in whatever language, mankind has affirmed the existence of invisible realms of being that simply cannot be accounted for on the basis of physical science and medicine alone. Such invisible realms imply grades of substance finer than physical matter, and subtle (non-physical) bodies as the appropriate vehicles of consciousness. The huge weight of evidence from diverse sources in favour of reincarnation strongly suggests that scientists should adhere to the spirit of science and be prepared to modify their materialistic paradigm and mechanistic theories to match the evidence—not dismiss the latter on the grounds that a satisfactory theoretical model and explanatory framework do not exist. After-death states of consciousness, reincarnation, and the phenomena of apparitions are discussed and explained in detail in Volume II, especially in Chapters 4 and 5.

Reincarnation is mankind's primeval affirmation

The Broader Implications of the Distant Views – A Good Case for Extraordinary Evidence?

'Extraordinary claims require extraordinary evidence' was a phrase coined by the American astronomer, astrophysicist, and cosmologist Carl Sagan (1934–1996). It has now become virtually a universal mantra embedded in the scientific ethos, and proffered as a key issue for critical thinking, rational thought, and scepticism for what is regarded as weak evidence. It is put about by the scientific community in order to disparage phenomena, such as telepathy or the paranormal, on the grounds that any evidence for them is highly questionable at best and offers little in the way of proof. Moreover, even if what evidence there is were accepted as being valid (and it is supposed to be highly debatable if it should), *limited and weak evidence is not enough to overcome the extraordinary nature of these claims.* (Refer back to Chapter 2 regarding Michael Shermer's counter-arguments against any claims about paranormal evidence.)

However, (and unfortunately for the convinced materialists), the examples of paranormal and *psi* phenomena cited above are so common that they cannot be dismissed or explained away on the grounds of weak evidence or mere coincidence or anomalous exceptions to natural law. On the contrary, they provide a strong case for a broader and deeper explanatory framework that cannot be grounded exclusively on materialism but must, perforce, embrace the minute and detailed accounts of Nature imparted by the *philosophia perennis*. Apropos, what counts as 'extraordinary evidence' will always remain ill-defined. The production of electricity, the electric light bulb, the fact that the behaviour of subatomic particles would depend on conscious observation, the penetrating power of x-rays, the splitting of the atom and fission of slightly less than one kilogram of uranium 235 releasing energy equivalent to approximately 15,000 tons of TNT (as in the Hiroshima atomic bomb), heavier-than-air flying machines, are just few examples of what would have been

'Extraordinary' soon becomes 'perfectly ordinary'

extraordinary claims at the time (with either weak or no evidence) but now, in the light of overwhelming evidence, seem commonplace and anything but extraordinary.

Indeed, in 1903 when the two American aviation pioneers Orville (1871–1948) and Wilbur (1867–1912) Wright made the first aeroplane flight in recorded history at Kitty Hawk, North Carolina, eight years earlier, the Scottish mathematician and physicist Sir William Thomson, Lord Kelvin OM (1824–1907), President of the Royal Society,[xxi] arguably the most prestigious scientific institution in the world, unambiguously declared that 'heavier-than-air flying machines are impossible.'[121] Clearly, this highly influential man of science was mistaken, but his supreme insight was absolutely correct: of one mind with Sir Isaac Newton—his legendary predecessor as President of the Royal Society— he held that the universe and man are 'shot through' with an intelligible design which reveals an intelligent and benevolent impersonal Mind. This is reflected in the quotations at the close of this Chapter.

Let us cite dramatic examples of extraordinary evidence in physics and astronomy, neuroscience and biology. The physicist Albert Michelson FRS (1852–1931)—of the famous Michelson-Morley experiment[xxii]—proclaimed that 'the more important fundamental laws and facts of the physical universe *have all been discovered* [writer's emphasis] and these are now so firmly established that the possibility of their ever being supplanted in consequence of new discoveries is exceedingly remote.'[122] Michelson went on to advise that 'our future discoveries must be looked for in the sixth place of decimals'.[123] At this time, towards the close of the nineteenth century, science felt secure in its understanding of physical laws: only such 'irritants' as the nature of the spectrum of radiation (light) emitted by a hot body still needed to be resolved. But Michelson's prophecy about the future course of science was demolished when, in 1900, Max Planck ushered in the era of quantum physics which literally shattered the backbone of deterministic classical physics, as previously explained. How and why this paradigm shift occurred warrants much consideration due to its profound implications.

Quantum physics undermines the deterministic paradigm of science

A spectacular U-turn in science in recent years concerns the condition of the planet Mars. At one time the Red Planet was unequivocally pronounced by astronomers to be dry, barren, and dead. In recent years, NASA missions and further astronomical observations have shown the presence of distinct polar ice caps. Additionally, an article in the scientific journal *Geophysical Research Letters* states that Mars also has belts of glaciers at its central latitudes in both the southern and northern hemispheres; and that new studies have now calculated the size of the glaciers and thus the amount of water in the glaciers—the equivalent of all of Mars being covered by more than one metre of ice.[124] The latest news is that liquid water has now been found coursing down the hillsides and canyons of Mars. 'Mars is not the dry, arid planet that we thought of in the past', says NASA scientist Jim Green (*b. circa* 1955), 'liquid water has been found on Mars.'[125] The presence of water clearly alludes to some form of life, biological or otherwise, existing at one time, or presently, on the once supposedly lifeless planet which billionaires and entrepreneurs now have advanced plans to colonize.

---

xxi Formally, the Royal Society of London for Improving Natural Knowledge.

xxii This was an experiment carried out in order to detect the ether believed to fill empty space. It is described in Appendix II-A of Volume II because of its strong bearing on the nature of light and on occult science in general. Other similar experiments are outlined in the same Appendix.

Leadbeater's large book, *MAN: Whence, How and Whither*[126] contains a record of his clairvoyant observations, including that of life on other planets. This book has been much derided (especially so by numerous Theosophists), his visions being put down primarily to what is known as unconscious *kriyashakti*, that is, the phantasy-producing power of the mind. Nevertheless, his imaginative forays contain more than a germ of truth, for he (clairvoyantly) foresaw the possibility of life on Mars, notwithstanding the fact that his descriptions were clothed in the imagery of his own mind (a hazard of the psychic researcher or medium untrained in science, as pointed out earlier).

Clairvoyance alludes to life on Mars decades before astronomical discoveries

In neuroscience the firmly established concept that the brain is a physiologically static organ has been displaced by the discovery of neuroplasticity, which shows that the brain changes throughout life; and brain functions are not confined to certain fixed locations. This exciting discovery is pursued in greater detail shortly, as it has a major bearing on the whole question of consciousness in mainstream science.

Brain once thought static is now regarded as 'plastic'

In biology, the burgeoning field of epigenetics is making deep inroads into what is known as 'the central dogma of molecular biology'. In the 1970s this dogma was upheld with a zeal tantamount to religious fundamentalism. It is an explanation of the flow of genetic information within a biological system, first proposed by Francis Crick in 1956[127] and re-stated by him in *Nature*[128] in 1970. It advances a strictly uni-directional transfer of sequential information (i.e., DNA sequencing as the process of determining the precise order of nucleotides within a DNA molecule) and states that such information cannot be transferred back from protein to either protein or nucleic acid. The logical outcome of this dogma, therefore, is that external or environmental factors can play no part in 'switching' genes on or off. This train of thought, along with the genome project in 2000 started a flurry of biological research into all sorts of diseases such as cancer and Alzheimer's disease on the basis that understanding the genetic mechanisms would supply the complete answer to such diseases. However, extraordinary evidence was not long forthcoming to undermine this hubristic self-confidence in biological and medical science.

Epigenetics outdoes dogma of molecular biology

Epigenetics is the study of cellular and physiological trait variations that are caused, not by changes in the DNA sequence, as in molecular biology, but from the interaction between genetic makeup and the environment (phenotypic variations);[xxiii] in other words, the study of external and environmental factors that switch genes on or off, controlling when and where genes are expressed.[129] It is now known that both the physical environment and psychological stress can have enormously significant effects on cellular activity; so can the role of emotions in the interaction and connection between psyche and body.[130] Thus, cellular function is influenced by both the bottom-up transfer of sequential information of molecular biology and the top-down factors shown by epigenetics. Moreover, such external influences are not limited just to the affected organism but can cross several generations. For example, the Dutch famine during the Second World War had a major impact on the genetic expression of the victims of starvation; moreover, the period of starvation affected not only the individuals directly exposed, but also their children and grandchildren who lived during a later time of no such deprivation.[131]

---

xxiii The same logic also applies to Gaia theory, i.e., the process is one of interaction between organism and environment.

Staying with biology, we would make a brief mention of what has been called 'junk DNA'. Soon after the genome project got underway, it became obvious that humans have too many genes in common with plants, animals, and even primitive animals, for genes to be regarded as the final blueprint of human intelligence and behaviour (refer also to the earlier sections in this Chapter about organismic and morphogenetic theories in biology that invoke organizing fields). Further studies have established that genome codes for proteins amount to only two per cent, with the remaining ninety-eight per cent relegated as junk with no real function. The latest evidence, however, shows that junk DNA is anything but 'junk'. On the contrary, it contributes in significant ways to our wellbeing, our physiognomy, and ability to lead a long and healthy life; also, to the intricate system of finely tuned functions within the cell, but in different (but possibly complementary) ways from the genes involved in coding proteins.[132]

So, all this *extraordinary* biological evidence has led to the extraordinary claim that genes alone cannot explain the unique characteristics of humans, as was once the dictum of biology. We confidently look forward to the time when extraordinary evidence will pave the way to an outlook on evolution that is primarily rooted in spirituality and consciousness, whilst not ignoring the physical Darwinian theory.

This contention would appear to be supported by the thoughts of the British naturalist, Alfred Russel Wallace (referred to earlier). After publishing his paper on the theory of evolution through natural selection—jointly with some of Charles Darwin's writings in 1858—and then in 1864 publishing a paper on human origins based on the theory of natural selection,[133] his thoughts subsequently turned to spiritualism on the grounds that natural selection alone cannot account for such human characteristics as mathematical, artistic or musical genius, as well as traits such as metaphysical musings and humour. He eventually said that something in 'the unseen universe of Spirit' had interceded at least three times in history. The first was the creation of life from inorganic matter. The second was the introduction of consciousness in the higher animals. And the third was the generation of the higher mental faculties in humankind. He also believed that the *raison d'être* of the universe was the development of the human spirit.[134] The teleological implications of these views obviously disturbed Darwin, who argued that spiritual appeals were unnecessary. However, for the rest of his life, Wallace remained convinced that at least some séance phenomena were genuine, no matter how many accusations of fraud sceptics made or how much evidence of trickery was produced.[135] It is regrettable that Wallace's forward looking ideas have not percolated through the strata of neo-Darwinism—the modern theory of evolution holding that species evolve by natural selection acting on genetic variations, whilst denying the inheritance of acquired characteristics and other non-material influences. (Refer to Chapter 3 and recall how developments in epigenetics regarding stable heritable traits cannot be explained by changes in DNA sequence, as stated above.)

Moving from terrestrial biology to astrobiology, 'panspermia' is a recent hypothesis about life existing throughout the universe, distributed by meteoroids, asteroids, comets, planetoids, and also by spacecraft in the form of unintended contamination by microorganisms. Such microscopic life forms are purported to survive the effects of space, becoming trapped in debris that is ejected into space after collisions between planets and small solar systems that harbour life. This would suggest that the ingredients of life—proteins and amino acids—may have formed in the depths of interstellar dust clouds and that life throughout the galaxy is universal. When the visionary English astronomer Sir Fred Hoyle FRS (1915–2001) first mentioned the idea back in the 1950s (but excluded any mention of spacecraft), it was regarded as so bizarre that, despite his prestige, no scientific journal would publish his paper: after all, in its early days planet Earth was supposed to be a fiery globe, inhospitable to life and any traces of life would not have survived those conditions. Many scientists began to wonder if Fred Hoyle had 'gone off the deep end'[136] Therefore, Hoyle cast his theory in the form of a science fiction novel *The Black Cloud*.[137] By 1975, Hoyle and his former student at Cambridge, the Sri Lankan-born British mathematician, astronomer, and astrobiologist Chandra Wickramasinghe (*b*.1939) were convinced that organic polymers were a substantial fraction of the dust.[138] Although considered wildly speculative at that time, these days, more astrobiologists take seriously the idea that life may not have originated on Earth but was brought about by comets soon after the Earth formed.

Fred Hoyle's ideas on astrobiology now taken seriously

Experimental evidence has been provided by the Rosetta spacecraft orbiting Comet 67P/Churyumov–Gerasimenko, which has found the presence of glycine, an amino acid and ingredient of proteins. Although traces of glycine had previously been detected in samples of dust returned to Earth in 2006 by NASA's Stardust mission, it is possible that the samples could have been contaminated by the Earth's atmosphere. However, Kathrin Altwegg (*b*.1951), principal investigator who made the measurements using the ROSINA instrument[xxiv] at the Centre of Space and Habitability of the University of Bern and the lead author of the associated paper published in *Science Advances*, commented: 'This is the first unambiguous detection of glycine in the thin atmosphere of a comet.' Altwegg goes on to state that 'at the same time, we also detected certain other organic molecules that can be precursors to glycine, hinting at the possible ways in which it may have formed.'[139] Traces of phosphorus, also an ingredient of proteins, were also found in the comet.

Recent discovery of organic molecules in atmosphere of comets

The latest evidence for panspermia (and therefore possible signs of life) is the discovery of phosphine (a toxic, colourless, malodourous gas) on Venus. Detected by the Venera 13 and 14 spacecraft, the quantity is regarded too great to be a passing phenomenon.[140, 141] Phosphine is considered to be a biosignature gas; i.e., a gas that is produced by life forms. So, on Earth, phosphine can be manufactured, or is produced, naturally by some species of anaerobic bacteria—organisms that live in oxygen-starved environments such as in marshlands and animal guts. But scientists are at a loss to explain how these microbes can survive in the hostile Venusian clouds that are mostly composed of sulphuric acid.[xxv]

Latest discovery of microbes in atmosphere of Venus

While the Rosetta, and later Venera, discoveries do not answer the greater question about extraterrestrial life, they provide further evidence that the ingredients of life are spread throughout interstellar space. Furthermore, they are examples of the provisional nature of scientific truths—what science has pronounced as a 'gospel truth' at one time has been overturned by the self-same science in the light of its own further discoveries that slowly, but inexorably, point towards the Eternal Wisdom which affirms that even the smallest

---

xxiv ROSINA (Rosetta Orbiter Spectrometer for Ion and Neutral Analysis) is an instrument designed to determine the gas properties and composition of the atmosphere and ionosphere of comet 67P.

xxv Instead of the scientific community jointly celebrating this discovery, it is disheartening to find the head of the Russian space agency Roscosmos boastfully claiming that 'Venus is a Russian planet', referring to the USSR's landing of a probe on its surface in the 1970s—*The Week*, 26 September 2020, 7.

corner of the universe is teeming with life and consciousness. What varies tremendously is the grade of matter (physical and non-physical) and associated forms, but not the fact of life and consciousness. Furthermore, the crucial role of comets in relation to the evolution of Earth is another important tenet of occult cosmogenesis.[142]

There are bound to be more such U-turns in science concerning extra-terrestrial planets and, indeed, concerning our own planet. The writer confidently foresees an imminent, major turnaround in geology (the signs are already in evidence) regarding the acceptance by mainstream science about the prehistoric continent of Atlantis and even the continents that preceded Atlantis.[xxvi] Whereas every occult teaching from antiquity (Plato and earlier) to modern times (Blavatsky, Steiner, Hall, and later) has declared the existence of great ancient civilizations on the basis of the accumulated wisdom of the ages and the testimony of generations of seers—see Endnote I-8—the corpus of geologists still choose to deny their existence. Without taking any cognizance of the weight of the occult teachings, their denial is based primarily on plate tectonics, the current theory in geology that the outer shell of the Earth is divided into several plates that glide over the mantle, the rocky inner layer above the core. However, even the geological evidence is by no means cast in stone. There are several anomalous facts and findings alluding to prehistoric continents.[143]

On reflection, it seems that major U-turns in science are grudgingly, at first, then universally accepted by the scientific community, as indeed by the writer, as part and parcel of the onward march and progress of science. But in the broad field of spirituality or psychic investigation, any uncertainties, vague definitions, or the smallest deviations from previously held views, are immediately pounced upon by establishment scientists (not all scientists), and both the subject and the researcher are snubbed with the usual hand-waving gestures of 'New Agey', 'woolly', or 'flaky'. Who has granted establishment science Crown immunity, or even divine immunity, from the charge of flakiness?

Extraordinary Quantum Discoveries – Even Great Minds Can Disagree!

One of the best examples of an extraordinary claim following extraordinary evidence based on the results of meticulous experiments, but questioned by one the greatest and most revered scientists of his time on the grounds of (to his mind) 'inadequate theory' comes from quantum physics, or quantum mechanics to use the older epithet. Readers are asked to revisit the earlier section in this Chapter where the principal discoveries of quantum physics that have undermined the deterministic paradigm of classical physics are summarized. Albert Einstein was deeply disturbed, one might almost venture to say psychologically upset, by these findings. He was a bitter critic of the following three chief (interrelated) tenets of quantum theory—here, forbearance is requested as it graphically illustrates how the greatest minds can be at variance when faced with new evidence and novel theories that fly in the face of well-established former theories:

1. The characterization of physical systems in terms of statistically formulated *probabilities*, or 'tendencies to occur' rather than actualities. In simplistic terms, a thing, if unobserved, cannot be said to exist as a definite entity in a specific location

Increasing geological evidence about prehistoric continents will be forthcoming

Scientists accept reversals and uncertainties in science but not in spirituality or psychic research

---

xxvi There is no dispute amongst occultists about the fact of these prehistoric continents.

at a specified time, but only with a (statistically calculable) probability of such existence. However, the act of observation (or measurement) collapses the probability into a certainty.

2. Heisenberg's uncertainty principle, which showed that indeterminacy is an inherent phenomenon in physical nature having nothing to do with any errors in measurement (see earlier). It showed that there is no absolute truth at the quantum level: we cannot know the entirety of nature with certainty, but only approximately. Heisenberg stated at the end of his paper, 'We *cannot* know, as a matter of principle, the present in all it details [italics in the original].'[144] This theory had become established in modern physics and Einstein could not reject it because he had no valid scientific arguments against it. Nevertheless, it disturbed him because it implied a randomness inherent in nature, which violated the 'strict' law of causality where every effect has its cause, and every cause its antecedent cause—refer to the section on causal closure in Chapter 3. It was the notion of mere probabilities (dice games) that so troubled Einstein, leading him to exclaim, 'I can't believe it, that God would choose to play dice with the world.'[145]

Quantum physics undermines dictates in classical physics of certainties, local causality, and objectivity

3. Non-causal correlations associated with non-locality, or non-local connections (instantaneous action-at-a-distance). This phenomenon, to reiterate, is the apparent ability of objects (specifically, micro-particles like electrons and photons) *instantaneously* to 'know' about and react to the state of each other, even when separated by large distances, potentially even billions of light years, hence the non-local connection. Non-locality further suggests that the universe is in fact profoundly different from our habitual 'common-sense' understanding of it, and that the apparently separate parts of the universe are in fact potentially connected in unseen, intimate, and immediate ways. A related phenomenon is quantum entanglement in which particles that have been coupled or interacted in the past, when separated, even billions of miles apart, will simultaneously change their state (for example, their polarization or the preferred direction of the rate of wave vibration) when the property of any one of the pair is measured. The two concepts of non-locality and entanglement go hand-in-hand: non-locality occurring due to entanglement, in that particles that interact with each other become permanently correlated, or dependent on the states and properties of each other, to the extent that they effectively lose their individuality and, in many ways, behave as a single entity, however much they may be apart in space.

Non-locality and entanglement central to quantum phenomena

Again, and not for the last time, Einstein's rejoinder to the concept of probability in Niels Bohr's interpretation of quantum mechanics was, 'Quantum mechanics is very impressive […] but I am convinced that God does not play dice [with the universe],'[146] to which Niels Bohr is supposed to have retorted, 'Stop telling God what to do!'[147]

In summary, Einstein's objections were that quantum theory undermined the notion of strict causality and precise determinism. They were a direct contravention of the principle of locality, that objects separated in space cannot *instantaneously* influence each other, and that an object is directly influenced only by its immediate surroundings; ideas on which physics (until then) was predicated. It is this violation of what Einstein called the 'principle of local action' that so worried him because of the clear implication of some form of superluminal (faster than the speed of light) communication or possibly even instantaneous

Quantum physics apparently inconsistent with relativity theory

action-at-a-distance, which contradicted (his) relativity theory that no signal can travel faster than the speed of light, hence nothing can link two particles instantaneously across space (because the linking would need a finite time determined by the separation in space and the speed of light). In fact, Einstein was so upset by the phenomenon of non-locality that on one occasion he is supposed to have declared that the whole of quantum theory must be wrong. Indeed, he pondered over the idea of non-locality until his dying day. It is this phenomenon that he called 'spooky actions at a distance'.[148] Accordingly, he devised a thought experiment to test quantum rules, specifically to show that Heisenberg's principle of indeterminacy was violated.

The experimental story is noteworthy. In 1935, Albert Einstein and his physicist collaborators, the Russian–American Boris Podolsky (1896–1966) and the Israeli Nathan Rosen (1909–1995) published a famous paper with the apposite title: 'Can quantum–mechanical description of physical reality be considered complete?'[149] It became known as the 'EPR paradox' because it highlights the non-logical nature (by ordinary common-sense standards) of the quantum world. They described a *Gedankenexperiment* (thought experiment) to show that quantum mechanics demands a non-local character, more precisely, that a measurement on one system can instantaneously influence another spatially separated system. However, and crucially, this non-local character violated their assumed non-existence of action-at-a-distance. They concluded that the quantum–mechanical 'wave function does not provide a complete description of physical reality',[xxvii] that the theory must be incomplete, if not outrightly wrong. Accordingly, they postulated a complementary, local causal theory, yet to be discovered. This caused a controversial discussion in the physics community and renowned physicists, like Bohr, disagreed with their line of argument.[150] Physicists tried to obtain direct, experimental proof of the EPR thought experiment, an updated version of which was suggested in 1952 by one of the most significant theoretical physicists of the twentieth century, the American, David Bohm, who provided a metaphysical dimension to quantum theory, neuropsychology, and the philosophy of mind.[151]

Thought experiment by Einstein and colleagues to test quantum theory

However, the discussion was focussed dramatically when matters were brought to a head by the Irish physicist John Bell FRS (1928–1990) who published a classic paper in 1964 drawing upon Bohm's concepts. Bell wanted to test the (then) fundamental premise of a 'local realistic' view of the world, the two key assumptions of which were objectivity and local causality. This meant that: *real things exist regardless of the existence of any observer; any signal or information cannot be propagated faster than the speed of light—hence, not instantaneously; and general conclusions could be drawn from repeatable and consistent observations or experimental findings*. Bell's theorem showed that the results predicted by quantum mechanics (as in experiments like that described by Einstein, Podolsky, and Rosen) could not be explained by any theory which preserved locality (or local causation).[152] Although at the time Bell could not foresee any experiments to check his theory, he presented his arguments mathematically in terms of an inequality that could (in principle) be tested experimentally. If the inequality were violated, then the two key assumptions of objectivity, and local causation pertaining to the local realistic view of the world, would be falsified; therefore, quantum theory on non-locality would be validated. Bell subsequently made

John Bell develops the thought experiment using mathematical arguments to argue that quantum theory is incompatible with local causality

---

xxvii A wave function (not to be confused with a wave equation) in quantum mechanics describes the quantum state of an isolated system of one or more particles.

further improvements of his original idea,[153] and twelve years later the American theoretical and experimental physicist John Clauser (*b.*1942) and the American physicist and philosopher Abner Shimony (1928–2015),[154] made it possible to test experimentally quantum mechanics against the theory of local action.

In 1972, John Clauser, working with the American graduate physicist Stuart Freedman (1944–2012) at the Lawrence Berkeley Laboratory at the University of California, actually performed experiments using photons to test Bell's inequality. Their results confirmed Bell's theorem.[155] Then in the mid-1970s, a variety of experiments were performed to show that Bell's inequality was violated. In 1976, for example, physicists at the Saclay Nuclear Research Centre in France used low-energy photons in an experiment to show that the local realistic view of the world was false. Later in 1979, the French theoretical physicist and philosopher of science Bernard d'Espagnat (1921–2015) argued that the materialistic doctrine claiming that the world is constituted of objects whose existence is independent of human consciousness, and that objects widely separated in space cannot affect each other, conflicts with the predictions of quantum mechanical theory as well as the facts established by experiments.[156] Significantly, in 2009 d'Espagnat won the £1 million Templeton Prize for his work on the philosophical implications of quantum mechanics. This prestigious award is presented annually to individuals who 'affirm life's spiritual dimension'. D' Espagnat's widely read paper provided the stimulus for the rigorous and sophisticated experiments, performed using photons, by the team at the University of Paris–South in 1982 led by the French physicist Alain Aspect ForMemRS (*b.*1947), noted for his experimental work on quantum entanglement. [157, 158] They effectively closed the last remaining loophole for the (materialistic) local realistic theory. Again, the results showed that Bell's inequality was violated, hence quantum mechanical theory and predictions were confirmed.

Alain Aspect's experimental verification of Bell's theorem thus validating quantum mechanical theory and predictions

Inferences and Implications of Quantum Discoveries

It is stressed that the experiments performed to test Bell's inequality were among the most carefully controlled and rigorous of their type in modern physics. The inescapable conclusion cannot therefore be explained away in terms of experimental error. And this conclusion from repeatable experiments clearly disagreed with the notion of local theories and confirmed quantum mechanical theories: that non-locality and entanglement do indeed rule the (quantum) world. Niels Bohr was correct, and Einstein was mistaken. 'Spooky action at a distance' is a fact that is rigorously demonstrable.

It is futile to argue on the basis that these experiments at the micro-world level are all very impressive but in the ordinary macro-world of tangible and visible things and objects such conclusions would be too far-fetched. The riposte is that reductionism is the overriding methodology of mainstream science on the grounds that a complex phenomenon or object can be explained by analysing its simplest, most basic physical constituents. This means that the simplest constituents must bear a relation to the object in question. Therefore, any macro-object embodies the character of its constituent micro-particles— if not, reduction has absolutely no meaning or use!

Entanglement and non-locality now fully accepted

Given that spooky action at a distance is now a scientifically proven fact, namely, that once two objects interact, they remain connected in space and time, Dean Radin (*b.*1952) argues in *Entangled Minds* that human minds are likely interconnected or entangled in the same way, and this interconnected fabric of reality is the key to those puzzling, yet profoundly significant, experiences called psychic phenomena.[159] Radin is Laboratory Director at the Institute of Noetic Sciences in California, having previously worked at AT&T Bell Laboratories and GTE Laboratories on advanced telecommunications systems, for nearly two decades conducted research on psychic phenomena in academia (Princeton University, University of Edinburgh, University of Nevada), and as scientist on a highly classified program investigating *psi* phenomena for the US government. Given his outstanding academic and research track record, his book clearly needs to be treated with utmost gravity by the scientific community as it shows how science has rigorously demonstrated genuine psychic phenomena and why these phenomena constitute the next frontier in terms of understanding ourselves.

Dean Radin postulates entanglement as key to explain psychic phenomena

The Breakdown and Abdication of 'Common Sense'

Would Einstein have changed his mind in the light of the extremely robust and repeatable experimental confirmation of non-locality being at the heart of quantum mechanical theory and action? It is singularly unfortunate that he died (in 1955) nine years before Bell published his original paper and over a quarter of a century before Alain Aspect's experiments supplied the definite evidence that confirmed Bell's inequality. One would like to think that Einstein would have had many second thoughts. But the great scientist once said that, 'creating a new theory is not like destroying an old barn and erecting a skyscraper in its place. It is rather like climbing a mountain, gaining newer and wider views, discovering unexpected connections between our starting point and its rich environment.'[160] We remark that the progress from Newtonian physics to general relativity did not entail 'destroying an old barn'. But the radical step change from classical physics to quantum physics did demand the destruction of the old order and the erection of a new skyscraper of thought.

A radical new theory invariably demands eradicating outworn concepts

Lessons Learnt from Quantum Physics

In conclusion then, we make no apology for labouring the following four 'lessons learnt' in the progression from classical to quantum physics:

1. The pronouncements of scientists, even as great as Einstein, are no basis upon which to disprove new evidence or theory on the grounds of weight of authority *per se*. In this wise, the history of quantum physics has shown that *so-called common sense and a preconceived view of the world can be most deceitful.*

   > Nature behaving *in actu* [in actuality] ever esoterically, and being, as the Kabbalists say, *in abscondito* [fugitive, or absconding], can only be judged by the profane through her appearance, and that appearance is always deceitful on the physical plane.[161]

2. 'New wine must be put into new bottles' is an old adage.[xxviii] *New evidence and new theories must be evaluated based on knowledge of the present moment, not the past.* It was this determined attempt to force-fit modern quantum theory and findings into

---

xxviii The old adage is from Mark 2:22. The King James Bible version is, 'And no man putteth new wine into old bottles: else the new wine doth burst the bottles, and the wine is spilled, and the bottles will be marred: but new wine must be put into new bottles.'

the paradigm of classical physics of the historical past that caused Einstein so much angst.

3   The complex, and at times painful, evolution of quantum physics has shown the *power of the scientific method at its best.* It was the unimpeachable enquiry and search for truth that spurred on the greatest scientific minds towards their legendary discoveries. We need to reiterate: the search for truth was the main drive, not the desire to win massive research grants or to maintain scientific respectability in journals, or amongst peer groups, or to gain personal accolades even though the latter were forthcoming aplenty. Needless to say, the search for truth has always been uppermost to real scientists.

4   Quantum physics has exemplified one of the principal, if not *the* principal tenet of the ageless wisdom: *that we live in a universe intimately interconnected at its deepest and fundamental level.* In this way quantum physics has paved the way in no uncertain terms for the consideration, if not yet the acceptance by mainstream science, of the perennial esoteric and occult sciences dealing with the unseen and invisible worlds. Indeed, Bernard d'Espagnat coined the term 'veiled reality' to allude to the elusive realm beyond the physical world which science can glimpse through the window of quantum behaviour and which, he argued, could be compatible with 'higher forms of spirituality' that we may intimate in ordinary life through such experiences as listening to sublime music.

    However, it is helpful to remember that d'Espagnat also maintained that quantum science cannot tell us anything about the existence, or otherwise, of God. And that is because science (meaning, of course, natural science) cannot reveal anything about the nature of being with absolute certainty; hence science cannot pronounce on what is not within its scope. Nonetheless, later, in Chapters 7 and 8 and in Chapter 11 of Volume III, we are at pains to point out that the term 'Science' in its fullest and truest sense concerns itself with Truth; hence, *knowledge of everything.* (Art, on the other hand, is the *practice* of Science in all fields.)

Enough has been said to demonstrate that it is as absurd, as it is unscientific, to use the Sagan cliché as a weapon to dismiss robust evidence that cannot be explained materialistically or mechanistically. This is not to deny that there are innumerable examples of charlatanry or claims to paranormal feats based on wishful thinking, deception or self-projection. However, spurious or sham claims say a lot about the falsity of the claims and the character of the claimant, but they say nothing whatsoever about independent, genuine evidence. Perhaps we may add that the *exclusively* materialistic world-view pronounced as an overarching scientific philosophy, rather than applied within its legitimate boundaries, and founded entirely on the assumption of the primacy of dead matter and a godless universe, is a claim for which it is difficult to find evidence, weak or strong, ordinary or extraordinary.

Clichés are impotent weapons to counter the weight of evidence

More examples of extraordinary evidence will be adduced shortly. Meanwhile, we vindicate when asking for extraordinary evidence is a legitimate demand.

Antecedent Probabilities

In his lectures on psychical research the philosopher of science the English epistemologist, historian of philosophy, and philosopher of science Charlie Dunbar Broad (1887–1971), usually cited as C. D. Broad, introduced the argument about antecedent probability.[162] He argued that it is right to demand a much higher standard of evidence for events that are allegedly paranormal than for those that would be normal, albeit unusual, such as a landslide, or abnormal, such as structural birth defects. For in dealing with evidence, we have always to consider the antecedent probability or improbability of the alleged event, i.e., its probability or improbability relative to all the rest of our relevant knowledge and well-founded beliefs (and assumptions) *other than* the special evidence just adduced in its favour. Thus, the more improbable the event would be antecedently, the stronger is the special evidence needed to force a reasonable person to conclude that such an event almost certainly did take place.

The unusual, abnormal, improbable, and experimenter motive, are collective considerations

Now it might be said that the antecedent odds are virtually infinite against the occurrence of an event which would be paranormal, i.e., which would conflict with one or more of the basic limiting principles which form the framework of all our practical activities and our scientific theories. On the other hand, to suppose that intelligent and careful persons, who are known to be honest in general and have no obvious motives for acting out of character, should on certain occasions have been careless or fraudulent, or both, to an extreme degree, is to suppose something which would be at most *highly abnormal*.

Alfred Russel Wallace, mentioned in the previous Chapter concerning his ideas on evolution, argues on similar lines to the above regarding anomalous evidence. In an interview published posthumously in 1913, the year of his death, he describes the slow and painful process by which new truths gain acceptance in these words: 'Truth is born into this world only with pangs and tribulations, and every fresh truth is received unwillingly. [Therefore] to expect the world to receive a new truth, or even an old truth, without challenging it, is to look for one of those miracles which do not occur.' This observation especially applies to psychical and paranormal phenomena which are invariably subject to ridicule and denounced by so-called authorities. Having noted, for half a century, the generally disdainful way that substantiated and repeatable psychical phenomena were received by scientists, Wallace counselled 'never to accept the disbelief of great men or their accusations of imposture or of imbecility, as of any weight when opposed to the repeated observation of facts [as to obscure psychical phenomena] by other men, admittedly sane and honest. The whole history of science shows us that whenever the educated and scientific men of any age have denied the facts of other investigators on a priori grounds of absurdity or impossibility, the deniers have always been wrong.' This, Wallace declared as his 'first great lesson in the inquiry into these obscure fields of knowledge'. [163]

Repeated observations overturn the prejudices of the highest authorities

Closing Reflections

In summarizing and reflecting on the above, however, we comment that when all things are considered there is no such thing as absolute, cast-iron objective evidence. What is 'normal' and 'abnormal'? What can be probable or is likely to be improbable? This is all a question of prior assumptions and presuppositions. Who is a reasonable person? And do our practical activities and our scientific theories remain fixed for ever, or subject to change? We have just mentioned the highly improbable case of aeroplane flight—until it happened. Lord Kelvin was hidebound by the prevailing scientific theories: not so the Wright Brothers, which is why they were able to break free of the scientific mould then prevailing. By the same token, astronomers confidently pronounced Mars to be a dry and arid planet—until they found flowing water on the Red Planet. In the realm of mind, the notion of group telepathy is regarded as abnormal and improbable in Western societies; however, it is quite normal, and highly probable, amongst aboriginal tribes having a group consciousness as Jung's research discovered.[164] Then, in biology, epigenetics has dented the hitherto impregnable dogma of molecular biology. So, we again come up against the central issue of *the subjective experience and beliefs (i.e., the mindset and consciousness) of the persons, and the presuppositions of the scientific bodies and institutions examining the evidence.* The peer review system adopted for academic publications is fine, in principle, as long as the ideas presented are compatible with the reviewing body. Otherwise, any new ideas, however thoroughly presented, that clash with the 'popular wisdom' are invariably filtered out swiftly or trashed by the proponents of scientism as we now describe.

Dogmas in science are eventually overturned by the weight of new evidence

Knowledge Filtration in Establishment Science

> And whenever we have been furnished a fetish, and have been taught to believe in it, and love it and worship it, and refrain from examining it, there is no evidence, howsoever clear and strong, that can persuade us to withdraw from it our loyalty and our devotion.
>
> Mark Twain[165]

Figure I-2 attempts to illustrate Mark Twain's witticism.[xxix] It shows how the scientific establishment deals with anomalous evidence by way of knowledge filtration.[xxx] Other than outright attack, as in the case of the American philosopher Thomas Nagel (*b*.1937), who dared to question Darwinian ideology (fully described in Volume II, Chapter 7), new ideas or discoveries are almost instinctively passed through a 'knowledge filter'. Those

Mainstream opinion still predominates over anomalous hard evidence

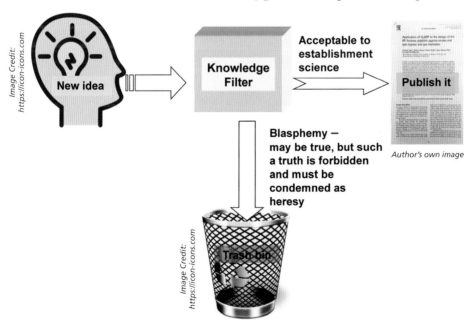

Figure I-2 Knowledge Filtration

xxix Mark Twain wrote the above in connection with the Shakespeare/Francis Bacon controversy, but his remarks could apply with equal force to the fetishist worship of enshrined scientific ideas.

xxx The writer has developed this idea from the excellent book *Forbidden Archeology: The Hidden History of the Human Race* by Michael Cremo and Richard Thompson discussed in detail in Volume III, Chapter 10.

ideas that agree with the establishment are allowed through and published; but any hard facts and evidence that do not uphold the orthodox opinion are swiftly mangled and dropped into a trash can, so to speak, even though they may be of considerable scientific merit. *The point is that the religious equivalent of heresy is not tolerated by the scientific community amongst any of its members who are not staunch 'defenders of the faith'.*

In an article about his book *The Shakespeare Enigma*,[166] the English geomancer and philosopher on Western wisdom traditions Peter Dawkins (*b*.1945) states: 'Dogma abounds, both in academic and scientific institutions. They are ruled by dominant people, or groups of people, with dogmatic views and vested interests, and it is dangerous to question such "authority". There are many taboos. To break such a taboo is to bring the vehement and dismissive fire of authority down upon one's head, and many brave searchers after truth have suffered badly and unfairly from such attack.'[167] Of course, Peter Dawkins is writing about the orthodox viewpoint concerning the authorship of the Shakespeare works, but his observations, like those of the American writer and humourist Mark Twain (1835–1910), apply equally to any situation where the dominant paradigm or belief is questioned, especially in science or religion—the virulence of the counterattack being in direct proportion to the weight of counter-evidence provided. One of innumerable examples of such dogmatic attitude is the nineteenth century German physician and physicist Hermann von Helmholtz FRS (1821–1894), who expressed his opinion with great force and clarity regarding telepathy: 'Not the testimony of all the Fellows of the Royal Society, nor even the evidence of my own senses, would lead me to the belief *in the transmission* [*sic*] of thought independently of the recognized channels of sense.'[168]

Breaking mainstream taboos invites trouble

Outright rejection of, or refusal to publish, robust empirical data supporting a non-materialistic world-view is merely ideology and contrary to the spirit and method of scientific inquiry, which maintains that new evidence that does not fit a pre-existing theory cannot be discounted by working from something that is already known in order to arrive at a conclusion about something new, i.e., a priori.

Knowledge Suppression Mechanisms

There is a vast amount of provocative evidence that blatantly contradicts currently accepted ideas in mainstream science. Such evidence—both qualitative and quantitative—in all fields of science has been systematically suppressed, forged, mutilated, ignored, allowed to be forgotten or brushed aside as 'witchcraft' or 'snake-oil'. We can discern two primary suppression mechanisms. The first is the deliberate attempt by a few politically powerful scientists to block any evidence that runs against established opinion (upon which large research grants and industrial funding also depend). A case in point is the research over decades by Robert Jahn and co-workers on the Princeton Engineering Anomalies Research (PEAR) project mentioned earlier, which was rebutted outright by the Nobel physicist Philip Anderson ForMemRS (*b*.1923) also, ironically, at Princeton University (more details in the Recapitulation to Volume I). The second is more in the nature of an on-going social process of knowledge filtration that appears insignificant in small doses, but has a major cumulative effect over time, whereby any kind of embarrassing evidence is quietly allowed to disappear into oblivion. The first suppression mechanism operates mainly in the fields of biology, cosmology, and physics; and the second in palæoanthropology and evolutionary theory. Glaring examples of these are provided in

Suppressing knowledge by attack or disregard

Volume II, Chapter 7 and Volume III, Chapter 10. In all cases however, the public at large do not get a balanced perspective and are, in effect, being deceived.

Categories of Knowledge Filtration

The numerous cases of knowledge filtration can be grouped broadly into the following four categories:

1 Scientific theories, data or discoveries that contradict Darwinian theory, as explained in Chapter 10 of Volume III.
2 Robust evidence for non-physical states of consciousness (i.e., consciousness 'beyond the brain') and related matters like organizing fields and morphogenesis, as described earlier in this Chapter, and further in Chapter 7 of Volume II.
3 Robust statistical evidence about *psi* phenomena, on subjects like telepathy, near-death experiences and consciousness beyond the brain, that contradict a neurobiological brain-based theory of thought and consciousness—see the previous sections of this Chapter.
4 The research and testimony of legendary scientists into the paranormal and non-physical realms of being.

Criticisms of Darwinism and non-physical findings are filtered out

The last category is revealing. In addition to the instances presented in earlier sections of this Chapter, two further cases of extraordinary evidence are noteworthy. The first is the ignoring of Newton's deep forays into the *prisca sapientia*, alchemy, and religion, until recently, when the sheer weight of scholarship, plus Lord Keynes's testimonial on the sobriety of the alchemical papers, made it unavoidable for academia to brush aside or deride these works and not to admit of their existence and worth. The second concerns the research discoveries of three French Nobel laureates: the physicists Marie Curie (1867–1934) and Pierre Curie (1859–1906), and the physiologist Charles Richet (1850–1935).

Suppression of Spiritualist Research Conducted by Nobel Laureates

Every physics student is told about the French husband and wife team who both received the Nobel Prize for their work in discovering radium, and this account is found in practically every introductory physics textbook. What the textbooks do not tell us is that the Curies were also heavily involved in psychical research. They were part of a large group of prominent European scientists, including other Nobel Prize winners, who were jointly conducting research into the paranormal in Paris early in the twentieth century. For two years, this group investigated the Italian spiritualist and medium Eusapia Palladino (1854–1918). In her biography of Pierre Curie, the contemporary Polish born historian Anna Hurwic notes that, 'he saw the séances as scientific experiments, tried to monitor the different parameters, took detailed notes of every observation. He was really intrigued by Eusapia Palladino.'[169]

About these séances with Eusapia Palladino, Pierre Curie wrote to his French physicist friend Louis Georges Gouy (1854–1926) in a letter dated 24 July 1905:

> We have had a series of séances with Eusapia Palladino at the [Society for Psychical Research]. It was very interesting, and really the phenomena that we saw appeared

inexplicable as trickery—tables raised from all four legs, movement of objects from a distance, hands that pinch or caress you, luminous apparitions. All in a locale [setting] prepared by us with a small number of spectators all known to us and without a possible accomplice. The only trick possible is that which could result from an extraordinary facility of the medium as a magician. But how do you explain the phenomena when one is holding her hands and feet and when the light is sufficient so that one can see everything that happens?[170]

Pierre Curie reported that on such occasions, the medium was carefully physically controlled by the scientists present.

A year later on 14 April 1906, Pierre Curie wrote again to Gouy about some further investigations that he and his wife had carried out:

> We had some sittings with the medium Eusapia Palladino (we had already had sittings with her last summer). The result is that these phenomena really exist and I can no longer doubt them. It is unbelievable but it is so and it is impossible to deny it, after the sittings that we had under conditions of perfect control. A fluid kind of limbs are formed from the medium (in addition to her ordinary arms and legs), and these more or less unformed members are able to forcefully grasp or push objects (Richet calls this ectoplasm). These fluid limbs are preferably formed beneath a piece of black cloth under her skirts behind a curtain. But sometimes they go out into the open air.
>
> What is extremely disturbing is that one feels very well [sic] that by admitting the existence of some of these phenomena one will gradually be led to admit all of them, even the ghosts of [Sir William] Crookes and [the French Nobel physiologist Charles] Richet. Also, we do not understand at all how such transformations of matter can be made so rapidly and without involving prodigious quantities of energy.[171]

Pierre Curie wrote these words a few days before his accidental death in 1906:

> There is here, in my opinion, a whole domain of entirely new facts and physical states in space of which we have no conception.[172]

Charles Robert Richet, the French physiologist who would later win the Nobel Prize in Physiology or Medicine in 1913, carried out decades of research into psychic phenomena and participated in the Curies's investigation of Palladino. He left his own account of a séance.[173] A fine account of Richet's exploration of psychic phenomena is given by Carlos Alvarado.[174]

We are therefore entitled to ask: given that three Nobel laureates (Marie Curie, twice, Pierre Curie, and Charles Richet) were seriously and sometimes contemporaneously involved in psychical research, moreover that Pierre Curie 'saw the séances as scientific experiments' (see above), why does the scientific establishment not also acknowledge and report this fact (whatever the results may have been) in the spirit of honest scientific enquiry, in addition to the much publicized accounts of their scientific researches that won them a total of four Nobel Prizes?

Such results, and many more like them from the hidden history of physics, biology, and psychology, suggest that there is associated with the human organism a mind element that can act on ordinary matter in ways that cannot be explained by known physical laws. The above cases—just two amongst several that could be mentioned, it bears repeating—have deliberately been chosen to illustrate the point that new facts and evidence that do not fit within the paradigm of materialistic science, and therefore cannot be explained by the known laws of physics, are filtered out, irrespective of their scientific validity, controlled experimental conditions, or the pre-eminence of the scientist.

In conclusion then, although this section refers to knowledge filtration in mainstream science, it must in all fairness be stated that such selective use of knowledge is not limited just to scientists. Far from it. It applies whenever people become obsessed with an idea or a theory, of another person or their own. When this happens, the theory possesses the man, so to speak and impartiality is compromised. The writer could cite numerous examples of Theosophists and religious people professing fair-mindedness, but in fact wedded to their sacrosanct book or writer and disdaining any views perceived to be to the contrary—see for example Appendix II-C to Volume II in connection with the Theosophical Society.

> **Cheating and deception involve not just the occasional, deliberate falsification or mutilation of data, but also failing to report, whether or not the motives be deliberate or unconscious, since the yearning for glory and power are also powerful drives amongst scientists.**

> Whenever we have been furnished with tar baby ostensibly stuffed with jewels, and warned that it will be dishonourable and irreverent to disembowel it and test the jewels, we keep our sacrilegious hands off it. We submit, not reluctantly, but rather gladly, for we are privately afraid we should find, upon examination, that the jewels are of the sort that are manufactured at North Adams, Mass [i.e. out of cheap plastic].
>
> Mark Twain[175]

The 'Church of Scientism'

Closely related to knowledge filtration are the various syndromes of scientism, which, to reiterate, is scientific materialism afforded a status tantamount to religious dogma—*not* materialism applied in its rightful context. *The Hidden Power* by the Irish journalist and historian Brian Inglis (1916–1993) contains well researched reflections on the menace of scientism, which is still the underlying world-view of mainstream science.[176]

Shown below are seven representative scientism syndromes that Inglis examines before demolishing their sceptical arguments:[177]

1   *Psi* phenomena across wide ranging fields like physics, botany, biology, shamanism, plus psychical research cannot exist because they are all contrary to accepted scientific laws—a classic case of 'the map dictating the territory'. Therefore, since there is no theoretical basis for *psi*, experimental evidence is fatally flawed and historical and anecdotal evidence is best accounted for, or explained away, by fraud—and this charge of being a dupe must necessarily include the Nobel laureate Charles Robert Richet who devoted many years to the study of paranormal and spiritualist phenomena, coining the term 'ectoplasm'.[178, 179]

2   *Festinger's syndrome* concerns itself with how people try to reach internal consistency, which illustrates cognitive dissonance and the reversal of opinions, when new information presents challenges to established beliefs and behaviours.[180] One notable instance of this was when the British physicist Professor John Taylor (1931–2012) in the late 1970s, after witnessing spoon bending by the Israeli psychic Uri Geller (*b.*1946), rejected his own experience on the grounds that he could find no unknown fifth force causing psychokinesis.[181]

The 'map' must fit
the 'territory' for
new theories or
evidence to be
acceptable to
orthodoxy

3   *Discrediting by smears* which is not the same as disproof: for example, Sir William Crookes who was first applauded for his courage in investigating paranormal phenomena, but then besmirched by mainstream scientists when he published positive results.[182]

4   *Polanyi's syndrome* proposed by the Hungarian–British polymath Michael Polanyi FRS (1891–1976), a critique of positivism, which maintains that contradictions between a popular scientific notion and the facts of experience are explained (away) in terms of other scientific hypotheses or simply dismissed not so much as untrue, but insignificant.[183]

5   *Medawar's syndrome* where the scientist does not ask questions until an outline of an answer appears; but if phenomena defy a materialistic understanding, then they should be denied or ignored.[184]

6   *Gregory/Mayo syndrome* which reaches back to the nineteenth century and derives from the split between the natural and the supernatural, the latter considered to be non-existent.

7   Finally, there are the '*lid-sitters*' and the '*hit-men*' of scientism. The former ignore or suppress contrary evidence partly for a fear of a return to what they consider mediæval superstition and the ridicule from their peers that could ensue. The latter are vociferous and include individuals such as the British psychologist C. E. M. Hansel (1917–2011)[185] and the Canadian–American stage magician James Randi (1928–2020),[186] both fellows of the Committee for Skeptical Inquiry, the program within the transnational American non-profit educational organization Center for Inquiry, which seeks to 'promote scientific inquiry, critical investigation, and the use of reason in examining controversial and extraordinary claims.' Notwithstanding the laudable claim of 'critical investigation, and the use of reason' their arguments are effectively dismembered by Brian Inglis.

The writer would like to suggest another syndrome: what he calls *Weinberg's syndrome*, after the American theoretical physicist and Nobel laureate, Steven Weinberg ForMemRS

Weinberg's
syndrome

(1933–2021). This syndrome holds that scientific knowledge is sufficiently advanced such that any alleged anomalous phenomena (like telepathy or telekinesis[xxxi]) can be condemned outright, without further investigation, on the basis of contravening the now well established laws of physics. This syndrome is elaborated in the Recapitulation.

Clearly, *psi* phenomena are particularly vulnerable to the above eight syndromes. What, then, can constitute universally acceptable, scientific proof of paranormal phenomena? This is best answered by the physicist, and highly acclaimed *psi* researcher, Stephen Phillips: 'Scientists insist that repeatable, double-blind tests performed under controlled laboratory conditions are prerequisite for an objective demonstration of the existence of a new, natural phenomenon. But such are the perceived revolutionary implications for science of *psi* faculties like ESP and telepathy that even highly significant statistical

Smearing the
character of the
researcher—the
last refuge of the
desperate sceptic

evidence of these abilities obtained under stringent, computer-controlled conditions may not satisfy some critics of parapsychology.' What happens when all else fails? 'If they cannot fault the experimental protocols eliminating cheating or unconscious use of

---

xxxi   The production of motion in objects without contact or other physical means.

sensory clues by the psychic, sceptics can, as a last resort, dismiss impressive findings either by suggesting that the researcher fabricated his data—a charge not easy to rebut— or by revealing a scandal [real or imagined] about his life in order to discredit his character and—by implication—his research.'[187]

The Canons of Scientism

Scientism: Science, Ethics and Religion is an important book by the Swede Mikael Stenmark (*b.*1962), Dean of the Faculty of Theology since 2008 and Professor in Philosophy of Religion at the Department of Theology, Uppsala University, Sweden.[188] Albeit published in 2001, it clarifies what scientism is, and proceeds to evaluate its four key claims that are, if anything, even more relevant now, namely:

1 The only kind of knowledge we can have is scientific knowledge.
2 The only things that exist are the ones to which science has access.
3 Science alone can answer our moral questions and explain as well as replace traditional ethics.
4 Science alone can answer our existential questions, explain the nature of mind and consciousness, and explain, as well as replace, traditional religion.[189]

Spirit of science imprisoned by scientism

If we were to take the words of Professor Stenmark to heart, it would appear that materialist science has morphed into scientism—the worship of science 'for its own sake'— tantamount to faith-based religion. Taken at face value, the undisputed assumption is that the ultimate truth is no more than the physical world which is held to be 'all that exists'. On this note, a story told by the renowned American scholar of religious studies Huston Smith (1919-2016) in his book *Why Religion Matters* is apposite. He had just given a university lecture on scientism and was answering questions afterwards. One member of the audience came up to him and remarked that there was only one problem with his careful distinction between science and scientism—that most scientists simply don't distinguish between them![190]

Nevertheless, the writer maintains that given its disregard for much of the empirical data and reasoned analysis, and its lack of awareness that the fundamental issue is a metaphysical one involving its own basic assumptions, scientism can be seen as more of a pseudoscience.

A Fine Scientific Definition of Pseudoscience

Nowadays it is certainly the case that a scientist embarking on his career, or even a world famous scientist who espouses unfashionable ideas and fails to conform, thereby daring to step outside the canons of scientism, is swiftly excommunicated and may well find his career and reputation in shreds. Woe betide a young researcher who wishes to embark on a career in parapsychology! Numerous such cases were adduced in this and previous Chapters and several more will come to light as we progress (especially in Chapter 7 of Volume II). The writer suggests, therefore, that the devotees who worship in the 'Church of Scientism' are, in fact, pseudoscientists. It would be difficult to find a better example of prejudice and unbridled dogma than 'Searching for the Impossible: Parapsychology's Elusive Quest'.[191]

Pitfalls awaiting researchers transgressing the establishment line

Earlier in this Chapter we quoted an extract from the presidential address to the American Statistical Association by the statistics professor at the University of California, Jessica Utts, confirming the statistical likelihood of remote viewing and precognition as being real effects in relation to intelligence gathering during the Cold War. In the same address Utts continues: 'Yet, most scientists reject the possible reality of these abilities without ever looking at the data! And on the other extreme, there are the true believers who base their belief solely on anecdotes and personal experience. I have asked the debunkers[192] if there is any amount of data that would convince them, and they generally have responded by saying, "probably not". I ask them what original research they have read, and they mostly admit that they haven't read any! Now there is a definition of pseudo-science—basing conclusions on belief, rather than data!'[193]

Do beliefs count more than data?

But are mountains of data more convincing than one strong personal experience?

Lots More Data or Just a Single Experience – Which is More Convincing?

Finally, in the same presidential address, Utts said: 'When I have given talks on this topic [remote viewing, precognition, etc.] to audiences of statisticians, I show lots of data. Then I ask the audience, which would be more convincing to you—lots more data, or one strong personal experience? Almost without fail, the response is one strong personal experience! Of course I'm giving you an extreme example, and I think people are justifiably skeptical, because most people think that these abilities contradict what we know about science. They don't, but that's the subject for a different talk.'[194]

Should statistics hold sway over experience?

All things considered, personal experience invariably gains the upper hand over data. And much of that experience (for which data around the world is mounting exponentially) concerns the class of phenomena, described earlier, which neither scientific materialism can explain nor scientism deride. But what seems so anomalous to materialism is perfectly natural when, along with physical nature, the spiritual and invisible Laws of Nature are also acknowledged and investigated by enlightened scientists as the following chapters will show.

Is Scientism then a Cult?

Scientists frequently disparage genuine spiritually orientated movements—Rudolf Steiner's Anthroposophy[195] being just one purely arbitrary example—as being pseudo-science or anti-scientific cults.[196] But what is a cult? One of the definitions in the Oxford English Dictionary is 'devotion or homage to a person or thing'.[197] On this basis, we are entitled to ask: 'In view of scientism's exclusive devotion to materialism would it be fair to refer also to scientism as a cult? Would it then be unreasonable to claim that being inimical to the true ethos of science, as evidenced in this section and earlier Chapters of this Volume, scientism is fundamentally anti-science, in fact pseudoscience, and that those who uphold it singularly belong to the cult of scientism?'

Are not science and scientism poles apart?

This Chapter has explained how the prevailing mechanistic paradigm of science has inhibited its march towards new ideas and discoveries, and the manner in which anomalous findings are discounted or discredited by the establishment. The next Chapter describes new vistas that come into focus when materialism is transcended, as the following quotes imply.

The day science begins to study non-physical phenomena, it will make more progress in one decade than in all the previous centuries of its existence.

NIKOLA TESLA[198]

A man should look for what is, and not for what he thinks should be.

ALBERT EINSTEIN[199]

Overwhelmingly strong proofs of intelligent and benevolent design lie around us … the atheistic idea is so nonsensical that I cannot put it into words.

LORD KELVIN[200]

Opposition to godliness is atheism in profession and idolatry in practice. Atheism is so senseless and odious to mankind that it never had many professors.

SIR ISAAC NEWTON[201]

This whole reductive programme—this mindless materialism, this belief in something called 'matter' as the answer to all questions—is not really science at all. It is, and always has been, just an image, a myth, a vision, an enormous act of faith. As Karl Popper said, it is 'promissory materialism', an offer of future explanations based on boundless confidence in physical methods of enquiry. It is a quite general belief in 'matter', which is conceived in a new way as able to answer all possible questions. And that belief has flowed much more from the past glories of science than from any suitability for the job in hand. In reality, not all questions are physical questions or can be usefully fitted to physical answers.

MARY MIDGLEY[202]

NOTES

1   Erwin Schrödinger, 'Nature and the Greeks' from the Shearman Lectures delivered at University College, London, 1948, in *Nature and the Greeks* and *Science and Humanism*, foreword by Roger Penrose (Cambridge: Cambridge University Press, 2014), 97, 98. See also Ken Wilber (ed.) *Quantum Questions: Mystical writings of the world's great physicists* (Shambhala, 1985), 75–97.

2   'Far more than 87m Facebook Users had Data Compromised, MPs told', *The Guardian*, 17 April 2018 <https://www.theguardian.com/uk-news/2018/apr/17/facebook-users-data-compromised-far-more-than-87m-mps-told-cambridge-analytica> accessed 14 November 2019.

3   Wolfgang Amadeus Mozart, *Die Sinfonien* [The symphonies] 1, trans. J. Branford Robinson (Kassel: Bärenreiter-Verlag, 2005), IX.

4   Richard Dawkins, *The Blind Watchmaker* (Harlow, England: Longman Scientific & Technical, 1986), 317.

5   'Albert Einstein', *Goodreads* <http://www.goodreads.com/author/quotes/9810> accessed 14 November 2019.

6   Arthur Ellison, *The Reality of the Paranormal* (London: Harrap, 1988).

7   This is a summarized account of a private communication to the writer by Professor Ellison in August 1996. An inaccurate version of the story is given in Kit Pedler, *Mind Over Matter* (UK: HarperCollins Distribution Services), 1982.

8   John Dupré, *Processes of Life: Essays in the philosophy of biology* (Oxford: Oxford University Press, 2012).

9   Hans Driesch: *The History & Theory of Vitalism*, trans. Charles Kay Ogden (London: Macmillan and Co., 1914); *Science and Philosophy of the Organism* (1908; 2nd edn, London: A. & C. Black, 1929); *Mind and Body: A criticism of psychophysical parallelism* (London: Methuen, 1927).

10 Ervin László, *Science and the Akashic Field: An integral theory of everything* (Rochester, Vermont: Inner Traditions), 2007.

11 Rupert Sheldrake, *The Presence of the Past: Morphic resonance and the habits of nature* (London: Fontana, 1989). See especially Chapter 9, 'Animal Memory', 159–81 and Chapter 12, 'Minds, Brains, and Memories', 210–22.

12 ——*A New Science of Life* (London: Icon Books, 2009).

13 ——*Morphic Resonance: The nature of formative causation* (Rochester: Vermont: Park Street Press, 2009), 38–41, 251.

14 Alexander Gurwitsch, 'Über den Begriff des Embryonalen feldes' ['About the concept of the embryonic field'], *Archiv für Entwicklungsmechanik der Organismen* [Archive for the development mechanics of organisms], 51/1 (December 1922), 383–415.

15 Paul Weiss, *Principles of Development* (New York: Holt, 1939).

16 C. H. Waddington, *The Strategy of Genes* (London: Allen & Unwin, 1957).

17 R. Thom, *Mathematical Models of Morphogenesis* (New York: Wiley 1983).

18 C. H. Waddington, *Towards a Theoretical Biology 2 – Sketches* (Edinburgh: Edinburgh University Press, 1969), 72–81.

19 'Appendix B, Morphic Fields and the Implicate Order: A Dialogue with David Bohm', in Rupert Sheldrake, *Morphic Resonance*, 251.

20 Alan Turing was also a long-distance runner of world-class standards. While working at Bletchley, Turing, occasionally ran the 40 miles (64 kilometres) to London when he was needed for meetings—see Anthony Cave Brown, *Bodyguard of Lies: The Extraordinary True Story Behind D-Day* (New York: Harper & Row, 1975). We may presume that Turing also ran the same distance back to Bletchley, probably on the same day.

21 Alan Turing, 'The Chemical Basis of Morphogenesis', *Philosophical Transactions of the Royal Society of London B*, 237 (1952), 37–72. Refer also to L. G. Harrison, *Kinetic Theory of Living Pattern* (Cambridge: Cambridge University Press, 1993).

22 D'Arcy Wentworth Thompson, *On Growth and Form* (Cambridge: Cambridge University Press, 2000).

23 Rupert Sheldrake, *Morphic Resonance*.

24 —— *The Presence of the Past*.

25 Wilder Penfield and Lamar Roberts, *Speech and Brain Mechanisms* (Princeton, New Jersey: Princeton University Press, 1959).

26 Karl Lashley, 'In Search of the Engram', *Symposia of the Society for Experimental Biology*, 4 (1950), 454–82.

27 Brian B. Boycott, 'Learning in the Octopus', *Scientific American*, 212/3 (1965), 42–50.

28 Karl Pribram, *Languages of the Brain* (Englewood Cliffs: Prentice Hall, 1971).

29 Rupert Sheldrake, 'The Hypothesis of Formative Causation', *The American Theosophist*, 70/10 (November 1982), 356–60.

30 Wilder Penfield, *The Mysteries of the Mind: A critical study of consciousness and the human brain* (Princeton, New Jersey: Princeton University Press, 1975).

31 John C. Eccles, *Facing Reality: Philosophical adventures by a brain scientist* (Berlin, Heidelberg, New York: Springer, 1974), 174. Quoted also in Karl R. Popper and John C. Eccles, *The Self and Its Brain: An argument for interactionism* (Berlin, Heidelberg, London, New York: Springer-Verlag, 1977), 558.

32 —— *op. cit.*, 559–60.

33 John C. Eccles, *Mind and Brain: The many-faceted problems* (Washington, DC: Paragon House, 1982), 97.

34 Norman Doidge, *The Brain that Changes Itself: Stories of personal triumph from the frontiers of brain science* (US: Viking Penguin, UK: Penguin, 2007).

35 Sharon Begley, *The Plastic Mind* (London: Constable, 2009).

36 Amongst several scholarly papers, a typical example is Peter Malinowski, 'Meditation and Neuroplasticity: Five key articles', *Psychological Science of Meditation* (March 2014) <https://meditation-research.org.uk/2014/03/meditation-and-neuroplasticity-five-key-articles> accessed 14 November 2019.

37 Rupert Sheldrake, *Morphic Resonance*, 162, 166, 173, 193–4.

38 'Remembering and Forgetting', in Rupert Sheldrake, *The Presence of the Past*, 197–209.

39 Myles Gough, 'Aboriginal Legends Reveal Ancient Secrets to Science', BBC News, 19 May 2015 <https://www.bbc.co.uk/news/world-australia-32701311> accessed 26 December 2019.

40 'Aboriginal Dreamtime', Artlandish Aboriginal Art Gallery <https://www.aboriginal-art-australia.com/aboriginal-art-library/aboriginal-dreamtime> accessed 26 December 2019.

41 Rupert Sheldrake, *Dogs That Know When Their Owners are Coming Home, and Other Unexplained Powers of Animals* (London: Hutchinson), 1999.

42 —— *The Sense of Being Stared At, and Other Aspects of the Extended Mind* (UK: Arrow Books, 2004). There are also technical papers providing further details on this controversial topic.

43 Morris Kline, *Mathematical Thought from Ancient to Modern Times* (1972; New York: Oxford University Press, 1990), i, 18–21.

44 David Brewster, *The Life of Sir Isaac Newton* (New York: Harper & Brothers, 1831), 198 [online] <https://books.google.co.uk/books?id=Jq43zQEACAAJ&printsec=frontcover&source=gbs_ge_summary_r&cad=0#v=onepage&q=verdict&f=false> accessed 10 July 2020. See also Richard S. Westfall, *Never at Rest: A biography of Isaac Newton* (Cambridge University Press, 1980), 698 et seq.

45 Thomas Sonar, *The History of the Priority Dispute between Newton and Leibniz*, Ger. orig., Eng. trans. Thomas Sonar, Keith Morton, and Patricia Morton (Basel, Switzerland: Springer International Publishing / Birkhäuser Verlag, 2018); quote from book review by Adhemar Bultheel, 'The History of the Priority Dispute between Newton and Leibniz', European Mathematical Society (29 May 2018) <https://euro-math-soc.eu/review/history-priority-dispute-between-newton-and-leibniz> accessed 11 July 2020.

46 Gustaf Strömberg, *The Soul of the Universe* (1940; 2nd edn, Philadelphia: David McKay Company, 1948).

47 —— *op. cit.*, vii-viii.

48 David Bohm, *Wholeness and the Implicate Order* (1980; rev. edn, London and New York: Routledge, 2002).

49 Gustaf Strömberg, *The Soul of the Universe*, 45. Quoted in part in C. J. Ryan, 'Dr. Gustaf Stromberg and the Invisible Structure of the Living Universe', *The Theosophical Forum* (August 1940) <http://www.theosociety.org/pasadena/forum> accessed 14 November 2019.

50 See also 'Book Review: The soul of the universe, by Gustaf Stromberg', *Popular Astronomy*, 48 (1940), 570.

51 Gustaf Strömberg, *The Soul of the Universe*, 303.

52 —— *op. cit.*, 303, 305.

53 —— *op. cit.*, 305.

54 Paul Kieniewicz, 'Andrew Glazewski and the Founding of the Scientific and Medical Network', *Journal of the Scientific and Medical Network*, 115 (2014), 3.

55 See also 'The Autonomous Field', *Journal of the Franklin Institute*, 239/1 (1945).

56 Roger Sperry, *Science and Moral Priority: Merging mind, brain, and human values* (New York: Columbia University Press, 1983). See also Roger E. Bissell, 'Can "Mentalist Monism" Save Mind and Morality from the Mechanistic Materialists?' Vera Lex, XIV/1–2 (1994), 84–7.

57 Roger Sperry, The Nobel Prize, 23 July 1997 <https://www.nobelprize.org/prizes/medicine/1981/sperry/article> accessed 14 November 2019.

58 Rollin McCraty, *Science of the Heart: Exploring the role of the heart in human performance*, 2 vols (HeartMath Institute) i 2001; ii 2015.

59 Bruce Goldstein, 'Cognitive Psychology', Wadsworth, Cengage Learning (2011), 374.

60 Refer to the publications on 'Psychical Research and Parapsychology' by the Society for Psychical Research <http://www.spr.ac.uk/page/spr-publications-parapsychology> accessed 14 November 2019.

61 Frederic P. Miller, Agnes F. Vandome, and John McBrewster, *Confirmation Bias* (Mauritius: VDM Publishing, 2009), 1.

62 Stephen W. Hawking, *A Brief History of Time* (London: Bantam Press, 1988), 67.

63 What follows is a summary from Edi D. Bilimoria, *The Snake and the Rope: Problems in Western science resolved by occult science* (Adyar, Chennai: Theosophical Publishing House), 276–7.

64 A. M. Turing, 'Computing Machinery and Intelligence', *Mind*, 59 (1950), 433–60.

65 Andrew Hodges, *Alan Turing: The enigma* (London: Random House, 2012). This is the official book behind the Academy Award-winning film *The Imitation Game*.

66 John Horgan, 'Brilliant Scientists Are Open-Minded about Paranormal Stuff, So Why Not You?' *Scientific American* (20 July 2012).

67 F. Song, S. Parekh, L. Hooper, Y. K. Loke, J. Ryder, A. J. Sutton, C. Hing, C. S. Kwok, C. Pang, and I. Harvey, 'Dissemination and Publication of Research Findings: An updated review of related biases', *Health Technology Assessment*, 14/8 (2010), iii, ix–xi, 1–193.

68 Etzel Cardeña, 'The Experimental Evidence for Parapsychological Phenomena: A review', *American Psychologist*, 73/5 (July–August 2018), 663–77.

69 'Selected Peer-Reviewed Journal Publications on Psi Research', Institute of Noetic Sciences (IONS) <http://noetic.org/blog/dean-radin/show-me-the-evidence> accessed 14 November 2019.

70 IONS, *art. cit.*

71 Titus Rivas, Anny Dirven, and Rudolf H. Smit, *The Self Does Not Die: Verified paranormal phenomena from near-death experiences*, ed. Robert G. Mays and Janice Miner Holden, International Association for Near-Death Studies, 2016.

72 Eben Alexander, 'Science Supports the Reality of the Soul', *Journal of the Scientific and Medical Network*, 122 (2016), 52.

73 Rajiv Parti (with Paul Perry), *Dying to Wake Up: A doctor's voyage into the afterlife and the wisdom he brought back*, foreword by Raymond Moody (Hay House UK), 2016, reviewed by David Lorimer in *Journal of the Scientific and Medical Network*, 122 (2016), 52–3.

74 Peter Fenwick and Elizabeth Fenwick, *The Truth in the Light: An investigation of over 300 near-death experiences* (New York: Berkley Trade, 1997).

75 Graham Coleman and Thupten Jinpa (eds), *The Tibetan Book of the Dead: First complete translation*, with commentary by Dalai Lama, trans. Gyurme Dorje (New York: Penguin Classics, Deluxe edition, 2007).

76 Kevin Williams, 'The Tibetan Book of the Dead and NDEs' <https://www.near-death.com/religion/buddhism/tibetan-book-of-the-dead.html> accessed 14 November 2019.

77 Sir E. A. Wallis Budge (Egyptian text transliteration and trans.), *Egyptian Book Of The Dead (The Papyrus of Ani)* (New York: Dover Publications, 1967).

78 Plato, *The Republic*, trans. with introduction by R. E. Allen (New Haven: Yale University Press, 2006).

79 Robert A. Monroe, *Journeys Out of the Body* (UK: Souvenir Press, 1989).

80 See Arthur J. Ellison, *The Reality of the Paranormal* (London: Harrap, 1988), 75–8, 79, 81, 83.

81 S. J. Muldoon and H. Carrington, *The Projection of the Astral Body* (London: Rider, 1929).

82 See E. Lester Smith, *Inner Adventures* (Wheaton, Illinois: Theosophical Publishing House, 1988), 132–55 passim.

83 S. LaBerge and H. Rheingold, *Exploring the World of Lucid Dreaming* (New York: Ballantine, 1990).

84 Carl Jung in a 1919 address to the Society for Psychical Research in England <http://www.spr.ac.uk> accessed 14 November 2019.

85 Peter Atkins, *On Being: A scientist's exploration of the great questions of existence* (New York: Oxford University Press, 2011), 90.

86 Arthur Ellison, *The Reality of the Paranormal*, 43.

87 Lecture by Professor Dr Peter A. E. Stewart, DSc, FREng, FRAeS, FInstP, 'An Engineering Life' (9 January 2008) <http://rpec.co.uk/rpec_new/pages/_Exc-11.html> accessed 14 November 2019.

88 Ingo Swan, 'The Ingo Swann 1973 Remote Viewing Probe of the Planet Jupiter' <https://www.thelivingmoon.com/44cosmic_wisdom/01documents/Ingo_Swann_Remote_Viewing_Jupiter.htm> accessed 14 November 2019.

89 'STAR GATE [Controlled Remote Viewing]' <https://fas.org/irp/program/collect/stargate.htm> accessed 14 November 2019.

90 Edwin C. May, Victor Rubel, Joseph W. McMoneagle, and Loyd Auerbach, *ESP Wars: East and West: An account of the military use of psychic espionage as narrated by the key Russian and American players* (Crossroad Press, 2018).

91 Jessica Utts, 'Appreciating Statistics', *Journal of the American Statistical Association*, 111/516 (2016), 1373–80.

92 Joseph McMoneagle, *Remote Viewing Secrets: A handbook* (Charlottesville, U.S.A: Hampton Roads Publishing Company), 2000.

93 *SD*-I, 'Gods, Monads, and Atoms', 612.

94 *ibid.*

95 '*Das Wesen der Materie* [The Nature of Matter]', speech at Florence, Italy, 1944, from Archiv zur Geschichte der Max-Planck-Gesellschaft, Abt. Va, Rep. 11 Planck, Nr. 1797, in Graham Smetham, *The Grand Designer: Discovering the quantum mind matrix of the universe* (Brighton: Shunyata Press, 2011), 377 n. 299.

96 Eugene Paul Wigner, 'Philosophical Reflections and Syntheses', in Part B/Volume VI of *The Collected Works of Eugene Paul Wigner*, annotated Gérard G. Emch, ed. Jagdish Mehra and Arthur S. Wightman (Berlin, Heidelberg: Springer-Verlag, 1997), 172.

97 For a fuller account of the empirical data, various theories proposed, and experiments devised to test such fundamental concepts as wave~particle, non-locality, and the role of conscious observation in the interpretation of quantum reality, see Edi D. Bilimoria, *The Snake and the Rope*, 33–47.

98 A. Aspect, J. Dalibard, and G. Roger, 'Experimental Test of Bell's Inequalities Using Time-Varying Analyzers', *Physical Review Letters*, 49/25 (1982), 1804–7.

99 J. C. Polkinghorne, *The Quantum World* (London: Penguin Books, 1984), 76–7.

100 Stuart Hameroff and Roger Penrose, 'Orchestrated Objective Reduction of Quantum Coherence in Brain Microtubules: The "Orch OR" Model for Consciousness', in *Toward a Science of Consciousness – The First Tucson Discussions and Debates*, ed. S. R. Hameroff, A. W. Kaszniak, and A. C. Scott (Cambridge, Massachusetts: MIT Press, 1996), 507–40.

101 —— 'Consciousness in the Universe: Review of the "Orch OR" theory', *Physics of Life Reviews*, 11/1 (March 2014), 39–78.

102 Roger Penrose, 'On the Gravitization of Quantum Mechanics 1: Quantum state reduction', *Foundations of Physics*, 44/5 (May 2014), 557–75.

103 D. D. Georgiev, 'Falsifications of Hameroff–Penrose Orch OR Model of Consciousness and Novel Avenues for Development of Quantum Mind Theory', *NeuroQuantology*, 5/1 (2007), 145–74.

104 Laura K. McKemmish, Jeffrey R. Reimers, Ross H. McKenzie, Alan E. Mark, and Noel S. Hush, 'Penrose-Hameroff Orchestrated Objective-Reduction Proposal for Human Consciousness is Not Biologically Feasible', *Physical Review E*, 80/2 (13 August 2009).

105 Jeffrey R. Reimers, Laura K. McKemmish, Ross H. McKenzie, Alan E Mark, and Noel S Hush, 'The Revised Penrose–Hameroff Orchestrated Objective–Reduction Proposal for Human Consciousness is Not Scientifically Justified: Comment on "Consciousness in the Universe: A review of the 'Orch OR' theory" by Hameroff and Penrose', *Physics of Life Reviews*, 11/1 (March 2014), 101–3.

106 Annie Besant and C. W. Leadbeater, *Occult Chemistry: Investigations by clairvoyant magnification into the structure of the atoms of the periodic table and of some compounds*, ed. C. Jinarâjadâsa, assisted by Elizabeth W. Preston (3rd edn, Adyar, Madras: Theosophical Publishing House), 1994.

107 Stephen M. Phillips, *The Mathematical Connection Between Science and Religion* (UK: Anthony Rowe Publishing, 2009). This book of peerless calibre was reviewed by Edi Bilimoria, *Journal of the Scientific and Medical Network*, 122 (2016), 52–3.

108 Sylvia Cranston (compiled and ed.), *Reincarnation: The phoenix fire mystery* (Pasadena, California: Theosophical University Press, 1994). The foreword is by Elisabeth Kübler-Ross MD (1926–2004), the Swiss–American psychiatrist and pioneer in near-death studies.

109 Peter and Elizabeth Fenwick, *Past Lives: An investigation into reincarnation memories* (UK: Headline Book Publishing, 1999).

110 Ian Stevenson, *Reincarnation and Biology: A contribution to the etiology of birthmarks and birth defects – Vol. 1: Birthmarks; Vol. 2: Birth defects and other anomalies* (Westport, Connecticut: Praeger Publishers, 1997). For a short, non-technical version, see Ian Stevenson, *Where Reincarnation and Biology Intersect* (Westport, Connecticut: Praeger Publishers, 1997).

111 —— *Cases of the Reincarnation Type – Vol. I: Ten cases in India, 1975; Vol. II: Ten cases in Sri Lanka, 1978; Vol. III: Twelve cases in Lebanon and Turkey, 1980; Vol. IV: Twelve cases in Thailand and Burma* (Charlottesville, US: University of Virginia Press), 1983.

112 —— *European Cases of the Reincarnation Type* (Jefferson, North Carolina and London: McFarland & Company), 2003.

113 —— *Cases of the Reincarnation Type – Vol. I: Ten cases in India* (Charlottesville, US: University of Virginia Press, 1975).

114   Ian Stevenson, *Children Who Remember Previous Lives: A question of reincarnation* (rev. edn, Jefferson, North Carolina and London: McFarland & Company, 2001).

115   Richard Silberstein, 'Bioelectric Fields: Where biology and reincarnation intersect', Lecture to the *Scientific and Medical Network*, London Group, 7 October 2019.

116   Ian Stevenson, *Children Who Remember Previous Lives*, 2.

117   Arthur Ellison, *The Reality of the Paranormal*, 52–3.

118   W. J. Crawford DSc, *Experiments in Psychical Science: Levitation, contact, and the direct voice* (New York: E. P. Dutton & Co., 1919).

119   —— *The Reality of Psychic Phenomena: Raps, levitations, etc.* (London: John M. Watkins, 1919).

120   One of the best detailed accounts is John G. Fuller, *The Ghost of Flight 401* (London: Corgi Books, 1979). An excellent summary is by E. Lester Smith, *Our Last Adventure* (London: Theosophical Publishing House, 1985), 40–6. Lester Smith was a Fellow of the Royal Society.

121   'Remarks by NASA Deputy Administrator Gregory Centennial of Flight Commemoration' (17 December 2003) <http://www.nasa.gov/audience/formedia/speeches/fg_kitty_hawk_ 12.17.03.html> accessed 15 November 2019.

122   Albert A. Michelson, *Light Waves and their Uses* (Chicago: the University of Chicago Press, 1903). Also quoted in L. Feuer, *Einstein and the Generation of Science* (New York: Basic Books, 1974), 253.

123   Michelson, *op. cit.*, 254.

124   N. B. Karlsson, L. S. Schmidt, and C. S. Hvidberg, 'Volume of Martian Midlatitude Glaciers from Radar Observations and Ice Flow Modeling', *Geophysical Research Letters*, 42/8 (April 2015), 2627–33. See also Nanna Bjørnholt Karlsson, 'Mars has Belts of Glaciers Consisting of Frozen Water', *Niels Bohr Institute* (7 April 2015) <http://www.nbi.ku.dk/english/news/news15/mars-has-belts-of-glaciers-consisting-of-frozen-water> accessed 15 November 2019.

125   *The Guardian*, 28 Sep 2015.

126   Annie Besant and C. W. Leadbeater, *MAN: Whence, how and wither* (Adyar, Madras: Theosophical Publishing House, 1913). Even though Besant co-authored the book, the clairvoyant accounts are principally by Leadbeater.

127   Francis Crick, 'On Protein Synthesis' *Symp. Soc. Exp. Biol.*, xii (1958), 138–63.

128   —— 'Central Dogma of Molecular Biology', *Nature*, 227 (8 August 1970), 561–3.

129   David Moore, *The Developing Genome: An introduction to behavioral epigenetics* (New York: Oxford University Press), 2015.

130   Jaak Panksepp and Lucy Biven, *The Archæology of Mind: Neuroevolutionary origins of human emotions* (New York: W. W. Norton, 2012).

131   Nessa Carey, *The Epigenetic Revolution: How modern biology is rewriting our understanding of genetics, disease and inheritance* (UK: Iconbooks, 2011).

132   Nessa Carey, *Junk DNA: A journey through the dark matter of the genome* (UK: Iconbooks, 2015).

133   Alfred Russel Wallace, 'The Origin of Human Races and the Antiquity of Man Deduced from the Theory of "Natural Selection"', *Journal of the Anthropological Society of London*, 2 (1864), clviii–xxxvii. For a modern version of this famous paper to a meeting of the Anthropological Society of London on 1 March 1864, see 'The Origin of Human Races and the Antiquity of Man Deduced From the Theory of "Natural Selection" (1864)', ed. Charles H. Smith (Alfred Russel Wallace Classic Writings, 2010), Paper 6.

134   Alfred Russel Wallace, *Darwinism: An exposition of the theory of natural selection with some of its applications* (London and New York: Macmillan and Company, 1889), 477.

135   'Chapter One: Belief and Spiritualism', in Charles H. Smith, *Alfred Russel Wallace: Evolution of an evolutionist* (Western Kentucky University, 2003). See also 'The Alfred Russel Wallace Page' <http://people.wku.edu/charles.smith/wallace/chsarw1.htm#top> accessed 15 November 2019.

136   'Hoyle and Wickramasinghe's Analysis of Interstellar Dust', *Cosmic Ancestry* <https://www.panspermia.org/astronmy.htm> accessed 27 December 2019.

137   Fred Hoyle, *The Black Cloud* (London: William Heinemann, 1957).

138   F. Hoyle and C. Wickramasinghe, 'On the Nature of Interstellar Grains', *Astrophysics and Space Science*, 66 (1979), 77–90.

139   Kathrin Altwegg, et al., 'Prebiotic Chemicals—Amino Acid and Phosphorus—in the Coma of Comet 67P/Churyumov–Gerasimenko', *Science Advances*, 2/5 (27 May 2016). See also 'Rosetta's

Comet Contains Ingredients for Life', *European Space Agency* (27 May 2016) <http://www.esa.int/Our_Activities/Space_Science/Rosetta/Rosetta_s_comet_contains_ ingredients_for_life> accessed 15 November 2019.

140 J. S. Greaves, A. M. S. Richards, W. Bains, et al., 'Phosphine Gas in the Cloud Decks of Venus', *Nature Astronomy* (September 2020).

141 Nadia Drake, 'Possible Signs of Life on Venus Stirs up Heated Debate', *National Geographic* (September 2020).

142 There are numerous references to this. Just two examples where the role and interaction of planets, comets, the solar system, and the Milky Way are elucidated are in *SD*-I, 'The Modern Nebular Theory', 593-4 and *CW*-X, 'Transactions of the Blavatsky Lodge', 402.

143 J. S. Gordon, *The Rise and Fall of Atlantis and the Mysterious Origins of Human Civilization* (London: Watkins Publishing, 2008).

144 Werner Heisenberg, 'On the Visualizable Content of Quantum Theoretical Kinematics and Mechanics', *Zeitschrift für Physik* (1927).

145 Philipp Frank, *Einstein: His life and times*' (New York: Alfred A. Knopf, 1947), 342.

146 Albert Einstein, Max Born, and Hedwig Born, *The Born–Einstein Letters: correspondence between Albert Einstein and Max and Hedwig Born from 1916–1955, with commentaries by Max Born* (London: Macmillan, 1971), 91. In a conversation with William Hermanns in 1943, we again find Einstein's exasperation: 'As I have said so many times, God doesn't play dice with the world.'

147 Jack Brown, 'I Visit Professor Einstein', originally published in Ojai Valley News, Ojai, California, 28 September 1983. See the Endnote to the Proem in Volume I for details and reference.

148 'Einstein's "Spooky Action at a Distance" Paradox Older Than Thought', *MIT Technology Review* (8 March 2012) <https://www.technologyreview.com/s/427174/einsteins-spooky-action-at-a- distance-paradox-older-than-thought> accessed 15 November 2015.

149 A. Einstein, B. Podolsky, and N. Rosen, 'Can Quantum–Mechanical Description of Physical Reality be Considered Complete?' *Phys. Rev.* 41 (1935), 777. This is the original EPR paper.

150 Niels Bohr, 'Can Quantum–Mechanical Description of Physical Reality be Considered Complete?' *Phys. Rev.* 48 (1935), 696. This is Niels Bohr's response to the EPR paper.

151 David Bohm, *Quantum Theory* (New York: Dover, 1989). Here Bohm discusses his ideas concerning non-local hidden variables.

152 John Bell, 'On the Einstein Podolsky Rosen Paradox', *Physics*, 1 (1964), 195.

153 John Bell, 'On the Problem of Hidden Variables in Quantum Mechanics', *Reviews of Modern Physics*, 38 (1966), 447–52. This classic paper is reprinted in J. S. Bell, 'Speakable and Unspeakable in Quantum Mechanics', in *Collected Papers on Quantum Philosophy* (Cambridge: Cambridge University Press, 1987; repr. 1989), 1–13.

154 John Clauser and Abner Shimony, 'Bell's Theorem: Experimental tests and implications', *Rep. Prog. Phys.*, 41 (1978), 1881.

155 John Clauser and Stuart Freedman, 'Experimental Test of Local Hidden Variable Theories', *Physical Review Letters*, 28 (1972), 938.

156 Bernard d'Espagnat, 'The Quantum Theory and Reality', *Scientific American* (1979).

157 Alain Aspect, Philippe Grangier, and Gérard Roger: 'Experimental Realization of Einstein-Podolsky-Rosen-Bohm *Gedankenexperiment* (Thought experiment): A new violation of Bell's inequalities', *Phys. Rev. Letters*, 49/91 (12 July 1982), 91–4.

158 Alain Aspect, Jean Dalibard, and Gérard Roger, 'Experimental Test of Bell's Inequalities using Time-Varying Analyzers', *Phys. Rev. Lett.*, 49/25 (20 December 1982), 1804–7.

159 Dean Radin, *Entangled Minds: Extrasensory experiences in a quantum reality* (New York: Simon & Schuster, Paraview Pocket Books), 2006.

160 Albert Einstein and Leopold Infeld, *The Evolution of Physics: The growth of ideas from early concepts to relativity and quanta* (Cambridge: Cambridge University Press, 1971), 152.

161 *SD*-I, 'Gods, Monads, and Atoms', 610.

162 Charlie Dunbar Broad, *Lectures on Psychical Research: Incorporating the Perrott Lectures given in Cambridge University in 1959 and 1960* (New York: Humanities Press, 1962).

163 Alfred Russel Wallace, 'Notes on the Growth of Opinion as to Obscure Psychical Phenomena During the Last Fifty Years (S478: 1893)' <http://people.wku.edu/charles.smith/wallace/S478.htm> accessed 18 November 2019.

164   Leon Petchkovsky, Craig San Roque, and Manita Beskow, 'Jung and the Dreaming: Analytical psychology's encounters with aboriginal culture', *Transcultural Psychiatry* (McGill University, Department of Psychiatry, June 2003).

165   Mark Twain, *Is Shakespeare Dead?* (New York: Harper & Brothers Publishers, 1909). Twain wrote the above in connection with the Shakespeare/Francis Bacon controversy, but his remarks could apply with equal force to the fetishist worship of enshrined scientific ideas.

166   Peter A. Dawkins, *The Shakespeare Enigma: Unravelling the story of the two poets* (UK: Polair Publishing, 2004).

167   Peter A. Dawkins, 'The Shakespeare Enigma' <https://www.peterdawkins.com/articles/pd_shakespeare%20enigma.htm> accessed 15 November 2019.

168   J. R. Smythies (ed.), *Science and ESP* (Routledge Library Editions: History and Philosophy of Science; New York and London: Routledge and Kegan Paul, 1967).

169   Anna Hurwic, *Pierre Curie* (Paris: Flammarion, 1995), 247.

170   Ken Ludden, 'Psychic Skills', in *Mystic Apprentice Master Volume with Dictionary* (US: Lulu, 2012), v, 434. Quoted also in Susan Quinn, *Marie Curie: A life* (New York: Simon and Schuster, 1995). This book was reviewed by Philip Morrison, 'Her Brilliant Career', *New York Times*, 2 April 1995 <https://www.nytimes.com/1995/04/02/books/her-brilliant-career.html> accessed 15 November 2019.

171   K. Blanc, *Pierre Curie: Correspondances* (Paris: Éditions Monelle Hayot, 2009), 643–4. Also cited in R. Evrard, 'Pierre Curie', *Psi Encyclopedia* (London: The Society for Psychical Research) <https://*psi*-encyclopedia.spr.ac.uk/articles/pierre-curie> accessed 18 November 2019.

172   Ken Ludden, 'Psychic Skills', *op. cit.* Quoted also in Sarah Dry, *Curie (Life & Times)* (UK: Haus Publishing, 2003), 69.

173   *ibid.*

174   Carlos Alvarado, *Charles Richet: A Nobel prize winning scientist's exploration of psychic phenomena* (UK: White Crow Books, 2019).

175   Mark Twain, *Is Shakespeare Dead?*

176   Brian Inglis, *The Hidden Power: Science, scepticism and psi* (UK: White Crow Books, 2018).

177   The seven syndromes listed are an elaboration of the review of Brian Inglis's book by David Lorimer in *Journal of the Scientific and Medical Network*, 127 (2018), 64–5.

178   Charles Richet, *Traité de Métapsychique* [Treatise on Metapsychics] (Paris: Librairie Félix Alcan, 1922).

179   —— *Notre Sixième Sens* [Our Sixth Sense] (London: Rider, 1928).

180   Leon Festinger, *A Theory of Cognitive Dissonance* (Stanford, California: Stanford University Press, 1957).

181   John Taylor, *Superminds: An enquiry into the paranormal* (London: Macmillan, 1975).

182   William Brock, 'Was Crookes A Crook?' *Nature*, 367/6462 (1994), 422.

183   Michael Polanyi: *Science, Faith, and Society* (Chicago, Illinois: University of Chicago Press, 2013); *Personal Knowledge: Towards a post-critical philosophy* (Chicago, Illinois: University of Chicago Press, 2015).

184   'The Medawar Lecture 2004: The truth about science', *Philos Trans R Soc Lond B Biol Sci.*, 360/1458 (29 June 2005), 1259–69. See also Peter Medawar, *The Limits of Science* (Oxford: Oxford University Press, 1988).

185   C. E. M. Hansel, *ESP: A scientific evaluation* (New York: Scribner, 1966).

186   James Randi, 'More Geller Woo-Woo', *Swift* (Newsletter) (9 February 2007). See also Adam Higginbotham, 'The Unbelievable Skepticism of the Amazing Randi', *New York Times*, 7 November 2014.

187   Stephen M. Phillips 'Extrasensory Perception of Subatomic Particles: I. Historical Evidence', *Journal of Scientific Exploration*, 9/4 (1995), 489–525.

188   Mikael Stenmark, *Scientism: Science, ethics and religion* (UK: Ashgate Publishing, 2001; repr. Oxford and New York: Routledge, 2018).

189   Paraphrased from The Galileo Commission [https://www.galileocommission.org/] *Newsletter* (April 2020).

190   Huston Smith, *Why Religion Matters: The fate of the human spirit in an age of disbelief* (San Francisco: HarperCollins Publishers, 2001).

191 Arthur S. Reber and James E. Alcock, 'Searching for the Impossible: Parapsychology's elusive quest', *American Psychologist* (13 June 2019).

192 See for example, Robert Todd Carroll, *The Skeptic's Dictionary: A collection of strange beliefs, amusing deceptions, and dangerous delusions* (US and Canada: John Wiley & Sons, 2003).

193 Jessica Utts, 'Appreciating Statistics', *Journal of the American Statistical Association*, 111/516 (2016), 1373–80.

194 —— *art. cit.*

195 David Gorski, 'A University of Michigan Medical School alumnus confronts anthroposophic medicine at his alma mater', *Science-Based Medicine: Exploring issues & controversies in science & medicine* (14 March 2011) <https://sciencebasedmedicine.org/a-university-of-michigan-medical-school-alumnus-confronts-anthroposophic-medicine-at-his-alma-mater> accessed 28 February 2020.

196 Michael Shermer (ed.), *The Skeptic Encyclopedia of Pseudoscience*, 2 vols (ABC-CLIO, 2002).

197 The Concise Oxford Dictionary of Current English (9th edn, ed. Della Thompson, Oxford: Clarendon Press, 1995), 327.

198 Nikola Tesler <https://www.amazon.com/non-physical-phenomena-progress-centuries-existence/dp/B01M3S41OM> accessed 15 November 2019.

199 Quoted in Dr Eben Alexander, *Proof of Heaven: A neurosurgeon's journey into the afterlife* (Great Britain: Piatkus, US: Simon & Schuster, 2012), 1.

200 *Proceedings of the Victoria Institute*, No. 124, p. 267.

201 David Brewster, *A Short Scheme of the True Religion. Manuscript quoted in Memoirs of the Life, Writings and Discoveries of Sir Isaac Newton* (Edinburgh, 1850); See also, 'A short Schem [*sic*] of the True Religion', *The Newton Project*, Keynes MS 7, King's College, Cambridge, UK (published online, February 2002) <http://www.newtonproject.sussex.ac.uk/view/texts/normalized/THEM00007> accessed 1 January 2020.

202 Mary Midgley, *What is Philosophy For?* (London: Bloomsbury 3PL, 2018), 100.

5 Straining Our Eyes to See Beyond – 'Uncomfortable Science'

Here, at Padua, is the principal professor of philosophy, whom I have repeatedly and urgently requested to look at the moon and planets through my glass, [telescope] which he pertinaciously refuses to do.

GALILEO'S LETTER TO JOHANNES KEPLER[1]

The absence of evidence is not evidence of absence.

MARCELO GLEISER, AWARDED THE 2019 TEMPLETON PRIZE[i]

SYNOPSIS

Chapter 5 takes up the theme, set out at the close of the previous Chapter, about the dogma of scientism; then continues with a historical timeline showing the gradual breakdown of materialism. Next, the question is posed whether brains, or other physical mechanisms, are an indispensable necessity for intelligence. This leads on to a catalogue of the fatal flaws in a theory of mind and evolution based exclusively on Darwinism and therefore points towards the need for a broader vision about the universe, life, and consciousness that are not necessarily limited to the physical realm or the five physical senses. This extended science, or what we prefer to call 'enlightened science', is slowly coming to the realization that consciousness is not a fixed thing but has an 'elasticity' rather like a radio receiver that responds to a range of tuning frequencies. Accordingly, the far vistas that come into focus are summarized in terms of the various levels of consciousness, ranging from physical consciousness to that of the group, and finally towards cosmic consciousness. Given that there is the possibility of consciousness extending beyond the physical realm, the final Chapter in the first section of Volume I must serve as a harbinger for the next step.

KEY WORDS: science and scientism, intelligence and brains, Darwinism criticized, post-materialist science, wider scientific paradigm, range of consciousness, matter and consciousness

At this juncture, it is as well for the writer to stress, in no uncertain terms, that he is not in any way anti-science or anti-scholarship—quite the reverse. But he is unequivocally against the blind literalism of the 'Church of Scientism' whose chief codes of belief were outlined at the close of the previous Chapter. Developing this theme, literalists and fundamentalists are not the unique preserve of orthodox religions; they can also be found abundantly in orthodox science. It is this intentionally blind type of prejudice in science which attempts to suffocate, or even obliterate, ideas at birth that it considers

Pro-science—anti-scientism

---

i Marcelo Gleiser (*b.*1959) is currently Professor of Physics and Astronomy at Dartmouth College, a private Ivy League research university in Hanover, New Hampshire, United States. The annual award from the John Templeton Foundation is for an individual 'who has made an exceptional contribution to affirming life's spiritual dimension'.

'alternative' or 'maverick', not on the grounds of a reasoned appraisal of their worth, but purely on the grounds that only highly qualified scientists can understand such matters. Moreover, this authoritarian science holds that even the most qualified individuals pursuing a scientific quest outside mainstream science should be summarily eliminated from the scientific community, or brushed aside as pseudo-scientists. Unsurprisingly, those scientists who have been thus anathematized by the orthodoxy are those who, whilst applauding the worth of materialism in its proper context, do not regard it as the sole and exclusive framework to explain such things as consciousness, paranormal phenomena, and the experience of life at all levels. Furthermore, some of the greatest discoveries in science have come from scientists following a completely different trajectory from the established one, for example, Max Planck who broke away from the rigid confines of classical physics; or from those initially academically unqualified but endowed with a highly intuitive faculty, such as the Russian chemist Dmitri Mendeleev (1834–1907) who developed the periodic classification of the elements and the Indian mathematician Srinivasa Ramanujan (1887–1920) who had practically no formal training in pure mathematics but made pioneering contributions to the subject, which eventually earned him a Fellowship of the Royal Society (see Chapter 9 in Volume III).

The establishment summarily 'burns' all heretics.

But 'heretics' have revolutionalized science

In his address to a symposium on energy in Hanover, the German–American physicist and rocket scientist Dr Rolf Schaffranke (1921–1994),[ii] assistant to the legendary German aerospace engineer and rocket scientist Werner von Braun (1912–1977), spoke of the extreme resistance of the scientific establishment towards new developments in science, always considering them 'unorthodox'. Schauffranke gave the example of the symposium of Nobel Prize winners in Lindau, Bodensee in 1973 where Paul Dirac (1902–1984) stated in his lecture *New Ideas in Space and Time*, 'The basic ideas about space and time are based on Einstein's Theory of Relativity. For the last few decades the physicists have accepted this theory of Space and have included it in their interpretation of all physical phenomena. There are, however, good reasons for the assumption that this should now be changed.'[2]

New developments invariably meet with establishment resistance

And here we should remember that towards the end of his life, on his seventieth birthday in 1949, Einstein wrote to his old Romanian friend, philosopher, and mathematician, Maurice Solovine (1875–1958):

> You imagine that I look back on my life's work with calm satisfaction. But from nearby it looks quite different. There is not a single concept of which I am convinced that it will stand firm, and I feel uncertain whether I am in general on the right track.[3]

Then in his penultimate year in a letter to another old friend, the Italian engineer Michael Besso (1873–1955):

Einstein's humility and self-doubt

> All these fifty years of conscious brooding have brought me no nearer to the answer to the question, 'What are light quanta?' Nowadays every Tom, Dick and Harry thinks he knows it, but he is mistaken.[4]

The humility behind these words speaks for Albert Einstein the man and the scientist declared 'High Priest' by his devotees. But history has taught us that even the best theories will ultimately need to be revised and the successful solution to the pressing scientific

---

ii Schaffranke was the youngest of the group of German scientists, including Werner von Braun, who were spirited out of Germany by American intelligence agents at the close of World War II and brought to the United States in order to advance the fledgling US rocket program. Schaffranke worked for the aerospace industry, and before retirement was on a NASA contract as a consultant to the propulsion laboratories in Huntsville, Alabama.

problems of today cannot therefore be left solely to the custodians of the past but will have to include the visionaries and pioneers of our time, many of whom have been suppressed, as cited above.

Useful lessons from history

Learning the lessons from history, then, the historical basis and genesis of materialism was outlined towards the end of Chapter 3; and Chapter 4 closed with examples of knowledge filtration in establishment science. Ironically, as also explained in Chapter 4, quantum science has undermined scientific materialism. It would therefore be useful to provide a historical timeline showing the developments in science that are slowly but inexorably signalling the breakdown of materialism whilst pointing to the perennial philosophy.

The Breakdown of Materialism – An Historical Timeline

We have furnished ample evidence to make our case for deeper insights into the workings of nature at all levels in order to complement the discoveries of mainstream sciences. But as this evidence comes from such diverse sources as physics and chemistry, psychology and parapsychology, neuroscience and biology, it would be useful to draw these disparate strands together by way of a chronological account of the principal milestones signalling the progressive breakdown of materialism from the nineteenth century to the present day. Accordingly, a historical summary with a timeline is shown in Appendix I-A for the progression of the physical sciences (physics and cosmology); and in Appendix I-B for the life sciences (molecular and developmental biology, evolution, and psychology).

A Paradox – Intelligence Without Brains?

Do we need good brains in order to think like the intelligent human beings we are supposed to be or to 'think like a scientist' as Michael Shermer would have it (see Chapter 2)?

Does Einstein's brain provide a clue to his mathematical abilities?

Having just mentioned Albert Einstein, the top half of Figure I-3 should prove interesting. It shows five views of Einstein's brain preserved in two fruit jars pickled in formaldehyde at the University of Pennsylvania, USA.[5] We are reliably informed by the contemporary Canadian professor of neurosciences Dr Sandra Witelson in the prestigious British medical journal *The Lancet* that a person's thinking capacity is largely explained by physical differences in the brain: that Einstein's brain was 15 per cent wider than average especially in crucial areas responsible for mathematical thought, namely, the inferior parietal lobule.[6] Witelson remarked, 'We held Einstein's brain in our hands and realized that this is the organ that was responsible for changing our perceptions of the universe, and we were in awe.'[7]

Even some mathematics graduates have no dectectable brain

But now switch to the bottom half of Figure I-3 where we find the Hungarian John Lorber (1915–1996), professor of paediatrics at Sheffield University, UK, informing us that some people have 'no detectable brain' (so obviously without any detectable parietal lobule), yet they have intelligence quotients around 120; and some are even *mathematics* graduates. He has identified several hundred people with very small cerebral hemispheres and even knows of one university *mathematics* student having less than one millimetre of cerebral tissue inside his cranium.[8, 9, 10, 11, 12]

Is it being too cynical to suggest that we may rely on science for (in)consistency? It is worth dwelling on this question of intelligence without brains. The Australian born

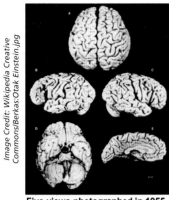

**Five views photographed in 1955
of Einstein's brain kept in two
fruit-preserving jars pickled in
formaldehyde at the University of
Pennsylvania, USA.**

**Dr. Sandra Witelson, neuroscientist of
McMaster University, Canada, reported in the
British medical journal _The Lancet_:**

- **Einstein's brain was wider than normal in
  crucial areas responsible for mathematical
  thought.**

- **Mathematical and spatial thinking
  'strongly dependent' on development of
  inferior parietal lobule.**

- **Person's thinking capacity largely
  explained by _physical differences_ in the
  brain.**

- **Einstein's brain was _15% wider_ than
  average.**

John Lorber, Professor of neurology at the University of Sheffield, UK:

- **A university mathematics student had less than _one millimetre_ of cerebral
  tissue inside his cranium.**

- **Identified several hundred people with very small cerebral hemispheres,
  but normal intelligence.**

- **Some people have '_no detectable brain_' but yet have:**
  - **IQ of 120;**
  - **and some are even _mathematics graduates_.**

Figure I-3   Are Brains Necessary for Intelligence?

research scientist in the fields of molecular biology, early development, and embryology Marilyn Monk (_b_.1939) informs us that the single cell paramecium, or the amoeba, displays remarkable intelligence in finding food and avoiding obstacles in its path without the benefit of a single brain synapse. In fact, most cells will move towards something nourishing and move away from something toxic or poisonous. Even more astonishing, however, is that the slime mould amoeba _Dictyostelium discoideum_ apparently has two levels of existence. Free-living amoebae eat decaying vegetation until the food runs out. The onset of starvation is a signal for the amoebae in a particular territory to aggregate to form a multicellular structure. To do this, specific amoebae pulse out a chemical signal of cyclic adenosine monophosphate ('cAMP'), which diffuses into the surrounding area. Other amoebae within range of the diffusing cAMP respond by making a movement step towards the source amoeba and they also themselves emit a signal of cAMP. Thus, the signal is relayed out in waves as bands of amoebae move in waves. Aggregating amoebae form wonderful spirals that look like galaxies. When all the amoebae have gathered they pile up and the heap falls over and forms a slug. The slug can move centimetres whereas a single amoeba can only move micrometres. So, the purpose of the slug is to move towards the heat and the light, namely, towards the surface of the soil—the organizer tip of the slug being thermotactic (temperature sensitive) and phototactic (responsive to light). Here, with the evaporation of ammonia, the slug transforms into an elegant fruiting body, that is, a head of spores held aloft by a cellulose stalk. During their time in the slug, the amoebae have differentiated into different cell types. A third of the amoebae sacrifice their lives to form the stalk of the fruiting body. From here the spores can be picked up by a passing insect and disseminated to find another feeding ground.[13]

Does Intelligence
always require a
brain?

The purpose of relaying this particular case study is, on the one hand, to applaud the triumph of materialistic science in discovering the intelligent behaviour of amoebae; but on the other hand, to bring to light that such science is completely at a loss to explain the design, source or nature of *inherent* intelligence in such simple cells. From whence comes the slug's senses, such that it can detect changes in temperature and light? According to what organizing plan do the cells differentiate in the specific and targeted manner that they do? Would morphic resonance and organizing fields provide a clue? If so, we have to look far beyond just physical mechanisms to discover how single cells seemingly display intelligence without brains. In fact, so-called simple cells are highly complex: so much so that according to the British consultant psychiatrist, doctor, writer, and former Oxford literary scholar Iain McGilchrist (*b.*1953), 'it has not been possible so far to model even a single cell, so complex is it [let alone a brain].'14

Science cannot explain inherent *intelligence— even in an amoeba*

But if scientists know all about the minute chemical ingredients and combinations of genes, chromosomes, etc., then why is it that a molecular biologist cannot assemble precise amounts of these building blocks to manufacture even an amoeba, let alone a midget or a monkey (let alone a man)? *What are the unseen factors and subtle influences that stand over and above physical biochemistry?*

But Not Really a Paradox

This intelligence-with-no-brains conundrum only exists if we unquestioningly accept the erroneous conclusion, based on the false assumption of a materialistic neuroscience, that intelligence and consciousness are solely physical functions of brain electrochemistry. However, the intelligence of an amoeba lacking a brain has just been demonstrated. The answer therefore lies in turning towards the perennial wisdom whereupon the paradox simply evaporates, because, in fact, there is no paradox other than what the intellect has fabricated for itself, and then makes itself miserable in trying to solve!

The philosophia perennis *resolves scientific paradoxes*

This wisdom demonstrates that there is no micro-particle in the universe that is not imbued with life and consciousness at its own level, as we shall show later.

Darwin's Dangerous Idea – Man from Ape: Really?

It is tantamount to blasphemy to dare to question Darwin's theories upon which mainstream science bases its dictate on human evolution, as summarized at the close of Chapter 3. Nonetheless, we are particularly uncomfortable about the following conundrums in evolutionary theory that mainstream science seems unable to answer satisfactorily without recourse to the *philosophia perennis*:

1   Natural science is centrally committed to discovering the physical mechanisms that drive the evolutionary process. But who are the 'Mechanicians' behind the mechanisms and the mechanics?

2   Scientific materialism speaks of 'chance' and 'accident' (sometimes in the guise of statistical improbabilities)—but great scientists of all ages like Newton, Einstein, Schrödinger, Pauli, Jeans, and Eddington have sensed Deity immanent and

transcendent, from the standpoint of deism or theism. Why is this, and what was their evidence?

3 Other than by blind chance or accident, purpose must come before function: science cannot account for purpose or cause. But why? Other than its philosophy of causal closure (see Chapter 3) why does natural science take scant, if any, cognizance of the interaction and interrelatedness of Aristotle's four causes needed to explain changes in the world: causes that are material—that out of which things are made; formal—the form or arrangement that makes a thing one particular thing rather than a different thing; efficient—the source of the change that made something happen; and final—that for the sake of which a thing is done, the purpose-driven goal towards which it directs?

4 Nucleic acids—DNA and RNA—are the principal substances of heredity. But WHY? What is so special about a couple of acids over and above other chemical compounds?

5 Granted that organisms and environment are reciprocally interacting, i.e., influences go both ways, however, when species become adapted to new environments, who is the adaptor; in other words, who is doing the adapting? Can Gaia (the Earth) itself be regarded as an organism with self-regulatory functions as postulated by the British scientist and environmentalist, James Lovelock?

6 If there is periodicity to mass extinctions, then what does this imply?

7 If biological mechanisms are just complicated machines, then can a machine regenerate, repair, and procreate itself?

8 Natural selection is a gradual process. How does it, along with molecular biology, account for the sudden appearance of geniuses born into families possessing no especial intellectual or artistic aptitude?

Darwinism cannot explain many crucial evolutionary features plus the enormous antiquity of man

9 If humans differs from the apes by one or two percent in their genetic units, then why do we find:
   i   such vast differences between the mentality of the 'brightest ape' and the dullest human;
   ii   such a collosal range of intelligence in humans only;
   iii but no comparable intelligence range in apes?

10 Does similarity of genetic constitution automatically imply similarity of mind?

11 If the genetic similarity between apes and humans supposedly demonstrates that the latter evolved from apes, is it absurd to suggest, on logical grounds, that apes could have been produced by a degenerative evolution from humans?

12 Why does natural science choose to ignore the weighty evidence from books like *Forbidden Archeology – The Hidden History of the Human Race*,[15] *Shattering the Myths of Darwinism*,[16] *Creative Evolution*,[17] and *Mind and Cosmos: Why the materialist Neo-Darwinian conception of nature is almost certainly false*[18] that seriously expose the flaws in the neo-Darwinian theory of evolution, for example, Darwin's idea of gradual change repudiated by the absence of transitional fossils?

13. The book *Forbidden Archeology* (fully discussed in Volume III, Chapter 10), is especially helpful in that it contains an immense database of artifacts and, fossil evidence. These historical records reveal that:

 i Human history can be pushed back to several millions of years when humans coexisted with primates.

 ii The orthodox evolutionary model has been built up on the shifting base of academic opinion and highly selective sampling of evidence, whereas anomalous hard evidence has simply been filtered out and trashed.

 iii Circular procedures are used to date rocks and fossils.

 iv Darwin's theory of 'man from ape' lacks any proof of a transitional species, the so-called evolutionary 'missing links'—the, as yet, indefinable sequence, or stage, that links different species.

Concerning the last item, Darwin avoided this problem by concentrating on objective changes within a single species or subspecies. In this limited sense Darwin was on the right track. The esoteric reason for the lack of evidence of a missing link is that intra-species transitions (i.e., within the same species) occur on both the subjective and objective side of nature, hence the physical evidence can be discovered. However, inter-species and inter-kingdom evolutionary transitions take place always within the subjective side of Nature; hence there is no material form, like a fossil or skeleton to provide objective, tangible evidence of a transitional link.

The 'missing link' is a perpetual thorn in Darwinian theory

The term *subjective* when applied to the human being means that which belongs to, and proceeds from, the individual consciousness or perception; hence entirely within the sphere of mind. By contrast, the term *objective* means 'existing external to the mind', hence not coloured by ideas, or perceptions. As an individual has a mind and memory giving rise to his habits, so also there is the collective mind and memory of Nature giving rise to the habits of nature as described by Sheldrake in *The Presence of the Past*.[19] By analogy then, when an individual decides to effect a change in his life (say, to move house) there is no external and physical transitional evidence of his mental decisions; so also there is no physical transitional evidence of the workings of the 'mind of Nature', only its objective manifestations.

Our conclusion is obviously that the existing, mainstream evolutionary model cannot be adapted or modified, but must be jettisoned entirely and replaced by a radical new model without preconceptions and with consciousness as its underlying premise. This is indeed a bold claim and is fully defended in Chapter 10 of Volume III, by which stage the inner and invisible (occult) governing laws and processes in Nature and man will have been expounded in detail.

Philosophical Postulates for a Broader Vision

We need an integral paradigm of science, embracing both subjective and objective aspects of man and cosmos

Our narrative continues with a prelude to the affirmations of occult science that are presented later in Chapter 8. We have shown, at some length, the limitations and deficiencies in the modern scientific picture of our world and ourselves. This discomfort with the establishment viewpoint, especially concerning mind and consciousness, has led avant-garde science to embrace a wider and deeper perspective. Whilst fully acknowledging the contributions of mechanistic theories and associated experimental research, a more complete and open paradigm is necessitated, as suggested in the logical sequence of seven viewpoints below:

1. The universe is a multi-dimensional, multi-levelled, organic and living entity;
   … consequently…
2. displays innate intelligence, order and purpose;
   … therefore …
3. why limit knowledge and experience to the physical realm or just the five senses;
   … so also …
4. consciousness need not be restricted to physical matter alone or solely to the brain;
   … in which case …
5. consciousness may survive the death of the brain;
   … what is more …
6. consciousness may even be fundamental rather than a by-product of material inter-actions;
   … and in fact …
7. consciousness may be unqualified and unconditioned and could display a spectrum of states with matter as its effect, rather than its cause.

Postulating transcendence (divine existence), not outright rejection of materialism

The chief insights for science, and associated benefits to humanity, accruing from this broader and deeper perspective regarding consciousness are that:

1. Consciousness and mind may represent the primordial aspect of reality, hence cannot be a derivative or epiphenomenon of matter or reduced to anything more elementary.

2. Mind being apparently unbounded, there may be a unity of minds implying a unitary One Mind which subsumes all individual minds.

3. There may be subtle connections between minds, and between minds and the physical world.

4. The brain may act as the transceiver and transducer of consciousness, meaning that mental functions use the brain as an instrument rather than a generator, or producer of thought. This assertion is, in fact, supported by a vast array of mounting evidence from OBEs and NDEs as typically occurring in cardiac arrest and accidents, plus scientific research into mediums, to suggest that consciousness survives bodily death.

Subtle interconnections exist at deeper levels of reality

5. The clear implication, therefore, is of other levels of reality that are non-physical for which non-physical, or subtle, bodies are the appropriate vehicle of expression of consciousness.

6. Focussed concentrated mind, applied as will or intention, may influence the individual mind and other minds, physical matter, and the state of the physical world operating in a non-local sense, that is, not confined to specific spatial locations (such as brains or bodies) nor to specific moments in time (like the present).

7. Given the non-local operation of mind, the expectations (along with the personal emotions, conditioning, and prejudices) of a scientific experimenter may never be

completely isolated from the experimental result, even in controlled, double-blind experiments.

The Present World Situation

Peer pressure and the existing politics of knowledge are still powerful factors impeding open-minded enquiry and scientific progress (refer to the close of Chapter 4 about knowledge filtration). Nonetheless, in consideration of the above postulates for a broader vision, there is no reason for scientists to shirk from open and rigorous research of spirituality and non-physical approaches to consciousness for fear of ridicule from colleagues that such investigations are not scientific or are pseudoscience, or else anti-science in motive: indeed, spiritual experiences represent the core of human life. For it has repeatedly been stressed that an enlarged science embraces and includes, but is not restricted to, a mechanistic science based on the properties of physical matter and applauds the scientific achievements that have resulted from empirical observations. However, by not restricting itself just to matter and physical mechanisms, there will ensue a deeper appreciation and expanded capacity to understand the finer and inner workings of nature and man, as well as a recovery of the pre-eminence of spirit and mind in the unfoldment and expression of the universe. When this happens, the logical outcome will be enhanced awareness and sensitivity towards our environment and increased human dignity by virtue of compassion and respect between ourselves, towards all beings and our whole planet. Let us remember that this expanded view of universe, nature, and man always was the bedrock of the *philosophia perennis*, alchemical practices, body-mind-spirit traditions, and the esotericism of both East and West: it has just been virtually forgotten during the past four hundred years or so and sorely needs to be recovered and restored to its rightful place. Even so, this vision of man understanding the workings of nature, spirit, and mind behind the expression of the universe, leading to sensitivity towards the environment, has always been so. However, at the moment humanity still seems to be working on the physical and objective level. This is because the sensitivity of the average person about the environment only seems to heighten as a result of fear of what might happen if the trajectory of economic growth, combined with environmental degradation, continues its present course unabated. With each natural disaster that fear arises and compounds. There is now a panic to do something about it. Unfortunately, however, 'fire fighting' without the enlightenment of the *philosophia perennis* seldom produces a long-lasting and positive outcome. The aftermath of the COVID-19 pandemic in 2020 may, unfortunately, prove the point that the ubiquitous saying 'business as normal' may no longer be the norm.

An enlarged science embraces both spirit and matter

Scientists should find the courage to research spirituality without fear of ridicule

Signs of Optimism – Post-Materialist Platforms for Science and Consciousness

Despite the current predominance of the machine paradigm, there are encouraging signs ahead. We mention four international initiatives, in chronological order, towards a post-materialist paradigm. The insights and information contained in these interrelated sources have provided the writer with much inspiration upon which to base the arguments in the preceding sections.

The first post-materialist initiative is the group work undertaken by the Esoteric Section of the worldwide Scientific and Medical Network (in which the writer participated and was one of the signatories), which culminated in a Manifesto arguing the case for an integral science of consciousness, as opposed to consciousness as a subject within mainstream science. This Manifesto opens by summarizing the paradoxical impasse of modern science and then moves on to highlight key philosophical assumptions that are prevalent in mainstream science. Thereafter, in connection with the cultural time-lag between avant-garde and orthodox science, the ontology and epistemology of the materialist stance is discussed as related to consciousness. In this regard, it is asserted that consciousness is fundamental to existence and the alleged primacy of matter is considered to be a grave and culturally conditioned fallacy. And from this emerges a new framework that transcends, yet includes, the presuppositions of modern science. The Manifesto concludes with the recognition that the 'oneness of life and consciousness has profound ethical implications that lead naturally to the formulation and application of a global ethic'.[20]

Insights from the Esoteric section of the Scientific and Medical Network

The second one is the Manifesto formulated by a group of internationally acclaimed scientists from a variety of scientific fields—biology, medicine, neuroscience, psychology, and psychiatry—who participated in an international summit on post-materialist science, spirituality, and society. The summit was held at Canyon Ranch in Tucson, Arizona in 2014 with the express purpose of discussing the impact of the materialist ideology on science, and the emergence of a post-materialist paradigm for science, spirituality, and society.[21] A key conclusion of the ensuing *Manifesto for a Post-Materialist Science* was that 'the shift from materialist science to post-materialist science may be of vital importance to the evolution of the human civilization. It may be even more pivotal [in its implications] than the transition from geocentricism to heliocentrism.'[22] The Manifesto concludes with this appeal:

Appeal by international scientists for a post-materialist paradigm

> We invite you, scientists of the world, to read the Manifesto for a Post-Materialist Science and sign it, if you wish to show your support.[iii]
> (see http://opensciences.org/about/manifesto-for-a-post-materialist-science.)

The third initiative comprises a seminal paper by the psychologist Etzel Cardeña submitted to the journal *Frontiers in Neuroscience*. It includes some one hundred co-signatories from internationally acclaimed scientists arguing for an informed study of all aspects of consciousness, but without preconceptions. The article reminds us that 'science thrives when there is an open, informed discussion of all evidence, and recognition that all scientific knowledge is provisional and subject to revision. This attitude is in stark contrast with reaching conclusions based solely on a previous set of beliefs or on the assertions of authority figures.'[23] Whereas some areas of consciousness, such as psychological dissociation, hypnosis, and preconscious cognition, are now well integrated into mainstream science, this has not generally been the case with research on phenomena such as purported telepathy or precognition, which some scientists dismiss a priori as pseudo-science or illegitimate.[24]

Internationally acclaimed scientists urge frank discussions and willingness to reassess the spirit of science

---

iii Manifesto authors were: Mario Beauregard, PhD, Neuroscience of Consciousness; Larry Dossey, MD, Internal Medicine; Lisa Jane Miller, PhD, Clinical Psychology; Alexander Moreira-Almeida, MD, PhD, Psychiatry; Marilyn Schlitz, PhD, Social Anthropology; Gary Schwartz, PhD, Psychology, Neurology, Psychiatry, and Surgery; Rupert Sheldrake, PhD, Biochemistry, Developmental Biology, Consciousness Studies; Charles T. Tart, PhD, Transpersonal Psychology.

As stated in the aforementioned journal, a good example of such 'pseudoscience' that has persisted for over a century is research on parapsychological phenomena (*psi*). Despite the taboo against investigating this topic, combined with virtually no funding, and professional and personal attacks against the scientists, *psi* research is being carried out in various accredited universities and research centres throughout the world by academics in different disciplines trained in the scientific method—for example, around eighty doctorates have been awarded in *psi*-related topics in the UK in recent years.[25] What is more, over twenty Nobel laureates, plus many other eminent scientists, have supported the study of *psi* or even conducted such research themselves.[26]

We referred earlier to the manner in which 'extraordinary claims require extraordinary evidence' is used as a prophylactic to reject anomalous evidence that does not fit the prevailing paradigm of the scientist concerned. We also gave many instances where initially weak evidence, or an extraordinary claim (such as heavier-than-air flying machines), later proved to be an incontestable fact. Etzel Cardeña and his co-signatories dismiss this platitude, citing the paper by the Danish sociologist Marcello Truzzi (1935–2003) which points out that the original intention of the phrase is typically misunderstood.[27] Also referenced in connection with Truzzi's article is the paper by the contemporary Italian cognitive and clinical psychologist Patrizio Tressoldi who, starting from the phrase 'extraordinary claims require extraordinary evidence', presents the evidence supporting the concept that human visual perception may have non-local properties (i.e., that it may operate beyond the space and time constraints of sensory organs), in order to discuss which criteria can be used to define evidence as extraordinary.[28] Cardeña, et al. further declare that 'even in its inaccurate interpretation what counts as an "exceptional claim" is far from clear.' They cite phenomena such as the existence of meteorites, the germ theory of disease, and more recently, adult neurogenesis,[iv] all of which were originally considered so exceptional that evidence for their existence was ignored or dismissed, by the scientists of the time, but are now accepted in mainstream science. Furthermore, they maintain that 'it is far from clear what would count as "exceptional evidence" or who would set that threshold. Dismissing empirical observations as a priori, based solely on biases or theoretical assumptions, underlies a distrust of the ability of the scientific process to discuss and evaluate evidence on its own merits'.

The fourth initiative is arguably among the finest. The epigraph to Chapter 2, and this Chapter, are of seminal importance. Both are quotes from letters written by Galileo to Kepler where Galileo complains that the learned men of science prefer to adhere to preconceptions rather than face evidence. In particular, Galileo cites the case of the principal professor of philosophy at Padua who laboured before the Grand Duke with logical arguments based on Aristotle (a classic case of the 'map ruling the territory'). He adds that Aristotle himself, as an empiricist, would surely have changed his mind on the basis of new evidence if he had had the opportunity of observing the moon and planets as Galileo did through his telescope.

Appropriately, then, the Galileo Commission is a recent project of the Scientific and Medical Network, one of whose principal aims is to challenge the adequacy of the philosophy of scientific materialism (scientism) as an exclusive basis for knowledge and values.

---

iv Neurogenesis is the process of generating new neurons which integrate into existing circuits after foetal and early postnatal development has ceased.

Scientists cite examples to illustrate the vagueness of 'extraordinary claims', 'extraordinary evidence', and 'exceptional claims'

The Galileo Commission invites scientists to look beyond preconceived ideas towards new evidence

The Galileo Commission is represented by a distinguished group of some one hundred scientific advisers affiliated to more than thirty universities worldwide. Many of these advisers were active contributors (including the writer) during the consultation process leading up to the publication of the Galileo Commission Report written by Professor Harald Walach (*b*.1957), a German researcher at the interface between medicine, psychology, and consciousness studies holding a double PhD in Clinical Psychology, and History and Theory of Science.[29, 30]

The Galileo Commission Report argues that this refusal to 'look through the telescope' has striking parallels today. In the seventeenth century, the infallibility of Scripture and Aristotle's doctrines were at stake; nowadays it is the infallibility of scientific materialism. For example, many scientists and academics are reluctant to take seriously the research evidence for consciousness beyond the brain because they have an unshakeable belief that consciousness is generated *in and by* the brain. The Galileo Commission Report is thus an invitation to scientists and academics to look dispassionately at such research evidence that is currently ignored or dismissed because it is philosophically incompatible with materialism.[31]

Striking parallels between scriptural dogma and scientism

The purpose of the Galileo Commission Report is to open up public discourse and to find ways to expand the presuppositions of science so that science: (*a*) is not constrained by an outdated view of the nature of reality and consciousness; and (*b*) is better able to accommodate and explore significant human experiences and questions that it is currently unable to accommodate for philosophical reasons. It anticipates that expanding science will involve: (*a*) new basic assumptions (an expanded ontology); (*b*) additional ways of knowing and new rules of evidence (an expanded epistemology); and (*c*) new methodologies flowing from these.

The Galileo Commission seeks to expand science and raise it to a higher metaphysic

The world today is dominated by science and its underlying assumptions. Yet these are seldom articulated even though they generate not only a methodology but also a particular worldview, an ideology generally known as 'scientism'. The Commission fully supports scientific methodology that is underpinned by a set of evolving rules, socially negotiated among scientists, but it is highly critical of scientism—of assumptions maintained by refusing to look through the telescope. Critical but open-minded readers are invited to do so.

Within an expanded science, existing 'hard' science would still be valid in the contexts where it was generated. Many areas of research could still be profitably undertaken within existing materialist assumptions. But if science, in its wider context, could be based on an expanded set of assumptions, and if they came to form the dominant philosophy of science, then that would open up new avenues and new possibilities. In other words, expanding science and its scope would transform the current worldview constrained by materialism.

In conclusion, enough has been said to provide reasonable grounds for doubting the supremacy of scientific materialism (not undervaluing its contribution within its legitimate context). We continue, appropriately, with unpacking what we mean by consciousness, a term that has so far been used in a general sense.

Consciousness – An Elastic Term

At this juncture, however, it is worth probing more deeply into the meaning behind that commonplace but disarmingly complex and elusive term 'consciousness'. Here a major obstacle is encountered: consciousness is an elastic term with a spectrum of meanings dependent on the context and the individual.

Consciousness is a phenomenon, not an object.ᵛ So it cannot be 'put into a box' with a label and rigidly defined, any more than can qualities such as love, generosity, kindness, cruelty, etc., which are not objective things, but are all concerned with our subjective experience. However, we may approach the essential meaning by understanding the genesis and evolution of the term. Upon a perusal of what follows, readers are urged to enquire whether consciousness—a subject that has engrossed the deepest minds since time immemorial—is an epiphenomenon (by-product) of brain mechanisms as the vast majority of scientists would claim, or whether it is something immensely more subtle and elusive that engages the very kernel of our being.

A phenomenon cannot be objectivized any more than a rainbow can be put into a box

The Idea of Consciousness – Etymology and Historical Perspective

'Consciousness' is absolutely central to Eastern (particularly Asiatic) philosophy and thought, and is expressed in the Sanskrit tongue in all its subtlety and fine shades of meaning. However, we will deal with its genesis in the West. The first reference to the adjective 'conscious' appeared in *circa* 1600 meaning 'knowing, privy to' from the Latin *conscius* 'knowing, aware', the latter derived from *conscire* meaning literally 'knowing with', or 'being mutually aware'; it is a compound verb derived from the prefix *con-* 'with, together' and *scīre* '(to) know' (source of the English 'science'). In 1689, the philosopher and influential Enlightenment thinker John Locke FRS (1632–1704) gave it the modern meaning of being 'inwardly aware', or 'sensible' using the phrase: 'If they say, that a Man is always conscious to himself of thinking; I ask, how they know it?' Locke then answered his own question with, 'Consciousness is the perception of what passes in a Man's own mind. Can another Man perceive, that I am conscious of any thing, when I perceive it not my self? No Man's Knowledge here, can go beyond his Experience.'³² In fact, the noun 'consciousness' first appeared in the 1630s meaning 'internal knowledge' and, from 1746, it was defined as a 'state of being aware'.

Consciousness is subjective

In 1805, the Oxford English Dictionary identified the usage of the phrase 'a state of consciousness or states of consciousness'; and in 1837 the conceptual use of the word 'consciousness' had progressed to 'the totality of the impressions, thoughts and feelings which make up a person's conscious being.' In 1863 we move towards the more modern usage when the word 'conscious' was defined in the Oxford English Dictionary as 'having an internal perception of consciousness'. The term 'consciousness raising' was first introduced in 1971.

Modern Usage

Scientists, psychologists, and consciousness researchers with a visionary and transpersonal outlook, like the American engineer and author associated with the human potential movement Willis Harman (1918–1997), use 'the word "consciousness" to connote the totality of conscious and potentially conscious states of mind, not in the limited sense of "conscious awareness" only [but also] meant to include awareness, creative, and volitional

---

v A simplistic example of the distinction between objects and phenomena is the rainbow. Each individual water droplet is an object that can be put into a box. But a rainbow is a phenomenon of the interplay of light and water: it cannot be thus confined.

aspects of mind, amongst others.'[33] This designation imparts a much wider, universal meaning to the word, not limited just to the individual person. The American psychologist and parapsychologist Charles Tart (*b.*1937) and others have coined the phrase 'altered states of consciousness' (aptly termed) to distinguish and differentiate such states from 'normal, everyday consciousness'.[34] These altered states can be attained by means of physical stimulants (like abnormal breathing practices and psychedelic drugs) or purely mental techniques as in the yogic traditions.

Consciousness is universal—not just individual

Increasingly nowadays, we find phrases with a self-reflexive content such as 'to become fully conscious entails being conscious of being conscious'. There is also the recognition that a fully conscious person is one who is aware of, is inwardly sensible to, and has the perception of their own internal reality of existence, of their emotions and thoughts, as well as the observation, feeling, and perception of the external reality of objects, other people and conditions. Accordingly, a state of consciousness is characterized by both: (*a*) the nature, and (*b*) the level of its awareness. Such awareness can be either general (a sort of overall, bird's-eye perspective) or an awareness focussed partly, or wholly, down to a centre, or point of attention. It is a common experience that the more focussed one is to the centre of attention, the more one is absorbed and therefore less aware of external peripheral activities and distractions. (This ability of complete absorption in the subject in question induces the state of inspiration and is the means whereby men of distinction have attained to genius. The secret lies in holding the ego in abeyance. Modern life with its ego-appeasing distractions, glamorous diversions, and idiotic electronic frivolities makes such a condition of internal quietude difficult to attain without strenuous effort and will power.)

The Spectrum of Consciousness

From the above, it should become apparent that the chief problems in understanding the meaning of the term 'consciousness', and therefore in relation to consciousness studies, are due to a general lack of understanding and appreciation of the diversity of consciousness, namely, the various levels of consciousness and their medium of expression for manifestation at each level—see Figure I-4. For this reason, the whole field of consciousness can, for analytical and explanatory purposes, be stratified into three broad, but highly overlapping 'wavebands' analogous to the three primary colours of the spectrum of light as now described. We stress that we are not in any way delving into the various topics from cognitive science to meditation. Our purpose is to outline the 'elasticity' of consciousness which spans the complete spectrum from the physical brain-only state to the non-physical realms beyond-the-brain.

Analogy between consciousness and light

Physical Consciousness

The basic level of consciousness is physical brain consciousness. By analogy, it can be likened to a radio or television receiver that is switched on with the electric power and internal circuits functioning, but not tuned, to a particular frequency, therefore not receiving any signals from the source carrier wave. Otherwise stated, all the flow of consciousness is internal. The physical consciousness, therefore, necessarily demands physical and materialistic approaches to enquiry and investigation—and quite rightly so, for we have previously emphasized, and need to do so again, that we have no quarrel with scientific materialism

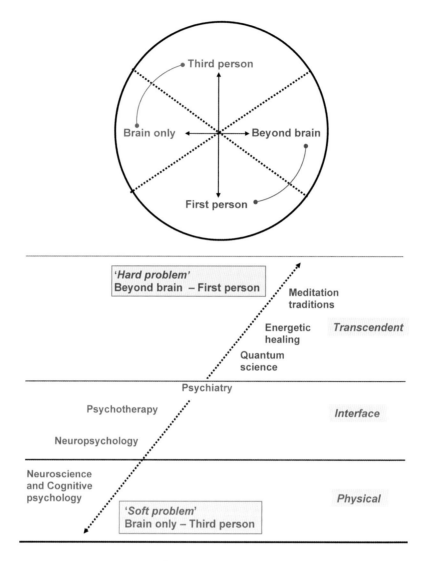

Figure I-4   The Spectrum of Consciousness

within its own limits, only when the materialistic paradigm is applied outside its legitimate context as the exclusive basis for understanding all realms of existence.

In this context then, what is popularly known as 'the unconscious' is the reservoir of feelings, thoughts, urges and memories that lie outside of our conscious awareness. This concept is often likened to an iceberg where everything above water, the 'tip of the iceberg', represents conscious awareness, while everything below water represents the unconscious. According to Freud, the unconscious continues to influence our behaviour and experience, even though we are unaware of these underlying influences. The unconscious may also be regarded as comprising those autonomous processes constantly in operation (even during sleep) concerned with the functioning and maintenance of the physical brain and therefore not under the direct control of the individual.

The 'soft problem' of consciousness is the normal waking state

Referring to Figure I-4 then, this 'brain-only consciousness' represents the third person perspective, consciousness being regarded as something that can be examined objectively in detachment from the self. It has been termed the 'soft', or 'easy problem' of consciousness by the philosopher David Chalmers since it is amenable to investigation by physical science, principally the standard methods of cognitive science, whereby a phenomenon is explained in terms of computational and neural mechanisms, which include the following:

- ability to discriminate, categorize, and react to environmental stimuli;

- integration of information by a cognitive system;

- reportability of mental states;

- ability of a system to access its own internal states;

- focus of attention;

- deliberate control of behaviour;

- difference between wakefulness and sleep.[35, 36]

Physical, 'brain only', consciousness is amenable to scientific investigation

Technically, the 'hard end' problem, or 'hard problem' is, 'How does the brain generate consciousness?' which, of course, presupposes that it does so in the first place. Nevertheless, hard problems are, by definition, those that seem to resist cognitive science, hence justifying the need to look beyond merely physical explanations and neural correlates.

'Hard problem' eludes scientific investigation

Reverting to the 'soft problem', or 'physical consciousness', this is the normal waking state of consciousness whereby an individual has a fairly clear consciousness of self, but invariably coloured and distorted by emotions and by internal and external stimuli. In this mode, an individual continually evaluates the input from sensory data, acquired from both the external environment and internal perceptual processes, and builds up his own unique model of reality upon which all his conscious decisions, volitions, and judgements are based. With no stimulus there is a clean 'circuit of consciousness' within the individual; however, the onset of any appropriate stimulus—whether external or internally generated by perception or imagination—may cause the emergence of any one of numerous psychological states that distort the original base-line consciousness. It is as though a variable distorting filter has been inserted into the circuitry of a radio set and the diversion of the operating 'current of consciousness' results in the individual experiencing a skewed version of reality, which is taken to be the one and only version of reality. The occurrence, intensity, and distribution of any number of such psychologically distorting states of consciousness will vary in individuals and also in groups, depending upon such distorting factors as propaganda, peer group pressure, advertising, manipulation by family and friends, and even the time and nature of the environment. The old adage 'Man, Know Thyself' is therefore never more appropriate, as we said right at the start in the Proem.

Physical consciousness in individual susceptible to internal and external stimuli

It may be worth revisiting the section in Chapter 3 which summarizes the 'soft' and 'hard' problems of consciousness in relation to the various versions of physicalism. Additionally, Endnote I-7 gives cursory details about some of the multi-disciplinary subjects and investigative methods that are encompassed by cognitive science.

Lower Consciousness

The next level of consciousness is the interface between the physical and the non-physical consciousness and so partakes of the nature of both. It corresponds to the waveband of, for want of a better term in English, the 'Lower consciousness' or the 'Lower mind', which acts, to continue our simile, as a tuner. In response to thoughts or trains of thoughts as

'Lower
consciousness'
pertains to the
mortal personality

packets of information, the Lower Consciousness tunes in so as to access external infor-
mation at a relatively low frequency, so to speak. Still continuing the simile, the Lower
Mind has four pre-programmed, or 'push-button' frequencies, namely, the Lower
Quaternary—the function of which will be explained in detail in Volume II.

At this stage however, suffice it to say that the Lower Quaternary encompasses the physical
body and three lower subtle bodies comprising the mortal personality of man. The lower
subtle bodies have their corresponding lower centres of consciousness, otherwise known
by the Sanskrit term *cākras*, pronounced chakras[vi] meaning a wheel, thus signifying a force-
centre. However, other than the terse description given in Chapter 9 of Volume III, the
subject of cākras will not be pursued further due to its inherent difficulties and immense
dangers. Such matters are best left to the instruction of those who are spiritually highly
advanced and know how to control latent forces that may well be evoked in the mind.

Higher Consciousness

'Higher
consciousness'
pertains to the
immortal
Individuality

The higher levels of consciousness correspond to the waveband of the 'Higher
Consciousness', or 'Higher Mind', acting as a tuner to access information at a higher
frequency level. To continue with the radio set analogy, the Higher Mind has three pre-
programmed, or 'push-button' frequencies, namely the Upper Triplicity, which encompasses the three higher subtle bodies comprising the immortal individuality of man (also
explained fully in Volume II). The higher subtle bodies have their corresponding higher
centres of consciousness (cākras), but for the same reasons as stated above, it serves no
purpose to describe their exact location, function, and manner of arousal.

A Spectrum of Consciousness

Consciousness is
homogeneous—
its expression is
heterogeneous

Viewed as a whole, the physical body and six subtle bodies (three lower and three higher),
and their corresponding centres of consciousness, form what may be described as a spectrum
of consciousness of 'ascending frequencies'. It cannot be emphasized too strongly that there
is no question of seven separate consciousnesses in impermeable frequency bands. There is
but ONE consciousness as continuum through all levels presenting different aspects, like overtones, of itself ranging from the lowest to the highest, rather like ice, water, and steam are
different phase states of the one H_2O at different conditions of pressure and temperature.

Mind and Brain

We have used the term 'mind' above. Like consciousness, this elusive term cannot be
pinned down to a rigid definition. Arguably, the most succinct meaning ascribed to mind
(again using the radio set analogy) comes from the American anaesthesiologist and
professor at the University of Arizona known for his studies of consciousness, Stuart
Hameroff (*b.*1947): '"a tuner" attuned to the ripples of space–time'.[37] We might add
'[…] ripples of space–time not limited to just the physical dimension'. In short, consciousness (like the carrier wave broadcast to the radio set) needs an instrument to 'flow through',
that is, to manifest and express itself. *Mind is the instrument of consciousness.*

---

vi The 'ch' pronounced as in the English 'chair', and not as in the French 'chateau'.

The next step 'downwards' towards the externalized expression of consciousness in phys-ical matter is of course the brain. *Brain is the instrument of the mind.*

Distinguishing mind from brain

The triple relation and interconnection between consciousness→mind→brain will shortly be clarified in the summary to this Chapter. Before that, we must consider the fact of group consciousness in animals and man.

Group Consciousness – Group Mind and Individuation

When we consider the high degree of organization involved in the construction of beehives or ant hills, the obvious deduction is some form of overshadowing consciousness, or group mind, that directs the process. Another familiar example is the beautifully co-ordinated flight patterns of a flock of birds, like geese or starlings, during their migration, where we are again led to infer that a group mind controls the flock and that the individual birds must be in some sort of telepathic communication with the former. The sophisti-cated aerobatics of hundreds of starlings in perfect co-ordination would certainly be a nightmare to explain in terms of reductionist theory. Promising scientific explanations come from complexity theory.[38] In the terms of developmental biology, this group consciousness would arguably bear some relation to the morphogenetic field.

Group mind discernible in the natural world

As stated earlier, group consciousness and group mind also exist amongst humans—racial violence, hysteria at rock concerts, and football hooliganism are obvious examples. It is questionable whether any member of a lynch mob would behave violently in the same way, if left to himself, as he would do when partaking of the 'mob consciousness'. Sometimes, and depressingly, committing an act of violence serves as an initiation process in the sense of a wake-up call to the person to mend his ways. Conversely, group consciousness and group mind exist in the absence of any obvious violent stimulus as amongst aboriginal communities and so called 'primitive' tribes as Carl Jung discovered (see Chapter 4).

Negative aspects of group mind in humans

Note, carefully, that mob consciousness is not restricted just to acts of physical violence and hooliganism. The intelligentsia have their own version of 'mob rule' as legendary scientists, who dared to step out of line with their peers, have found to the nemesis of their careers and reputations. For example, the English electrical engineer and Professor of Heavy Electrical Engineering at Imperial College, London, Eric Laithwaite (1921–1997), known as the 'father of maglev', for his development of the linear induction motor and maglev (magnetic levitation) rail system, had his Fellowship of the Royal Society of Great Britain cancelled and was obliged to retire in 1981, pretty much in disgrace. Why? Because in 1974 he gave the fourth prestigious Faraday Christmas Lecture at the Royal Institution in London, bringing with him an array of gyroscopes to demon-strate to his august audience that the former might be a hitherto unrecognized source of preternatural power that could challenge, or rather extend, the validity of Newton's Laws of motion and the laws of thermodynamics.[39] 'I thought my fellow scientists would be genuinely interested, so I wasn't prepared for the utter hostility of their reaction,' Laithwaite recalled later.[vii] Moreover, for the first time in its history, the Royal Institution of Great Britain failed to publish the Faraday Lecture that year.[40] Clearly, then, as regards

Scientific community also shares a group mind

---

vii The writer personally attended a lecture on similar lines given several years later by Eric Laithwaite at the University of Sussex and can testify to the legitimacy of what was presented both as theory, and experimental demonstrations with his gyroscopes.

the scientific orthodoxy, it is the theory (the collective mind set of the scientific estab-lishment) that determines what is allowed to constitute the evidence: in terms of the familiar truism, the map determines the territory.

Another causality, this time from the life sciences, is Thomas Nagel, Professor of Philosophy at New York University, who was (symbolically) torn apart by the literati for daring to explain in his book *Mind and Cosmos*[41] why mainstream thought on the workings of the mind is intellectually bankrupt. The fact that he presents his arguments with concise, meticulous thoroughness hardly counts: it seems that there is a powerful group consciousness amongst some mainstream academics devoted to guarding the materialistic paradigm of science and preserving, at all costs, the sanctity of their idols, chiefly Charles Darwin (see Chapter 7, Volume II for more details).

It is bad enough for a scientist to veer outside his subject areas and suggest that there might be hitherto undiscovered facts of nature, as in the examples just cited. But should a scien-tist, however well qualified, dare to mention religion, we may guarantee the outcome. On the eve of Darwin's bicentenary, the British educator and journalist Michael Reiss (*b*.1960), also professor of science education at the Institute of Education, University of London, and an ordained minister in the Church of England, agreed to step down (meaning he was probably eased out) from his role as education director of the Royal Society. What was his 'crime'? It was to suggest that there can be dialogue between religion and science.[42]

There is of course a positive side to group consciousness.

Extinction Rebellion and 'Greta effect'

A recent example is the Extinction Rebellion movement—a global environmental enter-prise with the stated aim of using non-violent civil disobedience to compel governments to take action to mitigate, and even reverse, 'tipping points' in the climate system which lead to biodiversity loss, and the risk of social and ecological collapse. The movement is inspired by the 'Greta effect', the work of the Swedish environmental activist Greta Thunburg (*b*.2003).[43] This shows that when an idea sweeps through a nation and, some-times, multiple nations, it is as if there is a kind of group consciousness about an 'idea whose time has come'. Another kind of uplifting group consciousness is seen when people are united in prayer or meditation in a sacred space, whether that be in the coun-tryside, a church or cathedral. Yet another kind of collective inspiration—this time in the arts—comes to mind in the form of the annual eight-week summer season of Henry Wood Promenade Concerts (the BBC Proms) held predominantly in the Royal Albert Hall in central London. What is known among aficionados as 'The Last night of the Proms' has a palpable atmosphere of group jubilation leaving everyone joyously energized.

There is also an online group consciousness. The negative features are too well known to warrant comment but the positive aspects should be acknowledged, as philosophically the positive always outweighs the negative, even if this cannot be seen at the time. 'Laughter is the best medicine' is an old adage that used to feature regularly in the American Reader's Digest family magazines. Nowadays, thanks to the advent of modern technology, Laughter Clubs are a recent development where individuals get together for fun and laughter. Clearly, this has a therapeutic effect and acts as a form of stress relief.[44] Again, campaigning communities, such as Avazz, provide a community platform on local, national, and international levels, allowing people to bring their collective pressure to bear and thus effect positive change in the world.[45]

The Swiss psychologist Carl Gustav Jung used the term 'individuation' to describe the process of becoming an individual whereby all potentials become actualised, i.e., fully conscious and operative. It is the hallmark of personal independence and freedom from 'keeping up with the Joneses' or succumbing to peer pressure and institutional directives on what to believe or disbelieve. In terms of Jungian psychology, it is a process of psychological integration. 'In general, it is the process by which individual beings are formed and differentiated; in particular, it is the development of the psychological *individual* […] as a being distinct from the general, collective psychology. Individuation, therefore, is a process of *differentiation* […], having for its goal the development of the individual personality.'[46] The differentiation referred to is from other human beings and the herd instinct of the crowd. Note, carefully, that to be aware of one's own individuality in no way implies an isolated, or self-enclosed consciousness. On the contrary, and paradoxically, strong individuals will invariably form, or be drawn to, societies having a common interest (such as musical societies) or to groups having a common altruistic, or charitable motive (like the Red Cross or the ecological movement). The collective consciousness of such societies and groups characterized by immense individual diversity within a unity of common purpose is radically different from the mindset of oppressive uniformity and imposed standardization found amongst totalitarian regimes.

Individuation means being oneself—not following the herd instinct nor 'keeping up with the Joneses'

> Individuation is closely connected with the *transcendent function*, since this function creates individual lines of development which could never be reached by keeping to the path prescribed by collective norms.
>
> C. G. Jung[47]

Cosmic Consciousness

This refers to the state whereby, after long processes of self-refinement, the individual consciousness voluntarily becomes fully merged in the universal field of consciousness (known in the East as *samadhi*). It is supposed to mark the full flowering and culmination of the human journey of self-development. As one might expect, this state occurs in various degrees, amongst people, or groups, with a strongly religious, mystical, philosophical or artistic bent, but it can also occur amongst (so-called) ordinary persons. In all cases, the person experiences flashes, or extended moments, of cosmic awareness; however, even one such genuine momentary occurrence is often enough to alter radically the course of the subject's life towards a more philanthropic and less worldly outlook. It is this life-altering feature of cosmic consciousness that clearly attests to the authenticity of the experience and distinguishes it from the common charge of being self-delusion or a hallucination (drug induced or otherwise). This is, of course, not to deny the fact of countless persons of unstable character claiming to have had a 'cosmic experience'. But to reiterate, it is the subsequent profound change in outlook, and associated lifestyle towards selflessness, that marks out a genuine experience from one of phantasy and delusion.

Hallmarks of a genuine experience

The Nature of Memory

We previously alluded to many instances where the nature of memory simply cannot be accounted for solely on the basis of physical processes in the brain, for example after an NDE, an OBE or a lucid dream. Especially regarding an NDE, how does the experiencer 'remember' what he has experienced when the brain is clinically dead? Furthermore, if reincarnation is a recurrent theme in cultural history, then why is it that the vast majority of people do not remember their past lives (notwithstanding the spectacular accounts of a few individuals who do claim to have vivid and detailed former life memories, as thoroughly investigated and documented by psychiatrists, such as Ian Stevenson, mentioned in the previous Chapter)? But what exactly is 'memory'?[48]

Memory cannot be restricted to the brain

Before enquiring into this question, we must dispose of one of the chief objections to reincarnation, namely, the average person's failure to recall his previous lives. The short answer is the complete inability of the best of modern mainstream psychologists to explain the nature of consciousness and mind (as distinct from brain); and their unawareness of their potentialities and higher states. Hence this objection is based on an a priori conclusion drawn from *prima facie* and circumstantial evidence more than anything else. We again ask: what is memory? Is it just the commonly accepted notion of the faculty in our mind (neuronal brain some would say) of remembering and of retaining the knowledge of previous thoughts, deeds, and events; or is there another dimension to be considered? There is indeed another major facet to be considered and it is this: memory is a *generic term* to encompass three faculties—remembrance, recollection, and reminiscence, and, despite some overlap, they are most certainly not synonyms.

Loss of memory does not refute reincarnation

Memory, strictly speaking, is the innate faculty in thinking beings (and even in animals) of reproducing past impressions by an association of ideas principally suggested by objective things or by some action on our external sensory organs. It is indeed a faculty depending entirely on the functioning of the physical brain. Remembrance and recollection are the attributes of memory—its handmaidens, or emissaries, so to say. But reminiscence is an entirely different thing. The philosopher John Locke, speaking of recollection and remembrance, says: 'When an idea again recurs without the operation of the like object on the external sensory, it is remembrance; if it be sought after by the mind, and with pain and endeavour found and brought again into view, it is recollection.'[49] However, Locke does not venture to explain reminiscence because it is not a faculty or attribute of memory dependent on the physical brain. Reminiscence is understood by modern psychology as something intermediate between remembrance and recollection, a kind of conscious process of recalling past occurrences, but without the specific and varied reference to the particular events which characterized the recollection.

Discerning remembrance, recollection, and reminiscence

We may further regard reminiscence in this way in the light of the *philosophia perennis*. While memory is physical and evanescent and depends on the physiological conditions of the brain, reminiscence is the longer lasting *memory of the soul*. And it is this memory of the soul which gives the assurance to almost every human being, whether he understands it or not, and before materialistic concepts attain their stranglehold, of his having lived before and having to live again. As the English Romantic poet William Wordsworth (1770–1850) puts it in *Intimations of Immortality*:

Reminiscence is soul memory

> Our birth is but a sleep and a forgetting,
> The soul that rises with us, our life's star,
> Hath elsewhere had its setting,
> And cometh from afar.[50]

Art can sometimes furnish finer intuitions

Indeed, poets and artists may have just as much to say, *sometimes more*, than scientists about divinity, nature, and mankind. The former speak from the standpoint of our human *condition*, the latter regarding our processes and mechanisms. The message to draw from the above is the clear distinction between memory and reminiscence. The former is a recording device that can easily malfunction and break down like the heads of a video recorder; but the latter is eternal, therefore imperishable, which is no figment of the imagination or wishful thinking. It is based on the profound teaching of Indian philosophy about *Akaśa* (Akasha), the equivalent Western term being Æther, or the misleading, because distorted, version, 'ether'. As succinctly explained by the Hungarian philosopher of science and founder of the Club of Budapest, Ervin László (*b.*1932), Akasha is 'an all-encompassing medium that *underlies* all things and *becomes* all things';[51] therefore, it is the womb from which everything manifested has emerged and into which everything will ultimately be reabsorbed.

Akasha: its significance

For this reason, '"The Akashic Record[s]" (also called "The Akashic Chronicle") is the enduring record of all that happens, and has ever happened, in the whole of the universe.'[52] The discoveries and theories of the very latest science are pointing strongly to this profound tenet of Indian philosophy. A consistent theme in philosophy and cultural history is that information is present, and preserved throughout nature, but it is a new concept in Western science. It requires acknowledgement that information is not just an abstract concept, but is 'in-formation', i.e. it has a reality of its own. And because it is present throughout the universe and nature, it is conceptualized in science as an extended field and like other fields, such as the gravitational or electromagnetic field, cannot be detected with the five physical senses, but is known and perceived through its effects.[53] That is why László calls the in-formation field the *Akashic Field*, or *A-field* for short. H. P. Blavatsky puts it in a slightly different context: 'The Universe is the periodical manifestation of this unknown Absolute Essence.'[54]

The Universal Memory of Nature

The subjective sense of time is a crucial factor in the different ways that we experience memory. In the broadest sense, remembrance, recollection, and reminiscence relate to time in the short, medium, and long term, respectively, in the experience of the individual. Consider, for example, a heart-rending piece of music you may have heard in your youth.[viii] A few days later, you might well remember the feelings of sadness along with details such as the title, composer, and singer. A few years later you might re-collect the feelings of sadness produced by the song and possibly remember a few details about the performance. Several years, or even decades later, when reflecting upon your youth, you may reminisce over the experience, even though most of the specific details might by now have been blurred. In rare circumstances, such reminiscence might even recall a love of music in a former life (the whole question of reincarnation is treated in detail in Chapter 5 of Volume II).

How time conditions memory

---

viii The example given applies of course to young people but is likely to be experienced more acutely in middle or old age.

Reminiscences are therefore the recall of long past impressions and experiences of significant poignancy that have percolated into the inner nature of the person, thus having much less to do with specific details and facts (or even forgetting about them) but involving the state of mind and feelings at the time. Accordingly, reminiscences pertain to the recall of the soul and are therefore more a faculty of the soul than the brain—working *through* the brain rather than being produced by it. (The meaning of 'soul' is defined in broad terms in the Recapitulation and, in detail, in Chapter 3 of Volume II.)

Innate ideas are the very fabric of the soul. The Platonic doctrine of recollection, or anamnesis, is the idea that we are born possessing all knowledge and our realization of that knowledge is contingent on our discovery of it. This is evident in the case of anyone born with a unique talent and starkly so in the case of geniuses, whether in the sciences or the arts—see Volume III, Chapter 9 for examples.

There is an old paradox that we can only learn what we already know. Logically, of course, it makes no sense; it is non-sense. Its meaning is best understood by the specific emphasis on recollection in the teachings of Plato, that is: we are born with innate ideas, like straightness or equality, and higher ideas like Justice and Truth. For this reason, when we say we 'learn' something, we are not so much learning as recalling what we once knew. This too is a case for life after so-called death, because as we did not learn these ideas at birth, or after birth—they were clearly there *before* we were born. Thus all knowledge is a recollection (literally, a 'collecting together') of what we once knew in essence, albeit rarely in detail. (Chapter 5 of Volume II explains this in detail in relation to death and rebirth).

Nature sometimes counts for more than nurture

We shall delve further into the whole question of mind and thought in Volume II where we investigate whether the brain is just a 'wet computer', to use a colloquial phrase.

Summary

We provide a summary of the preceding sections, on the unity and inter-relationship of consciousness, mind, and brain.

Consciousness at any level needs a suitable medium for expression

Consciousness is ubiquitous and ever-present. Being primary it is not, and cannot be, the product of something. However, it needs an appropriate instrument in order to manifest its potentiality. Mind *per se* is the instrument of consciousness. Moreover, mind cannot express on the physical level without its appropriate instrument. Brain is the physical instrument of mind. Hence, we have a triplicity from the non-physical to the physical: Consciousness (divine)—Mind (divine-physical interface)—Brain (physical). Mind in its Universal sense is also referred to as Soul in the generic sense.

Everything is consciousness but in different degrees of awakening and expression

Thus, from all that has been said, it should become increasingly clear that consciousness is not a thing or a (by)product of a some thing or other, but more in the nature of a universal field of intelligent-energy that presents manifold aspects of itself depending on the medium or vehicle that allows it self-expression and manifestation. By analogy with the musical scale (and its infinite variety of overtones) or the spectrum of light with wavebands of frequency-energy producing the seven colours of the rainbow (and an infinite variation of other colours, invisible to the eye), so also the spectrum of consciousness extends in descending frequencies from the most divine and spiritual—otherwise known as 'God'—down to physical consciousness. The latter means consciousness pertaining to physical matter, there being no particle of matter, however minute, that is not imbued with consciousness at its own level. What varies, as we move up the scale from physical matter to higher life forms, is the degree of awakened consciousness, arriving at man who is '*potentially*' fully self conscious, then man who is fully self conscious, or self realized, and ever upwards to Intelligences superior to man.

Although consciousness *per se* is omnipresent, the degree of its awakening, or expression, through forms is provided in an ascending scale by the mineral, vegetable, animal, human, and superhuman kingdoms. This is encapsulated in the Qabbalistic axiom: 'A stone becomes a plant, a plant an animal, an animal a man, a man a spirit, and a spirit a god.' Coupled with these ascending degrees of expression, this ubiquity of consciousness might be rephrased as follows: 'consciousness sleeps in the stone, stirs in the vegetable, dreams in the animal and awakens in the man.' This will all become clear in Volume III, Chapter 10 where evolution on all levels from the physical to the spiritual is explained in detail.

> **Physical matter does not generate consciousness. On the contrary, it provides the form for the expression of consciousness manifesting at the physical level.**

An Example to Illustrate the Omnipresence of Consciousness in Mind and Brain

We can illustrate this graduated scale of awakened consciousness by way of a modified version of an analogy that Newton used to illustrate the omnipresence of God the Father and to explain the pervasion of the Father through the Son and Holy Ghost.[55]

Imagine three bodies on top of one another as seen in Figure I-5 below.

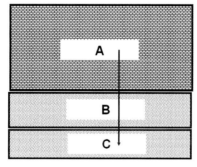

ONE FORCE BY COMMUNICATION AND DESCENT
ONE DIVINITY DERIVED FROM THE FATHER

Figure I-5   An Illustration of the Omnipresence of Consciousness

A is a heavy body, say a granite slab, bearing directly on two almost weightless bodies (such as polystyrene slabs) *B* and *C*. There is then a force in *A*, a force in *B* and the same force in *C*. But these are not three separate forces but ONE force originating in *A*, and by communication and descent, in *B* and *C*. Now if we let *A* represent consciousness, *B* mind, and *C* the brain, there is but one consciousness, in its unalloyed state, then received in the mind and in the brain by communication and descent. Just as slab *C*

Invoking Newton's analogy of force

cannot experience the force of slab *A* above without the interface slab *B* to communicate the force, similarly the brain needs the instrument of mind in order to 'receive' consciousness. The degree to which consciousness can express at any level is obviously limited by the 'attunement' and degree of refinement of its medium or instrument at that level. Physical consciousness therefore represents the lowest degree of conscious expression. Hence the need to elevate one's consciousness if one is to experience higher levels of being and reality.

This Chapter has revealed the glorious vistas that open up before our eyes when science decides to 'look through the telescope' and transcend (not reject) its materialistic stance. We are now entering the inner sanctum of the Mystery Teachings of the *philosophia perennis*. Before we take the plunge however, a few thoughts in the next Chapter about the prerequisite for a new mode of thinking, presaged by the following two quotes.

> *For a thing of this kind cannot be expressed by words like other disciplines, but by long familiarity, and living in conjunction with the thing itself, a light as it were leaping from a fire will on a sudden be enkindled in the soul, and there itself nourish itself.*
>
> Plato[56]

> *For nature is a perpetuall circulatory worker, generating fluids out of solids, and solids out of fluids, fixed things out of volatile, & volatile out of fixed, subtile out of gross, & gross out of subtile, Some things to ascend & make the upper terrestriall juices, Rivers and the Atmosphere; & by consequence others to descend for a Requitall to the former. And as the Earth, so perhaps may the Sun imbibe this spirit copiously to conserve his Shineing, & keep the Planets from recedeing further from him. And they that will, may also suppose, that this Spirit affords or carryes with it thither the solary fewell & materiall Principle of Light; And that the vast aethereall Spaces between us, & the stars are for a sufficient repository for this food of the Sunn and Planets.*
>
> Isaac Newton[57]

NOTES

1   Anton Postl, 'Correspondence Between Kepler and Galileo', *Vistas in Astronomy*, 21 (Pergamon Press, 1997), 325–30.
2   Rolf Schaffranke, article for the journal *Earth and Cosmos* published in German in the early 1980s.
3   Albert Einstein, Letter to Maurice Solovine, 28 March 1949, in Banesh Hoffmann (in collaboration with Einstein's secretary, Helen Dukas), *Albert Einstein: Creator and Rebel* (1st edn, US: Viking Press, 1 September 1972), 328. See also Claes Johnson, *Many–Minds Relativity* (2011), 89 [online] <http://citeseerx.ist.psu.edu/viewdoc/download?doi=10.1.1.441.6979&rep=rep1&type=pdf> accessed 9 July 2020.
4   Claes Johnson, *op. cit.*, 117.
5   William Kremer, 'The Strange Afterlife of Einstein's Brain', BBC World Service, 18 April 2015 <http://www.bbc.co.uk/news/magazine-32354300> accessed 20 November 2019.
6   Sandra F. Witelson, Debra L. Kigar, and Thomas Harvey, 'The Exceptional Brain of Albert Einstein', *The Lancet*, 353/9170 (19 June 1999), 2149–53.

7   'Sandra Witelson', *science.ca* <http://www.science.ca/scientists/scientistprofile.php?pID=273> accessed 9 July 2020.

8   William Reville, 'Remarkable Story of Maths Genius Who Had Almost No Brain', *The Irish Times* (9 November 2006). William Reville is associate professor of biochemistry and public awareness of science officer at UCC. See 'Public Awareness & Understanding of Science' <http://understanding-science.ucc.ie> accessed 20 November 2019.

9   'Living Without a Brain', in *Encyclopedia of the Unusual and Unexplained: Mysteries of the mind* <http://www.unexplainedstuff.com/Mysteries-of-the-Mind/Living-without-a-Brain.html> accessed 20 November 2019.

10   'Is Your Brain Really Necessary?' *Alternative Science News* (9 September, 2002).

11   Roger Lewin, 'Is Your Brain Really Necessary?' *Science* 210 (12 December 1980).

12   John Nolte, *The Human Brain: An introduction to its functional anatomy* (Philadelphia: Mosby Publishing, 2002).

13   An abridged version of Marilyn Monk, 'Recent Developments in Science and Medicine', *Journal of the Scientific and Medical Network*, 115 (2014), 16. References provided in the source article are: 'The Game is On', *Nature*, 509 (2014), 134; and F. Alcantara and M. Monk, 'Signal Propagation During Aggregation in the Slime Mould *Dictyostelium discoideum*', *J. Gen. Microbiol.*, 85 (1974), 321–34.

14   Taken from a lecture to the London Group of the Scientific and Medical Network on 12 November 2014. McGilchrist's major work, *The Master and His Emissary: The divided brain and the making of the western world* (rev. and enl. edn, New Haven and London: Yale University Press, 2019) is discussed in Volume II, Chapter 7.

15   Michael A. Cremo and Richard L. Thompson, *Forbidden Archeology: The hidden history of the human race* (Los Angeles, Bhaktivedanta Book Publishing), 1998. A condensed version is Michael A. Cremo and Richard L. Thompson, *The Hidden History of the Human Race* (Los Angeles, Bhaktivedanta Book Publishing), 1999.

16   Richard Milton, *Shattering the Myths of Darwinism* (Rochester, Vermont: Park Street Press, 2000).

17   Amit Goswami, *Creative Evolution* (Wheaton, Illinois: Quest Books, 2008).

18   Thomas Nagel, *Mind and Cosmos: Why the materialist neo-Darwinian conception of nature is almost certainly false* (Oxford: Oxford University Press, 2012).

19   Rupert Sheldrake, *The Presence of the Past: Morphic resonance and the habits of nature* (London: Fontana, 1989).

20   'Manifesto for an Integral Science of Consciousness', *Journal of The Scientific and Medical Network*, 75 (2001), 2–5 <https://opensciences.org/files/pdfs/Manifesto-for-a-Post-Materialist-Science.pdf> accessed 6 May 2020.

21   The Summary Report of the 'International Summit on Post-Materialist Science, Spirituality and Society' can be found on <http://opensciences.org/files/pdfs/ISPMS-Summary-Report.pdf> accessed 2 January 2020.

22   'Open Sciences' <http://opensciences.org/about/manifesto-for-a-post-materialist-science> accessed 20 November 2019. The complete manifesto is reproduced in 'Manifesto for a Post-Materialist Science', *Journal of The Scientific and Medical Network*, 115 (2014), 4–5.

23   Etzel Cardeña, 'A Call for an Open, Informed Study of All Aspects of Consciousness', *Frontiers in Human Neuroscience* (January 2014).

24   Irwin Harvey, 'The Major Problems Faced by Parapsychology Today: A survey of members of the parapsychological association', *Australian Journal of Parapsychology*, 14 (December 2014).

25   Etzel Cardeña, 'On Wolverines and Epistemological Totalitarianism', *Journal of Scientific Exploration*, 25 (2011), 539–51.

26   —— 'Eminent Authors from Other Areas', *Mindfield*, 5 (2013), 83–90.

27   M. Truzzi, 'On the Extraordinary: An attempt at clarification', *Zetetic Scholar*, 1 (1978), 11–22.

28   Patrizio E. Tressoldi, 'Extraordinary Claims Require Extraordinary Evidence: The case of non-local perception, a classical and Bayesian review of evidences', *Front. Psychol.* (June 2011).

29   Harald Walach, 'Report of the Galileo Commission Project', *Journal of The Scientific and Medical Network*, 128 (2018) 5–10. Downloadable digital summary report, in 'Galileo Commission Summary Report' <https://www.galileocommission.org/wp-content/uploads/2019/03/Galileo-Commission-Summary-Report-Digital.pdf> accessed 6 May 2020. Downloadable digital summary of

argument in English and eight foreign languages, in 'Beyond a Materialist Worldview' <https://www.galileocommission.org/report#summary> accessed 20 November 2019.

30 Harald Walach, 'Towards a Postmaterialist Science – Report of the Galileo Commission', *Society for Scientific Exploration* [video], YouTube (recorded 18 December 2019, uploaded 6 May 2020) <https://www.youtube.com/watch?v=ngFf Ytf-Aok> accessed 7 May 2020.

31 David Lorimer, 'The Galileo Commission: Towards a post-materialist science. An invitation to look through the telescope', *Journal for the Study of Spirituality*, 9/1 (2019).

32 John Locke, *An Essay Concerning Human Understanding*, ed. Peter H. Nidditch (Oxford: Clarendon Press, 1975), 115.

33 Willis Harman, 'The Scientific Exploration of Consciousness: Towards an adequate epistemology', *Journal of Consciousness Studies*, 1/1 (1994), 140–8.

34 Charles T. Tart (ed.), *Altered States of Consciousness* (New York: Doubleday, 1972).

35 David J. Chalmers, 'Facing Up to the Problem of Consciousness', *Journal of Consciousness Studies*, 2/3 (1995), 200–19; see also <http://consc.net/papers/facing.html> accessed 20 November 2019.

36 David Chalmers, *The Conscious Mind: In search of a fundamental theory* (New York and Oxford: Oxford University Press, 1997).

37 See the publications cited in 'College of Medicine Tucson, Department of Anesthesiology' <http://anesth.medicine.arizona.edu/faculty/stuart-r-hameroff-md> accessed 20 November 2019.

38 Vasileios Basios: 'The Century of Complexity', *Beshara Magazine*, Science & Technology, 6 (2017); 'Complexity, Complementarity, Consciousness', in Brenda Dunne and Robert Jahn (eds), *Being & Biology: Is consciousness the life force?* (Princeton: ICRL Press, 2017) <https://www.galileo commission.org/complexity-complimentary-consciousness-vasileios-basios-2017> accessed 6 May 2020. Vasileios Basios worked within the team of the Nobel laureate Ilya Prigogine at the Solvay Institutes for Physics and Chemistry at the University of Brussels.

39 'The Engineer Through the Looking Glass: Lecture 4, "The Jabberwock" ' [video] (recorded 1974, uploaded 6 May 2020) <http://www.rigb.org/christmas-lectures/watch/1974/the-engineer-through-the-looking-glass/the-jabberwock> accessed 7 May 2020.

40 Professor Eric Laithwaite, obituary by Brian Bowers, *The Independent*, 13 December 1997.

41 Thomas Nagel, *Mind and Cosmos*.

42 'On the Origin of an Essential Debate: Can science ignore faith?' *Times Higher Education* (27 November 2008), 27.

43 '#Where is Your Plan', *Extinction Rebellion* <https://rebellion.earth> accessed 26 December 2019.

44 'Laughter Clubs' <https://www.meetup.com/topics/laughter-club/> accessed 10 July 2020.

45 'Avazz', Wikipedia (last modified 5 July 2020) <https://en.wikipedia.org/wiki/Avaaz> accessed 10 July 2020.

46 C. G. Jung, *Psychological Types*, trans. H. G. Baynes, rev. R. F. C. Hull, foreword by John Beebe (Princeton: Princeton University Press, 1971; quotation from London and New York: Routledge, 2017), 411.

47 —— *op. cit.*, 412.

48 What follows is a paraphrasing and elaboration from *KT*, 'On Reincarnation or Rebirth: What is memory?' 124–5.

49 'Of the Modes of Thinking', in John Locke, *An Essay Concerning Human Understanding* (London: J. F. Dove, 1828; US: Oxford University Press, 2008).

50 William Wordsworth, *Ode: Intimations of immortality from recollections of early childhood,* in *The Oxford Book of English Verse: 1250–1900*, ed. Arthur Quiller-Couch (Oxford: Clarendon Press, 1919).

51 Ervin László, *Science and the Akashic Field: An integral theory of everything* (Rochester, Vermont: Inner Traditions, 2007), 76.

52 —— *op. cit.*, exordium, xii.

53 —— *op. cit.*, 72–3, 75.

54 *SD*-I, 'Summing Up', 273.

55 Newton's example is in *Yahuda* MS 14, ff. 173–3v; quoted also in Richard S. Westfall, *Never at Rest* (Cambridge: Cambridge University Press, 1980), 317.

56 Tim Addey, 'Plato's Seventh Letter', trans. Thomas Taylor, *Prometheus Trust*, 341c–341d <http://www.prometheustrust.co.uk/Seventh_Letter_-_extracts.pdf> accessed 3 August 2020. See

also: Kenneth Sayre, 'Plato's Dialogues in the Light of the Seventh Letter', in *Platonic Writings, Platonic Readings*, ed. Charles Griswold (New York: Routledge, Chapman & Hall, 1988); *Plato: Complete works*, ed. John M. Cooper, trans. Glenn Morrow (US: Hackett Publishing Company, 1997).

57 Letter to Henry Oldenburg, 7 December 1675, in *The Correspondences of Isaac Newton*, ed. H. W. Turnbull, J. F. Scott, A. Rupert Hall, and Laura Tilling, 7 vols (Cambridge: Cambridge University Press, 1959–77), i, 366.

6 A New Continent of Thought

Life, like a dome of many-coloured glass, Stains the white radiance of eternity.

PERCY BYSSHE SHELLEY[1]

SYNOPSIS

Chapter 6 depicts, in necessarily cursory fashion, the brain processes of a person whose thinking is entirely materialistic, in contrast with one who can function in a new continent of thought by discovering a gateway through materialism towards wider horizons. Regarding the latter faculty, mention is made of Goethean Science in the West and *Jñāna Yoga* (Yoga of the Mind) in the East, both of which stress the need for a universal and holistic approach in contrast to the predominantly analytical thinking in mainstream science in the Western world. The seminal insights of psychology are shown to undermine the dogma that thought is solely a function of the brain by realizing that functional dependence of the brain is not just a productive, or generative function, but also a releasing, or permissive function, and a transmissive function.

KEY WORDS: neuroplasticity, materialistic thinking, holistic thinking, brain experiments, sensory substitution, consciousness mechanisms, consciousness production, consciousness beyond the brain, William James, Lord Auckland Geddes

In the mid-twentieth century—a time of avid interest in mysticism, arcane teachings, New Age ideas, and the transcendent implications of quantum physics amongst some scientists—a book appeared bearing the title *A New Continent of Thought*.[2] Its purpose was to disseminate new ideas not as a question of belief or non-belief, but in an attempt to discover that attitude and mode of life by which the individual may become aware of the unknown life which exists behind ordinary mundane existence, as it does behind all forms of manifestation. Furthermore, that there exists a science of evolution, not restricted just to physical evolution, which stands in its own right as giving verifiable knowledge of this life-process in manifestation, knowledge of which is continually open to experiment and experience at all levels of individual progress.

Making the case for a new way of looking—a new mode of thinking

This is also our purpose here, which is why this Chapter bears the same title as the afore-mentioned book. Is it possible, therefore, to alter radically the way we ordinarily think along well-established tramlines of thought? Can such fixed patterns of thought be broken and transcended? Can our thoughts change the physical structure and functioning of our brains? The answer is a resounding 'yes'. Then, why do the materialists think the way they do, unable to appreciate a wider viewpoint?

Let us take up this theme by drawing on one of the most exciting discoveries in neuro-science—the plastic brain. It might be helpful to elaborate on the research conducted in support of this finding in order to unearth its implications in terms of moving from the

160

materialistic paradigm towards a new mode of thought. It is envisaged that such would include materialism but within holism and non-physical realms of being. Holism is the 'bigger picture', universal in its outlook and sees the universe, and especially living nature, in terms of interacting wholes. Such wholes are more than the sum total of their components and elementary particles and are to be examined as interdependent parts acting within the whole universe.

The Plastic Brain

We stated in Chapter 4 that brain plasticity, or neuroplasticity, is a generalizing term that encompasses both synaptic plasticity and non-synaptic plasticity, referring to changes in neural pathways and synapses due to changes in behaviour, environment, neural processes, thinking, emotions, as well as changes resulting from bodily injury.[3] Neuroplasticity has replaced the former well established position that the brain is a physiologically static organ, and explores how, and in which ways, the brain changes throughout life. The development of this topic is highly relevant to this work and is now summarized.

Brains can carve new neural pathways

The Brain That Changes Itself is a book by the Canadian analyst Norman Doidge (*b.*1950). It featured numerous case studies of patients suffering from neurological disorders and detailed how, in each case, the brain adapted to compensate for the disabilities of the individual patients, often in unusual and unexpected ways. Written by a psychiatrist and psychoanalyst, it created quite a stir by seeming to go contrary to conventional thought in neuroscience about brain functions being confined to certain fixed locations in the brain.[4]

However, the idea is not new: that the brain and its functions are not fixed throughout adulthood was proposed in 1890 by the psychologist William James, though the idea was largely neglected.[5] It then germinated in 1923 when the psychologist Karl Lashley conducted experiments on rhesus monkeys. By removing certain parts of the brain he demonstrated changes in neuronal pathways, which he concluded to be evidence of plasticity.[6] Despite this, as well as further examples of research suggesting neuroplasticity, the latter was still not widely accepted by neuroscientists. However, more significant evidence appeared in the 1960s and thereafter, particularly after the American neuroscientist Paul Bach-y-Rita (1934–2006) invented a device that allowed blind people to read, perceive shadows, and distinguish between close and distant objects. The six subjects of the experiment *were congenitally blind and had previously not been able to see*, but were eventually able to recognize a picture of the supermodel Twiggy. The capacity of the brain to adapt implied that it possessed plasticity. As Bach-y-Rita, known as 'the father of sensory substitution', said: 'We see with the brain, not with the eyes. You can lose your retina but you do not lose the ability to see as long as your brain is intact.'[7] What this implies is that, 'Persons who become blind do not lose the capacity to see.'[8]

Neuroplasticity has a historical basis

Incidentally, this finding might go a long way towards explaining how great composers, like Beethoven, were able to hear music despite the atrophy of the auditory organ.

Studies in the late 1990s onwards involving London taxi drivers not only interested scientists but also engaged the public and media worldwide and received much publicity. A well-known case is the research by the English neuroscientist Eleanor Maguire FRS (*b.*1970), which documented changes in hippocampal structure[i] (i.e., hippocampal plasticity) associated with acquiring knowledge of the layout of London streets in local taxi-drivers.[9, 10, 11] A redistribution of grey matter in the brains of those participating in the study was indicated in London compared to controls. A subsequent study to determine the effect of SatNav on the brains of London cabbies would be interesting! Similar studies involving musicians have shown increased development in the brain area associated with cultivation of a specific motor skill;[12] for example, the brain region corresponding to the left (fingering) hand of violinists which is used in a very different manner to the right (bowing) hand.

London taxi drivers and violinists show changes in specific brain regions

Brain reorientation is also well demonstrated in studies involving stroke patients who, although paralysed for years, were able to recover through the use of brain stimulating exercises. This showed that, 'under conditions of interest, such as that of competition, the resulting movement may be much more efficiently carried out than in the dull, routine training in the laboratory.'[13] A particularly poignant modern case is that of the American Harvard-trained neuroanatomist Jill Bolte Taylor (mentioned briefly in Chapter 4) who experienced a massive stroke that damaged the rational, logical, detail, and time-oriented functions of the left hemisphere of her brain. During this experience, she alternated between two distinct and opposite realities: the intuitive and emotional right hemisphere of the brain which engendered a feeling of euphoria, when she felt a sense of complete well-being and peace; and the logical left hemisphere, which enabled her to know that she was having a stroke. After her recovery lasting some eight years, Taylor completely reorientated her understanding of the world according to the insight gained from the right hemisphere of her brain.[14] The message here is what we take for granted as 'objective reality' is in fact highly influenced by the instrumentality of perception. Taylor's experience strongly vindicates William James's thesis (mentioned in detail later in this Chapter) about the brain being more like a filter or transducer, as opposed to the conventional view of just a producer, or generator of consciousness. The divided nature of thought as a result of the division of the brain into two hemispheres is the theme of a seminal book by the consultant psychiatrist Iain McGilchrist.[15] He argues that this division, whilst being essential to human existence, gives possibly incompatible versions of the world, with quite different priorities and values that, in turn, have had a strong, and occasionally detrimental, bearing in moulding our culture. The seminal importance of this work is discussed in Chapter 7 of Volume II in the context of the current conundrum in mainstream science, as to whether consciousness is generated by neural processes in the brain and if not, what might be an alternative explanation.

Brain hemispheres determine nature of thought and experience of the world

Michael Merzenich (*b.*1942) is an American neuroscientist who has been one of the pioneers of neuroplasticity for over three decades. He has made some of the most ambitious claims for the field—that brain exercises may be as useful as drugs to treat diseases as severe as schizophrenia, that plasticity exists from cradle to grave, and that radical improvements in cognitive functioning (how we learn, think, perceive, and remember) are possible, even in the elderly. Merzenich argues that neuroplasticity could occur beyond critical periods when, for example, the brain has to adapt following trauma. This was a

Brain is not 'hard wired' at birth and can change

---

i The hippocampus is a part of the brain that is involved in emotions, learning, and memory formation. There are two hippocampi, one in each side of the brain.

substantial breakthrough. Merzenich's experiments on monkey brains led him to conclude that if the brain map could normalize its structure in response to abnormal input, the prevailing view that we are born with a hard-wired system was undoubtedly wrong. The brain had to be plastic.[16, 17]

A number of studies have linked meditation practices to differences in cortical thickness or density of grey matter. One of the most well-known studies to demonstrate this was led by the contemporary American psychologist and psychiatry researcher Sara Lazar from Harvard Medical School in 2000.[18] Richard Davidson (b.1951), an American neuro-scientist at the University of Wisconsin, has led experiments in co-operation with the Dalai Lama on the effects of meditation on the brain.[19] His results suggest that the long-term, or even short-term, practice of meditation results in different levels of activity in brain regions associated with such qualities as attention, anxiety, depression, fear, anger, the ability of the body to heal itself, and so on. These functional changes may be caused by changes in the physical structure of the brain.

> Meditation can change brain structure

Brain plasticity is one of the finest fruits of modern neuroscientific discoveries for the world. There are enormous implications for our enquiry into consciousness and a new mode of thought as follows.

Conclusions and Implications for a Paradigm Transformation

Many of the experiments described above involved suffering to animals. Granted that (most!) humans do not possess monkey brains, what conclusions can we yet draw from this research, especially that which is of great importance to spiritual philosophy, namely, meditation? Presenting our case in stepwise fashion:

1. The brain is plastic and not 'hard-wired' from birth;
2. therefore, by implication, the same cognitive habits (thoughts) will necessarily involve the same brain pathways and brain regions;
3. however, if the brain pathways and regions are damaged, then the same cognitive habits performed under motivation will 'carve out' new pathways involving different brain regions;
4. and critically, as regards a new continent of thought, new cognitive habits and new ways of thinking will also carve out new brain pathways and stimulate hitherto unused regions of the brain resulting in the awakening of novel and increasingly subtle faculties of thinking. Therefore, it is entirely feasible to effect a transformation of the current machine paradigm of scientific materialism towards a more spiritual and universal world-view.

> Outworn, rigid habits of thought can be broken

> We can actually train ourselves to think differently and this has nothing whatsoever to do with deluding ourselves.[20, 21]

The Analytical Approach to Enquiry – Left-Brain Thinking

Psychologists refer to what is known as the 'hardening of the categories', a term used to describe how we remember things. Memory processes—specifically, remembrance and recollection (see Chapter 5, pages 152–4)—tend to work within three generalized categories:

1. If we do not have an appropriate mental category, or 'label' for something (such as a new scientific theory or philosophical doctrine), we are unlikely to perceive it and 'store' it in memory; still less able to retrieve (i.e., *re*-collect) it from memory later.
2. Or else, categories may be drawn incorrectly, in which case the perception and recall are likely to be distorted and inaccurately related.
3. But when information about phenomena or experiences that are disparate in important respects, hence belonging to different categories, nonetheless get lumped together and stored in memory under a single category or concept, the resulting analysis and exposition are bound to be biased and one-sided.

Assigning categories and labels helps the memory

The above explains why theologians have, in general, opposed any new knowledge (especially scientific) that cannot readily be fitted into a category hardened by the self-same theological concepts and dogmas over innumerable years. *It is essentially the same reason why materialist scientists are prejudiced against any ideas that have even a whiff of spirituality or imply non-physical influences.* Thus, it is easy to understand now why materialists think the way they do (we have cited the example of the palæontologist and evolutionary biologist Stephen Jay Gould—see Chapter 3). Their cognitive pathways and brain regions have been established and 'hardened' by the same old and familiar patterns of thought plus social pressures (Darwin's concepts in the case of Gould). The cerebral gramophone record is repeatedly playing the same 'conceptual tune' stuck in the same groove with nothing to nudge it out of the rut. What then provides the nudge? Intense motivation, as neuroscience research has shown. This can occur from an inner experience so extraordinary that conventional explanations provide no comfort, or perhaps an unquenchable thirst for knowledge and truth that leads a person to break out of the materialist paradigm and seek out deeper meanings and explanations, like Wilder Penfield exampled in Chapter 2. Unfortunately, the nudge, invariably the jolt, often comes from grave tragedy, intense suffering or severe illness (as for example, in the near-death experiences of the neurosurgeon Eben Alexander and anaesthesiologist, Rajiv Parti, described earlier in Chapters 2 and 4, respectively.)

Habitual thought patterns harden cognitive pathways

However, to apportion specific brain functions exclusively to one hemisphere or another is an erroneous concept. As stated above, the 'plastic' brain is now a well established fact; therefore, the brain acts as a whole and not in a compartmentalised fashion. But as McGilchrist (mentioned above) cogently argues, the differences in hemisphere function lie not, as has hitherto been supposed, in the 'what', but in the 'how'—that is to say, we should be concerning ourselves with not so much which skills each hemisphere possesses, but the way in which each uses them, and to *what end*. This is also elaborated in Volume II, Chapter 7.

Both brain hemispheres perform crucial functions. They are equally important

Moreover, readers should never form the impression that the suggestion is that the left hemisphere of the brain is being equated with the 'materialistic brain' and is by default inferior to the holistic thinking associated with the right hemisphere. Each hemisphere is of equal importance and value within the limits of its functioning and *within the context of its application*. Although it is undoubtedly true that the left brain alone might well lead to materialistic thinking, the left brain is just as valuable and quite 'neutral'. Problems arise when left-brained thinking is divorced from right-brained thinking. What is needed is the left brain led by the right brain—the 'emissary' led by the 'master'—as suggested in the next section.

The Holistic Approach to Enquiry – The Marriage of Left-Brain and Right-Brain Thinking: the Emissary Led by the Master

We have seen how ordinary intellectual activity moves along well beaten paths in the brain, and does not compel sudden adjustments and destructions in its substance; but a new kind of mental effort calls for something very different. Just as a sportsman develops specific muscles for the task in hand, the esotericist must develop his 'mental muscles' to acquire a higher faculty of thinking. In both cases, the endeavour is fatiguing, painful, and discouraging, as well as dangerous, if taken to extremes. But this is hardly a good reason to throw down the gauntlet for there is much fulfilment in the process, the freedom that such a challenge bestows on our earnest aspirations, and the Divine Grace which meets our efforts and lifts us up further than is possible when we try to 'go it alone'. Annie Besant (a senior pupil of H. P. Blavatsky) states how strenuous and continuous thought causes chemical activity, prompting the dendrons to shoot out from the neural ganglia,ii making connections and cross-connections in new directions—literally, new brain pathways of thought.22

New brain pathways can be forged using different 'mental muscles'

A major step forward in this direction is provided by Goethean Science, which promotes whole-brained thinking and a holistic world-conception (see Chapter 3). It is the natural complement to the predominantly left-brained thinking in mainstream science which, as impressively argued by Ian McGilchrist, has contributed significantly to the welfare of society albeit at the price of skewed approaches to science and medicine, philosophy, culture, and mental health care, especially in the Western world.

Further along similar lines, Blavatsky has given the following advice to her earnest students.23 She states that this new mode of thinking is what the Indians call *Jñāna Yoga*. As we progress in this Yoga of the Mind we find conceptions arising which, though we are conscious of them, we cannot express, nor yet formulate, into any sort of mental picture. As time goes on these conceptions will form into mental pictures. This is a time to be on guard and refuse to be deluded with the idea that the newly found wonderful picture must represent reality. It does not, for it is another map, hopefully a more accurate one; hence, those who are obsessed with precise and articulated definitions should pay especial heed. As we work on, we find the once admired picture growing dull and unsatisfying, and finally fading out, or being thrown away, altogether. This does not mean that we have become woolly thinkers, but simply that we have come up against another danger point. This leaves us seemingly 'high and dry'—as if, for the moment, trapped in a void without any conceptual scaffolding to support us. We may then be tempted either to give up altogether or to revive the cast-off picture, for want of a better one to cling to. The true student will, however, work on unconcerned, and presently further formless gleams come, which in time give rise to a larger and more beautiful picture than the last. But the student will now know that no picture will ever represent the Truth. This last splendid picture will grow dull and fade like the others. And so, the process goes on, until at last the mind and its pictures are transcended and the student enters and dwells in the World of No Form, but of which all forms are narrowed reflections. Thus, we slowly come to realize that all thought-concepts are 'mind maps', indispensable as stepping stones to

The 'map' is not the 'territory'. The concept is not the real

---

ii Neural ganglia are groups of brain nerve cells. Dendrons are nerve processes in the form of prolongations, or outgrowths, and consist of the matter of the cell enclosed in a medullary sheath (an insulating sheath around certain nerve fibres that allows the efficient transmission of electrical impulses along nerve cells).

This world of NO FORM is the mystic's vision. To articulate concepts in precise and definite terms is the triumph of the scientist but it is the bane of the mystic, for no words can possibly 'eff' the ineffable. That is why mystics of all ages have either retreated into silence or resorted to poetry, music, epic or allegory to convey some flavour of their indescribable and 'definition-less' experience of a transcendent reality.

The Thought Producer matters more than the myriads of thoughts produced

Reality, but never to be confused with the latter: as poetically expressed in this terse maxim: 'The Mind is the great Slayer of the Real.'24

The Indian sage Ramana Maharshi's constant advice to aspirants was similar to Blavatsky's—'Trace thought to its place of origin', was his tersely reiterated counsel: 'Watch for the real self to reveal itself, and then your thoughts [concepts, or mental pictures] will die down of their own accord.'25 Intellect then withdraws and is subsumed in its own ground, which is consciousness working unhindered by thought. We then perceive that the mind takes its rise in a transcendental source. Both Blavatsky and numerous other luminaries, like the sage Jiddu Krishnamurti, were pointing to exactly the same terminus: to discover the reality of the Thought *Producer*, without becoming fixated by identifying with thoughts, however useful they may be as stepping stones in the process of final attainment.

The Many and the One – Contrasting the Analytical Approach with the Holistic Approach to Enquiry

Figure I-6 provides a fanciful illustration of the contrasting insights into nature, the meaning of life, and the purpose of existence that ensue from two principal modes of enquiry: the analytical and holistic.

In the panel at the top of page 167, the picture to the left depicts the universal treasure trove of all knowledge and wisdom, likened to a garden of numerous, multi-coloured flowers. The birds, bees, and butterflies in the garden, attracted to different colours and varieties of flowers, are similes for truth-seekers each according to their own bent. Let us select three of the finest flowers as representative of the three main disciplines of human enquiry: Science, Philosophy, and Religion.

The flowers seen in the middle of the panel represent these distinct disciplines—Science, Philosophy, and Religion. Readers will see that each blossom is illuminated *individually* by an *external* beam of light. This represents the conventional analytical method of enquiry taught in schools and universities all over the world. It yields valuable facts and figures but invariably the analysis is based entirely upon the *objective* nature of the truths being explored. Without recognition of their *subjective* counterparts (or inner essence), these facts soon become ossified shells, stripped of life. Barren facts and figures, cut off from their vital essence, rarely inspire the seeker.

The picture to the right of the panel shows the three flowers tied with a nosegay constituting one bouquet—one entity—illuminated, not individually, *but as a whole* by a light from *within*. This is the holistic way of enquiry embracing Science, Philosophy, and Religion as an organic entity. The nosegay represents the common principle unifying apparently disparate subjects. This is the universal mode of instruction in Mystery Schools and centres of esoteric learning worldwide. This will be discussed at length in Chapter 9 and Recapitulation to this Volume.

 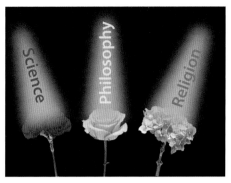 

The Garden of Universal Knowledge and Wisdom

The Fragmented, Anaytical Method of Enquiry Especially Favoured by the Mainstream Scientist

The 'Unific', Holistic Approach to Enquiry Favoured by the Integral Scientist and Mystic

Figure I-6   A 'Fragrant' Illustration Depicting the Fragmented, Analytical Approach to Enquiry in Contrast to the Holistic Approach to Enquiry

Image Credit: Artefact Design

In summary, then, the conventional analytical approach provides great detail about individual 'splinters' of truth at the expense of an understanding of the whole. In mainstream science this tends towards a materialistic and reductionist approach. By contrast, the holistic approach (the 'marriage' of left-brain with right-brain) forever maintains the organic unity and appreciates that the whole is always greater than the sum of its parts—albeit, with some loss of detail. In the case of the integral scientist the holistic approach takes the form of a systems approach because it is realized that complex and multifaceted systems exhibit nonlinear and often unpredictable characteristics that cannot be understood or controlled by simple mechanical, reductionist thinking and methods.

> Individual details and the whole picture are equally important in their context

A Gateway Through Materialism to Wider Horizons

The American philosopher, physician, and psychologist William James[26] was one of the leading thinkers of the late nineteenth century. Labelled by many as 'The Father of American psychology' (we would prefer to say, 'The Father of all psychology'), he was one of the most influential philosophers of his time and a principal founder of the discipline of functional psychology. His work impacted upon, and enlarged, the way science and psychology looked upon nature, the mind, and the body. In this regard he may have been influenced by the tenets of Theosophy, having been a member of the Theosophical Society for a number of years.[27] Many of his key ideas were also derived from the great German poet, playwright, and philosopher Friedrich Schiller (1759–1805). The pragmatism of James was much influenced by the similar humanistic philosophy of the German–British philosopher Ferdinand Canning Scott Schiller (1864–1937), who argued strongly against both logical positivism, especially that of the philosophers of science Otto Neurath and Carl Hempel of the Vienna Circle (see Chapter 3), as well as the absolute idealism of the German philosophers G. W. F. Hegel (1770–1831) and Friedrich Schelling (1775–1854) of the nineteenth century German idealist school. James was also influenced by Emanuel Swedenborg (1688–1772), the Swedish scientist, philosopher, theologian, and mystic, best known for his book on the afterlife, *Heaven and Hell*.[28] After reading daily

> Chief influences on William James

the works of Isaac Newton, Swedenborg travelled to England in 1710. Writing to his brother-in-law back in Sweden, he reported that he was indulging his 'immoderate desire' to learn about mathematics and science and attend lectures by the great man. Newton was living in London at the time, though it is uncertain whether Swedenborg ever succeeded in his quest to meet Newton in person. Nonetheless, in 1734 he entitled his own great three-volume philosophic work *The Principia; or, the first principles of natural things*[29] in response to Newton's own *Philosophiæ Naturalis Principia Mathematica*.[30] This background is important to an understanding of the cultural and philosophical currents that influenced James's own philosophy of mind.

In his lecture on human immortality,[31] and his book *Human Immortality: Two supposed objections to the doctrine*,[32] James's main purpose was to clear the way for constructive dialogue by removing the supposed objections to the doctrine by medical materialists associated with the established position of the anatomists, pathologists, physiologists, and psychologists who, with one voice, subscribe to 'the great psycho-physiological formula: *Thought is a function of the brain*.' Whilst not denying this assertion of *functional dependence*, James challenges the superficial and strictly one-sided interpretation of this statement by the 'puritanism of science' and asks us to look at the issue more closely. He points out that 'it is indeed true that physiological science has come to the conclusion cited; and we must confess that in so doing she has only carried out a little farther the common belief of mankind. Everyone knows that arrests of brain development occasion imbecility, that blows on the head abolish memory or consciousness, and [that] brain-stimulants and poisons change the quality of our ideas. The anatomists, physiologists, and pathologists have only shown this generally admitted fact of a dependence to be detailed and minute.'

<aside>James's criticism of medical and scientific orthodoxy</aside>

But the fatal flaw in the argument is not only what is assumed, but what is omitted in regard to functional dependence. He suggests three kinds of functional dependence: (*a*) productive function; (*b*) releasing, or permissive function; and (*c*) transmissive function. (It would be an extremely useful exercise to consider if these can be correlated with Aristotle's four causes. After all, the functional dependence of thought upon the brain could be rephrased as the brain being the cause of thought; but what kind of cause?)

<aside>Three types of brain functional dependence</aside>

First Functional Dependence – Productive

Now considering the first dependence, James writes: 'When the physiologist who thinks that his science cuts off all hope of immortality pronounces the phrase, "Thought is a function of the brain", he thinks of the matter just as he thinks when he says, "Steam is a function of the tea-kettle", "Light is a function of the electric circuit", "Power is a function of the moving waterfall". In these latter cases the several material objects have the function of inwardly creating or engendering their effects, and their function must be called productive function. Just so, he thinks, it must be with the brain.' So with this line of reasoning, a blow to the head would quite obviously impair memory and brain function just as a hammer blow to a watch would damage or destroy the time keeping mechanism.

<aside>Productive function has no bearing on immortality</aside>

Second Functional Dependence – Releasing

Whilst the above is true, it is not the whole truth and in fact represents a limited under-standing of functional dependence. Let James continue with the second functional dependence. 'In the world of physical nature productive function of this sort is not the only kind of function with which we are familiar. We have also releasing or permissive function ... The trigger of a crossbow has a releasing function: it removes the obstacle that holds the string, and lets the bow fly back to its natural shape.' The trigger, then, does not produce the flying arrow: it releases the obstruction to its flight. 'So [also] when the hammer falls upon a detonating compound. By knocking out the inner molecular obstructions, it lets the constituent gases resume their normal bulk, and so permits the explosion to take place.' The hammer does not produce the explosion: it removes the molecular impediment to the rapid expansion of the gases. Here we may also cite Aldous Huxley's metaphor of a 'reducing valve': the more open the valve, the more the flow of fluid through it.[33] The valve does not produce the fluid flow: it releases it. For 'trigger and arrow', 'hammer and explosion' or 'valve and fluid flow', read 'brain and thought', respectively.

Releasing function does not produce what it releases

Modern evidence for what William James declared well over one hundred years ago is to be found in several recent studies of the effects of serotonin-2a-type psychedelic drugs assessed through functional magnetic resonance imaging (fMRI) and in some cases also by magnetoencephalography (MEG). The most profound psychosomatic experiences correlated with the greatest *inactivation* of key junctional regions within the brain (notably the thalamus, the medial prefrontal cortex, and the anterior and posterior cingulate cortex).[34]

Psychedelic drug experiences attest to the releasing function

Third Functional Dependence – Transmissive

The third functional dependence, says James, is the 'transmissive function' as 'in the case of a coloured glass, a prism, or a refracting lens.' He continues: 'The energy of light, no matter how produced, is by the glass sifted and limited in colour, and by the lens or prism determined to a certain path and shape. Similarly, the keys of an organ have only a transmissive function. They open successively the various pipes and let the wind in the air-chest escape in various ways. The voices of the various pipes are constituted by the columns of air trembling as they emerge. But the air is not engendered in the organ. The organ proper, as distinguished from its air-chest, is only an apparatus for letting portions of it loose upon the world in these peculiarly limited shapes.'

Transmissive function does not produce what it transmits

Concluding Insights

Then follows a radical insight from the great psychological scientist who, virtually by definition, must also be a poet and a mystic. Drawing upon the three kinds of functional dependence, but especially the third, James continues in *Human Immortality* thus: 'My thesis is now this: that, when we think of the law that thought is a function of the brain, we are not required to think of productive function only; *we are entitled also to consider permissive or transmissive function* [emphasis by James]. And this the ordinary psycho-physiologist leaves out of his account. Suppose, for example, that the whole universe of material things—the furniture of earth and choir of heaven—should turn out to be a mere surface-veil of phenomena, hiding and keeping back the world of genuine realities. Such a supposition is foreign neither to common sense nor to philosophy. [See the doctrine of *māyā*, a central plank of Eastern philosophy, fully explained in Chapter 8 of Volume III.]

Brain function is productive, releasing, and transmissive

Common sense believes in realities behind the veil even too superstitiously; and idealistic philosophy declares the whole world of natural experience, as we get it, to be but a time-mask, shattering or refracting the one infinite Thought which is the sole reality into those millions of finite streams of consciousness known to us as our private selves.' This idea is beautifully stated by one of the most influential lyric and philosophical poets in the English language, the English Romantic poet Percy Bysshe Shelley (1792–1822), whom James quotes. Stated in the epigraph, it is worth reiterating:

> Life, like a dome of many-coloured glass,
> Stains the white radiance of eternity.

Figure I-7 is an attempt to illustrate this sublime couplet by way of an analogy with the refraction of white light through a prism.

If the 'dome of many-coloured glass' were opaque all over, the transmitted light would be a homogeneous dullness. But supposing now that the glass were rendered transparent, or indeed fractured in a few places, then a few beams of light would penetrate the interior and vouchsafe the original source of the light. If we 'admit now that *our brains* [emphasis again by James] are such thin and half-transparent places in the veil. What will happen? Why, as the white radiance comes through the dome, with all sorts of staining and distortion imprinted on it by the glass, or as the air now comes through [our] glottis determined and limited in its force and quality of its vibrations by the peculiarities of those vocal chords which form its gate of egress and shape it into [our] personal voice, even so the genuine matter of reality, the life of souls as it is in its fullness, will break through our several brains into this world in all sorts of restricted forms, and with all the imperfections and queernesses that characterize our finite individualities here below.' This explains why different people will experience exactly the same event in different ways, each according to the refractive index, so to speak, of the 'thin and half-transparent places in the veil'. For these reasons, the various reported experiences of several people of the same thing, seen or heard, generally have similarity, but not much commonality, due to each person's own psychological 'colouring'.

The 'refractive index' of our brains conditions our perception of reality

Thus, the releasing, or permissive function, and the transmissive function work hand-in-glove. For 'according to the state in which the brain finds itself, the barrier of its obstructiveness' [its permissive function] will determine the intensity and quality of the transmission. This threshold state of the brain may rise or fall, equivalent to the reducing valve closing or opening. When it drops, as when the brain is in full creative activity (valve opening), a person may be so overwhelmed by a flood of spiritual energy that outwardly he may appear to be insane: stories of ecstatic illumination amongst both artists and scientists abound (for example Beethoven and Newton). But when the threshold state rises (valve closing), such as through boredom or stupor, there will be few, if any, moments of illumination. 'And finally', James continues, 'when the brain stops acting altogether, or decays [through disease], that special stream of consciousness which it subverted will vanish entirely from this natural world. *But the sphere of being that supplied the consciousness would still be intact; and in that more real world with which, even whilst here, it was continuous, the consciousness might, in ways unknown to us, continue still* [writer's emphasis].'

Creativity is heightened by lowered brain threshold activity

Recent work at York University by the contemporary British neuroscientist Miles Whittington gives much neuroscientific credence to James's seminal insight that a relaxed brain would be the best state for creativity to flourish.[35]

White Light Refracted Through a   White Radiance of Eternity Stained by 'Refraction'
Prism into Seven Colours   Through Brain into Countless Streams of Consciousness

Figure I-7   An Illustration of the Analogy Between Light and Life
Image Credit: Artefact Design

The permissive–transmissive theory elucidates phenomena that are unsatisfactorily explained by the productive theory, such as instantaneous healings, premonitions, near-death experiences, and the whole gamut of psychic occurrences. For example, concerning NDEs, it is entirely reasonable to propose that when the normal brain function is held largely in abeyance (through accident, serious illness or impending death), its permissive function is correspondingly enhanced, thereby ushering in experiences and visions that would under everyday circumstances be opaque. One of many authentic cases in relation to this phenomenon is that of the British Assistant Professor of Anatomy at Edinburgh University, Sir (later Lord) Auckland Geddes FRSE (1879–1954) in an address given in 1937 to the Royal Medical Society of Edinburgh about the experience of a friend. He assured the audience that the experience was not fake, or else it would not have been brought to their attention. Later, however, he admitted that it was his own. We may infer that this was to avoid being branded a fool by his medical peers. Geddes narrated:

> A few minutes after midnight, I began to feel very ill … and was definitely suffering from acute gastroenteritis … by ten o'clock I have developed all the symptoms of acute poisoning … pulse and respirations became quite impossible to count, I wanted to ring for assistance, but found I could not and so I quite placidly gave up the attempt. I realised that I was very ill and very quickly reviewed my whole financial position. Thereafter at no time did my consciousness appear to me in any way dimmed, but I suddenly realized that my consciousness was separating from another consciousness which was also me.

These Geddes called 'A-consciousness' and 'B-consciousness', stating that the ego attached itself to the former. He saw the B-consciousness begin to disintegrate while

> the A-consciousness [the conscious self], which was now me, seemed to be altogether outside my body, which it could see. Gradually I realised that I could see, not only my body and the bed in which it was, but everything in the whole house and garden, and

Margin notes:

Non-physical and paranormal phenomena best explained by the permissive–transmissive function

Lord Geddes's experience of two states of consciousness

then realised that I was seeing, not only "things" at home but in London and Scotland, *in fact wherever my attention was directed* [emphasis added].'[36]

Here it needs to be stressed that there are not two separate consciousnesses, what Geddes called A- and B-consciousnesses, but different phases of one unitary consciousness, rather like ice and water are different phase states of H_2O. This simile was mentioned earlier and the reasons will become clearer in Volume II. Also, the reasons for the relative omnipresence that Geddes experienced in A-consciousness will be detailed in Volume III.

Heisenberg and Einstein allude to the transmissive function

Along similar lines, the permissive–transmissive theory could well account for the deepest insights gifted to advanced persons when approaching death, when normal brain function progressively ebbs. Here is a classic example. When he was dying in 1976, the great Nobel physicist Werner Heisenberg, who enunciated the principle of indeterminacy, said to his student, the German physicist and philosopher Carl Friedrich Freiherr von Weizsäcker (1912–2007): 'It is very easy: I did not know this before.' At another moment he said, 'I see now that physics is of no importance, that the world is illusion.'[37] What Heisenberg uttered through direct insight (unhindered by the brain) was similar to what the great sages and occultists have declared since time immemorial—that nature can be understood in her true Self, as opposed to her manifold, illusionary appearances (*māyā*), only by penetrating through the physical veil and reaching beyond. In similar vein, about a month before his own death in 1955, Einstein wrote the following in a letter to the family of his good friend Michele Besso who had just died: 'Now he has departed from this strange world a little ahead of me. That means nothing. People like us, who believe in physics, know that the distinction between past, present and future is only a stubbornly persistent illusion.'[38] *In this sense, the shadow of death may well become our tutor by bestowing fleeting moments of illumination on those profound matters that we perceived but dimly during life.*

Everything produced already exists in the transcendental world

The production theory needs to answer from what, and how, are such events produced. But on the permissive–transmissive theory proposed by James, 'they don't have to be "produced"—they exist ready-made in the transcendental world, and all that is needed is an abnormal *lowering* [emphasis added] of the brain-threshold to let them through', as happens when the personal ego is held in abeyance through intense concentration, devotional feelings or artistic ecstasy. 'We need only suppose the continuity of our consciousness with a mother sea, to allow for exceptional waves occasionally pouring over the dam.' Note again that creativity is associated with a lowering of brain activity. Whereas this may seem counter-intuitive at first, it explains why the meditative state, associated with the quietening of thoughts and resultant lessening of ego obstructiveness, is so conducive to inner illumination. The French philosopher and Nobel laureate for literature Henri Bergson (1859–1941) takes a similar view in his book *Creative Evolution*, which became an enormously influential work in the philosophy of science. Postulating an alternative account of the mechanisms underpinning Darwin's evolution, he explored the creative process, the role of intuition and its supremacy over rationality, going so far as to state, 'the intellect is characterized by a natural inability to comprehend life.' [39] This is tantamount to a restatement of Schrödinger's intuition (stated in the Introductory, page xli) that, 'We do not belong to this material world that science [operating as it does virtually exclusively using intellect] constructs for us.' Great minds do indeed think alike!

So as James again has it: 'The theory of production is therefore not a jot more simple or credible in itself than any other conceivable theory. It is only a little more popular. All that one need do, therefore, if the ordinary materialist should challenge one to explain how the brain *can* [emphasis by James] be an organ for limiting and determining to a certain form a consciousness elsewhere produced, is to retort with [the logical fallacy of] a *tu quoque* ["you also"], asking him in turn to explain how it can be an organ for producing consciousness out of whole cloth. For polemic purposes, the theories are thus exactly on a par. But if we consider the theory of transmission in a wider way, we see that it has certain positive superiorities, quite apart from its connection with the immortality question. Into the mode of production of steam in a tea-kettle we have conjectural insight, for the terms that change are physically homogeneous one with another, and we can easily imagine the case to consist of nothing but alterations of molecular motion. But in the production of consciousness by the brain, the terms are heterogeneous natures altogether [since the brain is physical and consciousness is mental]. Ask for any indication of the exact process either of transmission or production, and Science [*sic*] confesses her imagination to be bankrupt. She has, so far, not the least glimmer of a conjecture or suggestion—not even a bad verbal metaphor or pun to offer. *Ignoramus, ignorabimus* [we don't know, we won't know—to which we might add, we choose never to know], is what most physiologists, in the words of one of their number, will say here.' As scientists, even now, have no idea of how the brain produces consciousness (*their assumption*), this should engender some humility—in the words of the Cambridge Professor of Physiology Ian Glynn FRS (*b*.1928): '*una granda lacuna* [a large missing part].'

Why does science choose not to know?

Recall that several decades later, Schrödinger raised precisely the same objections in the words: 'Science sometimes pretends to answer questions in these [higher] domains, but the answers are very often so silly that we are not inclined to take them seriously' (see Introductory, page lxi). The situation is little different today. Despite the vast expense, time, energy, and experiments (on animals) expended in consciousness research, science, by its own admission, 'confesses her imagination to be bankrupt' concerning the origin of consciousness, having discovered just its neural mechanisms.[40, 41, 42, 43, 44, 45, 46]

In answer to the objection that we do not know how the brain might transmit consciousness, we may respond that orthodox neuroscience does not know how the brain produces consciousness either; correlation does not amount to causation. The view that the brain produces consciousness is in fact a postulate, or presupposition, rather than a scientific finding.

Résumé

William James's work has been of seminal value in bridging the divide between materialism and esotericism, especially regarding the whole question of mind and consciousness. He shows us 'that the fatal consequence is not coercive, the conclusion which materialism draws being due solely to its one-sided way of taking the word "function"'; and that 'it is not at all impossible, but on the contrary quite possible, that the life may still continue when the brain itself is dead'—when the many streams of consciousness transmitted through the brain organ, like the coloured rays of light transmitted through the dome of many-coloured glass, are merged back and subsumed into their source—the white light of pure Consciousness, or life *per se*.

William James provides a bridge from the material to the spiritual

The one-sided notion of consciousness being produced by the brain, then, was a worldwide enigma in the days of William James as it is to this day—unless and until we look beyond and seek an answer that is not at the same level of thinking that created the problem (as per Einstein's counsel). This seminal injunction from H. P. Blavatsky is addressed, of course, to the nineteenth century scientists of her day but is just as relevant for us today.

H. P. Blavatsky instructs on how to bridge the material–spiritual divide

> The naturalists refuse to blend physics with metaphysics, the body with its informing soul and spirit, which they prefer ignoring. This is a matter of choice with some, while the minority strive very sensibly to enlarge the domain of physical science by trespassing on the forbidden grounds of metaphysics, so distasteful to some materialists. These scientists are wise in their generation. For all their wonderful discoveries would go for nothing, and remain for ever *headless* bodies, unless they lift the veil of matter and strain their eyes to see *beyond*. Now that they have studied nature in the length, breadth, and thickness of her physical frame, it is time to remove the skeleton to the second plane and search within the unknown depths for the living and real entity, for its SUB-*stance*—the noumenon of evanescent matter.47

It is clear that both James and Blavatsky (who were close contemporaries) are conveying precisely the same message, 'to see beyond' in their different ways. But note also Blavatsky's eloquent account about the brain as an organ of transmission, entirely in accord with James's thesis:

Blavatsky affirms the releasing–transmissive function

> Physical man [his body and brain] is the musical instrument, and the Ego [the Inner or Soul nature], the performing artist. The potentiality of perfect melody of sound, is in the former—the instrument—and no skill of the latter can awaken a faultless harmony out of a broken or badly made instrument. This harmony depends on the fidelity of transmission, by word or act, to the objective plane, of the unspoken divine thought in the very depths of man's subjective or inner nature. Physical man may—to follow our simile—be a priceless Stradivarius, or a cheap and cracked fiddle, or again a mediocrity between the two, in the hands of the Paganini who ensouls him.48

The nature and close relation between the 'cracked fiddle' or the 'priceless Stradivarius' and the 'Paganini' will be explained at length in Volume II. Meanwhile we remark that all the above make it abundantly clear that as long as scientists limit their scope solely to investigating matter with physical instruments and using ordinary physical senses, they will work in a squirrel-cage of seemingly arbitrary effects ('headless bodies') rather than discovering the cause ('the noumenon of evanescent matter') on a higher plane, which must be accessed by lifting the veil of matter and straining to see beyond. That scientists fully (if not freely) admit their virtual '*ignoramus, ignorabimus*' about consciousness *per se* (only its neural correlates in the realm of matter, i.e., the brain) is surely fitting proof of James's advice and Blavatsky's forewarning to see beyond the physical frame and search for the living and real entity—the ensouling Consciousness.

Many scientists, like Rupert Sheldrake, have situated materialism in a wider scientific paradigm

Several other scientists of unimpeachable integrity nowadays, as indeed in Blavatsky's era,iii have seen through the fallacies and limitations of the purely materialistic scientific paradigm and have wisely invoked a more holistic world-view in their attempt to 'strain their eyes to see beyond'. A prime example of such a modern scientist who strives 'to enlarge the domain of physical science by trespassing on the forbidden grounds of metaphysics, so distasteful to some materialists' is none other than Rupert Sheldrake to whom we made significant reference earlier. What they have observed is that a brain-only based

---

iii For example, Sir Arthur Eddinghton OM FRS, Sir James Jeans OM FRS, Sir Oliver Lodge FRS, and Sir William Crookes OM PRS.

theory of consciousness presents serious obstacles in explaining the types of phenomena described at length in this and previous Chapters.

In closing this Chapter on the urgent need for a new continent of thought, it is affirmed that every mystical verse, metaphysical treatise, esoteric doctrine, and sacred text, such as the Bible, Qabbalah, the Vedas, and the Egyptian *Book of the Dead*, to mention but four from the West and the East, may be read in one of three ways:[49]

1. the literal and intellectual—corresponding to the physical plane and Lower self;
2. the symbolical and intuitional—corresponding to the astral planes and Higher Self;
3. the purely Divine and Spiritual—corresponding to the spiritual realms and the Soul.

Sacred texts reveal their meaning on different levels

(The terms 'Lower self', 'Higher Self', 'astral planes' and 'Soul' will all be explained fully in Volume II.)

In the broadest sense these three categories correspond to the three brain functions of productive, permissive, and transmissive, as elucidated by James. Hence, *the same text will impart a radically different meaning depending on the attitude of mind and mode of thought of the enquirer, as our exposition has sought to emphasize.*

This Chapter has described the brain processes associated with materialistic thinking and when such thinking is transcended. The latter is absolutely essential in order to apprehend the breadth and profundity of the mystery teachings of all ages, being the subject of the next Chapter. Meanwhile we close with two piquant warnings to scientists about the inadequacy of the use of *exclusively* intellectual/analytic arguments associated with reductionism and a simplistic use of statistical arguments to prove a point:

Water is simply H_2O (in other words, 2 parts hydrogen to 1 part oxygen). Try putting out a fire by squirting hydrogen and oxygen on to it!
H. P. Blavatsky (attributed)

To upset the conclusion that all crows are black, there is no need to seek demonstration that no crow is black; it is sufficient to produce one white crow; a single one is sufficient.
William James[50]

NOTES

1   Percy Bysshe Shelley, *Adonais*, Stanza 52.
2   William J. Ross, *A New Continent of Thought* (Wheaton, Illinois: Theosophical Publishing House), 1956.
3   A. Pascual-Leone, et al., 'Characterizing Brain Cortical Plasticity and Network Dynamics Across the Age-Span in Health and Disease with TMS-EEG and TMS-fMRI', *Brain Topography*, 24 (2011), 302–15.
4   Norman Doidge, *The Brain That Changes Itself: Stories of personal triumph from the frontiers of brain science* (US: Viking Penguin, UK: Penguin, 2007).
5   William James, *The Principles of Psychology* (US: Dover Publications, 2000).

6   K. S. Lashley, 'Basic Neural Mechanisms in Behavior', Address of the President of the American Psychological Association before the Ninth International Congress of Psychology at New Haven, 4 September 1929. First published in *Psychological Review*, 37 (1930), 1–24.

7   Paul Bach-y-Rita, et al., 'BrainPort', *Mindstates.tribe.net*, topic posted, 30 March 2005.

8   P. Bach-y-Rita and S. W. Kercel, 'Sensory Substitution and the Human–Machine Interface', *Trends in Cognitive Science*, 7/12 (2003), 541–6.

9   E. A. Maguire, R. S. Frackowiak, and C. D. Frith, 'Recalling Routes Around London: Activation of the right hippocampus in taxi drivers', *The Journal of Neuroscience*, 17/18 (1997), 7103–10.

10 K. Woollett and E. A. Maguire, 'Acquiring "the Knowledge" of London's Layout Drives Structural Brain Changes', *Current Biology* 21/24 (2011), 2109–14.

11 E. A. Maguire, D. G. Gadian, I. S. Johnsrude, C. D. Good, J. Ashburner, R. S. J. Frackowiak, and C. D. Frith, 'Navigation–Related Structural Change in the Hippocampi of Taxi Drivers', *Proceedings of the National Academy of Sciences*, 97/8 (2000), 4398–403.

12 Ana Carolina Rodrigues, Maurício Alves Loureiro, and Paulo Caramelli, 'Musical Training, Neuroplasticity and Cognition', *Dementia e Neuropsychologia*, 4/4 (São Paulo: 2010).

13 Victor A. Colotla and Paul Bach-y-Rita, 'Shepherd Ivory Franz: His contributions to neuropsychology and rehabilitation', *Cognitive, Affective & Behavioral Neuroscience*, 2/2 (2002), 141–8.

14 Jill Bolte Taylor, *My Stroke of Insight: A brain scientist's personal journey* (UK: Hodder Paperbacks, 2009).

15 Iain McGilchrist, *The Master and His Emissary: The divided brain and the making of the western world* (rev. and enl. edn, New Haven and London: Yale University Press, 2019).

16 Dean V. Buonomano and Michael M. Merzenich, 'Cortical Plasticity: From synapses to maps', *Annual Review of Neuroscience*, 21 (1998), 149–86.

17 M. M. Merzenich, R. J. Nelson, M. P. Stryker, M. S. Cynader, A. Schoppmann, and J. M. Zook, 'Somatosensory Cortical Map Changes Following Digit Amputation in Adult Monkeys', *Journal of Comparative Neurology*, 224/4 (1984), 591–605.

18 S. Lazar, C. Kerr, R. Wasserman, J. Gray, et al., 'Meditation Experience is Associated with Increased Cortical Thickness', *NeuroReport*, 16/17 (2005), 1893–7.

19 Richard Davidson and Antoine Lutz, 'Buddha's Brain: Neuroplasticity and meditation', *IEEE Signal Processing Magazine* (January 2008).

20 Meghan O'Rourke, 'Train Your Brain: The new mania for neuroplasticity', *SLATE* (25 April 2007) <http://www.slate.com/articles/life/brains/2007/04/train_your_brain.html#p2> accessed 21 November 2019.

21 Mark R. Rosenzweig, 'Aspects of the Search for Neural Mechanisms of Memory', *Annual Review of Psychology*, 47 (1996), 1–32.

22 Annie Besant, *A Study in Consciousness: A contribution to the science of psychology* (Adyar, Madras: Theosophical Publishing House, 1972), 125.

23 Adapted from Bowen Notes, 10–11. The Bowen Notes are extracts from the notes of personal teachings given by H.P. Blavatsky to private pupils during the years 1888 to 1891. These are published in a pamphlet entitled *Madame Blavatsky on How to Study Theosophy* (London: Theosophical Publishing House, 1960).

24 *VS*, Fragment I: The Voice of the Silence.

25 Paul Brunton, *A Search in Secret India* (New York: Samuel Weiser, 1994), 304.

26 William James: *Writings 1878–1899* and *Writings 1902–1910*, Library of America <https://www.loa.org> accessed 7 January 2019.

27 Kurt Leland, 'Alarums and Excursions: William James and the Theosophical Society', *Theosophical History*, 19/4 (October 2018).

28 Emanuel Swedenborg, *Heaven and its Wonders and Hell From Things Heard and Seen* (1758; New York: Swedenborg Foundation), 1946.

29 Emanuel Swedenborg, *The Principia; or, the first principles of natural things, being new attempts toward a philosophical explanation of the elementary world*, trans. Rev. Augustus Clissold (London: W. Newbery and H. Bailliere; Boston: Otis Clapp, 1846); [online facsimile] <https://archive.org/details/b29324919_0002/page/n5/mode/2up> accessed 30 July 2020.

30 See 'David Bodanis on Isaac Newton – Swedenborg Birthday Lecture 2018' <https://www.swedenborg.org.uk/events/david-bodanis-on-isaac-newton-2/> accessed 29 July 2021.

31 William James, 'Human Immortality (1898)'
    <http://www.uky.edu/~eushe2/Pajares/jimmortal.html> accessed 21 November 2019. All quota-
    tions are taken from this lecture.

32 William James, *Human Immortality: Two supposed objections to the doctrine* (UK: Andesite Press,
    2015).

33 Aldous Huxley, *The Doors of Perception* (London: Chatto & Windus, 1954); [online version]
    <https://www.mescaline.com/huxley.htm> accessed 21 November 2019.

34 R. L. Carhart-Harris, et al. 'Neural Correlates of the LSD Experience Revealed by Multimodal
    Neuroimaging, *PNAS*, 113/17 (26 April, 2016), 4853–8. See also Eben Alexander, 'Consciousness
    and the Shifting Scientific Paradigm', *Journal of the Scientific and Medical Network*, 127 (2018), 3–8.

35 See The University of York, The Hull York Medical School, Centre for Neuroscience
    <https://www.hyms.ac.uk/research/research-centres-and-groups> accessed 21 November 2019.

36 David Lorimer, *Survival? Death as a Transition* (Hove, UK: White Crow Books), 2017; quotations
    from 1st edn, *Survival? Body, Mind and Death in the Light of Psychic Experience* (London: Routledge &
    Kegan Paul, 1984), 249–50.

37 *NPB*-6, Part 2: *From Birth to Rebirth*, 'The Event of Death', ¶104, 16.

38 'Michele Besso', Wikipedia (last modified 13 July 2019)
    <https://en.wikipedia.org/wiki/Michele_Besso> accessed 14 February 2020.

39 Henri Bergson, *Creative Evolution*, trans. Arthur Mitchell (US: University Press of America), 165.

40 Colin McGinn, 'Can we Solve the Mind-Body Problem?' in *Mind*, 98 (1989), 349–66.

41 —— *The Problem of* Consciousness (Oxford: Blackwell, 1991).

42 Ned Block, 'On a Confusion about the Function of Consciousness', *Behavioral and Brain Sciences*, 18
    (1995), 227–47.

43 David Chalmers, *The Conscious Mind: In search of a fundamental theory* (New York and Oxford:
    Oxford University Press, 1996).

44 Ned Block, 'The Harder Problem of Consciousness', *The Journal of Philosophy*, 99/8 (2002),
    391–425.

45 Joseph Levine, 'The Explanatory Gap', in *The Oxford Handbook of Philosophy of Mind* (Oxford:
    Clarendon Press; New York: Oxford University Press, 2009)
    DOI:10.1093/oxfordhb/9780199262618.003.0017.

46 Rocco Gennaro, *The Consciousness Paradox* (Cambridge, Massachusetts, MIT Press, 2012).

47 *SD*-I, 'Gods, Monads, and Atoms', 610.

48 *CW*-XII, 'Genius', 15.

49 *Occult Mysteries: The path to light* <http://www.occult-mysteries.org/symbolism.html> accessed 21
    November 2019.

50 The quote is from one of William James's lectures in 1890, in Brian A. Schill, *Stalking Darkness:
    Surveillance and investigation techniques for paranormal investigators*, International Parapsychology
    Research Foundation (US: printed Lulu.com; 2nd edn, 2008), 49.

7 The Mystery Teachings of All Ages – A General Overview

The Mysteries had evolved a method whereby the mind was so trained in the fundamental verities of life that it was able to cope intelligently with any emergency which might arise. Thus the reasoning faculties were organized by a simple process of mental culture, for it was asserted that where reason reigns supreme, inconsistency cannot exist. Wisdom, it was maintained, lifts man to the condition of Godhood, a fact which explains the enigmatical statement that the Mysteries transformed 'roaring beasts into divinities'.

MANLY P. HALL[1]

SYNOPSIS

Chapter 7 presents an overview of the teachings imparted in the Mystery Schools that lie at the root of both Western and Eastern cultures. The location of these great centres of wisdom, ancient and modern, and their emissaries, are also touched upon. A route map is provided to show how science, religion, philosophy, and culture are the tributaries fecundated by the stream of universal wisdom, or *philosophia perennis*—one in essence and from one source—since time immemorial.

A major portion of this Chapter comprises a necessarily meticulous explanation of terms and this is especially the case in relation to the term 'occult science'. To use such a term is virtually guaranteed to evoke a reaction of contemptuous disdain, or a charge of derangement and dabbling with the black arts. We therefore spare no effort to explain the precise meaning of this sacred, yet most misunderstood of terms, and to justify our reasons for insisting upon using it in order to show the wisdom it bequeaths to the sincere seeker after Truth. However, at this stage it would be useful to throw more light on the elementary definition given in the Proem and add that the science of the secrets of nature involves the totality of the physical and psychic, mental and spiritual realms.

Related, but not equivalent, terms to occult science, are esoteric science, theosophy, mysticism, psychism, and metaphysics. Unfortunately, out of pure ignorance, these terms have been assigned meanings which do not belong to them. This has resulted in no end of sloppy use and, indeed, plain misuse. Accordingly, they are carefully defined and the insights revealed by their nuances of meaning are elucidated.

Having thus cleared the decks of prejudicial clutter, in the following Chapters we show how occult science throws much needed light upon our understanding of man at all levels, from the physical to the spiritual.

KEY WORDS: Mystery Teachings, Mystery Schools, qualifications for initiation, adepts, occultism, esotericism, theosophy, mysticism, psychism, metaphysics

This Chapter represents a turning point and upwards 'gear shift' in order to aspire towards the teachings of the *philosophia perennis*, generally known as the 'Mystery Teachings', about consciousness and life.

Our Journey So Far

Our journey so far has been long and admittedly, arduous at times. But our sojourn in some regions of rough territory has been necessary to make a robust case for the *philosophia perennis* as an indispensable complement to the scientific view of the world. This, it is hoped, has been accomplished by explaining in detail, supported by copious references, the philosophy and methodology of science and, as a corollary, its attendant strengths and weaknesses. Considerable evidence for the need to transcend—not jettison—the current scientific paradigm has been adduced from renowned scientists (including many Nobel laureates, like Schrödinger who has been periodically mentioned) working within the scientific camp to demonstrate the limits and limitations of materialism; hence, dictating the urgency of incorporating the latter within a wider and deeper paradigm that also embraces non-physical realms, including the implications arising from phenomena such as near-death experiences, out-of-the-body experiences, remote viewing, and paranormal phenomena. Having prepared the ground, we are now equipped to plunge into the majestic and awe-inspiring Mystery Teachings.

The Mysteries transcend the materialistic paradigm

The Mysteries – A Preamble

The degrees of initiation of the Mysteries are three in number. They were commonly imparted in ancient times in temple chambers which represented the three great centres of the human and Universal bodies. If possible, the temple itself was constructed in the form of the human body. The candidate entered between the feet and received the highest degree in the point corresponding to the brain. Thus the first degree was the material mystery and its symbol was the generative system; it raised the candidate through the various degrees of concrete thought. The second degree was given in the chamber corresponding to the heart, but represented the middle power which was the mental link. Here the candidate was initiated into the mysteries of abstract thought and lifted as high as the mind was capable of penetrating. The aspirant of the third degree then passed into the third chamber, which, analogous to the brain (in the human body), occupied the highest position in the temple but, analogous to the heart, was of the greatest dignity. In the brain chamber the heart mystery was given. Here, for the first time, the initiate truly comprehended the meaning of those immortal biblical words: 'As a man thinketh in his heart, so is he.'[2] The above is just a taster before expanding on the profound analogies and symbolism regarding the human body in Chapter 4 of Volume III.

Three degrees of initiation into the Mysteries

What follows, then, is a necessarily brief elucidation of the Mystery Teachings based upon a digest of the writings principally of H. P. Blavatsky and Manly P. Hall, supplemented by other information garnered from the works of the American scholar, linguist, and esoteric philosopher Gottfried de Purucker (1874–1942), Nicholas Goodrick-Clarke (1953–2012), the British historian and professor of Western Hermeticism at the

University of Exeter and Director of the Exeter Centre for the Study of Esotericism,[i] and other arcane sources that are referenced in the appropriate places.

Equipped then, with our new mode of thinking, as outlined in the closing sections of the previous Chapter, let us tread carefully into the arcana of the Mystery Teachings taught in the Mystery Schools of all ages and cultures since time immemorial. 'Mystery Teachings' is the generic term given to esoteric teachings concerning the sacred teachings concealed within the rituals, allegories, and observances of all ages, mostly kept secret from the profane or uninitiated masses, and concerning the origin of things, the nature of the human spirit, its relation to the body, and method of its purification and restoration to a higher life. These teachings are also known under a whole variety of other terms conveying a similar flavour, such as the secret teachings, theosophy, esotericism, occultism, and the Secret Doctrine (not to be confused with H. P. Blavatsky's epic book *The Secret Doctrine*, which contains a portion of the universal Secret Doctrine relevant to our scientific epoch). At the outset, let the reader be clear that the mystery aspect of these teachings has nothing to do with mystique or any deliberate attempt to obfuscate or mislead. These teachings about the invisible Laws of Nature, and the powers latent in man, have been taught in the Mystery Schools of great civilizations (like India, Egypt, Persia, Greece, Mexico) since the dawn of time, but because the teachings concern the inner workings, or secrets, of Nature and man rather than the outward form, as taught in the conventional schools of science, the information is revealed only to students who are suitably qualified (see below). This stipulation is no different, in principle, from any school or college where a student has to qualify himself to attend the course he desires: except that in the Mystery Schools— ancient and contemporary—the proven qualifications are based upon nobility of character and moral attainment in addition to intellectual aptitude, so that the teachings imparted would not be misused for selfish or personal reasons.

Mystery Teachings are worldwide and imparted only to worthy candidates

So for this reason, the Mysteries in every country are divided into two general parts: the 'Lesser' and the 'Greater'. In ancient times, for example in Egypt, the Lesser Mysteries were sacred to Isis and the Greater Mysteries to Serapis and Osiris; and in Greece the Lesser Mysteries were the Eleusinian and the Greater Mysteries the Orphic and Dionysian. In all cases, the Lesser Mysteries largely comprised dramatic rites or ceremonies, alongside some teaching; whereas the Greater Mysteries were composed of, and conducted, almost entirely on the grounds of study, and the doctrines taught in them were proved later by personal experience in initiation. The first philosophers of antiquity were all initiated in the Mystery Schools. To a greater or lesser degree, then, the mysteries of cosmogony and nature, in general, were personified by the priests and neophytes, who enacted the parts of various gods and goddesses, repeating the scenes—allegories—from their respective lives. These were then explained in their hidden meaning to the candidates for initiation and incorporated into philosophical doctrines.

The Greater and Lesser Mysteries

Mystery traditions lie at the roots of both Western and Eastern cultures, taught by the ancient masters of wisdom who laid the foundations for the world we now live in, first to chosen disciples, who then disseminated the teachings on a wider front. It has become common in the West to turn to Eastern sources for real understanding and enlightenment; however, as constantly emphasized in this work, Western culture, albeit highly

---

i Dedicated university chairs in esotericism are also at the Sorbonne and the University of Amsterdam.

materialistic, is underpinned by a tradition of incredible wisdom and significance, which we need now, more urgently than ever, to rediscover and reclaim. To that end the works of the Canadian-born occultist, philosopher, and prodigious researcher of esoteric and mythological lore, Manly P. Hall (see Profiles at the end of Volume III), and more recently, the British philosopher, Cambridge scholar, and mystic Peter Kingsley (b.1953), provide an invaluable service.[3] The Preface to the Diamond Jubilee Edition of Hall's magnum opus was written in 1988. It mentions the author's despair that 'materialism was in complete control of the economic structure, the final objective of which was for the individual to become part of a system providing an economic security at the expense of the human soul, mind, and body.'[4] He goes on to remark that, 'with a very few exceptions', the works of classical authors on all systems of idealistic philosophy, and the deeper aspects of comparative religion, have been downgraded by modern authorities 'and scholarship was based largely upon the acceptance of a sterile materialism.' In the same vein, he continues, 'we are now coming to the end of the twentieth century, and the great materialistic progress which we have venerated for so long is on the verge of bankruptcy'; therefore, 'to avoid a future of war, crime, and bankruptcy, the individual must begin to plan his own destiny, and the best source of the necessary information comes down to us through the writings of the ancients.' Accordingly, his volume 'is a tribute to the memories and labors of the noblest of mankind.'

Mystery Teachings are the saviour of humanity

The 'writings of the ancients' are of course known as the Mystery Teachings. But as this is an abstruse subject it is as well at this early stage to define some key terms in common use in the literature of the Mysteries. But first, we need to dispense with the charge frequently levelled against mysticism and occultism that they are merely a throwback to an earlier age of superstition now effectively supplanted by modern exact science.

The Charge of Mediæval Superstition

'But all that's just mediæval and woolly mysticism' is the contemptuous retort one invariably hears about astrology, divination, and spiritual healing, to take just a few arbitrary examples of subjects under the general heading of the esoteric and occult sciences that are largely scorned by those who have never bothered to enquire into such matters. These terms will shortly be defined in the wider concept of science, which simply means 'knowledge' derived from the Latin *scīre*, 'to know', hence applying to all departments of human enquiry, which of course includes, but is not restricted to, the scope of Western science. It is a truism that 'empty vessels make the most noise', meaning that facetious remarks always come from those dominated by popular sensationalist journalism (espousing scientific materialism exclusively) who have never troubled to investigate, seriously, what these subjects really mean. As Goodrick-Clarke notes: 'The intellectual status of such topics was denigrated, and they were kept in epistemological quarantine lest they cause a relapse from progressive rationalism. Just as the established churches had once excluded heterodox doctrine as heresy, the modern post-Enlightenment world rejected magic and occultism as a violation of reason, its dominant criterion of acceptable discourse.'[5] Goodrick-Clarke further observes that far from being regarded as superstition or outmoded knowledge and a 'casualty of positivist and materialist perspectives during the nineteenth century', esotericism is slowly gaining the historical pre-eminence it deserves as a worldview. This is borne from its illuminating influence on the progress of scientific,

Superstition is invariably a label for ignorance or lack of understanding

religious and philosophical thought. Exhaustive research and historical scholarship, from impeccable sources, have shown how esotericism lies at the core of science and spirituality that has characterized and fecundated both Eastern and Western thought in various schools and movements from antiquity to the present age. Major academic sources on Western esotericism are given in Endnote I-6.

Indeed, there is a great deal of mediæval superstition that is just that; and it raises its ugly head rather more frequently than we like to admit. But superstition is the distorted outer garb concealing an inner lining of truth. Therefore, we must look through irrational credulity and the surface meaning, namely, the 'dead-letter' interpretation of words and phrases.

A Matter of Definitions

We now move to an understanding of some key terms: 'spirit' and 'spiritual', 'philosophy' and 'philosopher', 'theosophy', 'mysticism', 'esotericism' and 'exotericism', 'occultism' and 'psychism', and 'metaphysics'. These words have a considerable overlap of meaning, which is a source of confusion; hence an understanding of the origin of such terms, and their individual nuances of connotation, will avoid much confusion and misunderstandings as we proceed.

Etymology helps to reveal the inner meaning of words

Definitions can sometimes be arbitrary. This particularly applies to highly abstract terms like the ones just mentioned. Our approach, therefore, is to coax out the essential meaning of a term from its etymology, which elucidates the origin, or 'seed-meaning' of the term, and the way in which its meaning has evolved throughout history.

Spirit and Spiritual – What Do They Imply?

The literature of religion, mysticism, and philosophy abounds in liberal (and often vague) use of the terms 'spirit' and 'spiritual'. Spirit connotes the eternal and immortal element in all of nature, man, and the universe; and Matter (or Substance), its correlate. It must constantly be borne in mind that these terms are abstractions, referring to universal principles (hence capitalized)—generalized expressions of which energy and matter (in the terminology of modern science) are the physicalized manifestations.

The need to distinguish the abstract from the concrete

By implication then the term 'spiritual', as commonly understood, is a view of life that recognizes the continuity of an immortal element that is untouched by the death and change of the form of its expression: in man, this of course refers to some kind of surviving entity after the death of the mortal, physical body.

Later on we shall clarify, in detail, the difference between spirit and soul. For now, suffice it to say that soul is the vehicle of spirit and so the two terms are not synonymous.

Philosophy – What Is It, and Who is a Philosopher?

Who is a philosopher? On the first page of his magnificent Chapter, 'The Life and Philosophy of Pythagoras', Hall intriguingly states: 'Pythagoras was said to have been the first man to call himself a *philosopher*; in fact, the world is indebted to him for the word *philosopher*. Before that time the wise men had called themselves *sages*, which was interpreted to mean *those who know*. Pythagoras was more modest. He coined the word *philosopher*, which he defined as *one who is attempting to find out*.'[12] Thus, a philosopher is one who takes full cognizance of the spiritual dimension of life and the universe. In this wise, it is worth reminding ourselves that philosophy is the love of wisdom and Truth, and not merely the accumulation of intellectual knowledge and dry facts, which is a debasement of the true meaning of philosophy. The term derives from the Latin *philosophia* meaning 'knowledge', 'body of knowledge'; and from the Greek *philosophia* meaning 'love of knowledge', 'pursuit of wisdom', derived from the compound *philo-* 'loving' and *sophia* 'knowledge', 'wisdom', from *sophos* 'wise', 'learned'.

Pythagoras, the supreme philosopher

Theosophy – What Does It Mean?

The term 'theosophy' derives from the Greek *theosophia* meaning 'Wisdom-Religion', or 'Divine Wisdom' derived from the compound *theos-* 'a divine being', 'a god' and *sophia* 'wisdom'. It is not 'Wisdom of God' (as mistranslated by some) but, as just stated, Divine Wisdom such as possessed by the gods (not by 'God' in the ridiculously anthropomorphic sense in which the word is used today), the plural term signifying the various powers, forces, and intelligences in Nature which are impersonal, but personified in terms of various deities in the popular mythologies, legends, and traditions of world cultures, and known collectively as 'the gods'). The origin of the term, which is several thousand years old, comes from the Alexandrian philosophers, called 'lovers of truth', or Philalethians, from the Greek *philo-* 'loving' and *aletheia* 'truth'. The term 'theosophy' originates from the third century of our era, beginning with Ammonius Saccas (175–242), the Greek philosopher who started the School of Alexandria, and who is often referred to as one of the founders of Neoplatonism. It was Saccas and his disciples, chiefly the Greek philosopher Plotinus (*circa* 204/5–270) who founded the Eclectic Theosophical system in order to reconcile every system of ethics based on eternal verities, by demonstrating their identical origin in one universal system.

Theosophy concerns Divine Science; it is not a religion

Theosophy and its doctrines, then, are emphatically not a religion[ii] but Divine Consciousness, or Divine Science; and in its practical bearing theosophy is Divine Ethics. It is the exact equivalent of the Eastern term *Brahmā-Vidyā*, Divine Knowledge. However for our purposes, theosophy is the sub-stratum and basis of all the world religions, sciences, and philosophies as taught and practised by the elect few of humanity, who are referred to by such terms as seers and sages, initiates and adepts. Accordingly, to reiterate, theosophy is not a religion; nor is it a syncretistic religion-science-philosophy system of thought or belief which has been put together piecemeal like a jigsaw-puzzle from various sources. On the contrary, just as white light is broken into the separate colours of the solar spectrum by the prism, theosophy is a single, self-consistent, organic system and systematic formulation of the facts of Nature—both visible and invisible—which, when expressed through the 'prism' of the illumined human mind, takes the apparently separate

---

ii The definitions in dictionaries, based on religious prejudice and ignorance, are invariably inaccurate and misleading at best, or at worst, pure nonsense.

forms (like 'colours') of religion, science, and philosophy. Likewise, theosophy may be described as the formulation in human language of the nature and structure, origins and destiny, and operations of the Universe—seen and unseen—and of the multitude of beings which dwell in it. The principal aim of modern theosophy is essentially the same as that of its predecessor, the Eclectic Theosophical School.

Theosophy and the Perennial Philosophy – What Is Their Relation?

The simple answer to the question of the relation between theosophy and the *philosophia perennis* is that the two terms are practically synonymous in their essential meaning. Then why not use any one term instead of both? The reason is to promote better clarity and nuances of meaning. *Philosophia perennis* is used as an overarching and generalizing term encompassing the three broad categories of 'theosophy'. This is depicted in Figure I-8 which is a flowchart that attempts to summarize and represent the evolutionary develop-ment and progression of the *philosophia perennis* as characterized by: (*a*) *theosophia*, its quintessential meaning of Divine Consciousness, or Divine Wisdom—REALITY, the 'territory', so-called; (*b*) theosophy, its various teachings and doctrines—the several ways of looking at REALITY—the intellectual concepts, the 'maps' and 'models', so to speak; and (*c*) Theosophy, its modern synthesis—a specific set of 'maps', drawn from diverse sources, ancient and modern.

Common source of diverse teachings

We draw particular attention to the third inset in Figure I-8: Theosophy (capital *T*), which is a contemporary presentation through a scientific idiom by the modern Theosophical Society of the universal theosophy, or *philosophia perennis* underlying all religions, sciences, and philosophies the world over.

Mysticism – What Really Is It?

Popularly stated and understood, mysticism represents a state of transformation resulting in union with a Higher Power, by whatever name, such as REALITY, the Absolute, the Infinite, or God. So a mystic is one who may be said to experience intimations, or intuitions, of the existence of inner and superior worlds (transcending the physical) and who attempts to ally himself or come into self-conscious communion with them and the beings who inhabit these inner and invisible worlds. Mysticism is common to all religions and all cultures, and each religion has its own mystical tradition. The significant point to note is that, univer-sally, mystics report that their personal boundaries dissolve as they experience not just union with a higher reality, but a merging with this supernal realm such that they are one existence.

Mysticism is the common property of all religions

The mystic state has innumerable shades ranging from vague intimations of superior worlds to an elevated state, such as *Henosis* (Ancient Greek: ἕνωσις)—union with the 'One and All'. The latter comprises a conviction based on inner vision and knowledge of the existence of spiritual and ethereal universes of which our physical universe is the outer garment, or shell, so to speak; plus the inner knowledge that such higher dimensional universes (worlds, planes, or spheres), with their hosts of inhabitants, are intimately connected with the origin, destiny, and present nature of the world that surrounds us, which we inhabit. (Of course, there are gullible or neurotic people who claim to have experienced superior visions that are in fact none other than their own delusions. But delusion says everything about the

Mysticism is characterized by the merging of the personal with the impersonal reality

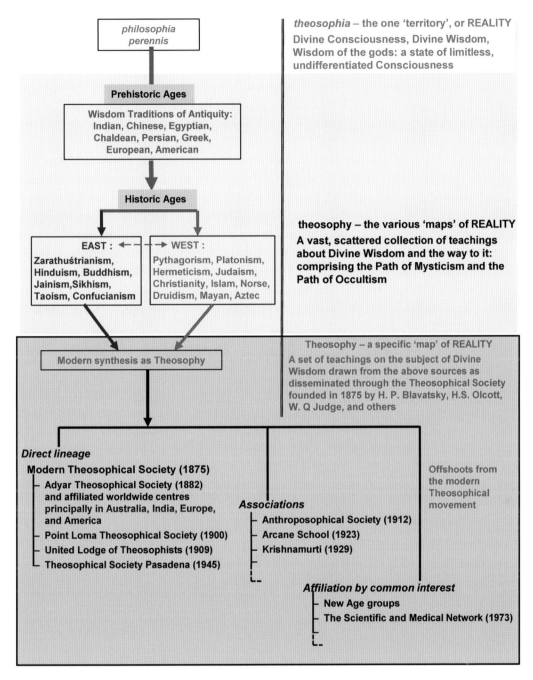

Figure I-8 The Outpouring of *theosophia* – One Source: Many Tributaries

deluded person and nothing about the innumerable authentic accounts to be found in the allegories, poems, literature, and sciences the world over.)

When the consciousness of the mystic-seeker approaches 'at-onement' with the essence of the object of his search, then with this attainment, it becomes virtually impossible to describe in the language of the outer and objective world what is seen and experienced in the inner, spiritual worlds because of their highly qualitative, subjective nature and unimaginable splendour.

We must perforce dispose of the all-too-frequent charge that mysticism is woolly and vague. In fact, it is the very opposite: it is, as just implied, a condition of absolute clarity where the mystic has penetrated the veil of conceptualizing intellect to touch a deeper level of reality that transcends thought and language. The oft-heard jibe about 'woolly mystics' therefore displays complete ignorance about the true nature of the attainment. As an exercise, readers are invited to describe their dreams in full detail—not just the scenes, but the experience of them. This will give an indication of the virtually insurmountable difficulties in attempting to describe the ineffable, internal landscape in words—which is why so many mystics have resorted to poetry, allegory, metaphor, and music to convey their intuitions—or wisely, remained silent. In point of fact, sacred metaphor, symbolism, allegory, and paradox are not only necessary, but indispensable to convey some flavour of the inward experience. Many a mystic may not be trained in science or mathematics, or may even be illiterate, hence the *expression* of his inner realization may well be imprecise and nebulous. Newton is, arguably, the supreme example of an ardent mystic and occultist (as defined shortly), who famously succeeded in harnessing his intuitions through the language of mathematics, much of which he invented himself, as also through his original experiments in optics[6] and alchemy.[7]

Mysticism is a state of perfect inner clarity

The English writer and pacifist Evelyn Underhill (1875–1941) known for her numerous works on religion and spiritual practice, in particular Christian mysticism, encapsulates the mystic vision thus:

> Mysticism is the art of union with Reality. The mystic is a person who has attained that union in a greater or lesser degree, or who aims at and believes in such attainment.[8]

> The visionary is a mystic when his vision mediates to him an actuality beyond the reach of the senses.[9]

Although the above extracts speak of the unific approach of the mystic (over the analytical methods of the scientist), it needs to be made perfectly clear that no true mystic would automatically disdain an intellectual approach to problems (Newton, the obvious and supreme example as just stated). However, when problems become intractable at the intellectual level, instead of wallowing in a morass of conflicting theories (as do the intellectualists), he sees the need for a different approach: to transcend the limitations of the physical senses and the material world. The difference between the scientific and mystic-esoteric methods of investigating nature—both equally valid in their respective contexts— is explained later.

Ironically, because of its all-inclusive approach, mysticism could, in a sense, be said to be even more committed to the scientific ethos than science itself. In *Dialogues with Scientists and Sages*, Renée Weber (1929–2017), who was a professor of philosophy at Rutgers, the State University of New Jersey, and a member of the Board of Directors of the Theosophical Society in America,[iii] has put this very eloquently:

Mysticism is truer to the scientific ethos than even science

> It is mysticism, not science, which pursues the Grand Unified Theory with ruthless logic—the one that includes the questioner within its answer. Although the scientist wants to unify everything in one ultimate equation, he does not want to unify

---

iii Weber's book is dedicated to the American, Fritz Kunz (1888–1971), lecturer, educator, editor, writer, and leading member of the Theosophical Society in India and America.

consistently, since he wants to leave himself outside that equation. Of course, with the advent of quantum mechanics, that is far less possible than it was in classical physics. Now observer and observed are admitted to constitute a unit. But the full meaning of this has not yet caught up with most of the community of scientists [especially, the biologists] who, despite quantum mechanics, believe they can stand aloof from what they work on.[10]

Esotericism and Exotericism – What Do They Mean?

We have just explained that in the approach to the psycho-spiritual world, the mystic is concerned primarily with the intensity of his inner experience and its repetition. Such questions as 'Why?', 'How?', 'For what purpose?', 'In what context?' are of secondary concern, if at all, to the mystic. But they are of absolutely major concern to the esotericist and occultist who, as the English scholar and author on Theosophy and esotericism John Gordon (1946–2013) admirably elucidates, 'sees and recognizes the "inner world" as a progressive theophany (subjectively visual perception of divine organization) of far greater extent and reality than the objectively visible world.'[11]

Esotericism then, is a somewhat generalizing term for the entire body of the Esoteric Philosophy, or Doctrine, the term derived from the Greek *esôterikos* (esotericos) 'inner', 'concealed', 'hidden', 'secret', 'pertaining to the innermost'. Its antonym is exoteric, or profane—see below.

Esotericism provides the key to unlock hidden meanings

Accordingly, the Esoteric Doctrine is the body of mystical and sacred teachings—about the Universe, Nature, and Man—reserved for students of high and worthy character. So in this sense, esoteric also means 'equipped with a key'—a key to unlock the inner meaning of a Mystery Teaching. Using the example of the Qabbalah in the Western Mystery tradition, it represents the broad stream of the hidden wisdom (mystical and occult) contained in the Hebrew Scriptures, derived in turn from the older secret doctrines concerning cosmogony and other divine things. It taught that there existed within the sacred writings a hidden doctrine which was the key to those writings.

The Esoteric Doctrine has always been the heritage of mankind, but not the common property of the masses. Since time immemorial, it has been held in the guardianship of exalted persons—the seers, sages, initiates, and adepts—who periodically disseminate those portions of it to the world when the intellectual and spiritual needs of mankind are ripe. The form in which such portions of esotericism is revealed is necessarily dependent upon the intellectual capacity and spiritual propensities of the human minds in question. This readily accounts for the diverse world-religions and world-philosophies seeming to have little in common (or even appearing to be contradictory). But on reflection and careful study, the root cause of such differences is realized to be not in the contents, but in the different forms which each religion and philosophy took as having been the best means of expressing an aspect of the eternal verities for the epoch in which it was promulgated. So if all the great religions and philosophies are placed side by side, so to speak, and critically examined, the fundamental principles in each will be found to be identical; for this reason, the aggregate of all these world-religions and world-philosophies contains the entirety of the Esoteric Doctrine, but it is invariably expressed in exoteric form.

Esotericism is the highest common factor in world religions, sciences, and philosophies

Why the charge of
silence?

As we are informed in *Ancient Freemasonry* by the American Masonic and Rosicrucian scholar, and authority on ritual and ceremonial magic, Frank C. Higgins (*circa* 1860–*circa* 1920): 'The pupils of the Pythagorean School were divided into "exoterici", or pupils in the outer grades, and "esoterici", after they had passed the third degree of initiation and were entitled to the secret wisdom. Silence, secrecy and unconditional obedience were cardinal principles of this great order.'[12] The word 'exoteric' in contrast to 'esoteric' also seems to have been used in the Peripatetic School of Greece, initially by Aristotle. There are parallels also in Gnosticism.[13]

The Qabbalah and
its offshoots

The best example from the Western Mystery tradition is surely the Qabbalah. Besides being the priceless heritage of the Jews it provided the underlying philosophy and framework for later esoteric societies such as the Rosicrucians (early seventeenth century and influential today) and the Hermetic Order of the Golden Dawn (late nineteenth and early twentieth centuries). 'Without the key which the Qabbalah supplies', writes Hall, 'the spiritual mysteries of both the Old and the New Testament must remain unsolved by Jew and Gentile alike. The Old Testament—especially the Pentateuch—contains not only the traditional account of the creation of the world and of man, but also, locked within it, the secrets of the Egyptian initiators of Moses concerning the genesis of the god-man (the initiate) and the mystery of his rebirth through philosophy. Yet familiarity with the three Qabbalistical processes termed Gematria, Notarikon, and Temurah makes possible the discovery of many of the profoundest truths of ancient Jewish superphysics.'[14]

The exoteric is the outer covering, or 'skin' of the esoteric; the esoteric is the inner meaning disguised beneath its surface appearance and descriptions.

However, in relation to the above, 'exoteric' does not mean deliberately misleading or false, but refers to teachings of which the keys to unlock the inner meaning have intentionally not been given out openly in order to protect the sacred nature of the latter, but rather alluded to through allegory, parable, and simile. Recall the words of Jesus the Christ: 'Therefore speak I to them [the multitude] in parables: because they seeing see not; and hearing they hear not, neither do they understand'—Matthew 13.13 (King James Version). However, to his disciples He revealed the secrets: 'But blessed are your eyes because they see, and your ears because they hear'—Matthew 13.16 (King James Version). An example may help. Pre-empting the detailed account given in Chapter 5 of Volume II, we cite here, by way of an appetizer, the true meaning gleaned from the exoteric account of the doctrine of reincarnation written in the form of a parable in the fourth Gospel. Verses 1 to 6 in Chapter XV of St. John (King James Version) state: 'I am the true vine, and my Father is the husbandman. Every branch in me that beareth not fruit he taketh away […]. As the branch cannot bear fruit of itself, except it abide in the vine; no more can ye, except ye abide in me. I am the vine, ye *are* the branches […]. If a man abide not in me, he is cast forth as a branch, and is withered; and men gather them, cast *them* into the fire, and they are burned.'

Biblical example
of esoteric
meaning hidden
in parable

Now if we eschew the literal dead-letter interpretation for disbelieving in the theological hell-fires as the underlying threat to the physical branches of wood and instead hold to the hidden (esoteric) meaning, we find that these verses are none other than a terse outline of the principle of reincarnation, as also the annihilation of the mortal personality after death. The Father–Husbandman stands for *Ātma*, the symbol for the infinite, impersonal Principle, while the vine stands for the Spiritual Soul, Christos; and each branch represents the personality in a new incarnation. It is entirely reasonable to ask what proofs there are to support such an apparently arbitrary interpretation. The answer is universal symbology, which is a warrant for its correctness and that it is not arbitrary. For example, Hermas[15] says of 'God' that he 'planted the Vineyard', that is, He created mankind. In the Qabbalah, it is shown that the Aged of the Aged, or the 'Long Face', plants a vineyard, the latter typifying mankind; and a vine, meaning Life.[16]

Turning to the East, we find a similar teaching using the symbol of a living tree:

Universal symbology in scriptures of the West and the East

> Pervaded by the self, the tree will keep drinking juice and living happily. But if the self leaves a branch of a tree, that branch withers away and dies. […] If the self withdraws from the whole tree, then the whole tree will die. […] When the self leaves the body, the body surely dies. The self, however, never dies.
>
> Chāndogya Upaniṣad, Verse 6.11[17]

We may reinforce our case that sacred scriptures should never be understood in the literal sense by citing the example of the Gnostic philosopher Origen Adamantius (184/5–253/4), the most mystical of the anti-Nicean fathers who was one of the main exponents of the mystical and esoteric Christianity. He taught the Hermetic concept of the pre-existence of souls. In his preface to St. John, he admits the twofold nature of all theological revelations, stating very astutely however that:

> To the literal-minded [or exoterici] we teach the Gospel in the historic way, preaching Jesus Christ and Him crucified; but to the proficient, fired with the love of divine wisdom [the esoterici], we impart the Logos [the Greek term for the 'Lost Word', i.e. *Nous*, or the Universal Mind as Source of all existence and from which all forms are derived].[18]

Origen further affirmed that several of the statements described in the Gospels must be understood not as historical incidents but as spiritual allegories, i.e., in the purely esoteric sense.[19] Several centuries later, but in similar vein, Albert Pike (1809–1891) the American poet, orator, jurist, and high ranking Freemason writes without mincing his words:

Truth must be protected from the profane

> Fictions are necessary for the people, and the Truth becomes deadly to those who are not strong enough to contemplate it in all its brilliance. In fact, what can there be in common between the vile multitude and sublime wisdom? The Truth must be kept secret, and the masses need a teaching proportioned to their imperfect reason.[20]

It can now be grasped why it is that when taken to extremes, the exoteric, literal doctrinaire statement of sacred esoteric truths becomes a source of utter confusion, distortion, and mayhem, not to say, hatred begetting violence. One need only think of the innumerable wars that have been fought *in the name* of religion 'because it says so in the Bible' or because 'the Qur'an says it'. Such dogmatic, dead-letter interpretations simply display the utter failure to see the deeply allegorical and symbolic nature of the scriptures that must be understood, it bears repeating, primarily in their psycho-spiritual context and only secondarily in their historical setting. One also needs to be wary of reading too much into the texts that have been edited and doctored over the ages. It is indispensable to bear these points in mind at all times. The scriptures and esoteric literature reveal a hidden knowledge only when considered allegorically and esoterically. Any seeker who accepts the wording of the Bible, or any other scriptures and esoteric works, in a dead-letter, literal sense will only hit a blank wall and never succeed in entering the inner sanctuary of truth.

Perils arising from literal interpretation of scripture

Regarding the allegories used to veil the secrets of alchemy, the celebrated English anti-quary and astrologer Elias Ashmole (1617–1692), who donated most of his collection, his antiquarian library, and priceless manuscripts to the University of Oxford to create the Ashmolean Museum, describes in his *Theatrum Chemicum Britannicum* the methods employed by the alchemists to conceal their true doctrines: 'Their chiefest study was to wrap up their *Secrets* in *Fables*, and spin out their *Fancies* in *Vailes* and *shadows*, whose *Radii* seems to extend every way, yet so, that they meet in a *Common Centre*, and point only at One thing.'[21]

The Esoteric–Exoteric Contrast in Relation to Religion

As just stated, the contrast between the esoterici and exoterici is of supreme importance. Above all, this applies to the whole field of religion. We therefore reinforce this theme by explaining their differences by way of a commentary on Figure I-9 showing the esoteric approach contrasted with the exoteric.[iv] In practice, of course, the contrast is not as black-and-white as such necessarily schematic depictions tend to convey.

> Without exception, religious founders have had a transformative experience

The starting point in both cases, as shown in the top centre of the diagram, is someone—invariably the founder of a religion—having an experience that is transformative. This applies to all religious founders, whether in the East or the West. Suffice it to give three examples. The Buddha did not formulate the Four Noble Truths—the core teaching of Buddhism—because He gained a PhD in theology; it was His revelation, the fruit of His enlightenment under the Bodhi Tree at Bodh Gaya. The Christ's transcendent Teachings were the outcome of His transformative experience of baptism—not because Jesus went to a rabbinical college.[22] And Muhammad's[v] revelation following the visitation by the Archangel Jibrīl (Gabriel), and his Ascension to Heaven, was not because the Prophet read books on how to raise consciousness. ('Heaven' here obviously refers to an inner state of consciousness. What this elusive term means exactly will become clearer as we proceed, as Chapter 5 of Volume II, and several Chapters of Volume III explain.)

Such a life-changing experience is naturally recognized by others who then gather around the transformed person wanting to become his disciples and followers in order to re-enact his experience. Whether such experience is re-enacted or interpreted marks the contrast between the esoteric and exoteric version of the same religion.

Esoteric Re-enactment of Religious Experience

In the esoteric route, shown to the left of the diagram, the transformative experience would not be represented in terms of scripture but re-enacted through symbol. Scriptures read in the customary manner tend to be an historical record of past events. Hence the use of icons, which are radically different from symbols. An icon has a fixed meaning whereas a

---

iv This diagram, and the ensuing narrative, is an extract from the lecture entitled 'Mysteries: Ancient and Modern' given to the Theosophical Society in England on 31st July 1996 by Professor John Algeo, a former Vice President of the Theosophical Society.

v Jane I. Smith, professor of Islamic Studies, associate dean of academic affairs and lecturer in comparative reli-gion at Harvard University and co-director of the Hartford Seminary Foundation states that the more appro-priate transliteration is Muhammad rather than Mohammad, and Qur'an rather than Koran, as stated later.

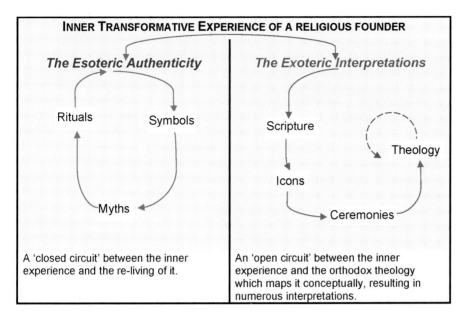

Figure I-9 *Esoterici* and *Exoterici* – A Schematic Representation of their Contrast

symbol has no definite connotation but a range of interrelated meanings on different levels. An obvious secular example of the former would be a red traffic light. No one would argue that it meant other than 'stop'. But regarding the latter, Christians, for example, would ascribe several meanings to the Cross: suffering, sacrifice, spirit over matter, redemption, to name but a few. All meanings are valid; there is no correct one. However, and this is important, for 'born again Christians', the Cross would have a fixed meaning—redemption. This shows that in religion (obviously not in secular matters), the same thing can be either an icon or a symbol. The difference lies in the mind of the person, not in the thing in itself.

The difference between symbols and icons

Following on from symbols comes myth and ritual instead of ceremony and theology. Myths are narratives usually involving imaginary or superphysical[vi] characters to embody natural events and phenomena—for example, the theatrical culture of Ancient Greek drama that flourished in ancient Greece from *circa* 700 BC. (The legendary Indian epics *Mahābhārata* and *Rāmāyaṇa* also convey such drama and tragedy but it is highly conjectural whether they were actually dramatized in theatre as with the Greeks.) Ritual is radically different from mere ceremony. Whereas ceremonies imitate, or commemorate, the original experience in some form or other, rituals *evoke* it—a person is *changed* by it. Such eureka moments signal a 'closed circuit', i.e., a continuity of the connection, from the founder's experience to its *experiential* re-enactment through ritual.[vii] Therefore it is a deeply personal affair where the disciple seeks to re-embody—not describe in words—

Myth and ritual in contrast to ceremony and theology

---

vi We insist on using this term over the customary term 'supernatural', which, strictly speaking, is a misnomer. There is nothing whatsoever that is outside the natural order, but much that lies in non-physical realms. Because of the common, but wrongful, association of the natural order solely with the physical domain, phenomena and events inexplicable in physical terms are then deemed super-natural.

vii The exultant cry of 'eureka', meaning 'I have found it!' announcing a discovery or experience is attributed to the legendary Greek mathematician and scientist Archimedes of Syracuse (*circa* 287 BC – *circa* 212 BC).

the original experience in his own life. It cannot be stressed sufficiently that this is not just an ordinary kind of experience but one that is life-changing, invariably, one of death and resurrection: death to the old and resurrection of the new, not in terms of reincarnation, but dying (i.e., letting go) and being re-born in the here and now at each moment in life.

But, as with icons and symbols, a ceremony can remain as such or become a ritual. The difference lies not so much in what happens but how the individual responds to it. For example, the bar mitzvah is a Jewish religious ceremony and family celebration commemorating the religious adulthood of a boy on his thirteenth birthday. But the ceremony would become a religious ritual if the boy were changed as a result of his experience of it. Significantly, the term 'ritual' is etymologically the same as the Sanskrit word *Ṛta* 'the natural rule and order of things', the principle of natural order which regulates and co-ordinates the operation of the universe and everything within it—which is precisely what ritual seeks to re-enact.

Exoteric Interpretations of Religious Experience

The exoteric route, shown to the right of the diagram, has marked differences. Exactly the same transformative experience would not be re-enacted as symbol but recorded by disciples in terms of scriptures: for example, the Buddhist Sūtras, Christian Gospels, and Holy Qur'an in Islam. Icons and pictures would represent some aspect of the originating Teaching, like the Wheel in Buddhism and the Cross in Christianity. Islam eschews pictures and icons, regarding them as idols; nevertheless, the Arabic decorative motifs (as inscribed on the arches of the Taj Mahal) are tantamount to icons. Furthermore, ceremonies are created to represent the experience of the founder.

Exoteric interpretations are descriptive

From this medley a theology emerges with speculations rife on two fronts: the meaning of the scriptures and the significance of the icons and ceremonies; and then an analysis of *itself*, educed by questions such as—what is the nature of knowledge, how do we know that we know and what we know, ad nauseam. This basically results in a dead end—a closed loop of never ending conjecture leading to the obvious differences of opinion that invariably run a downhill course towards intolerance, conflict, and religious wars. Why? Because there is an 'open circuit', i.e., a break in the connection, between the founder's inner experience and its innumerable outward representations as descriptions (mind maps), rather than an actual analogous experience by his followers. (Refer back to Chapter 3 regarding the numerous hair-splitting versions of physicalism with no definite consensus. The point being made is that whether in science, philosophy of mind, or religion, doubts and uncertainties are bound to reign when the intellectual concepts usurp the reality behind them.)

Religious authorities control by imposing blind belief

Blind belief and worship of the outer form are critical to maintaining the status quo of the exoteric form of religions by the religious authorities. There is no shortage of such superstitious genuflection by the masses in front of statues and portraits, as in India, and other predominantly Catholic countries. Nonetheless, it must be admitted that the genuflection may sometimes be genuine and not superstitious, i.e., honour being paid to the idea and quality *behind* the icon, painting or statue. Even though the worship of an outward form, it is a step up from nihilism.

All this clearly shows why the great instructors of all religions, especially in ancient times, rarely wrote down their own teachings and on the few occasions when they did, it was in highly cryptic allegorical form that could be understood only by those acquainted with the inner meaning. More often, however, their instruction was transmitted orally to chosen disciples to disseminate in the manner best suited to their times and culture. Such illumined souls knew that once something was written down, it would be 'set in stone', the inner living message suffocated by the outer crust of rigid interpretations. But does that necessarily mean that sacred writings are merely an interpretation of the founder's teaching? When read esoterically, they convey an ever-present, life-affirming message. As with icons and symbols or ceremonies and rituals, exactly the same thing—in this case scripture—can either be a description of the past or if its esoteric import (necessarily hidden) can be discerned, then what was once a dry set of rules and guidelines for living becomes transformed into life-changing insights in the present moment. It all depends on the sensitive response of the reader rather than what is read.

Descriptions of the experiential become ossified

In summary: the exoteric religions and esoteric religions are not discrete religious entities. They are the descriptive and the experiential versions, respectively, of the *same* religion: in the former, the religious experience of the founder is represented outwardly through scripture, icons, ceremonies, and theology; in the latter, the inward re-enactment of the founding experience is through symbols, myths, and rituals. For this reason the esoteric version of all religions is sometimes referred to as a 'Mystery religion'. The inner experience does not bypass the labelling, pigeon holing, and 'interpretizing' intellect: it transcends it. That is because the experience is not informational—so much knowledge to be gained, facts to be learned, etc.—but *transformational*.

Summary of Key Precepts

So, in summary, we may say that whereas esotericism *reveals* the inner meaning and truth, exotericism masks, or '*re-veils*', the truth by presenting it in the form of the outward and popular (literal) interpretations found in the public rituals, and ceremonies of orthodox religions. To this we may add that the self-righteousness of ignorance *reviles* the truth. Esotericism is also known as the 'Doctrine of the Heart', namely, seeing into the inner meaning of a subject or object using the awakened spiritual eye; whereas exotericism is referred to as the 'Doctrine of the Eye', that is, seeing the outward form and appearance with the physical eyes of flesh. This distinction is to be found in the scriptures and theologies of all nations and races. Referring again to the Qabbalah as a typical example, Hebrew theology was divided into three distinct parts (which correspond to the three degrees of initiation outlined in the Preamble to the Mysteries at the opening of this Chapter): the first was the law, the exoteric part taught to all the children of Israel; the second part was the *Mishna*, or the soul of the law, being the partially esoteric Teaching revealed to the Rabbins and teachers; the third part was entirely esoteric, namely, the Qabbalah, the soul of the soul of the law, artfully concealed, such that only the highest initiates among the Jews were instructed in its secret principles. (In fact the word Qabbalah means 'the secret, or hidden tradition, the *unwritten* law'.) Why unwritten? Because the inner and fuller meaning of these symbols and cryptic writings cannot, and may not, be revealed by writing or even by word of mouth, but must be divined by the student as the result of study and meditation. In the *Sepher ha Zohar*, the foundational text of esoteric Jewish mysticism, it is written that there is a garment—the written doctrine—which every man may see. This is the exoteric doctrine, the written law. Those with understanding do not look upon the

Qabbalah cited as an example of exoteric and esoteric teachings

garment, meaning the outer appearance, or literal interpretations, but at the body beneath it, namely, the intellectual and philosophical code. The wisest of all, however, look at nothing other than the soul or inner meaning, the spiritual doctrine, which is the eternal and ever-springing root of the law.

We reiterate that the exoteric doctrines should not therefore be regarded in themselves as being superficial or puerile. Far from it. It all depends on whether we are reading with the eyes of flesh—the Doctrine of the Eye—or through the eyes of spirit—the Doctrine of the Heart. There is a fine essay on this uncertainty between the exoteric and esoteric reading by the Swiss–German philosopher of perennialism, metaphysician, poet, and painter, Frithjof Schuon (1907–1998).[23] In fact, a huge number of esoteric insights can be gleaned from a careful reading of the exoteric accounts. For example, as Hall writes: 'An inkling of the substance of Rosicrucianism—its esoteric doctrines—can be gleaned from an analysis of its shadow—its exoteric writings.' One of the most important of their 'clouds' [protecting veils[viii]] is the *Confessio Fraternitatis* where in Chapter V we find 'God has surrounded us with His clouds and His protection so that no harm may come to us, and God has decreed that we of the Order of R.C. can no longer be seen by mortal eyes unless they have received strength borrowed from the eagle [the spiritual eye of the initiate that can penetrate the veiled or clouded].'[24] Then in Chapter III of the same work we are told: 'We cannot describe fully the marvels of our Fraternity lest the uninformed be overwhelmed by our astonishing declarations and the vulgar ridicule the mysteries which they do not comprehend. Like blind men living in a world full of light, they discern only through the sense of feeling.'[25] In this context, 'feeling' refers to the material senses, or seeing with the fleshly eyes, as opposed to spiritual cognition, which is seeing through the inner spiritual eyes.

Likewise, 'the creation myths of the world are acroamatic cryptograms,[ix] and the deities of the various pantheons are only cryptic characters which, if properly understood, become the constituents of a divine alphabet. The initiated few comprehend the true nature of this alphabet, but the uninitiated many worship the letters of it as gods.'[26]

Occultism and Occult Science – What Exactly Do They Mean?

The reader will by now have appreciated that esotericism deals not only with the phenomena and perception of the interrelationships between forces and beings at every level of subjective and objective existence, but also with understanding their underlying causes. Occultism takes this a stage further by dealing, not just with the characteristic nature of all the energies and forces in the universe, again whether objective or subjective, but also the techniques by which they work and can be controlled. As John Gordon remarks: 'The former [esotericism], while not exactly theoretical, does not concern itself with quite the practical, "hands-on" involvement of the latter [occultism].'[27]

But we need to define, and then justify, using the word 'occultism' with utmost care—and with good reason—because few words occasion more mindless hysteria from people in

The esoteric is never overt. It is revealed by penetrating the exoteric veil

Occultism takes esotericism a major step further

---

viii   These veils are there to safeguard the sacred teachings from misuse. This is explained later in the section on the Language of the Mysteries.

ix   Acroamatic cryptograms are pictorial ciphers drawn in words and their symbolism must be so interpreted.

both the scientific and religious orthodoxy than the word 'occult'. One invariably feels rather hesitant about using a word that has unpleasant and wrongful associations, even in the minds of educated persons, let alone 'ignorant vulgars', (to use Newton's term when referring to the common, uneducated folk) as standing for dark practices. So what does this word really mean, and why do we insist upon using it in its rightful context? Moreover, why is it that despite its spectacular triumphs in the material world, Western science has singularly failed to achieve an understanding of occult science, even cursorily—so important for apprehending the mysteries of the universe and man? As mentioned earlier, the origins of words reveal their inner meaning. What then is the etymology of the word 'occult'? Moreover, why do we insist on referring to it as a science? These are the questions we shall now consider.

Importance of understanding precisely what 'occult' means and reasons for using it

Etymology

All the meaningless and asinine 'knee-jerk' associations with black magic and witchcraft notwithstanding, the word 'occult' simply means 'secret', 'hidden', or 'concealed'. It derives from the Latin *occultus*, past participle of *occulere* 'hide', or 'cover over', a compound verb formed from the prefix *ob-* and an unrecorded **celere*, a relative of *cēlāre* 'to hide' (which forms the second syllable of the English 'conceal').[28] So anything that is occult is, etymologically speaking, hidden, or concealed from the five physical senses.

What then is occult science? (The next section justifies our use of the term 'science' in this connotation.) It is a generic term referring to the Hermetic or Esoteric Sciences, which explore the essential, or hidden, secrets of Nature—physical and psychic, mental and spiritual—rather than, but not excluding, her outward appearance and mechanical behaviour which natural science, mainly in the West, studies to virtual perfection. Occult science is the science of the secrets of Universal Nature; so Western science, which studies objective nature on the physical plane may therefore be regarded, arguably in one sense, as a distant subset of all-inclusive occult science.

'Occultism' is therefore a generalizing term for the entire body of occult sciences. Occultists are those who both study and practice occultism, as just defined. Mankind has never ceased asking profound questions about whether there was ever a time that the Universe was not, how the universe came into existence, and his own place in it.[x] Since time immemorial, he has pursued his quest along the traditional lines of philosophy, religion, science, and art. Occultism, however, refers not merely to the subject, but rather to the standpoint and attitude brought to bear on whatever is being examined. Philosophy, religion or science can be studied either from the conventional or orthodox perspective of intellectual speculations based on physical appearances; or from the occult standpoint, focussing on unearthing and actively harnessing the inner, core principles buried in the myriad forms in which such subjects are presented.

The deeper issues of life and the laws of nature are hidden from the physical eye, i.e. occult

The Word 'Occult' Used in Two Different Senses

In the light of the above, it is important to make a clear distinction between two different uses of the word 'occult'—both referring to hidden qualities—that can be a source of much

---

x Readers are asked to refer to the Definitions in Volume IV which point out the distinction between 'universe' and 'Universe'; the former material and objective, the latter subjective—as an Idea in Divine Mind.

Hidden qualities
as an excuse to
explain away and
mask ignorance

confusion.[29] The first use is as just defined and explained. However, hidden qualities also figure in the Aristotelian philosophy. Regarding the latter use, occult qualities were invoked to explain certain phenomena or properties that could not be perceived directly. For example, such qualities as heat, or the colour red, were not occult since they could be perceived directly. However, the quality by which, for example, the bindweed drug scammony acted as a stimulant to purge was occult; the quality itself, i.e., its purgative effect in the stomach, could not be perceived, although the effect it produced certainly could. When does this superficial refuge in occult qualities happen? According to the American philosopher and logician Willard Van Orman Quine (1908–2000), 'meaning is what essence becomes when it is divorced from the object of reference and wedded to the word.'[30] Quine further argues that the danger of an idea is that its use engenders an illusion of having explained something, whereas it may only have explained it away.[31] Here he cites, as an example, the appeal to a *virtus dormitive* (a substance possessing sleep-inducing properties) in a passage in *Malade Imaginaire* (The Imaginary Invalid) which satirises scholastic philosophy. In the said passage from the three-act *comédie-ballet* by the French playwright Molière (1622–1673), a candidate for a degree in medicine is asked, during his examination, why it is that opium makes people sleepy? To loud acclaim from his examiners and the chorus, the candidate replies that it is because opium has a 'dormitive virtue'. The phrase has entered philosophical folklore as a paradigmatic example of an explanatory façade, but in fact it is a non-explanation.[32]

In that case why did Newton insist on using the term occult? And in what sense was he using it?

Newton's Defence of Occult Qualities

There is, arguably, no better example of the distinction between the two uses of occult qualities, as just enumerated, than that applied by Newton. Regarding his concept of universal gravitation, Newton's opponents on the continent accused him of reviving occult qualities in the scholastic sense, which the mechanical philosophy had banished.[33] In his response to Leibniz's dismissal of Newtonian gravity as '*une qualité occulte scholastique*' (an occult quality as per the scholastics), Newton forcefully stated: 'He [Leibniz] [*sic*] changes the signification of the words Miracles & Occult qualities that he may use them in railing at universal gravity […] occult qualities are decried not because their causes are unknown, but because the Schoolmen believed that those things wch were unknown to their Master Aristotel [*sic*], could never be known.'[34] Presumably for this reason, Newton added an anti-Aristotelian rider to his phenomenological defence of occult qualities in his 1717 edition of *Opticks*. Having declared that active principles are 'manifest Qualities, and their Causes only are Occult', Newton wrote:

> And the *Aristotelians* gave the Name of occult Qualities, not to manifest Qualities, but to such Qualities only as they supposed to lie hid in Bodies, and to be the unknown Causes of manifest Effects […]. Such occult Qualities put a stop to the Improvement of natural Philosophy, and therefore of late Years have been rejected.[35]

Then, in further defence of properly resorting to occult principles in mechanical philosophy, he added:

> To tell us that every Species of Things is endow'd with an occult specifick Quality by which it acts and produces manifest Effects, is to tell us nothing: But to derive two or

three general Principles of Motion from Phænomena, and afterwards to tell us how the properties and Actions of all corporeal Things follow from those manifest Principles, would be a very great step in Philosophy, though the Causes of those Principles were not yet discover'd. And therefore I scruple not to propose the Principles of Motion above-mention'd, they being of a very general Extent, and leave their Causes to be found out.[36]

Hidden qualities investigated to discern the true nature of things and advance learning

In summary, Newton upheld the notion of using occult principles in a mechanical philosophy in the true meaning of real and active, but hidden powers—amenable to experimental investigation and advancement of wisdom, *yet to be discovered*, as opposed to occult qualities invoked as a mere excuse and refuge for ignorance—destroying attempts at 'Improvement of natural Philosophy'. As it happens, occult qualities in mechanical philosophy have a history before Newton. Indeed, the investigation and demonstration of occult qualities in matter were major factors in establishing the experimental method as the safest and surest way to truth in natural philosophy, which is why leading members of the Royal Society were attempting to promote various experimental research programmes, such as the English architect, geometer, and anatomist Sir Christopher Wren PRS (1632–1723) in his 1662 lecture to the Society advocating the chemical investigation of bodily fluids.[37]

Specific Use of the term 'Occult' in this Work

'Occult science' in this work refers to the hidden laws of Nature amenable to study and to resolve intractable problems in the physical sciences

Needless to say, the extensive use of the term 'occult' in this work bears no reference to the scholastic meaning of the term. Accordingly, occult science, used as an overarching term, refers to the entire body of sciences of the hidden laws of Universal Nature, both objective and subjective. Similar terms, but with subtly different shades of meaning, are Hermeticism, Esoteric Philosophy, and Esoteric Science. We stress that occult science embraces not only the structure and operations, origins and destiny of the universe and its inhabitants, but also equally, the physical, physiological, psychological and spiritual aspects of man's being—the human dimension of course being the core thesis of this work. Furthermore, whilst the various phenomena in nature and man are studied in depth, occult science, in contrast to the conventional sciences, penetrates deeply into the causal mysteries of Being.

In this work, as indeed in common practice, the term 'occultism' is used as a generalizing term when dealing with occult matters of a general or philosophical nature; the term 'occult science' being reserved for matters of a more technical nature dealing with the hidden laws, mechanisms, and processes in nature. The writer hopes that, even at the expense of labouring the point, readers will understand the importance of injecting clarity into key terms in this work.

Occult science is the science of the hidden Laws of Nature that lie at the root of all life and pertain to the unseen and higher realms of existence that, even so, constitute the ground of physical existence. Therefore, it refers to the Hermetic or Esoteric Sciences which explore the essential, or hidden, secrets of Nature—physical and psychic, mental and spiritual—rather than, but not excluding, her outward appearance and mechanical behaviour which natural science studies to virtual perfection.

What is 'Science' in the Context of Occult Science?

Properly understood, then, occult science embraces not only the physical and physiological, psychological and spiritual dimensions of man's being, but has an equal and wider range in the enquiry into the origin and destiny, as well as the structure and operation of the universe, seen and unseen. For this reason, it needs emphasizing that the term 'science' should not be restricted solely to the philosophy and associated methodology of modern science (i.e., from the time of the Scientific Revolution in the seventeenth century), upon which the dominant paradigm of our age is based. What is the *essential* meaning of science?

Etymologically 'science' means 'what is known', 'knowledge', 'knowledge (of anything or something) gained by study'. It derives via Old French *science* from the Latin *scientia*, a noun formed from the present participle of the verb *scīre* '(to) know'. The derivative, 'scientist', was coined in 1840 by the English polymath, scientist, Anglican priest, philosopher, and historian of science, William Whewell (1794–1866): 'We need very much a name to describe a cultivator of science in general. I should incline to call him a Scientist.'[38]

Science, in its original meaning and fullest sense, then, becomes the operation of the human mind in its endeavour to research, discover, and understand the 'purpose', 'how', and 'what' of things, not just any one aspect, but in their totality—the thing in itself; hence, science *per se* can be defined as, ordered and classified knowledge on any subject. However, such science is one phase of a triform method of understanding Universal Nature in its multiform and manifold workings; and this phase cannot be separated from the other two—religion and philosophy—in order to gain a true picture of things *as they are in themselves*. Moreover, both religion and philosophy can, in this perspective, be regarded as Science, in the sense that they are amenable to the inquisitive, systematic researching and classifying functions of an enquirer who wishes *to know*.

Occult science is Science in the truest sense

The above makes it plain that there is no restriction placed upon Science (or a scientist) to limit the scope of enquiry solely to physical matter (the province of modern science especially in the West). That being the case, we are fully entitled to refer to the methodical and structured investigation of nature's invisible and hidden processes as a science, albeit an occult, or hidden science. All this will become much clearer in the next Chapter when we explain the different methods employed by modern Western science and occult science to investigate Nature.

True Occultism and the Black Arts – The Essential Difference of Meaning

True occultism is a Sacred Science which stands for real and transcendent knowledge of the highest truths of nature and man; and therefore demands the practice of altruism and purest spirituality. It has nothing to do with pseudo-occultism with which it is often confused. It is the misuse of occult science by the selfish and unethical that leads to the traditional charge that occultism deals with the black arts. But any power and force in nature can be so exploited and abused. It is crucial to distinguish the practice from the practitioner. For example, is nuclear physics to be held culpable for the horrors of atomic bombs over Japan; do we denounce biochemistry because of the thalidomide disaster of thousands of limbless babies; when hackers create mayhem in corporations by stealing personal data, shall we blame the force of electricity that powers their computers? Shall we then condemn the science or some of its deluded practitioners? So why condemn occult science because of the malpractices of some unscrupulous practitioners? This

Man's abuse of the Laws of nature is no fault of nature

brings us to the distinction between white magic, sorcery, and black magic which all relate to the use and misuse of nature's powers and forces, seen and unseen, as we now elaborate, first in terms of an allegorical account of general principles.

The Use and Misuse of the Secrets of Nature

It is emphasized that any force in nature, or discovery by man, is completely impersonal in itself: to be used by man to uplift humanity or, conversely, misused and exploited with dire consequences, all depending upon the motive of the user. So, the unpleasant connotations in the mind of the average person about occultism having dealings with black magic or witchcraft have everything to do with the abuse of this sacred science in wrongful hands for personal and selfish reasons—we might as well decide to jump from the top of the Eiffel Tower and then accuse the force of gravity of being intrinsically evil when faced with impending death! Has gravity killed us or our own foolishness? Therefore, it is worth repeating that practitioner and practice have to be distinguished clearly: the misuse of occultism in the hands of unscrupulous practitioners has no bearing on its rightful practice by philanthropic persons motivated by a selfless desire for universal good.

The Laws of Nature are impersonal. Their use, or misuse, lies with man himself and his motives

This message is well encapsulated in the Book of Revelation, often called the Apocalypse, accredited to St. John. It is one of the most important (but arguably the least understood, hence most criticized) of the works of Gnostic Christianity. In this work the Lamb signifies the purified candidate, he who is worthy to receive, and be entrusted with, Nature's secrets by virtue of his purity, illumined reason, and perfected sense-perceptions. The Lamb holds a book with seven seals. When the final seal—the seventh—was broken, a catastrophe ensued. A star fell from the heavens on to Earth, a portent that Nature's secrets—the universal Secret Doctrine, or Occult Science of the ancients—had been entrusted to men who had blasphemed it and hence caused the wisdom of the gods (i.e., the forces and powers in Nature, intelligent but impersonal) to become a destructive agency. And then, another star fell from heaven, another omen that the divine reason of the initiate had been subverted by the false light of human reason, i.e., materialistic and dead-letter thinking, which was then used as the key to the bottomless pit (Nature), which it opened, causing a host of evil entities to issue forth.[39] We cite a few striking examples that follow directly on from the allegorical tale just expounded.

Gnostic allegory on misuse of Nature's secrets

Among the ancient civilizations resplendent during their acme, but then degenerating through misuse of occult knowledge, we can especially cite the examples of the Atlanteans, Egyptians, and American Indians (the Red race). The iniquity of these races during the final stages of their epoch stands in inverse proportion to their supernal majesty during the zenith of their era. In the case of the Egyptians and American Indians, white magic degenerated into sorcery and subsequent black magic with attendant appalling rituals resulting in the eventual degeneration of those once lofty civilisations. The same applies with even greater force to the rise and fall of the prehistoric Atlantean civilization and the catastrophic destruction over long periods of time of that once majestic continent, whose existence is forever an uncomfortable enigma to the 'fact finding' archaeologist and historian, or to the scientist wedded to a particular geological ideology—but never to the truth-inspired occultist. Readers are encouraged to consult the source references stated in Endnote I-8 for convincing accounts that prehistoric continents are not mere idle fable or phantasy.

Historical example of abuse of Nature's secrets

In modern times, the blatant abuse of occult knowledge by the leaders of the Third Reich should provide ample evidence of the appalling catastrophes and the tragic consequences to the evil-doers resulting from attempting to twist nature's secrets for selfish, power-seeking motives.[40] However, it must be clearly understood that black magic is neither a fundamental science nor an art of its own accord; it is the nefarious misuse of science and art. (A far-fetched simile would be that dis-ease is not a fundamental condition but rather a deviance of health, which is our natural birthright.) For this very reason *it has no symbols or emblems of its own but distorts or perverts the symbols of white magic* (such as the pentagram) to signify aberrant practice of total self-concern and deliberate evil to others. No better example than the reversal of that ancient and sacred symbol, the Swastika, by the Nazis indicative of their misunderstanding and criminal misuse of occult knowledge. The reader may rightly ask whether the black magician can conceal his felonious activities under the camouflage of the symbols of white magic. The answer is he can never do that, for to use the symbol ethically is to invoke the opposite forces of white magic, which would run counter to his motives. Thus we see that nature is not deceived. A man has to be true to his colours: he cannot work evil wearing a mask of benevolence.

Modern example of abuse of Nature's secrets

White Magic, Sorcery, and Black Magic – What are the Differences?

White magic is referred to in occult literature as choosing to follow the Right-Hand Path. It is a general term referring to a totally altruistic, philanthropic, and utterly impersonal use of occult powers directed solely and entirely towards the physical but especially the moral and spiritual elevation of humanity. There are in truth no miracles and magic. Everything operates under law, but when we cannot recognize the secret mechanisms of nature we resort to words like 'magic' to come to terms with what appears on the surface to be unfathomable.

Conversely, unclean practices, such as witchcraft and voodoo, are not based entirely on superstition as many sceptical and naïve people assume without ever bothering to study and investigate these matters. Despite the considerable amount of charlatanism, fraud, and superstition enveloping such pseudo-occult phenomena, there is still a solid basis of truth that underlies them. This basis is none other than the misuse of nature's secret powers—occult powers—for personal and selfish ends. The acquisition of power and control over others is invariably the prime motive. Any such misuse of powers for personal gain is known in general as sorcery and referred to as following the Left-Hand Path. At its worst it is black magic and will exact a terrible price of *self-generated* suffering upon the wrongdoer. We obviously have absolutely no truck with this.

As Hall informs us, the pagans and ancient philosophers used nocturnal birds as symbols to signify both white and black magic. The latter because it cannot function in the light of truth—daylight—and is powerful only when enveloped in ignorance—the darkness of night. The former because those possessing the keys to wisdom are able to penetrate the darkness of materiality and ignorance. Hence, bats and owls were often associated with either wisdom or dark practices.[41]

Different degrees of use and misuse of nature's secrets

But it is of the utmost importance to understand that highly evil people can be highly evolved people; except that they have chosen to take what we have defined above as the Left-Hand Path of black magic, instead of the Right-Hand Path of white magic. Hence, although we understandably tend to regard evolved persons as spiritually beneficent individuals and a major force for the good of society, yet the evolutionary status by itself of individuals says nothing about their *spiritual* status.

Finally, from all this, we can realize why the word 'esoteric' is understandably used as a safe alternative to 'occult' on account of the unsavoury associations but this is not an accurate substitution of terms.

Psychic and Psychic Powers – What Are They?

'Psychic' and 'psychic powers' are also terms encountered widely in arcane literature. Psychic, from the Greek *psyche*, refers to the intermediate nature of man—that which lies between spirit and body, namely his soul in the generic sense. (This will become clear in Chapters 2 and 3 of Volume II.) Psychic powers, then, are the exercise of the powers corresponding to the lower strata of man's soul nature. One cannot therefore consciously exercise psychic powers without some degree of esoteric knowledge. In appropriate circumstances, with guidance and training, such powers can be evoked, but the dangers to health and sanity are immense if any attempt is made to force their development prematurely. Needless to say, this is not the business of this work. More profitably, we may point out that psychic powers are the lower manifestation of occult powers. When misused for selfish reasons, to gain power and control over people, the result is sorcery, or black magic at worst. The exalted use of occult powers is sometimes referred to as 'spiritual powers', exercised, needless to say, for totally impersonal and altruistic purposes. Thus, 'occult powers' is a collective term encompassing psychic powers at the lower pole to spiritual powers at the upper pole.

> Psychic powers are a lower aspect of occult powers in general

> Spiritual powers are to psychic powers as the words of a mature philosopher are to baby-talk.

Mysticism, Esotericism, Occultism, and Psychism – Subtle Shades of Meaning

At this juncture it would be sensible to provide a résumé of the terms that we have defined, and illustrate both their overlap and their fine distinctions of meaning by way of a simile.

The mystic is primarily concerned with attaining a state of union with the divine, or the object of his devotion and contemplation. So the esotericist and the occultist are both mystics at heart, but the mystic is not necessarily an esotericist or an occultist. When the mystic decides to subject his mystical visions and intuitions to rigorous scientific scrutiny and understand the causes and interrelationships between the various realms of nature, seen and unseen, and to unfold the (metaphysical) basis and mechanisms by which they express themselves, he becomes what is known as an 'esotericist'—a dissatisfied mystic who yearns to probe deeper.[xi] And when, additionally, he is able to influence, and control, the invisible forces of nature that he investigates, he becomes worthy of the name 'occultist'. This shows that esotericism occupies the middle ground of overlap between mysticism

---

xi However, this is not to imply that all esotericists were once dissatisfied mystics.

and occultism; whereas occultism represents their culmination and highest common factor (refer back to the meaning of these terms given earlier).

Importance of understanding nuances of meaning in closely related terms

In essence then, mysticism is concerned primarily with feeling, esotericism with meaning and understanding, and occultism with function. *Esotericism is the intellectual arm of mysticism, and occultism is the practical, or functional arm of esotericism.* By way of a simplistic analogy then, the difference between the mystic, the esotericist, and the occultist is the difference between being intensely sensitive to music, having deep musical knowledge with some performing ability, and performing expertly as a concert musician. It is mystic experience and esoteric understanding that pave the way for occult powers in the same way that a feeling for music, combined with an understanding of musical theory and notation, provide the basis for the actual performance of music. For this reason, white magic, or the Right-Hand Path, is better understood as the philanthropic use of occult powers (and black magic, or the Left-Hand Path, their misuse) rather than esoteric knowledge.

Following on from the above, a man may be said to acquire or possess occult powers or psychic powers but it is not, strictly speaking, meaningful to talk of esoteric powers.

Metaphysics – What Is It?

Metaphysics is an elusive term to define, but an understanding of which is central to any comprehensive enquiry into reality as a whole, and the underlying basis and assumptions upon which such enquiry is based. In the most abstract sense, metaphysics is the branch of philosophy that examines the fundamental nature of reality; in other words: a theory of reality concerned with existence and the nature of things that exist. The subject-matter therefore concerns 'being as such', or the essential nature of reality, the first causes of things, and that which is not subject to change. Examples of metaphysical concepts are: Being, Existence, Purpose, Universals, Property, Relation, Causality, Space, Time, and Event. They are fundamental, because all other concepts and beliefs, whether in science, religion or philosophy, rest on them. Ontology is a branch of metaphysics dealing with the nature of Being; whereas epistemology is Knowledge of Being, and the theory of knowledge (generally related to a specific discipline) especially with regard to its methods and validation.

The etymology of the word 'metaphysics' can lead to misunderstanding. The word derives from the Greek words μετά (*metá* 'after') and φυσικά (*physiká* 'physics'). In the English language, the word comes by way of the Mediæval Latin *metaphysica*, the neuter plural of Mediæval Greek *metaphysika*.[42] It was first used as the title for several of Aristotle's works, because they were usually anthologized after his works on physics in complete editions. But Aristotle himself did not use that title, or even describe his field of study as 'metaphysics'; the name was evidently coined by the first century AD editor who assembled the treatise we know as Aristotle's *Metaphysics* out of various smaller selections of Aristotle's works. For that reason, the prefix *metá-* indicates that these works come 'after' the chapters on physics and thus gives the impression that metaphysics is a study that somehow 'goes beyond' physics—a study devoted to matters that transcend the mundane world described by physics. This impression is mistaken. In fact, metaphysics is not that which 'goes beyond' but that which 'comes before' in the sense of that which underlies and constitutes the foundational basis and groundwork upon which a particular branch of science or philosophy or religion is erected. Thus *metá-* is meant in the literary historical sense concerning the sequential order in which Aristotle's books were written, having nothing to do with its subject-matter, as explained above. Furthermore, readers should not assume that metaphysics is restricted solely to a study and application of Aristotle's groundwork on the matter.

Used as an overarching and generalizing term, metaphysics subsumes the 'sub-meta-physics' of the numerous philosophies, religions, and sciences constituting the manifold and varied disciplines within the overall field of enquiry into the nature of reality. Hence, there are several schools of metaphysics all based on their discipline-specific foundational assumptions. Thus, the various schools of philosophy, such as British empiricism, analytic philosophy, rationalism, and positivism, have their underlying metaphysics. So too, the world religions like Buddhism and Islam. Occult science also has its foundational meta-physic as will soon become apparent.

Metaphysics refers to the foundational basis of any subject of study or enquiry

Likewise, the entire edifice of science is based entirely upon its foundational metaphysics and assumptions. In no uncertain terms this includes contemporary scientific materialism—the outgrowth of logical positivism—also known as logical empiricism. Those scientists in academia who promulgate what is now fashionably known as the 'public understanding of science' would have the public believe that science, meaning materialism, is the *proven* basis of reality and that literally all problems regarding the universe and man, including the nature of subjective experience, psychological states, and the nature of consciousness, will ultimately be solved through physics and chemistry. This is completely erroneous as, in the final analysis, physics and chemistry themselves are based on unprovable assumptions about the nature of physical matter. Metaphysical concepts therefore involve all branches of scientific enquiry. Physics is permeated with metaphysics. As will become increasingly evident as we progress, current mainstream science makes unempirical and irrational assumptions, even while assuming that it makes no assumptions; moreover, materialist science, imperative in its rightful context, is at an impasse as a foundation for comprehending our reality.[xii]

Science is honeycombed in metaphysics

Summary of Key Ideas

The preceding sections have explained, in some detail, the definition and nuanced differences of meaning of abstruse terms that are central to the literature of Mystery Teachings and the *philosophia perennis*.

At this point, it may be helpful to readers to have a summary of the core meaning of these terms showing their strong overlap of meaning and interconnection. This can be set out as follows:

❖ The Mystery Teachings are special teachings and specific instructions imparted to candidates of high intellectual and moral standing concerning the hidden Laws of

---

xii This sentence is rephrased from the writings of Eben Alexander, neurosurgeon and author of *Proof of Heaven* (see Chapter 2) of worldwide acclaim; and Iain McGilchrist, neuropsychiatrist and author of the best-selling book *The Master and his Emissary: The divided brain and the making of the Western world* (see Chapter 6).

Nature and the powers latent in man, in order that the latter may be unfolded to render
the candidate an educator for the spiritual and moral advancement of humanity.

❖ 'Spirituality' is a term used to convey the general idea that a person feels within himself
that purely physical matter and mechanical explanations about the workings of nature
and man (i.e., scientific materialism) are inadequate to explain deeper questions about
life, purpose, and destiny. Spirituality is a vague term intimating shades of religion,
mysticism, divinity, and 'something that lies beyond'.

❖ Philosophy is the love of wisdom and truth in all departments of nature. It is not merely
an accumulation of data, facts, and intellectual knowledge. A 'philosopher' is not so
much one who knows, but one who is attempting to find out. Socrates declared, 'I
know that I know nothing' which is a shorter version of his actual words, 'I neither
know nor think that I know.'[43]

❖ *Theosophia* is similar in meaning to the *philosophia perennis*, which is the overarching
and generalizing term encompassing the three broad categories of the former, as
depicted in Figure I-8 on page 185, for better clarity of meaning. These categories are:
(*a*) REALITY (Divine Consciousness); (*b*) the various teachings and doctrines about
REALITY; and (*c*) a synthesis of these doctrines about REALITY drawn from diverse
sources, ancient and modern, by the Theosophical Society.

❖ Mysticism is the universal feeling of union with nature, especially her subtler and invisible realms.

❖ Esotericism (esoteric science) is the study and understanding of the secret knowledge
of Nature's hidden forces and energies rather than the outer and public (i.e., exoteric)
forms that conceal their hidden meaning.

❖ Occultism (occult science) is the study of the secret knowledge of Nature's forces and
energies and how they can be manipulated and controlled to bring about a desired end.

❖ Psychism is a wide term used to denote every kind of mental or paranormal phenomenon such as mediumship and clairvoyance. As commonly understood, however, it
refers to the manifestation of the powers pertaining to the lower strata of man's soul
nature.

❖ Metaphysics is concerned with the underlying basis of reality as a whole. In any branch
of science, philosophy or religion, it constitutes its groundwork and assumptions.

The Language of the Mysteries and the Use of 'Blinds'

Finally, in this section on meanings and definitions we deal with the frequent charge that
the language and literature of the Mysteries (chiefly, occultism) is full of waffle and jargon
unintelligible to the ordinary person—and, to complicate matters, it may appear in
Sanskrit or some other foreign tongue. Whilst we fully accept that one should call 'a spade
a spade' and not 'an agricultural implement', there are two important aspects to the use of
so-called occult jargon.

First, is it not the case that each discipline draws upon a language best suited to
communicating its message? Of course, merely using jargon in no way implies that the

user understands its meaning (and in fact jargon used in that way is waffle and serves only to confuse). For example, merely to use words like 'differentiation', 'integration', and 'calculus' in no way suggests that the user of such words is a mathematician; however, it would be impossible to find a single mathematician who does not understand the meaning of such terms. Moreover, is it not the case that the exact sciences, like physics, chemistry, and physiology, use words in Greco-Latin terminology in their books? Is it not also the case that musicians resort to Italian or German in their scores, botanists to Latin for their taxonomy, lawyers to Latin phrases? For example, would a layman, however intelligent but untrained in molecular biology, know that 'apoptosis' means 'a genetically determined process of cell self-destruction that is marked by the fragmentation of nuclear DNA'?[44] Then why should not occultism resort to the pristine clarity of Sanskrit, or the Tibetan tongue, when no equivalent words exist in a European language, including English? 'Rich as the English language is in media of expression', as Manly Hall correctly avers, 'it is curiously lacking in terms suitable to the conveyance of abstract philosophical premises. A certain intuitive grasp of the subtler meanings concealed within groups of inadequate words is necessary therefore to an understanding of the ancient Mystery Teachings.'[45]

Every branch of study has its own terminology; so why should the Mystery Teachings be an exception?

Secondly, such 'jargon' fulfils a double necessity: to communicate facts to the worthy, and protect those facts from falling into unscrupulous hands and being perverted. For this reason the Mystery Teachings were conveyed in an outer wrapping in what is known as 'blinds': a word, or symbol, used as an allegorical surrogate or proxy for its real meaning. The Mystery language was the sacerdotal secret jargon employed by initiated priests and used only when discussing sacred things. Every nation had its own 'Mystery tongue' unknown save to those admitted to the Mysteries. In consequence, those who were versed in esoteric and occult matters would be able to unwrap the outer covering and find the terminology to be terse and clear—revealing the kernel of truth within. But for the profane, the terminology would seem meaningless gobbledygook (which is no different, in principle, from a kindergarten child struggling with basic arithmetic, who would find the symbols and language of calculus to be meaningless drivel); and this is for good reason—for example, neither Darwin nor Stephen Jay Gould had any insight into Plato's *Phaedo* and therefore imposed their own materialistic interpretation on the esoteric meaning behind the doctrine of archetypes and the pre-existence of the soul (see the close of Chapter 3).

The language of the Mysteries is clear to the initiated; but nonsense to the profane

It has been stated above, and it bears repeating, that occult facts are highly dangerous in unworthy hands. So the *apparently* gibberish nature of occult terminology is simply a way to ensure that the secrets about the inner workings of nature, and latent powers in man, will not fall into undeserving hands but will be understood only by those who are worthy to receive them. In Hall's words: 'In a single figure, a symbol may both reveal and conceal, for to the wise the subject of the symbol is obvious, while to the ignorant the figure remains inscrutable. With the needs of posterity foremost in mind, the sages of old went to inconceivable extremes to make certain that their knowledge would be preserved. [For example] their knowledge of chemistry and mathematics they hid within mythologies which the ignorant would perpetuate, or in the [geometrical proportions of] spans and arches of their temples which time has not entirely obliterated.'[46] This is something that Isaac Newton clearly realized. His last book, *The Chronology of Ancient Kingdoms Amended*, contains descriptions and drawings of King Solomon's Temple along with a detailed numerological analysis of the mysteries embedded in its sacred proportions.[47] Why did

How the
Mysteries have
been safeguarded
in myth,
allegories, sacred
geometry, ciphers,
etc.

its architecture hold a special fascination for him? His passion for unlocking hidden truths and secrets—whether in mathematics, natural philosophy, alchemy or theology—led him to view all these studies as connected and interconnected; and towards the end of his life he became convinced that sacred architecture was also a repository of arcane wisdom, and so he began studying the temples of the ancient world. It is heart-breaking nowadays to witness the destruction of the ancient temples and archaeological sites in Iraq and Syria (like the ancient Semitic city Palmyra) by the murderously fanatical Islamic gangs— having naught to do with the true Teachings of the Prophet of Islam. One therefore shudders to think what would happen if the ancient secrets about nature's finer forces and powers were to fall into their unworthy hands. The need for secrecy is apparent. Then, regarding the Rosicrucians, Hall informs us that 'Whatever initiatory ritual the Order possessed was so closely guarded that it has never been revealed. Doubtless it was couched in chemical terminology.'[48] An example of such a chemical 'blind' is *The Chymical Wedding of Christian Rosenkreutz*[xiii] often described as the third of the original manifestos of the mysterious Fraternity of the Rose Cross.

Another instance of concealed meanings, again reliably stated by Hall, is this passage:

> Doubt has always existed as to whether the name Rosicrucian came from the symbol of the rose and cross, or whether this was merely a blind to deceive the uninformed and further conceal the true meaning of the Order. [The British antiquarian, mythographer, and religious historian] Godfrey Higgins [1772–1833] believes that the word *Rosicrucian* is not derived from the flower but from the word *Ros*, which means dew.[49] It is also interesting to note that the word *Ras* means wisdom, while *Rus* is translated concealment. Doubtless all of these meanings have contributed to Rosicrucian symbolism.

Concealed
meaning in the
symbol of the
Rose and the
Cross

> [The American-born British mystic, occultist and writer] A. E. Waite [1857–1942] holds with Godfrey Higgins that the process of forming the Philosopher's Stone with the aid of dew is the secret concealed within the name Rosicrucian. It is possible that the dew referred to is a mysterious substance within the human brain, closely resembling the description given by alchemists of the dew which, falling from heaven, redeemed the earth. The cross is symbolic of the human body, and the two symbols together—the rose on the cross—signify that the soul of man is crucified upon the body, where it is held by three nails.[50]

What these 'three nails' are will become apparent in Chapter 4 of Volume II. Suffice it to state here that they are the psycho-spiritual platforms acting as foundations, or anchor points, for the organization of the subtle bodies of man.

> The arcana of the ancient Mysteries were never revealed to the profane except through the media of symbols. Symbolism fulfilled the dual office of concealing the sacred truths from the uninitiated and revealing them to those qualified to understand the symbols. Forms are the symbols of formless divine principles; symbolism is the language of Nature. With reverence the wise pierce the veil and with clearer vision contemplate the reality; but the ignorant, unable to distinguish between the false and the true, behold a universe of symbols.[51]

The problem of secret meanings and confusing terminology is explored further in Volume II, Chapter 1.

———

xiii Its anonymous authorship is attributed to the German theologian Johann Valentin Andreae (1586–1654).

Meanwhile, we draw this section to a close by touching on the subject of crop circles. Although Southern England seems to be peculiarly well endowed when it comes to the appearance of crop circles, it is in fact a worldwide phenomenon spanning several centuries. Naturally, they have always attracted attention but never more so than in the twentieth and twenty-first centuries. Having looked at the way in which the Rosicrucians shrouded their secrets in chemical technology, it is perhaps more than idle speculation to conjecture that crop circles may encode mathematical symbols. For example, a crop circle, measuring three hundred feet across, which recently appeared in England in the county of Wiltshire, is thought by some serious researchers to have a connection with one of the most elegant theorems by the Swiss mathematician Leonhard Euler (1707–1783).[52] Unfortunately, mainstream scientists have been dissuaded from taking these mysterious appearances seriously due to disinformation, propaganda, and for fear of looking foolish in front of their peers. Nonetheless, there seems to be compelling, and mounting evidence that the sudden appearance, intricate pictograms, and perfect symmetry of crop circles suggest that they cannot all be explained away in terms of freak atmospheric conditions, or human fakes and counterfeits, and whereas orthodox science prefers to ignore any speculation about extraterrestrial communication, some serious scientists have given this matter much consideration.[53]

Do some crop circles convey a meaning hidden in symbols?

The Charge of Secrecy

We now deal with the related charge of secrecy: that besides being expounded through allegories and blinds, Mystery Teachings were never publicly stated; moreover, even what was stated had vital elements missing and the seeker had to go to extraordinary lengths to find the hidden secrets of the teachings. What we have just stated above, underpinned by the quotation below, should make it plain why the initiates of Mystery Schools have closely guarded their secrets and never revealed them on demand to the unworthy:

> Occult philosophy divulges few of its most important vital mysteries. It drops them like precious pearls, one by one, far and wide apart, and only when forced to do so by the evolutionary tidal wave that carries humanity on, slowly, silently, but steadily [onwards]. For once out of the safe custody of their legitimate heirs and keepers, those mysteries cease to be occult: they fall into the public domain and have to run the risk of becoming in the hands of the selfish—of the *Cains* of the human race—curses more often than blessings.[54]

The charge of silence and secrecy to shield 'pearls cast before swine'

The true occultist, then, contributes immensely to the sum total of human knowledge and wisdom, whilst maintaining silence about his personality and the organization, or brotherhood, to which he belongs. What is the nature of that silence?

It is symbolized in the mysteries by the closing of the eyes and the closing of the mouth. Closing of the eyes has nothing to do with inducing temporary blindness. Quite the contrary: by shutting out external distractions, the internal vision becomes magnified and clarified—every serious meditator knows and experiences this. As for the closing of the mouth, this is not just because the secrets may not be communicated (for reasons just explained) but that they *cannot* be communicated. It is as impossible to describe in words the taste of wine to he who has never drunk of it, as it is to impart secrets to a neophyte who has not been initiated into their meaning.

As for the complaint amongst the zealous that a vital piece of the esoteric jigsaw is being left out of the teachings imparted or the missing clue deeply hidden in blinds and symbols, this is because the initiated philosophers realized that once man understands the complete workings of any system, he may accomplish a prescribed end (often motivated by personal power or greed), but he would not necessarily be qualified to deal with, or control, the effects so produced. This is well illustrated in *Der Zauberlehrling (The Sorcerer's Apprentice)*, the poem by Goethe written in 1797.[55] The story tells of an old sorcerer who departs his workshop, leaving his apprentice with chores to perform. Tired of fetching water using buckets, the apprentice enchants a broom to do the work for him, using magical powers which he only partially understands and in which he is not yet fully trained. The floor is soon flooded with water, and the apprentice realizes that he cannot stop the broom because he does not know how to do so. In desperation, he splits the broom in two with an axe, only to find that each of the two pieces becomes a whole new broom and takes up a bucket and continues fetching water, now at twice the rate. When all seems lost, the sorcerer returns and quickly breaks the spell. The poem finishes with the old sorcerer chiding his apprentice for meddling in things the latter only half-understands and warning him that powerful spirits should only be evoked by the master himself.

Why a little knowledge is dangerous: Goethe's tale of *The Sorcerer's Apprentice*, set to music in 1897 by the French composer Paul Dukas (1865–1945)

In Chapter XI of the Rosicrucian manifesto *Confessio Fraternitatis* we find this warning, and a fitting example of the great misuse of power by the obliterating forces of dogmatic Christian ideology:

> When to a man is given power to heal disease, to overcome poverty, and to reach a position of worldly dignity, that man is beset by numerous temptations and unless he possess true knowledge and full understanding he will become a terrible menace to mankind. The alchemist who attains to the art of transmuting base metals can do all manner of evil unless his understanding be as great as his self-created wealth. We therefore affirm that man must first gain knowledge, virtue, and understanding; then all other things may be added unto him. We accuse the Christian Church of the great sin of possessing power and using it unwisely; therefore we prophesy that it shall fall by the weight of its own iniquities and its crown shall be brought to naught.[56]

How Christian dogma has obliterated truth

It would not be entirely unreasonable to argue that such prophecy has indeed come to pass, given the moribund state of orthodox Christianity in the public eye these days.

And in Chapter XIV of the same work there is the further warning that even otherwise upright men who may be overturned and 'dazzled by the glitter of gold or […] might be turned by great riches to a life of idleness and pomp' should not attempt to penetrate into the arcana of adepts. For 'though there be a medicine which will cure all diseases and give unto all men wisdom, *yet it is against the will of God that men should attain to understanding by any means other than virtue, labour, and integrity* [emphasis added].' The penalty of transgressing this law is none other than insanity or loss of life.

The Rosicrucian credo for safeguarding secrets

The French metaphysician and writer, René Guénon (1886–1951), wrote widely on topics ranging from sacred science and comparative religion to symbolism and initiation but made some entirely inaccurate and misleading remarks about Blavatsky and the Theosophical Society,[57] effectively invalidated by Joscelyn Godwin (*b.*1945), the British author known for his work on paganism, hermeticism, and Theosophy.[58] Nevertheless, Guénon upholds the same moral of the Rosicrucian manifesto that certain schools in the West, since antiquity, have remained closeted, especially in the Middle Ages, for the simple reason that they were philosophical schools whose doctrines were expressed only under the veil of symbolism that remained forever obscure to those who did not possess the key to them. That key is the higher, or esoteric, standpoint, which includes the exoteric interpretations lying beneath it. In a discussion on 'Esotericism and Exotericism', he writes that:

> This key was given only to adherents who had made certain pledges and whose discretion was sufficiently proven, whilst their intellectual capacity was deemed adequate [because] it was a question of doctrines so profound as to be totally foreign to the popular mentality [...].59

These sequestered schools or societies were typically the Alchemists, Rosicrucians, Freemasons, Cathars, Gnostics, Templars, and Theosophists, the latter concerning the theosophy of the German philosopher, Christian mystic, and Lutheran Protestant theologian Jakob Böhme (1575–1624) and the Christian theosophy of the seventeenth and eighteenth centuries. Each of these movements was, at one time or another, virulently opposed by the Catholic Church, which thought nothing of persecuting, torturing, burning, butchering, or, at best, excommunicating their members. Even the modern Theosophical Society received its fair share of malicious attacks from the Christian Missionaries in nineteenth century India. It is for this reason that such schools, particularly during the Middle Ages, had to pursue their spiritual and esoteric functions under the cloak of disguises and blinds. By contrast, other major religions, especially in the East, have shown far more tolerance towards their esoteric brothers than official Christianity. But even in Christianity we easily discern the use of blinds, otherwise known as sacraments, which are religious ceremonies regarded as an outward and visible sign of an inward and invisible reality, like baptism, confirmation, the Eucharist, etc.

The Catholic Church and the fate of esoteric societies

The qualified initiate, then, was taught in stages how to develop the occult powers hidden within his own nature, but what these were, and how they could be unfolded, was never revealed to the unregenerate, for fear of misuse and the acquisition of powers for selfish gain. Even a cursory glance at the current world situation where we see a rampant craze for power, and its dreadful misuse, in the hands of unscrupulous politicians and business leaders, as also in pseudo-spiritual fads dominated by powerful cult figures—let alone terrorists—should make it crystal clear why long periods of arduous probation were imposed on the occult neophyte, so that the knowledge of how to become as the gods might remain the sole possession of the worthy. This is the significance of the allegory of Goethe's *The Sorcerer's Apprentice*, just described, in order to illustrate the reason why the initiates and occultists guarded their secrets so closely.

Why arduous probation is indispensible before secrets are revealed

But nowadays, spurred by the march of natural science, the veil of secrecy has been unveiled, albeit partially, by the modern Theosophical Society. The correspondences between the occult powers latent in the organs, orifices, channels, and centres in the human body with planetary and terrestrial influences, has been disseminated by Blavatsky in the form of the *Inner Group Teachings of H. P. Blavatsky*. Needless to say, Blavatsky does not instruct Inner Group members on how to evoke the occult powers; it is sufficient to draw attention to their relationship and correspondences with the organs of the body—something that was never divulged publicly until then. These further facts with references are given in Chapter 9 of Volume III.

Why some secrets were partially unveiled by the Theosophical Society

It is obvious that knowledge is power and those who would fathom nature's secret processes, or solicit the company of the adepts, would have the power to wreak untold havoc in the world, unless they possessed full control and absolute power over themselves. The passionate desire of the occultist to see things hidden is the counterpart of his apprehension that what he sees may also be seen by the unworthy. Accordingly, we now describe the qualifications and necessary preparation for the teachings imparted in the Mystery Schools.

Apropos it is worth pointing out that occult secrets have been protected almost as effectively, if entirely unwittingly, by modern scientific scepticism as they have been in the past by blinds, sacraments, and secrecy.

Adepts and Initiates – Who, or What Are They?

At this stage it is as well to explain the meaning of two terms that we shall meet frequently in the course of this work: 'initiate' and 'adept'. Who, or what are they? In short, an initiate is one to whom the Mystery Teachings have deservedly been imparted at a level appropriate to his grade of development. An adept is one who has attained full mastery over himself and the mysteries (i.e., secrets of nature) to which he has had access and been entrusted. It stands to reason therefore, that an adept is a fully fledged occultist. It would be helpful to unpack these somewhat terse descriptions.

The term 'initiate' derives from the Latin *initiatus*, past participle of *initiare* 'to begin', or 'originate'. It is the designation of anyone who was received into, and had revealed to him, the mysteries and secrets of the occult sciences, whether this be through traditions of the East or the West—the Qabbalah, Rosicrucianism, or Masonry being prime examples of the latter. In bygone days, the arcane knowledge was imparted to the chosen neophyte by the hierophants[xiv] of the Mysteries. In modern times there are still teachers capable of instructing initiants worthy of the teaching, but these are necessarily few and far between. Note the distinction between the 'initiant', one who is beginning, or preparing for, an initiation, and an 'initiate', one who has successfully passed at least one initiation. Obviously, then, an initiate is always an initiant when he prepares for a higher degree of initiation. In the Masonic tradition for example, the Entered Apprentice is an initiant to the next degree of Fellow Craftsman, after which initiation he becomes an Initiant to the next higher degree of Master Mason.

An initiate has deserved the teachings imparted to him

Logically extending the argument, the adept is one who has obtained the highest initiation. The term derives from the Latin *adeptus* 'having reached', 'attained', past participle of *adipisci* 'to come up with', 'arrive at'. In occultism it signifies one who has reached the stage of a master in esoteric wisdom and occult philosophy. If all this sounds a little far-fetched we need only look at the way the term is used in everyday parlance. We tend to refer to anyone who is highly skilled and attained mastery over their profession as being adept at it, be it in sport, culinary arts, science or music. There is no logical reason why such adeptship cannot sensibly be extrapolated to include not just mastery over a chosen skill, but full mastery over the complete human nature at all levels, physical, emotional, psychic, and mental. This, then, represents the highest attainment of the human kingdom after which, as it is taught, the adept may progress to states and planes of consciousness out of the human kingdom into still higher kingdoms of nature.

---

xiv 'Hierophant' is derived from the Greek *Hierophantes*, literally, 'One who explains sacred things', a title belonging to the highest teachers and expounders of the Mysteries in the temples of antiquity.

An equivalent term to adept is 'master', or the generic Indian term *mahātmān* ('mahātmā' when applied to a specific august being). It is a Sanskrit term meaning 'Great Soul', derived from *maha-* great and *ātman* soul. The term 'master' was later adopted for 'mahātmā' in the West. It is an aptly descriptive term since a master is an appellation assigned to one who has overcome the hurdles of his chosen endeavour; and in the spiritual realm a master is one who has conquered and surmounted all the challenges of life—physical, emotional, and mental.

That such mysterious men did exist there can be little doubt, as their presence is attested by scores of reliable witnesses. However, these adepts were polyonymous individuals (i.e., known by several names) who were able unexpectedly to appear and disappear at will, leaving no trace of their whereabouts (refer to Chapter 4 of Volume II where the phenomenon of creating the *Māyāvi-rūpa*, or 'body of illusion' is explained). There are indications that a certain degree of organization existed among them. The most powerful of such hierarchies in the West and the Middle East were the Rosicrucians, the Illuminati, and certain Arabian and Syrian sects; and in the East the Great White Brotherhood. However, it would not be sensible to draw hard-and-fast distinctions between the various organizations since they are, in a sense, the overtones emanating from the central parental keynote of Universal Wisdom.

> Terms like 'initiate' and 'adept', or 'master' and 'mahātmā' refer to ascending degrees of self-mastery and powers over the secrets of nature

It is further asserted that they are still to be found by those who have qualified themselves to contact them. The philosophers taught that like attracts like, and that when the disciple has developed a virtue and integrity acceptable to the adepts they will appear to him and reveal those parts of the secret processes that cannot be discovered without such help. In summary, an adept is one of those rare, illumined, souls who has been entrusted with the perpetuation and dissemination of the arcana of the transcendental and superphysical realms of nature (which has always been the province of the pagan hierophants). To attain that end the adept may promulgate as much of such wisdom as he is lawfully entitled to do, either on his own or by admission into a fraternal organization as one of its principal representatives, or through chosen initiates as his messengers and envoys (as exampled by H. P. Blavatsky).

Why All the Mystery Surrounding the Lives and Whereabouts of Adepts and Masters?

The perennial wisdom tradition has always taught about Intelligences ('gods' from planetary and solar schemes higher than our own) watching over and guiding the spiritual evolution and consciousness of nascent humanity, and intervening at critical moments to provide the impetus and assist its evolutionary progress, much as in the same way a parent–teacher passes on its wisdom to its child–pupil. Known variously as masters and adepts, or the Indian term mahātmās, as just stated, this idea has captured the imaginations and fired the aspirations of seekers past and present, both East and West. However, this same idea has become prey to the most serious misunderstandings and misconceptions. This has resulted in absurdly anthropomorphic phantasies and grotesquely materialized, personalized, and even carnalized, concepts about their lives and true spiritual stature. There is no shortage of self-appointed 'masters' coveting personal aggrandizement along with power and control; and credulous idolatry is rampant.

Self-appointed
'masters' and
genuine masters
are poles apart in
wisdom

This is why the whereabouts of real masters, and other details concerning them, are closely guarded secrets open only to those initiates and advanced seekers qualified to gain access and contact with them. An exception to this general rule may be cited. The pioneering Madame Blavatsky, principal founder of the modern Theosophical movement, was the first to reveal openly, and for the first time, in a manner widely accessible to the public, some of the facts of the Mahātmās (Masters); and to confirm that the movement she spear-headed, along with the teachings promulgated, were the project and offspring of her two principal Mahatmic instructors with whom she confirmed direct communication, instruction, and experience. Alas, this excessive divulging of facts, which Blavatsky herself regretfully admitted should never have been made public, has caused seismic disturbances within the Theosophical Society itself, not to mention the personal calumny, charges of fraud, and character assassinations that she personally had to bear, for example the infamous 'Hodgson Report'.[60] For this reason we again affirm that there is no obfuscating mystique concerning genuine adepts, or masters of any age or epoch: only a protective veil of MYSTERY that may not be penetrated by the sensation-seeking, the ill-wishers or the profane.

Is there, then, no way that such lofty individuals (in physical existence) can be contacted by the earnest and dedicated seeker of truth, who does not happen to be an initiate?

Can the Adepts be Contacted – If so, How?

The guarded answer is in the affirmative and it is this. While the intellectualist invariably flounders amongst contradictory theories, the mystic and occultist treats the problem of the relationship between the seen and unseen worlds in an entirely different manner. He believes (or rather, knows) that the true occult fraternity consists of a school of superhumans (like the fabled mahātmās of India), being an institution existing not just in the visible world but primarily in its spiritual counterpart, which he sees fit to call the 'inner planes of Nature'; and that the Brothers can be reached only by those who are capable of transcending the limitations of the material world. To substantiate this viewpoint, we cite two seminal passages from the occult literature of the West and the East.

From the Confessio Fraternitatis of the Rosicrucians:

> A thousand times the unworthy may clamour, a thousand times may present themselves, yet God hath commanded our ears that they should hear none of them, and hath so compassed us about with His clouds that unto us, His servants, no violence can be done; wherefore now no longer are we beheld by human eyes, unless they have received strength borrowed from the eagle.[61]

In mysticism, the eagle is a symbol of initiation, as we said earlier, and by this is explained the inability of the unregenerate world to understand the Secret Order of the occult fraternity.

A more encouraging note is sounded in a letter written in 1882 by one of Blavatsky's Adept instructors:

Sincerity and
purity of motive
are the surest
ways to attract
the attention of a
mahātmā

> Nature has linked all parts of her Empire together by subtle threads of magnetic sympathy, and, there is a mutual correlation even between a star and a man; thought runs swifter than the electric fluid, and your thought *will find me* if projected by a pure impulse, as mine will find, has found, and often impressed your mind. We may move in cycles of activity divided—not entirely separated from each other. Like the light in the

sombre valley seen by the mountaineer from his peaks, every bright thought in your mind, my Brother, will sparkle and attract the attention of your distant friend and correspondent […] and it is our law to approach every such an one [*sic*] if even there be but the feeblest glimmer of the true 'Tathāgata'[xv] light within him—then how far easier for you to attract us. Understand this and the admission into the Society of persons often distasteful to you will no longer amaze you.62

There are three factors of deepest significance. The first sentence conveys two ideas: instantaneous action-at-a-distance by way of sympathetic resonance (the linking of all parts of Nature's Empire); and non-locality (the mutual correlation between a star and a man, implying that the intervening distance is of no consequence). This is one of the clearest, yet most poetical statements presaging the principal breakthroughs of quantum physics eighteen years later in 1900.[xvi] Secondly, it is made crystal clear that pristine purity of motive is the signal that will attract the attention of an adept, however weak or unqualified one may be in other respects. Thirdly, most reassuringly, that it is a spiritual law that any advanced being must seek out such a pure aspirant for wisdom. This is the real truth behind the popular saying (also depicted in paintings): 'Take one step towards the divine, and the divine will take nine steps towards you', which really means, 'God helps those who help themselves'. How an advanced being seeks out and contacts the earnest aspirant is too complex a subject to enter into here. Suffice it to say that it is never at our personal convenience or behest. The contact is very rarely in person and mostly in the form of synchronous occurrences that impel the inner nature towards the higher life—for example, finding just the right book or acquiring an exceptional friendship at just the right time in life. Needless to say, any accelerated growth process invariably involves suffering and hardship in the personal life during the period of the transition.

Spiritual law dictates that a mahātmā seeks out an earnest aspirant

The Mystery Schools and Their Teachings

Whereas it would be foolish to pretend that what follows is anything more than a bare outline of the necessary qualifications and essential secrets divulged to chosen candidates in the Mystery Schools, yet we may profitably elucidate some broad doctrines imparted that are common to the Mystery Teachings the world over—in the Brahmanical Schools of India, the ancient Persian and Egyptian Schools, the Odinic Mysteries of Scandinavia, the Eleusinian, Orphic, and Dionysiac Mysteries of Greece, and the Druidic Schools of ancient England, to name but a few of the chief centres of esoteric learning and instruction.

Objectives and Purpose

The principal objective of the Mysteries is to enable the struggling human person to re-awaken, and hence re-claim, the spiritual fire lying dormant within himself but walled in and suffocated by the smoke of the lust, selfishness, and decadence of his baser nature

---

xv 'Tathāgata' is the Sanskrit term for an honorific title of a Buddha, especially the Buddha Gautama, or a person who has attained perfection.

xvi The writer's conviction is that world-shattering scientific discoveries do not happen by chance; and that the impulse for quantum physics was given out on the inner planes by the Masters and Emissaries of the Mystery Schools to minds prepared and attuned to receive it—see the next section.

The Mysteries
unfold the higher
nature; never
pander to the
personality or
respond to
personal needs

(Wagner's epic opera *Siegfried* provides dramatic evidence[xvii]). The whole purpose of the secret processes of the Mysteries was thus to enable certain centres of the brain to be stimulated so that the consciousness could be liberated and extended to bequeath vistas of elusive interior, invisible landscapes that remain entirely opaque to everyday consciousness.[xviii] Accordingly, all the arcane writings are allegorical expositions of profound mystic and philosophic truths whose hidden (occult) meaning may be unlocked and comprehended only by those with the key (esoteric) of a prepared mind and elevated consciousness. For that reason, the ancients always taught—scientists please note—what was so eloquently pronounced by the Christ: 'Neither shall they say, Lo here! or, lo there! for, behold, the Kingdom of God is within you,'[63] meaning that a man does not know the gods (divine forces and powers) by logic and intellect alone, or by external activities and influences, *but primarily by realizing the presence of the gods within himself.*

However, never in their entire history have the Mysteries in their purity and spiritual integrity ever catered to the personal and emotional nature and needs of the candidate. It is precisely to free the soul of limitation, to purify the heart and discipline the mind, that the Mystery training is so severe, for in initiation only spiritual strength, underpinned by unimpeachable strength of character, can withstand the searching ordeal.

There is ample evidence about the pre-eminence of the doctrines promulgated by, and through, the Mysteries. From the unqualified testimony of such reputable authorities on the Western Mysteries as the Greek pantheon comprising the dramatist Aristophanes (445–385 BC), Epictetus (50–135) the Stoic philosopher, Proclus (412–485) the Neoplatonist philosopher, and Plato, then the Roman orator and lawyer Cicero (106–43 BC) and the Christian theologian Clement of Alexandria (150–215); and on the Eastern Mysteries from H. P. Blavatsky and Paul Brunton, the Initiates of India, Egypt, Greece, and other ancient civilizations—came the correct solution to those great cultural, intellectual, moral, and social problems which, in an unsolved state, confront the humanity of all times, as our present century of political unrest, terrorist violence in the name of religion, and ecological disasters bears ample witness. This does not mean, as Hall clarifies, 'that antiquity had foreseen and analysed every complexity of this [or any other] generation, but rather that the Mysteries had evolved a method whereby the mind was so trained in the fundamental verities of life that it was able to cope intelligently with any emergency which might arise. Thus the reasoning faculties were organized by a simple process of mental culture, for it was asserted that where reason reigns supreme, inconsistency cannot exist. Wisdom, it was maintained, lifts man to the condition of Godhood, a fact which explains the enigmatical statement that the Mysteries transformed "roaring beasts into divinities."'[64] Likewise, the writer maintains that much of what passes for mainstream education these days aims at narrow specialization in one or other department of the sciences, arts or humanities. This assumes that each individual is a blank canvas needing to be spoon-fed so called facts which are foreign to the former; whereas the true meaning

The Mysteries are
a universal
training school to
meet the
challenges of any
age

---

xvii Wagner memorialised the Odinic mysteries in musical language, with artistic liberties, in his monumental Ring Cycle (*The Ring of the Nibelung*) of four epic operas, in sequence: *Das Rheingold* (The Rhine Gold), *Die Walküre* (The Valkyrie), *Siegfried* (a legendary hero of Germanic mythology), and *Götterdämmerung* (Twilight of the Gods).

xviii Psychedelic drugs also act on the brain centres. However, other than in carefully controlled experiments, the obsessive drug-taker is hardly likely to be prepared in the manner of a candidate of the Mysteries for his experiences; hence the invariably disastrous consequences of his addiction.

of education is to *educe*, meaning, to bring out, or develop, the knowledge which is innate but latent within. This is a far cry from the total culture of the mind inculcated by the classical education in the *seven liberal arts* comprising first the trivium (grammar, logic, and rhetoric) and then the quadrivium (arithmetic, geometry, music, and astronomy).[65] In the same vein, it was Plato who taught his adherents to rely solely on principles in order to determine the truth of any particular question or situation. For this not only did the gnostic faculties have to be known and exercised, but the 'Good', or virtuous, life lived fully, that is, through the whole gamut of the human being.

Location of the Mystery Schools – Ancient and Modern

'Śambhala' (Shamballa) is the Sanskrit place-name of highly mystical significance—the mythical location and abode of the divine Kumaras, those mighty INTELLIGENCES who are the real Guides of our planetary Life as a whole, not only of man. Its abode is said to exist in invisibly ethereal substance somewhere to the north of the Tibetan plateau. Just as the heart pumping blood into the circulatory system and vital organs maintains the vitality and function of the physical body, so it is with the spiritual body of the Earth and humanity, whose mystic heart-centre is Śambhala from whose ventricles the esoteric life-blood flows into organic Mystery-centres of esoteric and occult learning and instruction. But whatever its historical basis, the reality of Śambhala is best regarded as being primarily visionary and spiritual, and only secondarily, physical or geographical. See Chapter 9 for further details on the primeval location of this fabled land and the outpouring of spiritual emissaries from it.

Śambhala connotes a spiritual focus rather than a physical centre

Every Mystery-centre, then, is an organic focus owing spiritual allegiance to the mystic heart-centre. Accordingly, the Mysteries were taught in specially created Schools by priest–hierophants who developed extraordinary techniques to assist candidates to achieve higher states of consciousness. However, as intimated above, a Mystery School is not dependent on location as such (even though it might have one). Rather it is an association, or brotherhood, of spiritually disciplined individuals bound by one common purpose—the spiritual and moral elevation of humanity, a service intelligently and compassionately rendered because born of love and wisdom. Modern examples would, arguably, be the Theosophical Society, on the one hand, which has its international headquarters in India, acting as the focal centre for disseminating the esoteric wisdom to various national Centres around the globe; and, on the other hand, the Scientific and Medical Network which has no physical headquarters of its own, but spreads its knowledge through channels of journals and web-based publications, conferences and lectures to regional centres and also to a worldwide audience. Nonetheless, it is a fact that certain locations appear to be more favourable to success in spiritual matters than others. Why, for instance, were the ancient seats of the Mysteries almost invariably in rock-temples or subterranean caves, in forests or mountain passes, in pyramid chambers or temple crypts? Because the thought currents and atmosphere prevailing in such remote locations would be calmer, more peaceful, and cleaner the farther removed from the 'madding crowd' of cities. So rarely, if ever, would one find a seat of esoteric training near a large metropolis. (Do we not experience greater calm and heightened awareness when we take a trip away from the noisy bustle of the city to the solitude of the unspoilt countryside?)

Location of Mystery-centres worldwide

We show pictures of two of the most famous rock-cut cave-temples from the thousands excavated in the hills in South India. The Elephanta Caves, shown in Figure I-10, are a network of sculpted caves hewn from solid basalt rock located on Elephanta Island, or Gharapuri (literally 'the city of caves') in Bombay (Mumbai) Harbour, ten kilometres to the east of the City.

Image Credit: Wikipedia/Elephanta Caves

Figure I-10 Elephanta Caves, a UNESCO World Heritage Site located off the coast of Bombay – A conglomeration of complex temple structures

The Ellora Caves, shown in Figure I-11, represent the epitome of Indian rock-cut architecture. They are a complex of thirty-four cave structures excavated out of the vertical basalt rock face of the Charanandri hills north-west of the City of Aurangabad.

Image Credits: https://pixabay.   *Writer's own photograph*   *Wikipedia/Ellora Caves*
com/photos/ellora-cave-spirituality-
structure-4988785

Figure I-11 Ellora Caves, a UNESCO World Heritage Site located near Aurangabad in Maharashtra – Thirty-four monasteries and temples, extending over more than 2 km, dug in the wall of a high basalt cliff

Pythagoras
instructed in India
by the Brahmins

It is of deepest significance that after he made his historic venture through Media and Persia into Hindustan, the legendary Pythagoras (*circa* 570 BC – *circa* 495 BC) remained for several years as a pupil and initiate of the learned Brahmins of Elephanta and Ellora; and in fact the name of Pythagoras is still preserved in the records of the Brahmins as *Yavancharya*, the Ionian Teacher—see *Ancient Freemasonry*.[66] It is of equal import that Newton revered the Teachings of Pythagoras (and Plato).

Indian philosophy
has seeded
worldwide
religions and
philosophies

Then, after returning from his travels, Pythagoras established his famous school (or university as it has sometimes been called) at Crotona in Southern Italy. There he taught the secrets of occult mathematics, music, and astronomy, considered by him to be the triune foundation of all arts and sciences. And so it is no exaggeration to say that the wisdom of the East has seeded and fecundated the greatest science and philosophy the world over. This point is argued with great elegance and clarity by the philosopher and statesman Sir Sarvepalli Radhakrishnan in *Eastern Religions and Western Thought*, which describes the leading ideas of Indian philosophy and religion and then traces the probable influence of Indian mysticism on Greek thought and Christian development, through Alexandrian

Judaism, Christian Gnosticism, and Neoplatonism.[67] The author argues that Christianity, which arose out of an Eastern background, became allied with Graeco-Latin culture and will find rebirth in a renewed alliance with this Eastern heritage. These ideas and the exposition in the final chapter of Radhakrishnan's book, about the meeting of religions, furnishes added evidence in support of a principal theme of this work: the unity of religions rooted in the *philosophia perennis*, hence understood in their mystical and esoteric content stripped of orthodox accretions. Says Radhakrishnan in the Preface:

> Modern civilization with its scientific temper, humanistic spirit, and secular view of life is uprooting the world over the customs of long centuries and creating a ferment of restlessness. The new world cannot remain a confused mass of needs and impulses, ambitions and activities, without any control or guidance of the spirit. The void created by abandoned superstitions and uprooted beliefs calls for a spiritual filling.[68]

Do Mystery Schools, or Mystery-centres (not necessarily location-dependent) exist these days? There is no doubt that the Mystery Schools have withdrawn from public knowledge, but that does not automatically imply that the perennial link with Śambhala has been severed: rather the link is now preserved under a veil of secrecy which is not synonymous with non-existence. Such Mystery-centres are to be found the world over, for, as Blavatsky declares, 'the Secret Association is still alive and as active as ever',[69] even though the exact location of these centres, guarded with zealous care by their protectors, is undiscoverable except by the worthy. In point of fact, owing to the increased need for light and truth nowadays, 'the esoteric groups of Mystery-Schools are perhaps more numerous today than they have been for thousands of years.'[70] This theme is continued later in Chapter 9.

Mystery-centres will always exist

Emissaries of the Mystery Schools and Their Fate

Who are the emissaries of the Mystery Schools and how have they been regarded in the eyes of the world? In the broadest sense, emissaries are those who have made their appearance on the world stage with the express purpose of revealing a portion of the Mystery Teachings appropriate to the epoch in question, in order to elevate the consciousness of humanity, whether this be in the realms of religion, philosophy, science or culture. Their presence has exerted a profoundly beneficent influence on human society and changed the course of history. (Admittedly, human society and history have also been radically altered by tyrants and dictators who have wielded unimaginable power. As explained in detail earlier, this again suggests some degree of contact with occult teachings. In such cases, of course, these teachings have been grotesquely perverted and misused for selfish gain.) It would be unwieldy, and in fact quite pointless, to enumerate a long list of names of Initiate–Teachers. Much better, therefore, to cite a few representative examples as indicative of the general pattern.

In spiritual science and religion, Zarathuśtra (Greek, Zoroaster) the prophet of Persia (*circa* 628–*circa* 551 BC), the Vedic seers like Vyâsa, Śankara, and Kapila and, as the evidence suggests, the Christ,[71] were clearly emissaries of the great centres of esoteric learning. In modern times the writings of the Bulgarian sage Peter Deunov (1864–1944) provide clear indications of contact with the Mystery Teachings of Christianity, as do the works of the Indian sages Ramana Maharshi and Śrī Aurobindo. In philosophy, the names of Pythagoras (instructed in India, as previously stated), Plato who taught in the Mystery Schools of Egypt, and the Roman Hypatia (*circa* 350/370–415), the Hellenistic

Mystery Teachers worldwide from East and West

Neoplatonist philosopher, astronomer, mathematician, and head of the Alexandrian School of Neoplatonism, spring to mind from the wellspring of antiquity; and in our day, Paul Brunton, disciple of the sage Ramana Maharshi. In science, Galileo, Newton, and Planck are outstanding examples. In culture, we have souls of the calibre of Dante Alighieri (1265–1321), Johann Sebastian Bach (1685–1750), Wolfgang Amadeus Mozart (1756–1791), and Ludwig van Beethoven (1770–1827). The Italian occultist and healer The Comte di Cagliostro (1743–1795) and his instructor, the immortal German alchemist and adventurer The Comte de St.-Germain (1712–1784) were both men way beyond their times. In recent times, the Japanese author and scholar Daisetsu Suzuki (1870–1966) was another venerable soul who was instrumental in spreading Zen philosophy to the West.

By way of clarification, it is not being suggested that individuals with unusual facility in their fields, like Bach, Mozart and Beethoven, or Planck, Schrödinger and Einstein, physically attended an official 'Mystery School' or were taught by a 'Mystery Teacher'. In the case of Newton, the picture is not so clear, given the phenomenal forays he made into penetrating the arcana of sacred wisdom, plus his numerous contacts with alchemical and Rosicrucian adepts of the Renaissance and Age of Enlightenment periods in Europe. Nonetheless, as explained above, the Mystery Schools do not necessarily have to be in dedicated geographical locations, although some undoubtedly were and still are. So for contact with the Mystery Teachings, whether this be by way of formal instruction by an initiate in a Mystery School, or not, as the case may be, the central issue is really a matter of internal contact, by way of spiritual resonance between the Higher Self of an aspirant with the radiating consciousness of august beings unknown to the world at large; and there is no denying the radical and lasting change that occurred in the course of science and music from such 'resonant contact' by great scientists and musicians.

How has the world at large treated its ambassadors of Truth—those advanced souls who, out of compassionate love for 'the "great orphan," Humanity'[72] sought to uplift common humanity to witness and live the spiritual life conjoined to the material existence? Their lot has rarely been a happy one, particularly in the Middle East and the West. All the resplendent sages and saints mentioned above, and others too numerous to mention, were streets ahead of their times in mental, intellectual, and spiritual capacities, and so, with few exceptions, like the Buddha, had to suffer the resentfulness and suspicions of the unthinking multitude, who labour under the delusion that advanced ideas and divine truths can be forever obliterated by murdering, persecuting, incarcerating, exiling or slandering those who sought to bequeath them to the world. The iniquities perpetrated against the emissaries of Truth makes depressing reading: among the prophets and religous mystics, Zarathuśtra killed by the assassin's spear according to legend; the crucifixion of the Christ; the flight from Mecca of Muhammad (*circa* 570–632); the imprisonment and execution of the Persian Sūfī masters Manṣūr al-Ḥallāj (857–922) and Shihâboddin Yahya Sohravardi, al-Maqtul (*circa* 1154–1191/2), the former beaten, half-killed, and left on a gibbet until the next day, when he was decapitated, and his body burned,[73] and the latter, it is thought, died through starvation;[74] then among the great philosophers, Socrates (*circa* 469/470–399 BC) executed by drinking poison hemlock; the defenceless Hypatia dragged from her chariot by a Christian mob and excoriated to death; and Giordano Bruno (1548–1600), the Italian Dominican friar, philosopher, mathematician, poet, and cosmological theorist suffered the clamping of his mouth with a nail driven horizontally

Spiritual resonance with a master is the foremost mode of learning

Historical examples of cruelty and ingratitude suffered by the brightest lights of humanity through both cheeks and another vertically through his lips before being burned at the stake; likewise, the Italian poet Dante Alighieri dying in exile from his beloved city of Florence; and the fall from high office and persecution of the English philosopher, statesman, scientist, jurist, and probable author of the so-called Shakespeare plays, Francis Bacon (1561–1626)—the list is a long and sad one. Even the legendary Pythagoras was not spared. Accounts of the philosopher's death vary but not the fact of his untimely and unhappy end. According to some, he was murdered with his disciples; others say that, on escaping from Crotona with a small band of followers, he was trapped and burned alive by his enemies in a little house where the band had decided to rest for the night. Another account states that, finding themselves trapped in the burning structure, the disciples threw themselves into the flames, making of their own bodies a bridge over which Pythagoras escaped, only to die of a broken heart a short time afterwards as the result of grieving over the apparent fruitlessness of his efforts to serve and illuminate mankind.[75]

No better example of slander in modern times than the great occultist H. P. Blavatsky, who had to drink to the last dregs from the poisonous cup of calumny.[76] Even the quiet philosopher and sage Peter Deunov of whom Einstein said, 'All the world renders homage to me and I render homage to the Master Peter Deunov from Bulgaria' was persecuted by the Bulgarian clergy and accused of corrupting the minds of people.[77] Another notable example is Mahatma Gandhi (1869–1948),[xix] the great Indian political leader who campaigned for Indian independence by employing non-violent principles and peaceful disobedience. Though controversial, apparently he exclaimed 'Hey Ram,' ('Oh God') when he was assassinated. Was he recognizing the divine spark, even in the perpetrator? A misunderstanding world has invariably persecuted those who understood the secret workings of nature, seeking in every conceivable manner to exterminate the custodians of divine wisdom. That these illimitable elevators and saviours of mankind were invested with holiness in no way guaranteed, with rare exceptions, that their personal lives would be spared from suffering and powerful strains.

Modern examples of vindictiveness and brutality meted out to saviours of mankind

However, as exemplified by the long list of immortal men and women who have epitomized the Mysteries of the *philosophia perennis* to the world, the sublime verities of the Sacred Science are beyond the range and reach of ordinary mortals and are reborn in every age in those Emissaries who take them forward. The spiritual culture and Teaching from Divine institutions in the world of men has always existed and will continue to do so, as borne witness by the golden chain of initiates and advanced souls of the various Mystery Schools of the past and the present.

Truth and its Emissaries can never be exterminated

But why is such ingratitude shown towards its instructors for which common humanity has, and continues to pay a terrible price? As is invariably the case with geniuses, their outspokenness evokes personal and political hostility both in full measure. In each and every case it is because of the clash between the 'new' and the 'old': the clash between the visionary and the dyed-in-the-wool establishment clergy, between the prophet of the new and the priest of the past. Quite simply, the Emissaries of Truth brought forth a living and new message that threatened the status quo of the *establishment*—the church, the synagogue, the mosque, the temple—entrenched in their own past. And following on from

Authorities are always fearful of new ideas that upset orthodox canons

---

xix The honorific Mahatma (Sanskrit: 'great-souled', 'venerable') was first applied to Mohandas Karamchand Gandhi in 1914 in South Africa.

the above, what was the 'crime' committed by these advanced beings who strove to uplift the bar of humanity's threshold of consciousness? The answer is really quite simple. Each one of them in his or her own way encouraged people to substitute blind belief for a questioning attitude, not to accept the status quo as the final verdict on truth, to seek fresh insights, to break through the crust of outworn ideas, customs, and rituals. As the establishment sees this tidal wave of change, it girds up its loins in ever more ferocious (and even fanatical) attempts to push back the surge, but Truth is too powerful for it and although the fatalities, as named above, may be great, Truth will eventually prevail.

How establishment science and medicine treat their own emissaries

The situation is no different in science and medicine now when research grants, prestigious prizes, and powerful positions are at stake. In science, Galileo was forced to recant his ideas in physics that ran counter to the established Church and sentenced to imprisonment at the pleasure of the Inquisition, which, on the following day, was commuted to house arrest, for the rest of his life. Nowadays, what springs to mind is the vitriol from establishment biology heaped against Rupert Sheldrake for his advanced ideas on the formative principles of life, and the way in which Thomas Nagel has been figuratively mutilated by academia for daring to question (with facts and figures) some aspects of the establishment dictate on Darwinian evolution, as we mentioned earlier. In medicine, Paracelsus (1493–1541) was probably assassinated; these days, naturopaths, and other complementary medicine therapists, inexplicably suffer 'heart attacks' or quietly 'disappear' when their remedies attract sufficient publicity and are seen to threaten the profits of the pharmaceutical multinationals;[78] Eben Alexander's experience of consciousness surviving clinical death of the brain was relegated to a delusional story by establishment neuroscience wedded to a materialist view of 'brain death means extinction of consciousness' (see Chapter 2). Again, the list is depressingly long. (More details on Sheldrake, Nagel, and Alexander are given in Chapter 7 of Volume II.)

Qualifications for Initiation in the Mystery Schools

In the previous sections we have stressed that in any school of learning there are qualifications before a neophyte is accepted. How does one qualify for initiation? Put another way, how does one become an initiate or an occultist? The answer is disarmingly simple, but the simplest answers are the most difficult to apply! A concert pianist, however supremely talented he may be from birth, does not become an international performing artist just by listening to others playing the piano; a neurosurgeon does not qualify for his job only by reading books about brain anatomy. In any field of human endeavour, we must work towards our aspirations; and such work always entails a fine balance between theory and practice. Equally then, an occultist is not ready-made but has to *make himself such*. The German Franz Hartmann MD (1838–1912) was a medical doctor, occultist, geomancer, astrologer, for some time a co-worker of Helena Blavatsky at Adyar, and the founder of the German Theosophical Society in 1896. His works include several books on esoteric studies, peerless biographies of Jakob Böhme (Jacob Boehme) and Paracelsus, and a translation of the *Bhagavad Gītā* into German. As he forcefully states in regard to the initiates and occultists of the Rosicrucian movement:

> Names have no meaning if they do not express the true character of a thing. To call a
> person a Rosicrucian [or an occultist or Theosophist for that matter] does not make him

one, nor does the act of calling a person a Christian make him a Christ. The real Rosicrucian or Mason cannot be made; he must grow to be one by the expansion and unfoldment of the divine power within his own heart.

Why spiritual societies fall far short of their highbrow ideals

And then the author continues with this remark of *deepest import*:

> The inattention to this truth is the cause that many churches and secret societies are far from being that which their names express.[79]

The above statement should serve to jolt at least one, and possibly more, sections of the Theosophical Society in Europe, out of their sanctimonious complacency, which, nowadays, is very 'far from being that which their names [at one time] express[ed].' Tin gods preaching 'brotherliness', whilst presuming to judge the 'brotherliness' or 'unbrotherliness' of others, and merely quoting large tracts of Theosophical doctrines, like so many garrulous parrots, are a far cry from evolved human beings, who sincerely strive to realize the divinity within their own hearts and, as the great German Theosophist Hartmann says, take active steps to *make themselves* into what they preach, namely, to bring forth their latent divine faculties into objective and active manifestation—in popular terms, 'to walk the talk'.

Do fine feathers make fine birds?

But here we need to make a careful distinction between ignorance on the one hand, and idiocy, or stupidity, on the other hand. By 'idiocy' we do not refer to an unfortunate condition of congenital brain damage or the illiteracy of simple country folk, but to those who have allowed their minds to become closed to any new avenues of exploration or enquiry. In this sense an idiot may well be, and often is, a highly intellectual person whose mind is so over-stuffed with intellectual furniture that the light of wisdom cannot penetrate the internal gloom. Wisdom, therefore, cannot be awakened in such a person because the seed of wisdom within him has been suffocated; but wisdom can be aroused in an ignorant person, however ignorant he may be, because the seed of wisdom lies buried within him and can be grown and developed through learning, application, and culture. Hence a philosopher, or a wise man, is an ignorant man within whose nature the seed of wisdom has grown. It is no exaggeration to say that ignorance is greatly preferable to the attitude of a closed mind. An illiterate village peasant in India is far more receptive to, and qualified to receive, spiritual truths than a closed-minded materialist who may have written a hundred academic papers, but is incapable of stepping outside the stronghold (and stranglehold) of his preconceptions—something that the writer has personally discerned on numerous occasions.

Intelligent but uneducated is as possible as idiotic but intellectual

Given the above provisos, we now explain the qualifications laid upon candidates who would seek initiation in the Mystery Schools. The general principles apply to all Mystery Schools the world over, since the overall purpose is to test, to the very limit, a candidate's mettle before he can be entrusted with the secrets of nature and man.

We take as typical examples the rites of Mithras of ancient Persia and the degrees of the Pythagorean School. These had a far-reaching effect upon the civilization of the Western world, being interwoven with, and influencing, Christianity (as Radhakrishnan has observed) following the first century after Christ. Like initiation into several other Mystery Schools and ancient schools of philosophy, and after a period of suitable preparation, the ordeal for the candidate always comprised three important degrees.

Preparation for the Degrees of Initiation

Preparation, or pre-qualification, for the initiation degrees involved three disciplines: (*a*) self-purification; (*b*) building up of the intellectual powers; and (*c*) mastery over the animal nature.

The reasons for such preparation are self-evident and have been outlined above; however, they bear further disclosure. Any system or mechanism, from the most basic to the most subtle, needs to be of an appropriate grade of cleanliness so as not to interfere with the purpose for which it is intended. At a simplistic level, cooking utensils must be sufficiently free from grime and dirt, which would otherwise contaminate the food. A motor engine needs to be rust free so as not to contaminate the fuel or clog the mechanism with debris. How much more important is it, then, for the human vessel to be pure and refined in order that the knowledge imparted may not become defiled through impure personal agendas.

Next, the intellectual powers must be fully functioning in order to discriminate truth from falsehood, reality from appearance, dogma from certainty—and never more so in the present climate of façades and fake news. Here we need to stress that the development of the intellect involves a keen discernment of the 'maps from the territory', namely the distinction between intellectual concepts and structures from reality. It is not a matter of acquiring great intellectual acumen, but rather jolting the mind awake in the sense of Aristotle's remark that thoughts in themselves should not be taken too seriously since 'it's the mark of an educated mind to entertain a thought without accepting it.'[80] Similarly, in *The Voice of the Silence*, a devotional classic of occult instruction by Blavatsky, we are warned 'The Mind is the great Slayer of the Real. Let the Disciple slay the Slayer.'[81]

Intellect on its own is insufficient to qualify for initiation

Finally, control and mastery over the animal nature is a *sine qua non* to ensure that the knowledge imparted be directed towards altruistic and philanthropic ends rather than the appeasement of the lower, sensual nature. Note that all three pre-qualifications must be developed to a high degree: over-development of any one does not compensate for deficiency in another. For example a highly intellectual man may be an utter slave to his sensual passions: there are far too many examples in history to enumerate here.

Degrees of Initiation

The three degrees of initiation into the Mithraism cult were as follows:

In the first degree the candidate was given a golden crown on the point of a sword and instructed in the mysteries of the hidden power of Mithras. The sword probably symbolised the cutting edge of Truth wielded by the power of the intellect. (We find a similar allegory in the Japanese martial arts where the sword represents self-mastery, or killing of the base nature as enemy, having nought to do with the killing of another person.) The crown represented the candidate's spiritual nature, which had to be unfolded and objectified before he could truly glorify Mithras, for Mithras was none other than his own soul standing as mediator between Ormuzd, his SPIRIT (divine essence) and Ahriman, his animal nature. (This dynamic and the role of the soul is explained briefly in the Recapitulation and in detail in Volume II, Chapter 3.)

In the second degree the candidate was given the armour of purity and intelligence (a potent combination) and banished into the darkness of subterranean pits to fight the beasts of passion, degeneracy, and lust.

Finally, in the third degree, he was given a cape upon which were drawn the signs of the zodiac and other astronomical symbols. To those acquainted with their use, such strange hieroglyphic figures and symbols gave unlimited power and control over the unseen forces of nature. Throughout the entire ritual, repeated reference was made to the birth of Mithras as the Sun God, his sacrifice for man, his death in order that man might have eternal life, and finally his resurrection and the saving of all humanity by his intercession before the throne of Ormuzd. (The parallels with the story of Jesus the Christ are obvious.)[82]

Inner nature unfolded in ascending degrees of initiation

We have cited the Mithraic degrees, but every country has its own methods of preserving the knowledge and tradition of the Mysteries. In the Pythagorean School, for example, the first degree was that of 'Mathematicus', assuring the candidate proficiency in mathematics and geometry. The second degree was 'Theoreticus', which imparted a superficial application of the exact sciences. Finally, the degree of 'Electus', which entitled the candidate to pass forward into the light of the fullest illumination which he was capable of absorbing. The degrees are variously reckoned, sometimes four, five, seven, or even ten; but whatever the divisions, they can be recognized under the three major categories just described, because, without exception, they all honoured the one divine purpose of arduous training in order to consummate the spiritual marriage of the Higher Self with the awakened human soul, from which union springs the seer, the adept, and the master of life.[83]

Degrees of initiation in the Pythagorean School

Notwithstanding the ravages of time and unholy priestcraft, plus the distortions and contortions in which exoteric rites are enmeshed, one can still perceive the venerable tradition even in the orthodox and tampered versions of the world religions.

> The initiates of the various Mystery schools of past ages form a veritable golden chain of supermen and superwomen connecting heaven and earth. They are the links of that Homeric 'golden chain' […] an illustrious line—founders of sciences and philosophies, patrons of arts and crafts, supporting by the transcendency of their divinely given power the structures of world religions erected to do them homage. Founders of doctrines which have molded [sic] the lives of uncounted generations, these Initiate–Teachers bear witness to that spiritual culture which has always existed—and always will exist—as a divine institution in the world of men.[84]

This Chapter has gone to some lengths to explain the meaning of terms commonly used in the Mysteries. By now, the reason should not be difficult to fathom, since abstruse terms conjure up meanings ranging from the absurd to the muddled and imprecise, though it must be pointed out that the subtlety and strong interconnection amongst diverse esoteric doctrines makes it unrealistic to give dry, clear-cut definitions and meanings. Clarity and definiteness are wonderful in themselves, but there can also be an illusion of clarity based on arbitrary definitions. More instructive than definitions, which tend to convey a fixed meaning, is insight into the origin of words. For this reason, we have elucidated the etymology of recondite words since an understanding of word origins furnishes a clue about their inner meaning at different levels and in different contexts—many abstract terms resist cut-and-dried definitions, but are clearly perceptible to those who are in sympathy with the subject by virtue of penetrating through the veil of ratiocination and beyond the limitations imposed by language.

Having now established the groundwork for an understanding of the Mysteries in general, we are now in a position to expound, in the next Chapter, what these worldwide teachings affirm and their contrast with science.

We close with a quote that makes it clear why teaching of a recondite and occult nature must be sheltered from the fury of the mob ('scientific' or 'religious') and should be divulged only to the deserving few.

> *Wisdom is as a flower from which the bee its honey makes and the spider poison, each according to its own nature.*
>
> As spoken by an unknown Adept[85]

NOTES

1   *STA*, 'The Mysteries and Their Emissaries', CXCVII.
2   *STA*, 'The Human Body in Symbolism', LXXIV. The full passage in the King James Version of the *Holy Bible*, Book of Proverbs, Chapter 23, Verse 7 is, 'For as he thinketh in his heart, so is he: Eat and drink, saith he to thee; but his heart is not with thee.'
3   Peter Kingsley, *Reality* (Inverness: Golden Sūfī Center, 2003).
4   Manly P. Hall, *The Secret Teaching of All Ages – An Encyclopedic Outline of Masonic, Hermetic, Qabbalistic and Rosicrucian Symbolic Philosophy* (Los Angeles, California: The Philosophical Research Society, Inc. 1988), Preface to the Diamond Jubilee Edition.
5   Nicholas Goodrick-Clarke, *The Western Esoteric Traditions: A historical introduction* (New York: Oxford University Press, 2008), 4.
6   Isaac Newton, *Opticks, Or, A Treatise of the Reflections, Refractions, Inflections & Colours of Light* (London 1730; 4th edn, New York: Dover Publications, 1979).
7   The Newton Project <http://www.newtonproject.ox.ac.uk/search/results?keyword= alchemy&all=1> accessed 9 January 2019.
8   Evelyn Underhill, *Practical Mysticism* (US: Createspace Independent Publishing Platform, 2014), 23.
9   —— *op. cit.*, 28.
10 Renée Weber, *Dialogues with Scientists and Sages: The search for unity* (London and New York: Routledge & Kegan Paul, 1986), quoted in Dean Radin, *The Noetic Universe: The scientific evidence for psychic phenomena* (London: Corgi Books, 2009), 305.
11 J. S. Gordon, *The Path of Initiation: Spiritual evolution and the restoration of the Western mystery tradition* (Rochester, Vermont: Inner Traditions, 2013), 2.
12 *STA*, 'The Life and Philosophy of Pythogoras', LXVI. See also Frank C. Higgins, *Ancient Freemasonry* (1923 edn; facs. edn, US: Kessinger Publishing, 1993).
13 James Robinson, *The Nag Hammadi Library in English* (San Francisco: Harper & Row, 1978).
14 *STA*, 'The Tree of the Sephiroth', CXXI.
15 *Hermas Pastor*, similitude v, 6.
16 Marginally reworded from *KT*, 'On the Nature of our Thinking Principle', 186–7.
17 *Chāndogya Upaniṣad: Following Śaṅkara's commentary*, trans. Swami Lokeswarananda (Kolkata, India: Ramakrishna Mission Institute of Culture, 2017).
18 John Jr. Yarker, *The Arcane Schools* (US: Cosimo Classics, 2007), 163.
19 See Origen, *Philocalia*, trans. G. Lewis (Edinburgh: T&T Clark, 1911), 1, 17.
20 Albert Pike, *Morals and Dogma of the Ancient and Accepted Scottish Rite of Freemasonry: Prepared for the Supreme Council of the Thirty Third Degree for the Southern Jurisdiction of the United States* (US: Charleston, 1871; US: Reprint Services Corp, 1999).

21 Elias Ashmole, *Theatrum Chemicum Britannicum* (London: Nath. Brooke publishers, 1652; facs. edn, US: Kessinger Publishing, 1992), 101. Quoted also in *STA*, 'The Theory and Practice of Alchemy: Part One', CLV.

22 Paraphrased from a conference talk by Rupert Sheldrake, 'Science and Spiritual Practices: Ways to go beyond and why they work', *The Scientific and Medical Network – Beyond the Brain 2019*, 2 November 2019.

23 Frithjof Schuon, 'The Ambiguity of Exoterism', in *Studies in Comparative Religion*, xv, No. 3 & 4 (Summer–Autumn, World Wisdom, 1983). See also Frithjof Schuon: *In the Face of the Absolute – A New Translation with Selected Letters*, ed. Harry Oldmeadow (US: World Wisdom, 1994); *Splendor of the True* (New York: State University of New York Press, Albany, 2013).

24 *Confessio Fraternitatis* (Emperor Norton Books, Cincinnati, Ohio, 2000). See also *STA*, 'Rosicrucian Doctrines and Tenets', CXLI-II.

25 *STA*, 'Rosicrucian Doctrines and Tenets', CXLI.

26 *STA*, 'The Cryptogram as a Factor in Symbolic Philosophy', CLXXI.

27 J. S. Gordon, *The Path of Initiation*, 33.

28 John Ayto, *Bloomsbury Dictionary of Word Origins* (London: Bloomsbury Publishing, 1990), 370.

29 Florian Sprenger, 'Insensible and Inexplicable – On the Two Meanings of Occult', *Issue 1, Occult Communications: On instrumentation, esotericism, and epistemology*, iv (September 2015), Article 2.

30 Willard Van Orman Quine, *From a Logical Point of View* (Cambridge, Massachusetts: Harvard University Press, 1953), 22.

31 —— *op. cit.*, 48.

32 Cathy Legg, 'Extension, Intension and Dormitive Virtue' (Philosophy Program, Research School of Social Sciences, Australian National University, 1999), in *Transactions of the Charles S. Peirce Society*, 35/4 (US: Indiana University Press, Fall, 1999).

33 I. Bernard Cohen and Richard S. Westfall (eds), *Newton* (New York and London: W. W. Norton & Company, 1995), 426.

34 Draft of letter from Newton to Abbé Conti, 26 February 1715/1716 in response to Letter from Leibniz to Conti, November/December 1715; quoted in A. Koyré and I. Bernard Cohen, 'Newton and the Leibniz-Clarke Correspondence, with notes on Newton, Conti & Des Maizeaux', *Archives Internationales d'Histoire des Sciences*, xv (1962), 70, 74, and 110, 113 for drafts which make similar comments. Quoted also with commentary in John Henry, 'Occult Qualities and the Experimental Philosophy: Active principles in pre-Newtonian matter theory', *History of Science*, 24/4 (1986), 362.

35 Isaac Newton, *Opticks*, 401. Quoted also with commentary in John Henry, *op. cit.*, 362–3. This extract does not appear in the earlier 1704 and 1706 editions of *Opticks* before Leibniz's censure of Newton's reference to occult qualities.

36 Isaac Newton, *op. cit.*, 402–3; John Henry, *op. cit.*, 363.

37 John Henry, *loc. cit.*

38 William Whewell, *The Philosophy of the Inductive Sciences, Founded Upon Their History*, 2 vols (London: J. W. Parker, 1840), ii, 560.

39 Paraphrased from *STA*, 'The Mystery of the Apocalypse', CLXXXV–CLXXXVIII.

40 Nicholas Goodrick-Clarke, *The Occult Roots of Nazism* (New York: New York University Press, 1992). The use of the term 'occult' in the title is correct, but singularly unfortunate. We stress that the term as used in Goodrick-Clarke's book refers to the utter misuse of occultism by the Nazis. Readers should never automatically equate the occult with heinous crimes – see p. 200.

41 *STA*, 'Fishes, Insects, Animals, Reptiles, and Birds: Part Two', LXXXIX.

42 'Metaphysics', in *American Heritage® Dictionary of the English Language (5th edn) 2011* <https://ahdictionary.com/word/search.html?q=metaphysics> accessed 23 November 2019.

43 'Plato, Apology 21d', in *Plato in Twelve Volumes*, trans. Harold North Fowler with introduction by W. R. M. Lamb (Cambridge, Massachusetts: Harvard University Press; London: William Heinemann, 1966), i.

44 'Medical Dictionary' <Merriam-Webster https://www.merriam-webster.com/browse/medical> accessed 23 November 2019.

45 Manly P. Hall, *The Secret Teaching of All Ages*, preface to original 1928 edn, V.

46 *STA*, 'The Fraternity of the Rose Cross', CXXXIX.

47 Sir Isaac Newton, *The Chronology of Ancient Kingdoms Amended* (London: Printed for J. Tonson, J. Osborn, and T. Longman, 1728; repr. London: Histories & Mysteries of Man Ltd., 1988), 332–46. An explanatory drawing of King Solomon's Temple is given between pages 346 and 347.

48 *STA*, 'The Fraternity of the Rose Cross', CXXXIX.

49 See Godfrey Higgins, *Anacalypsis: An attempt to draw aside the veil of the Saitic Isis or an inquiry into the origin of languages, nations and religions* (London: Longman & Co., 1836). This book of 1436 pages has scrupulous references to hundreds of books.

50 *STA*, 'The Fraternity of the Rose Cross', CXXXIX.

51 *STA*, 'The Cryptogram as a Factor in Symbolic Philosophy', CLXIX.

52 [*Daily Mail* reporter] 'Crop Circle Hiding "Beautiful" Maths Formula Appears in Rape Seed Field', *MailOnline* (7 June 2020) <https://www.dailymail.co.uk/sciencetech/article-1280930/Complex-crop-circle-appears-rape-seed-field--does-mean.html> accessed 7 June 2020.

53 Jerry Kroth, *Messages from the Gods: A scientific exposition on the extraterrestrial origin of crop circles* (Kindle edn, 2019). The author of this book of 513 pages is an Associate Professor in the graduate counselling psychology program at Santa Clara University and a member of the International Psychohistorical Association.

54 *SD*-I, 'The Coming Force', 558.

55 'The Sorcerer's Apprentice by Goethe', trans. Zeydel (1955) <https://www.scottish-country-dancing-dictionary.com/sorcerers-apprentice.html> accessed 23 November 2019.

56 *Confessio Fraternitatis* (Cincinnati, Ohio: Emperor Norton Books, 2000), as quoted in *STA*, 'Rosicrucian Doctrines and Tenets', CXLII.

57 René Guénon, *le Théosophisme, histoire d'une pseudo-religion* [Theosophy, History of a Pseudo-Religion], trans. Alvin Moore, Jr., Cecil Bethell, Hubert and Rohini Schiff (Hillsdale: New York: Sophia Perennis, 2004).

58 Paul Bertrand [Georges Méautis], *Theosophy and Theosophism: Response to a criticism of Theosophy by René Guénon*, trans. with introduction by Joscelyn Godwin (Paris: Publications Théosophiques, 1922). Reproduced in *FOTA*, Newsletter of the Friends of The Theosophical Archives, Special Edition (Autumn 2016) <http://hypatia.gr/fota/images/newsletter/Fota_Newsletter_Special_Ed_Autumn2016.pdf> accessed 23 November 2019.

59 René Guénon, *Introduction Générale à L'étude des Doctrines Hindoues* [Introduction to the Study of the Hindu Doctrines] (Paris: Véga, 2014). See also, Joscelyn Godwin, 'Layers of Meaning in "The Magic Flute" ', *The Musical Quarterly*, 65/4 (Oxford: Oxford University Press, 1979), 475.

60 See the 'Report of the Committee Appointed to Investigate Phenomena Connected with the Theosophical Society', *Proceedings of the Society for Psychical Research*, 3 (December 1885), 201–400. It is commonly called the 'Hodgson Report' since the bulk of it was written by Richard Hodgson. This report was revisited in 1985 and its claims declared as being utterly worthless by the SPR, the same body that commissioned the original report. See Vernon Harrison, ' "J'Accuse": An examination of the Hodgson Report of 1885', *Journal of the Society for Psychical Research* (London, April 1986); and the associated book, Vernon Harrison, *H. P. Blavatsky and the SPR: An examination of the Hodgson Report of 1885* (Pasadena, California: Theosophical University Press, 1997). But in the hundred year intervening period between 1885 and 1985, immense damage was done to the Theosophical movement and the message of its chief founder.

61 *Confessio Fraternitatis* (Cincinnati, Ohio: Emperor Norton Books, 2000) quoted in *STA*, 'The Fraternity of the Rose Cross', CXL.

62 *ML*, Letter No. 47.

63 Luke 17:21 (King James Version).

64 *STA*, 'The Mysteries and Their Emissaries', CXCVII.

65 See: John Martineau (ed.), *Trivium: The classical liberal arts of grammar, logic, & rhetoric* (UK: Wooden Books, 2016); E. B. Castle, *Ancient Education and Today* (UK: Penguin Books, 1969), 59; 'Philosophy and the Liberal Arts' <https://www.liberalarts.org.uk/philosophy-and-the-liberal-arts> accessed 26 August 2020.

66 Frank C. Higgins, *Ancient Freemasonry: Introduction to Masonic Archeology* (1923; facs. edn, US: Kessinger Publishing, 1993).

67 Sarvepalli Radhakrishnan, *Eastern Religions and Western Thought* (Oxford: Oxford University Press, 1940).

68 —— *op. cit.*, Preface, vii.

69 *IU*-II, 'Christian Crimes and Heathen Virtues', 100.

70 G. de Purucker, *Studies in Occult Philosophy* (Pasadena, California: Theosophical University Press, 1973), 637.

71 Paul Brunton, *The Inner Reality* (London: Rider, 1923); repr. as *Discover Yourself* (US: Weiser Books, 1971).

72 The poignant phrase used by H. P. Blavatsky in *CW*-XII, 'Recent Progress in Theosophy', 308.

73 Dr Massoud Homayouni, *The Origins of Persian Gnosis*, trans. F. J. Stone (London: Mawlana Centre, 1992), 14.

74 —— *op. cit.*, 16.

75 *STA*, 'The Life and Philosophy of Pythagoras', LXV.

76 To give but two examples: 'The Hodgson Report' by the Australian psychic researcher Richard Hodgson (1855–1905)—see Note 60 above; *A Modern Priestess of Isis* (London and New York: Longmans, Green and Co), 1895 by the Russian historical novelist Vsevolod Solyvov (1849–1903).

77 David Lorimer (ed.), *Prophet For Our Times: The life & teachings of Peter Deunov*, foreword by Dr Wayne W. Dyer (UK: Hay Hous, 2015).

78 Nick Redfern, 'Mysterious Deaths in the Holistic Community?' *Mysterious Universe* (2 December 2016) <https://mysteriousuniverse.org/2016/12/mysterious-deaths-in-the-holistic-community> accessed 8 January 2020. A rebuttal alleging, unsurprisingly, that such claims are false is by Alex Kasprak, 'Have Sixty Holistic Doctors Died Suspicious Deaths In the Past Year?' *Snopes* (3 May 2017) <https://www.snopes.com/fact-check/holistic-doctor-death-conspiracy> accessed 2 December 2019. Readers are therefore encouraged to do their own research free from personal or institutional bias.

79 Franz Hartmann MD, *Cosmology, Or Universal Science, Cabala, Alchemy, Containing the Mysteries of the Universe, Regarding God Nature Man, the Macrocosm and Microcosm, Eternity and Time, Explained According to the Religion of Christ, By Means of the Secret Symbols of the Rosicrucians of the 16th and 17th Centuries Copied and translated from an old German manuscript, and provided with a Dictionary of Occult terms* (US: Boston Occult Publishing Company, 1888), 7; [online facsimile] <https://www.thelemiSTAs.org/PDF/Hartmann-Secret_Symbols_of_the_Rosicrucians.pdf> accessed 7 May 2020.

80 Attributed to Aristotle in Lowell L. Bennion, *Religion and the Pursuit of Truth* (US: Deseret Book Company, 1959), 52. See also Robert Welch, *American Opinion*, 24 (incorporated 1981), 23—possibly a discombobulation of Book 1 of the *Nicomachean Ethics* 1094b, line 24.

81 *VS*, 'The Voice of the Silence: Fragment I', 1.

82 The above passage is a digest from *STA*, 'The Ancient Mysteries and Secret Societies Which Have Influenced Modern Masonic Symbolism', XXIV.

83 The above passage is a digest from *STA*, 'The Life and Philosophy of Pythagoras', LXVI.

84 *STA*, 'The Mysteries and Their Emissaries', CXCVII.

85 *STA,* 'The Theory and Practice of Alchemy: Part Two', CLVII.

8 What Occult Science Affirms – its Contrast with Natural Science

Until a person is able to travel inwardly to his own heart and to penetrate to the meaning of the mysteries of his own inner life, he will never be capable of interpreting the spiritual message of the Doctrine of Illumination. For the Doctrine has been written as an enigma, so that only the enlightened may solve it.

AL-SHAHRAZURI[1]

SYNOPSIS

Chapter 8 commences with a careful description of the methods of science and occult science, emphasizing the fact that they are complementary and not antagonistic. Then follows a global overview of occult science leading to summaries of key occult principles and essential characteristics, the latter particularly in regard to evolution. Particular stress is laid on the Hermetic Axiom—the all-important *modus operandi* of occultism—about the indissoluble relation and correspondences, at all levels, between the greater and the lesser, or the macrocosm and the microcosm. Three versions of the Emerald Tablet of Hermes are presented, including the translation by Sir Isaac Newton currently lodged in King's College Library at Cambridge University. A few examples of the operation of macro-microcosmic correspondences are outlined. What is further revealed in the floodlight forms the context of the next Chapter.

KEY WORDS: scientific method, logical positivism, occult method, fundamental precepts of occult science, evolution, Hermetic Axiom, *Corpus Hermeticum*, Newton

The preceding Chapter on the Mystery Teachings will have given the reader a fair appreciation of what the occult and esoteric sciences affirm in contrast (not in opposition) to natural science. This Chapter should make the distinction clearer by describing first their different methodologies, and then elucidating the fundamental tenets of esoteric science and occult science. However, the effort to achieve maximum clarity and consistent use of terms can sometimes sink into excessive pedantry. So to avoid this danger, the term 'esoteric' will be used in its appropriate context; however, the term 'occult' will henceforth be used as a generalizing term for both 'esoteric and occult'. This decision is justified on the basis that the occult necessarily subsumes the esoteric as explained in the previous Chapter.

Scientific and Occult Methods of Investigating Nature and Man

Having explored the distinctive contributions of occult science and natural science in investigating nature, it would be apposite to summarize their different working methods abridged from the full treatment provided in *The Snake and the Rope*.[2]

The Method of Science

> One of the most highly developed skills in contemporary Western civilisation is dissection: the split-up [*sic*] of problems into their smallest possible components. We are good at it. So good, we often forget to put the pieces back together again.
>
> Alvin Toffler[3]

The above pithy statement forms the opening words of the foreword to a book entitled *Order Out of Chaos: Man's new dialogue with nature*. The foreword was penned by an American writer and associate editor of *Fortune* magazine, one Alvin Toffler (1928–2016). The book was co-authored by the Russian physical chemist Ilya Prigogine (1917–2003), a Nobel laureate and former honorary member of the Scientific and Medical Network, and Isabelle Stengers (*b.*1949), a Belgian philosopher distinguished for her work in the field of the philosophy of science. It is a stark warning of the ingrained dependence on reductionism in our scientific culture (such as the attempt to understand the mystery of consciousness by reducing the brain to ever smaller components like neurons, neuroglia, dendrites, axons). Prigogine was a pioneer in systems, or complexity science, which overcomes the Cartesian–reductionist fallacy by recognizing that the whole is both greater than, and different from, the sum total of its parts. This is a major step towards occult science which amply fulfils what is missing in so much of contemporary science, namely the synthesising component. Newton taught the 'Method of Analysis' for which he is justly revered; but he also taught the 'Method of Composition' (i.e., putting back together): 'As in Mathematicks, so in Natural Philosophy, the Investigation of difficult Things by the Method of Analysis, ought ever to precede the Method of Composition.'[4] The progress of science has been hampered by virtual neglect of the latter at the expense of the former.

Reductionism without synthesis presents a one-sided picture

Newton taught that Composition should follow Analysis

Briefly stated, the scientific method moves from the particular to the general, rather like assembling individual pieces of a jigsaw puzzle: discrete observational data are collected and gradually fitted into a general picture, the latter being a mental representational model of the physical effects observed. This is the 'bottom-up', inductive Aristotelian method. The instruments of investigation are limited to, and conditioned by, the five physical senses, and their extensions as telescopes and microscopes, etc. The result is a precise description of the appearances, behaviour, and physical mechanisms of the universe— nature in her *manifold appearances*. The mind process is predominantly intellectual, applied by orthodox science, for the most part, in a linear, sequential mode. Nonetheless, it must be admitted that laws, theories, and hypotheses in science are related more like a web than a superstructure model as taught by the proponents of the Vienna School of Logical Positivism. Furthermore, it was Einstein who stated that there is no such thing as a 'crucial' or 'ultimate' test of a theory (or hypothesis), since all such tests assume the truth of other laws and theories in their formulation and execution.[5] For example, the famous test of relativity—that strong gravitational fields bend light rays—assumed the accuracy and validity of astronomical observations (i.e., the 'proper' position of certain stars during an eclipse) and the various laws of light in physics.

The inductive method of natural science

Science is therefore a series of approximations to the truth. The truth investigated by science is therefore relative and not absolute as its theories are ever liable to change (many examples of this were given in Chapter 4). At no stage can a scientist claim to have reached finality as any theory must be revised in the light of new facts. Experiment is, and always will, remain the final court of appeal in deciding the fate of any scientific theory. We should always remember the words of Einstein's close colleague at the University of Berlin, Leopold Infeld (1898–1968), the Polish physicist and Rockefeller fellow at Cambridge University:

Scientific progress
is an asymptotic
(ever closer)
approach to truth

> Scientific theories arise, develop and perish. They have their span of life, with its successes and triumphs, only to give way later to new ideas and a new outlook.[6]

The Occult Method

Occult science works from universals to particulars within the 'Ring Pass-Not' (i.e., limiting boundaries of evolutionary growth) of every world system: the overall, grand picture is first realized in its essential nature, and the way this presents itself as particular effects is then expounded. The mind process is essentially holistic, applied in an all-inclusive mode. This is the 'top-down', deductive Platonic method. The instruments of investigation are *not* limited to the physical senses; in fact, the senses are *transcended* rather

The deductive
method of occult
science

than *extended* as is the case with natural science. This gives profound insights into the origin, essential nature and manifestation of Nature in her *true self*. Further elaboration of the scientific and occult approaches is now given. Whereas science has a rigorous and organized method based upon a problematic philosophical foundation, the philosophical basis of occult science is completely secure and unchanging, although it adopts a less formal method, as mentioned above. For these reasons, natural science provides enormous factual information on individual physical phenomena, but knows less about their intrinsic nature, besides having a tenuous grasp of the overall picture. By contrast, occult science reveals the grand plan, but can sometimes provide inaccurate details about specific, vital physical mechanisms, which are best left to natural science.

Method of Research

The method of research and analysis of texts and literature of an occult nature is not dissimilar, in principle, to the literature survey that students undertake when embarking on their chosen topic of research for their doctoral thesis.

A fine case in point is the method used by Newton concerning his research and analysis of esoteric, alchemical, and prophetic texts from diverse sources. In two incomplete treatises on prophecy known as *The Language of the Prophets* we find his instruction thus:

> He that would understand a book written in a strange language must first learn the language & if he would understand it well he must learn the language perfectly. Such a language was that wherein the Prophets wrote, & the want of sufficient skill in that language is the main reason why they are so little understood. Iohn [John] did not write in one language, Daniel in another, Isaiah in third, & the rest in others peculiar to them selves; but they all wrote in one & the same mystical language as well known without doubt to the sons of the Prophets as the Hieroglyphic language of the Egyptians.[sic] to their Priests. And this language so far as I can find, was as certain & definite in its signification as is the vulgar language of any nation whatsoever.[7]

Newton stresses
importance of
learning language
of Scripture

Having established this basic premise, Newton continues:

> So that it is only through want of skill therein that Interpreters so frequently turn [i.e. manipulate] the prophetic types & phrases to signify whatever their ffansies and

Hypotheses lead them to. He therefore that would understand the old Prophets (as all Divines ought to do) must fix the significations of their types & phrases in the beginning of his studies.[8]

Then, in a manner reminiscent of the Rules at the beginning of Book III of *Principia* ('The System of the World'), he inserts the seminal statement:

Newton discerns common overlap from plurality of sources

> The Rule [for fixing the signification of the Prophets' types and phrases] I have followed has been to compare the several mystical places of scripture where the same prophetic phrase or type is used & to fix such a signification to that phrase as agrees best with all the places, & if more significations then [than] one be necessary to note the circumstances by which it may be known in what signification the phrase is taken in any place & when I had found the necessary significations to reject all others as the offspring of luxuriant fansy. For no more significations are to be admitted for true ones then can be proved.[9]

Nor does Newton confine his language to the Western tongue, when he adds:

Newton consults both Western and Eastern sources

> I have not feared sometimes to call in to my assistance the eastern expositors of their mystical writers […]. ffor the language of the Prophets being hieroglyphical had affinity with that of the Egyptian Priests & eastern wise men & therefore was anciently much better understood in the East then it is now in the west.[10]

Finally, ever acknowledging the Hermetic Axiom, Newton says:

Newton derives inspiration by analogy with nature

> I received also much light in this search by the analogy between the world natural & the world politique[i]. ffor the mystical language was founded in this analogy & will be best understood <IIr>[*sic*] by considering its original.[11]

One of the finest studies of Newton's alchemy and theology is *The Foundations of Newton's Alchemy* by Betty Jo Teeter Dobbs (1930–1994), the American professor of history at the University of California. The author draws our attention to, 'the rational matter-of-factness of Newton's approach […], as well as his willingness to draw upon the several techniques of textual comparisons, cross-comparison to other systems of mystical interpretation, and comparisons of the prophetic language with the natural world in which it was founded by "analogy".'[12]

One example of Newton's rule 'to compare the several mystical places of scripture where the same prophetic phrase or type is used' should suffice. In substantiation of his affirmation in the General Scholium of the omnipresence of God, Newton provides the following evidence in a footnote:

Example of Newton's comparative approach

> This was the opinion of the Ancients. So Pythagoras in Cicer. de Nat. Deor. lib. i. Thales, Anaxagoras, Virgil, Georg. b lib. iv. ver. 220. and Æneid. lib. vi. ver. 721. Philo Allegor. at the beginning of lib. i. Aratus in his Phænom. at the beginning. So also the sacred Writers, as St. Paul, Acts xvii. ver. 27, 28. St. John's Gosp. Chap. xiv. ver. 2. Moses in Deut. iv. ver. 39. and x. ver. 14. David, Psal. cxxxix. ver. 7, 8, 9. Solomon, 1 Kings viii. ver. 27. Job xxii. ver. 12, 13, 14. Jeremiah xxiii. ver. 23, 24. The Idolaters supposed the Sun, Moon, and

---

i In general, the 'world politique' means those in a position of power who put the success and well-being of their state above all else. Note that the transcript of this passage from Keynes MS. 5, King's College, Cambridge, UK, in *The Newton Project* (online March 2003) <http://www.newtonproject.ox.ac.uk/view/texts/normalized/THEM00005> accessed 17 February 2020, states 'the world natural & the word politique'; but this is very likely in error as the next paragraph continues with 'The whole world natural consisting of heaven & earth signifies {illeg} whole world politique […].'

Stars, the Souls of Men, and other parts of the world, to be parts of the supreme God, and therefore to be worshipped: but erroneously.[13]

The writer maintains that this singular failure on the part of both mainstream science and orthodox theology to follow Newton's counsel—

Reasons why science flounders when faced with religion and mysticism

1. about attaining 'sufficient skill' in understanding the 'strange language' of the scriptures and 'learn[ing] the language perfectly' (the Holy Bible and the Qur'an are particularly unfortunate 'victims');
2. about 'the language of the Prophets being hieroglyphical'—not verbatim;
3. that the Prophets 'all wrote in one & the same mystical language';
4. that such language is 'much better understood in the East then it is now in the West';
5. the 'analogy between the world natural & the world politique';

has resulted either in the blathering of 'luxuriant fansy' or the blind literalism of scientific materialism and religious fundamentalism leading to acrimony, conflict and, finally, to war.

Likewise does H. P. Blavatsky remark outspokenly:

But do the men of Science understand the innermost thought of Newton, one of the most spiritual-minded and religious men of his day, any better now than they did then? It is certainly to be doubted.[14]

The innermost thoughts and ideas of Newton were perverted, and of his great mathematical learning only the mere physical husk was turned to account. Had poor Sir Isaac foreseen to what use his successors and followers would apply his 'gravity,' that pious and religious man would surely have quietly eaten his apple, and never breathed a word about any mechanical ideas connected with its fall.[15]

Blavatsky adopted a similar approach to Newton in the way she collected huge tracts of arcane literature from diverse epochs and cultures in order to underscore their common origin in the Mystery Teachings of antiquity and to demonstrate their highest common factor running as a thread binding them into a coherent whole. In her words:

It is, therefore, impossible to treat this subject [of archaic and occult texts] as one would the ordinary evolution of an art or science in some well-known historical nation. It is only by bringing before the reader an abundance of proofs, all tending to show that in every age, under every condition of civilization and knowledge, the educated classes of every nation made themselves the more or less faithful echoes of one identical system and its fundamental traditions [the Secret Doctrine, or Mystery Teachings]—that he can be made to see that so many streams of the same water must have had a common source from which they started. It is […] the desire to do so, which has led the writer [Blavatsky] to be constantly bringing ancient and modern evidence as a corroboration of the Archaic and quite unhistoric Past [concerning] the various and widely-separated periods of history and tradition.[16]

Like Newton, Blavatsky abstracts highest common factor from plurality of sources

Thus it can be argued that Newton and Blavatsky both resorted to the method of consilience: gathering together and linking multiple, generally unrelated facts and theories across disciplines to create a common synthesis of knowledge converging towards a definite conclusion. Consilience is further explained in the Recapitulation to this Volume.

The Test of Truth

What, therefore, are the litmus tests of Truth? We have already mentioned self-consistency of doctrine concerning all departments of nature. Another one is universality: has it been taught by all those who have received the sunlight of initiation into nature's deeper secrets? So, for example, did Gautama the Buddha in the East instruct his disciples in the self-same doctrine that Jesus the Christ did in the West? Did Śankaracharya (788–820) of India teach the same occultism that Pythagoras and Empedocles (495–430 BC) of Greece did? Were the religious reformer and prophet Zarathuśtra of Iran (Persia) and the Tibetan religious philosopher Tsong-kha-pa (1357–1419) born into their adepthood through initiation processes similar to those of the Greek Neopythagorean philosopher Apollonius of Tyana (15–100), the legendary musician, poet, and prophet Orpheus of Greece, or the philosopher Lao-Tzu (*circa* 605–*circa* 531 BC) of China and the father of Taoism? Have Persia, Egypt, Greece, China, ancient America, Iceland, Wales, and Babylonia all received a Wisdom-teaching which, stripped of outer vestments, is one in essentials? *Most assuredly, it is so,* for such patterns have been woven on one loom—the ageless loom of Truth embedded in the *philosophia perennis* under names such as occultism, esotericism or theosophy. This is why legendary scientists (like Newton) have spared no effort in recovering these archaic truths before theological encrustations, idolatry, and superstition progressively suffocated the original meaning.

Universality and self-consistency are the hallmarks of emissaries of Truth of all Ages

Scientific and Occult Methods Contrasted

The legendary sage and philosopher Paul Brunton tersely encapsulated the vital difference between the scientific and the occult methods of investigating nature and man thus:

> There is this vital difference, that whereas the scientist can only observe the object into which he is investigating, the mystic [and occultist] can participate in the one upon which he is meditating. In the first case, there is a knowing in separation [detachment] from it; in the second, a knowing in [vital] union with it.[17]

It is the difference between, so to say, knowing from the outside and understanding from the inside. To elucidate the above by way of a simplistic example, one can discover the physical mechanisms of bird flight by examining the structure of the wings of a dead bird under a microscope. But in order to discover the secrets of flight one has to be in union with the living creature, namely, to be one with it in one's consciousness. This is not as far-fetched as it may seem on first appearance. Let us expand on this theme as it provides crucial insights into the manner in which revolutionary discoveries are made.

Knowing in union versus knowing in separation

Throughout history, artists, musicians, poets, mystics, and lovers have known and written about the experience that occurs through the loss of self, being that state whereby the personal ego dissolves or is held in abeyance, resulting in a state of subjective fusion with an idea, a subject of enquiry, or an object of knowledge. Many scientists would like to pride themselves on their capacity to distance subject from object, claiming that such detachment results in 'pure' observation, free from personal bias. But scientists are no exception to the rule. The greatest of scientific discoveries have come from those who were able to turn object into subject, that is, to participate actively in the inner state, or consciousness of whatever they were investigating. A recent example in biology would be Barbara McClintock FRS (1902–1992), the American scientist and cytogeneticist

Examples of fruits of knowing in union

(a branch of genetics that is concerned with the study of the structure and function of cells, especially chromosomes) who was awarded the 1983 Nobel Prize in Physiology, or Medicine. McClintock described her experience when researching genetic mechanisms thus: 'I wasn't outside. I was part of the system.' Later she spoke of the 'real affection' one gets 'as you look at these things, they become part of you and you forget yourself. The main thing about it is, you forget yourself.'[18]

Mystic Meditation Technique

Is it then the case that 'genius is one percent inspiration, ninety-nine percent perspiration', the saying attributed to an early member of the Theosophical Society—the great American inventor Thomas Edison (1847–1931)?[19] That would certainly seem to apply to Isaac Newton, arguably England's greatest mystical scientist. In the first of four letters written in 1692 'containing some Arguments in Proof of a Deity', addressed to the English classical scholar, theologian, and Master of Trinity College, Cambridge Richard Bentley (1662–1742), Newton imputed all his merit to 'nothing but industry & a patient thought'.[20] But what about the vital remaining one percent? How, and from where, does inspiration arise? Newton famously declared to the English politician and Master of the Mint, John Conduitt (1688–1737)[ii] that an irregular life was attended with an irregular head and that truth was, 'the offspring of silence and unbroken meditation.'[21] He intimated as much when asked how he came to his discoveries: 'I keep the subject constantly before me, and wait till the first dawnings open slowly by little and little into the full and clear light.'[22] Mystics who focus upon a single point have uttered similar words to describe the means for receiving divine revelation. Lord Keynes, who bought a large proportion of Newton's alchemical treatises and studied them assiduously declared: 'I believe that the clue to his mind is to be found in his unusual powers of continuous concentrated intro-spection. I believe that Newton could hold a problem in his mind for hours and days and weeks until it surrendered to him its secret.'[23] Einstein who, so to speak, became one with a photon during his work on light and the theory of relativity wrote, 'the state of feeling which makes one capable of such achievements is akin to that of the religious worshipper, or of one who is in love.'[24] Is it surprising that Einstein mentions the word 'love'? Clearly, a prerequisite for this capability of direct intuitive knowing (transcending the intellectual brain) is the deep and abiding love of the subject of enquiry (be that physics or biology) or the object of knowledge (say, the nature of gravity), enabling the merging of subject into object—the being-in-love state of mystical union.

The margin note reads: Newton's and Einstein's inspiration from meditation: knowing in union

The basic activity required of the creative scientist is that of preparing, and then main-taining, a *state of attunement* to sensitize him to the manifestations of intelligibility, however fleeting, that are presented by his focus of research. Then, as soon as a lead appears, he has to follow it to its very end. This essential aspect of scientific innovation is hampered by following well-trodden conceptual pathways.

However, this subject–object merging is a technique that can be learned. The essence lies in forgetting oneself, or the disappearance of the self-conscious 'I', as just stated. The

---

ii John Conduitt married Sir Isaac Newton's pretty half-niece and adopted daughter, Catherine Barton, in 1717. He later succeeded Newton as Master of the Mint and preserved a mass of Newton's personal papers and anecdotes of his life.

technique known as *Samyama* is a yogic siddhi[25] (psychic power) 'in which subjects are able to learn about whatever they wish, without the use of intellectual intermediaries, by merging themselves with the chosen object.'[26] Physicist Stephen Phillips from Cambridge uses the terms 'micro-psi vision', or the Sanskrit *anima*, meaning 'to become very small', for this capacity of extrasensory perception when directed towards investigating the objective world at the nuclear level of atomic and subatomic particles. He states that, 'the experience of a person in this state is not that of a passive spectator peering down a microscope. Instead, it is characterized by a vivid, subjective sense of actually being in the microcosm, of being suspended in space amid particles in great dynamical activity.'[27] Phillips has related past micro-psi research by Besant and Leadbeater to contemporary particle physics as outlined in Chapter 4.[28, 29]

Merging of subject with object key to creative insights

Chapter 9 of Volume III concerning the latent powers in man supplies a few more details on the *Samyama* technique of attaining extended consciousness and the powers conferred.

Summary

By way of a summary of the contrasting methods of natural science and occult science, the former is concerned mainly with epistemology, hence operates according to the inductive Aristotelian empirical method of a posteriori reasoning (i.e., from known facts, therefore past events to their causes); whereas the latter is concerned primarily with ontology, hence functions according to the abstract Platonic deductive method of a priori reasoning (i.e., from known causes to their necessarily related effects). Given their different *modus operandi*, scientific instruments provide extensions of the physical senses and the result is precise descriptions of physical nature and the body of man in appearance and mechanisms; however occult science seeks to transcend, rather than extend, the senses to gain insight into the purpose and workings of the hidden laws of nature and the powers latent in man.

Differentiating epistemology from ontology. Extending the senses versus transcending the senses

But there is no question whatsoever of science and occult science working in isolated, watertight compartments. Each is, so to say, reflected in the other: the inductive method of science includes the deductive method in the background, i.e., theories derived by induction are subsequently used to deduce predictions based upon such theories; and the deductive method of occult science also incorporates the highest application of the inductive principle to test, and independently corroborate, the spiritual visions and experiences of adepts. As the following quotation from Blavatsky implies, the two disciplines of science and metaphysics (the philosophical underpinning of science—see Chapter 7) have to be blended.

> Science is honeycombed with metaphysical conceptions, but the Scientists will not admit the charge and fight desperately to put atomo-mechanical masks [i.e., espouse materialistic concepts based on physical atoms] on purely incorporeal and spiritual laws in nature, on our plane—refusing to admit their substantiality even on other planes, the bare existence of which they reject *a priori*.[30]

Science cannot be divorced from its bedrock metaphysics

Occult Science – A Global Overview

In the spirit of the above quotation, let us now go beyond the safe limit of our vision and strain to see what really lies beyond. What facts do occult science legitimately and lawfully divulge?

Occultism (and its near-twin, esotericism) is in radical contrast to the mainstream scientific viewpoint that the universe is basically inanimate and that all life is a fortuitous concurrence of physical atoms in the fullness of time with consciousness a by-product, or epiphenomenon, of purposeless physical processes; and mind is a correlate of brain function. Unlike the changing scientific theories on cosmology and consciousness, to give but two contemporary examples,[31] occult principles (as encapsulated in modern Theosophy) are the cumulative independent testimony of countless generations of sages of all times—ancient and modern, of all races and all religions. There is total consistency in what they have declared, in necessarily diverse tongues and forms, from their own utterly direct experience by incessant observations and rigorous independent corroboration. By 'direct experience', we mean strictly the *spiritual* visions and experiences attained after the most arduous and rigorous training and practice, never to be confused with the glamour-producing illusions of the psychic planes. There are many who claim to have had 'spiritual visions', which are nothing other than the distorted and delusional images from contact with the lower astral levels.

Blavatsky wrote in a scholarly manner amenable to academic scrutiny

This occult doctrine received its clearest, most detailed, and forceful exposition from Blavatsky in her writings, notably, *Isis Unveiled, The Secret Doctrine, The Key to Theosophy, The Voice of the Silence* and *The Collected Writings*, which, collectively, have provided a unique service to humanity by drawing together the priceless but abstruse and far-flung flowers of a universal wisdom-tradition into one bouquet for which she provided the nosegay—see below. Much to the point, her writings are *eminently verifiable* by way of literally thousands of specific and detailed references, as in a learned scientific paper, which all readers can verify independently.

Thus, there are no conflicts or anomalies between the great occult traditions, once the dogmatic interpretations and outer forms of expression are stripped out to reveal the bare inner meaning. The works of the great sages are utterly unique, their manner of expression as individual as they are illimitable, *but all have been written with their pens dipped into the self-same inkwell of universal truths.* As we have seen, universality is a hallmark and an indication of truth.

Occult philosophy connects diverse sciences, religions, and philosophies

Indeed, the occult philosophy, or the esoteric doctrine, is known as the 'thread doctrine' since, as Blavatsky explains:

> Like Sūtrātman, in the Vedānta philosophy, it passes through and strings together all the ancient philosophical religious systems, and reconciles and explains them all. It does more. It not only reconciles the various and apparently conflicting systems, but it checks the discoveries of modern exact science, and shows some of them to be necessarily correct, since they are found corroborated in the ancient records. All this will, no doubt, be regarded as terribly impertinent and disrespectful, a veritable crime of *lèse-science* [insulting the sovereignty of Science]; nevertheless, it is a fact.[32]

The Occult Doctrine

The depth and sophistication of occultism is prodigious. However, key occult axioms are few: just three in number. Their peerless formulation was given out as the Three Fundamental Propositions, or Axioms, by Blavatsky in *The Secret Doctrine*[33] in words of simplicity and brevity out of all proportion to their depth, universality, and inexhaustibility of meaning. However, owing to the imperious nature of the language used in that monumental work, the following simplified, paraphrased version below is offered instead.

Three Fundamental Axioms – Unity, Periodicity, Reunification

❖ FIRST FUNDAMENTAL AXIOM – *Keyword*: UNITY

The Fundamental Unity of All Existence: an Absolute Principle of Unity behind diversity. The Causeless Cause behind all causes, unthinkable by human expression or comparisons, therefore ineffable and unpronounceable.

ELUCIDATION OF FIRST AXIOM: This Unity is not the same as the common notion of unity, such as when we say an orchestra is united by a common interest in music or an army is united in waging war. 'It is that existence is ONE THING, not any collection of things linked together. Fundamentally there is ONE BEING.'[34]

'Thus this Earth resembles a great animall or rather inanimate vegetable,[iii] draws in æthereall breath for its dayly refreshment & vitall ferment & transpires again w th [with] gross exhalations, And according to the condition of all other things living ought to have its times of beginning youth old age & perishing,' wrote Newton, foreshadowing the modern Gaia theory implying the dynamic balance, harmony, and organic unity of all existence on planet Earth.[35] It is significant that Blavatsky made many prominent references to Newton, who, as we saw earlier was deeply versed in both the precepts and practical import of the esoteric and alchemical literature and philosophy and was, most likely, an Initiate in these Arts.[36, 37, 38]

If 'this Earth resembles a great animall', then the UNIVERSE must surely also resemble a great ANIMALL.

Viewed through a mechanistic lens, however, the living universe of supernal order, beauty, and orchestration appears like a machine—the so-called 'clockwork universe' wrongly ascribed to Newton. The true case, as is substantiated by the quotation above, is in fact the converse—he saw the universe as a *living being*.

❖ SECOND FUNDAMENTAL AXIOM – *Keyword*: PERIODICITY

Eternal Periodicity and Cyclicity: Universes appear and disappear, i.e., from subjective (implicate) realms to objectivity (as evolution, manifestation) and from objectivity withdrawn into subjectivity (as involution, dissolution).

ELUCIDATION OF SECOND AXIOM: It is easy to see this fundamental Law of the Universe as, for example, the universal alternations of day and night, sleeping and waking, life and death, ebb and flow of the tides; and on a larger scale, evolution and involution, cosmic awakening and cosmic slumber.[iv]

Such ideas are also fundamental to the cosmology of Walter Russell, one of the

(margin note) Three keys that unlock Universal Wisdom

---

iii 'Inanimate nature means everything other than the animal world'—*The Concise Oxford Dictionary*, ed. Della Thompson (9th edn, Oxford: Clarendon Press, 1995), 685. It means inert, or inactive; it does not mean dead, or lifeless. Thus there is no contradiction between 'a great animall' and an 'inanimate vegetable' insofar as both are living and the Earth resembles inanimate nature.

iv Through the lens of physical cosmology, cosmic awakening and cosmic slumber could, conceivably, be seen as 'Big Bang' and 'Big Crunch', respectively.

leaders of the New Thought Movement in America and regarded by many as a poly-math and a Renaissance man for the twentieth century—see Chapter 9.

❖ THIRD FUNDAMENTAL AXIOM – *Keyword*: REUNIFICATION

The fundamental identity of all souls with the Universal Over-Soul: the latter an aspect of the Unknown Root; and the necessity for every Soul to realize and re-claim, in full consciousness, its intrinsic Divinity.

ELUCIDATION OF THIRD AXIOM: Every spark of life from the lowest to the highest seeks to be united with its parent source. So there is involution (the progressive descent of spirit into matter) followed by evolution (the progressive ascent of spirit from matter). This means that there is a force or power in every creature that impels it to ascend towards ever higher forms of life, for example, the plant kingdom strives towards the higher consciousness of the animal kingdom; the animal kingdom towards the self-consciousness of the human kingdom; and the human kingdom to superhuman realms of consciousness.

The bud of occultism enclosed by the Three Fundamental Axioms acting as sepals will now be unfurled to reveal the flower of seven petals—the seven principles of occultism. In more prosaic language, the Three Axioms can be expanded into Seven Principles—the latter is explicate, the former, implicate.

Seven Principles

❖ FIRST PRINCIPLE: *An Absolute, incomprehensible (to the brain intellect) and Supreme Deity*, or infinite essence as the root of all nature and all there is, visible and invisible, manifest and unmanifest, immanent and transcendent.

IMPLICATIONS OF FIRST PRINCIPLE: Therefore everything is pervaded by, and ulti-mately *is*, this essence. Pertains to the Universe as a whole in its seen and unseen aspects. The macrocosm, as an organic entity, a living process; and man, the micro-cosm, seen as subsumed under the same laws and processes that operate in the wider macrocosm.

The septenate spectrum of Universal Principles

❖ SECOND PRINCIPLE: *The hylozoic principle* which says that there is absolutely nothing in the universe such as dead matter; that everything from below the mineral kingdom to beyond the human kingdom is conscious and interacts with, and responds to, its environment with intelligence and purpose. What varies, as we progress from sub-mineral to superhuman, is the *degree*, but not the fact of consciousness. The higher on the evolutionary ascent, the more awakened is the consciousness, because increasingly released from matter; the lower down the scale the more consciousness is dormant because progressively enmeshed in materiality. This is beautifully encapsulated in the proverb: *I slept in the stone; I stirred in the plant; I dreamt in the animal; and I awoke in the man*. This refers to the Qabbalistic doctrine, referred to earlier in Chapter 5, that man becomes a stone, a plant, an animal, a man, a spirit, and finally a god, thus accom-plishing his obligatory cycle from the point where he started and returning to the same point on a higher turn of the spiral, so to say. By 'man' of course we mean the enduring spiritual entity, not his physical vestures. This theme will be taken up again in Volume III in connection with symbolism and evolution.

IMPLICATIONS OF SECOND PRINCIPLE: The 'I' as the sleeper-stirrer-dreamer-awakener is therefore *the one self-same consciousness* in different modes of operation working through progressively more complex vehicles of manifestation in the various kingdoms of nature that allow it increasingly sophisticated function and refined forms of expression.

❖ THIRD PRINCIPLE: *That man is a radiation of the Universal Soul* and of an identical essence with it.

IMPLICATIONS OF THIRD PRINCIPLE: The immortal nature of man, i.e., the spiritual entity and not the physical body. This distinction is explained in the Recapitulation to this Volume.

❖ FOURTH PRINCIPLE: *The Great Hermetic Axiom*, often abbreviated, 'As Above, So Below'. This describes the relationship between the macrocosm—the universe as the great ordered whole—and the microcosm—man as its reflection. In one of the many translations it is stated thus, 'As is the Inner, so is the Outer; as is the Great so is the Small; as it is Above, so it is Below: there is but ONE LIFE AND LAW; and he that worketh it is ONE. Nothing is Inner, nothing is Outer; nothing is GREAT, nothing is Small; nothing is High, nothing is Low, in the Divine Economy.'[39]

What this means, no less, is that the human mind is a microcosm of Divine Mind. As the modern thinker Thomas Troward explains it, our innermost centre is the divine within us, so we are co-creators with God, being His instrumentality to radiate His purpose into the world. Troward's philosophy is summarized in Chapter 9 (along with that of Ralph Waldo Emerson and Ralph Waldo Trine).

IMPLICATIONS OF FOURTH PRINCIPLE: The principles of analogy and correspondence, such that events that are related as having occurred in the external world, are regarded as expressing operations and experiences of the human soul. For this reason, the disciples of Ammonius Saccas (like Plotinus) were also called 'Analogeticists' because of their practice of interpreting all sacred legends and narratives, myths and mysteries by the rules and principles of analogy and correspondence.

The ramifications of these cardinal principles are amplified later in this Chapter along with different translations of the Hermetic Axiom.

❖ FIFTH PRINCIPLE: *Theurgy*, meaning '*divine work*', or producing a work of the gods, derived from the Greek *theoi* 'gods' and *ergein* 'to work'.

IMPLICATIONS OF FIFTH PRINCIPLE: Theurgy is the application of esoteric principles, therefore truly an occult practice (see Chapter 7). By making oneself as pure as the divine, i.e., by reverting to one's pristine purity of nature, man can move the gods (i.e., command the forces and powers in nature) to impart to him divine mysteries. This is the only aspect that need concern us, other than to stress that divine theurgy requires supreme holiness and austerity of life if the practice is not to degenerate into unholy mediumship or, much worse, black magic, with terrible, self-inflicted results to the practitioner and his circle (see again Chapter 7).[v]

---

v The lives of occultists such as Aleister Crowley demonstrate the consequences of veering towards the Left-Hand Path of the misuse of ceremonial magic in the service of the ego.

❖ SIXTH PRINCIPLE: *The Law of Karma* which adjusts effects to their impelling causes, both individually and collectively.

IMPLICATIONS OF SIXTH PRINCIPLE: The doctrine of rebirth, sometimes known as reincarnation, is not unique to mankind alone. It is a particular instance of periodicity and the eternal cyclicity of action and inaction, activity and rest, that may be observed in the natural world and recognized as the alternation of birth and growth, decay and death pertaining to the form.

❖ SEVENTH PRINCIPLE: *Evolution* which proceeds on three fronts: the spiritual, the intellectual, and the physical—the last of course being the only evolution that natural science knows about and acknowledges. One way of looking at this is that consciousness—the universal primary—ever seeks vehicles of increasing complexity, refinement, and subtlety in order to express[vi] increasing amounts and degrees of its potentiality at infinite levels from the most spiritual to the gross material.

IMPLICATIONS OF SEVENTH PRINCIPLE: Firstly, it is clear that there is active intelligence behind the Laws of Nature, such that evolution may occur in the first place. Secondly, concerning man, occult anthropogenesis affirms three cardinal principles about his evolution:

1. Man is of polygenetic origin, meaning that new types, or species of mankind, have originated from more than one ancestral species.
2. There was a variety of modes of procreation before humanity fell into the ordinary (sexual) mode of generation.
3. The evolution of animals—of the mammalians at any rate—follows from that of man instead of preceding it.

The next section is essentially a development of the three points made above.

The Occult Doctrine on Evolution

Regarding the first point, the American microbial geobiologist and biogeochemist Felisa Wolfe-Simon (*b.*1978) at the National Aeronautics and Space Administration (NASA) and her team have found a bacterium whose DNA is completely alien to what we know today, working differently and unlike anything currently living on the planet. Instead of using phosphorus, the newly discovered microorganism—called 'GFAJ-1' found in Mono Lake, California—uses poisonous arsenic for its building blocks. [40, 41] NASA is saying that this is 'life as we do *not* know it'.[42] The celebrated English physicist Paul Davies (*b.*1946) wrote an article in the *Wall Street Journal* in support of the finding of Felisa Wolfe-Simon that arsenic can replace phosphorus because 'I had the advantage of being unencumbered by knowledge. I dropped chemistry at the age of 16, and all I knew about arsenic came from Agatha Christie novels.' He added: 'Well, I would be astonished if this was the only arsenic-based organism on Earth and Felisa just happened to scrape it up from the bottom of Mono Lake on the first try, [*sic*] It's quite clear that it is the tip of an iceberg. I think it's a window into a whole new world of microbiology. I think we're going to see a whole new domain of life here.'[43] What is the reason for this imminent 'whole new domain of life'?

Arsenic building block for new life form discovered

---

vi Ex-press, meaning 'to press out of'.

All life on Earth is supposed to be composed mostly of six principal components: carbon, hydrogen, nitrogen, oxygen, sulphur, and phosphorus. Every being, from the smallest amoeba to the largest whale, shares the same life stream. Our DNA blocks are all the same. That was true until now. However, the possibility of using arsenic to build DNA, RNA (Ribonucleic acid), proteins, and cell membranes changes everything.[44] Although these discoveries have supposedly been contested (it is argued that the DNA of the microorganism contained no arsenic at all[45]), they touch upon the occult tenet that there is no such thing as dead matter, and that life uses different materials and vehicles of expression not necessarily carbon based. While we are on the subject, terms such as 'alien DNA' are not entirely nonsensical, but a caricature of the true fact about the polygenetic origin of man. It is not so much that our physical DNA is extra-terrestrial: rather that our inner principles—our 'spiritual DNA' is not of this Earth. (This will become plainer as we proceed.)

Life may not all be carbon based

The second and third principles above are bound to raise many an eyebrow amongst Darwinian evolutionists. However, the evidence from occult sources is overwhelming—see Endnote I-9—and there is increasing evidence forthcoming nowadays from palæontology. For example, a scholarly paper on the mating of Neanderthals and humans states that 'the skeleton of a 4-year-old child, recently unearthed at the 24,500-year-old site of Lagar Velho in Portugal, represents not merely a casual result of a Neanderthal/modern human mating, but rather is the product of several millennia of hybridization among members of the resident Neanderthal population and the invading *Homo sapiens*.'[46] Recently, researchers in Germany discovered that the 50,000-year-old remains of a Neanderthal woman recovered from southern Siberia carried traces of *Homo sapiens* DNA; and the analysis indicated that it was the result of one or more of her ancestors interbreeding with a human some 100,000 years ago. Whereas it is known that some people even today carry up to 4 per cent Neanderthal DNA (the implications of which regarding consciousness and behaviour are fascinating), the above discovery shows for the first time that human DNA has been discovered in a Neanderthal.[47] By demonstrating the interbreeding and cross-breeding between different species with man these discoveries do not prove, but allude to, the above assertion about the coexistence of animals with man and the logical possibility of the evolution of the former following, rather than preceding, that of the latter.

Recent scientific discoveries of Neanderthals breeding with humans

However, this work is not concerned with the fascinating subject of evolution as a whole, but on its bearing that man, writ large, is vastly more complex and subtle an entity than just a supposedly evolved ape as per the neo-Darwinian hypothesis. (This stance is fully explained in Chapter 10 in Volume III.) It is therefore totally erroneous to declare, as do the Darwinians, that man is a secondary twig on the evolutionary tree. Such an assertion displays the common mistake of confusing and conflating the human form with the human state, or condition. The former concerns the human body, which indeed will change as it has in the past; the latter is to do with the informing principle of mind, which is the origin of the word 'man', connected to the root *men- 'to think', which would make the elementary sense of man as 'one who has intelligence'. Clearly then, the term 'man' must not be understood to be merely the physical creature with a body on two legs, with two arms, and a head, but rather as a stage in the evolution of consciousness; in other words, humanity should be regarded as a kingdom of nature just like the mineral, plant, and animal kingdoms. For this reason, man needs appropriate vehicles, other than his

Important to distinguish human body from the human being. See Definitions in Volume IV

physical body, in order to manifest and actuate the vast range of his potentiality ranging from the physical to the spiritual via the intermediary of the emotional–mental characteristics of his soul. Suffice it to quote Blavatsky's words:

> That they [certain ancient and mediæval occultists on evolution] antedated Darwin, embraced more or less all his theories on natural selection and the evolution of species, and largely *extended the chain at both ends* [writer's emphasis]. Moreover, these philosophers were explorers as daring in psychology as in physiology and anthropology. They never turned aside from the double parallel path traced for them by their great master Hermes. 'As above, so below', was ever their axiom; and their physical evolution was traced out simultaneously with the spiritual one.[48]

> The whole order of nature evinces a progressive march towards *a higher life*. There is design in the action of the seemingly blindest forces. The whole process of evolution with its endless adaptations is a proof of this. The immutable laws that weed out the weak and feeble species, to make room for the strong, and which ensure the 'survival of the fittest', though so cruel in their immediate action—all are working toward the grand end. The very *fact* that adaptations *do* occur, that the fittest *do* survive in the struggle for existence, shows that what is called 'unconscious Nature' is in reality an aggregate of forces manipulated by semi-intelligent beings (Elementals) guided by High Planetary Spirits (Dhyāni Chohans [Archangels]), whose collective aggregate forms the manifested *verbum* of the unmanifested LOGOS, and constitutes at one and the same time the MIND of the Universe and its immutable LAW.

> Nature taken in its abstract sense, *cannot* be 'unconscious', as it is the emanation from, and thus an aspect (on the manifested plane) of, the ABSOLUTE consciousness. Where is that daring man who would presume to deny to vegetation and even to minerals *a consciousness of their own*. All he can say is, that this consciousness is beyond his comprehension.[49]

Alas! Such a 'daring man' can easily be found amongst the invincible materialists today—and in droves. Nonetheless, this quotation makes it plain, as we have said previously, that occult science does not reject the Darwinian theory so much as pointing out its severe limitations and incompleteness when it is proposed as the sole explanatory mechanism of evolution. Moreover, the very title of Darwin's book *On the Origin of Species by Means of Natural Selection* is misleading. It does not deal with origins but with physical evolution *at a certain moment in time onwards*;[vii] in contrast, the occult doctrine has 'extended the chain at both ends' as avowed above. Apropos, such extension takes cognizance of the triple nature of the generic evolutionary sequence comprising:

1. *Involution* (i.e., the inverse of the process of evolution) being the enwrapping, or infolding, of what previously existed; the so-called 'descent into matter' as the infolding and progressive densification of the spiritual potencies (consciousness) into material vehicles.
2. *Evolution* (properly understood) as the unwrapping, unfolding, or rolling out of the spiritual potencies (consciousness) contained within matter and form (because of the limitation imposed by that form to express the full spiritual potentiality).
3. *Devolution* meaning the liberation from one cycle into another (generally lesser) cycle of being and consciousness.

Margin notes:

Occultists have greatly extended Darwinian-type ideas

Nature is ever evolving. Active intelligence is the principle that impels

The Origin of Species a misrepresentative title

Three components of the advance of nature

---

vii This was pointed out to the writer by the late Dr Julian Candy, a psychiatrist and a senior member of the Scientific and Medical Network.

The above three components are explained in depth in Chapter 10 of Volume III, which deals with the whole scheme of evolution from the Darwinian and occult perspectives.

But let us revert to the statement, 'what is called "unconscious Nature" is in reality an aggregate of forces manipulated by semi-intelligent beings […] guided by High Planetary Spirits […] whose *collective aggregate* [writer's emphasis] […] constitutes at one and the same time the MIND of the Universe and its immutable LAW.' The British-born American mathematical physicist and Templeton prizewinner Freeman Dyson FRS (1923–2020) and the mathematician and philosopher Alfred North Whitehead FRS asserted that even elementary particles are endowed with a form and a level of consciousness. Dyson said: 'Matter in quantum mechanics is not an inert substance but an active agent […]. It appears that mind, as manifested by the capacity to make choices, is to some extent inherent in every electron.'[50] Brian Goodwin argues that natural selection is a 'too weak force' on its own to explain evolution and only operates as a filter mechanism.[51] He claimed that modern evolutionary biology failed to provide an explanation for the theory of biological form and had ignored the importance of morphogenesis in evolution—see Chapter 4. A more forthright statement is shown below. It is a verbatim account, including underlining, of seven crucial points made in a slide from a talk by the Welsh Nobel physicist Brian Josephson FRS (*b.*1940), which the writer attended:

> Alfred North Whitehead, Freeman Dyson, and Brian Goodwin identify limitations of natural selection

1. Physics has things back to front
2. Observers are important
3. Observation is done by agents (subjects, observers)
4. <u>Agents are the source of physics – not v/v [vice versa]</u>
5. This is a taboo idea ([because it smacks of] intelligent design)
6. Physics needs to come to terms with agents
7. [We need to move] Towards a Science of Agents.[52]

> Brian Josephson calls attention to the noumena of physics, i.e. causative agents of physics

Regarding 6. above, Josephson stated that even Stephen Hawking agreed about the necessity for agents, e.g. to 'inform' pre-Big Bang events, but backed off when asked what these agents are.

On another occasion, echoing the thoughts of Dyson and Whitehead, Josephson has said, 'There may be elements of intelligence in every atom of matter.'[53] This is entirely in line with the earlier thoughts of the American psychologist George Trumbull Ladd (1842–1921), Professor of Philosophy at Yale University, that '*Every organ*—indeed, every area, and every element—of the nervous system *has its own memory;*'[54] in turn, fully corroborated by occultism: 'Every organ in our body *has its own memory*. For if it is endowed with a consciousness "of its own kind," every cell must of necessity have also a memory of its own kind, as likewise its own *psychic* and *noëtic* action.'[55]

> Intelligence intrinsic to, not a product of, matter and its interactions

The writer therefore speculates that in mentioning the agents that 'physics needs to comes to terms with', Josephson has suggested the same general idea about the collective aggregate of intelligently guided forces constituting the noumena of what physicists see on the material plane as phenomena, namely, the immutable laws of nature. Otherwise, why suggest that intelligence may inhere 'in every atom of matter'? Furthermore, the importance given to observers surely suggests the crucial role of consciousness, as quantum physics has shown.

Man, matter, and
nature are neither
chance nor
random events

Considered collectively, all this is convincing proof that neither matter nor mankind are the product of blind forces of nature or merely random evolutionary adaptations. On the contrary, both the visible and the subtle counterpart of the human body, down to the minutest speck of matter, are structured according to the cosmic blueprint (prototype) of the 'image of God' referred to in mystical and religious traditions, such as in Christianity, Genesis 2:27. But the reader should *beware* that terms such as 'design', 'agents', and 'active intelligences' have absolutely nothing to do with the naïve and literal creed of 'intelligent design by a Creator-God' propounded by the Christian creationist–fundamentalists; they have all to do with pointing towards our transcendent origins—divinity mirrored in us.

Essential Characteristics of Occultism

Nicholas
Goodrick-Clarke's
contribution to
Western
esotericism

We have just enumerated the key principles of occultism. How do we recognize their operation in practice? A useful account has been provided by Antoine Faivre (*b.*1934), the prominent French scholar of Western esotericism, who held a chair in the École Pratique des Hautes Études at the Sorbonne.[56] As summarized by Nicholas Goodrick-Clarke (Professor of Western Esotericism at the University of Exeter), Faivre deduced six fundamental characteristics taking into account Hermeticism, Qabbalah, the Renaissance concordance of Neoplatonism, as well as alchemy, astrology, and the magic tradition. The first four characteristics Faivre described as 'intrinsic' in the sense of all of them being necessary for spirituality to be understood as esoteric (and of course, occult); the last two are not indispensable but are frequently found together with the first four in esoteric traditions. Although Faivre has based his findings strictly on Western occultism (strictly speaking, esotericism) the six characteristics apply equally to Eastern traditions. They are stated below along with this writer's brief commentary.

❖ FIRST CHARACTERISTIC: *Correspondence*—between all parts of the universe, the macrocosm and the microcosm and at all levels seen and unseen.

  IMPLICATIONS OF FIRST CHARACTERISTIC: We have referred to this earlier as the 'Hermetic Axiom' upon which we lay great stress. It means that all kingdoms of nature at all levels—natural, celestial, super-celestial, and human—are linked through a series of correspondences, or analogies through the idea of the macrocosm (universe and heavens) being reflected in the microcosm (nature and the composition of the human being). We devote a separate section below to amplifying the meaning of this cardinal teaching.

❖ SECOND CHARACTERISTIC: *Living Nature*—as a vital, hierarchical, complex, plural, and organic whole—there being no such thing as 'dead matter'. Newton wrote that even a stone has soul and spirit.[57] In our time, Freeman Dyson, Alfred North Whitehead, and Brian Josephson suggest that intelligence inheres in every atom of matter, as we mentioned above.

  IMPLICATIONS OF SECOND CHARACTERISTIC: If there is no such thing as dead matter, life, therefore, cannot be just the product of blind forces between the constituent parts of inorganic matter. For this reason, there is a vital, responsive connection between the universe as a whole, nature in all her parts, and man—underlying the Principle of Correspondence at all levels, as stated above.

The vitality in nature is the basis of the practice of *magia naturalis* (natural magic) whereby the magician, or the healer, knows the technique of exploiting the antipathies and sympathies that link crystals, stones, herbs, and other substances, as well as colour, sound, and planetary influences; for example, to effect healing using the influences of crystals and therapeutic effects of sound, or to invest talismans with power for protective or other purposes.[viii]

❖ Third Characteristic: *Mediation*—in the form of intermediaries such as gods and spirits, elementals, and nature spirits; also symbols and mandalas.

IMPLICATIONS OF THIRD CHARACTERISTIC: These can be seen in Faivre's notion of a 'mesocosm' being a semi-independent world of spiritual intermediaries and world hierarchies (spirits, devas, angels as emanations of Deity like the *sephiroth* in the Qabbalah) acting as hypostases, or a sort of spiritual ladder, linking the macrocosm and microcosm. (The simile of electrical transformers positioned between the source of power generation and the receiver is apposite.)

❖ FOURTH CHARACTERISTIC: *Transmutation*—the experience of the soul through evolutionary purification and ascent.

IMPLICATIONS OF FOURTH CHARACTERISTIC: That esoteric knowledge not only far extends comprehension about the Universe *in toto*, but also provides an understanding that fundamentally transmutes what would otherwise be an intellectual and speculative subject into an inner experience. This is the true meaning of alchemy where, just as there is a change in state from the base to the noble, so there is a change in being (in consciousness) of the esotericist as a result of his illumined knowledge. The illumination and inner metamorphosis of the esotericist is analogous to the processes of refinement and purification of the alchemist. A contemporary example of this process is to be found in Carl Jung's *Psychology and Alchemy*, concerning the analogies between alchemy, Christian dogma, and psychological symbolism.[58] Alchemy is central to Jung's hypothesis of the collective unconscious and Jung reminds us of the dual nature of alchemy, comprising both the chemical process and a parallel mystical component. In using the alchemical process to provide insights into individuation, Jung emphasises the importance of alchemy in relating to each person the transcendent nature of the psyche.

Universal characteristics of occultism drawn from the West and the East

❖ FIFTH CHARACTERISTIC: *Concordance*—as found in the tendency to establish similarities, or resonances, between the various esoteric traditions.

IMPLICATIONS OF FIFTH CHARACTERISTIC: That the similarities found extend further than mere intellectual similarities, but rather point to a single, unified, and divine source as the trunk of an ancient wisdom (*prisca sapientia*, or *prisca theologia*) of which the various traditions represent the branches. By way of comparative studies, modern Theosophy has magnificently demonstrated that all religions, sciences, philosophies, and esoteric traditions have been inspired by an ancient, unified wisdom tradition at their root—what Newton strove to demonstrate all his life.[59] (See also Chapters 6 and 7.)

---

viii Comprehensive tables showing these correspondences are shown in Volume III, Chapter 5.

❖ SIXTH CHARACTERISTIC: *Transmission*—of the secrecy and profound nature of the teachings through a defined path of initiation.

IMPLICATIONS OF SIXTH CHARACTERISTIC: This concerns the authenticity of the transmission of teachings through the ages and the enduring validity of their message. Whereas it is certainly true that the field of esotericism (and occultism) in general is afflicted by questionable claims and all manner of half-baked concepts, not to say outright phantasies promulgated as facts, yet a serious enquirer into the profound literature of the various spiritual and esoteric traditions will find in them a remarkable consistency— a consistency greater than can be found in natural science.[60] Why should this be? How did the sages and adepts establish the *factual basis* of their teaching? The answer comes from Blavatsky—and in a manner similar to the scientific spirit of our age:

> By checking, testing, and verifying in every department of nature the traditions of old by the independent visions of great adepts; *i.e.*, men who have developed and perfected their physical, mental, psychic, and spiritual organisations to the utmost possible degree. No vision of one adept was accepted till it was checked and confirmed by the visions—so obtained as to stand as independent evidence—of other adepts, and by centuries of experiences.[61]

This suggests that adepts—using their own special methods and instruments (the power of extended and heightened consciousness) of occult research—adopted the utmost care and rigour in their investigations of nature, in all her departments, as modern science does in its enquiries into physical nature through its own methods of analysis and experimental verification.

The Hermetic Axiom – The *Modus Operandi* of Occultism

Hermetic Axiom resolves innumerable problems in science

The Hermetic Axiom concerns the relation between the macrocosm and the microcosm. Many concepts in science nowadays are deprived of their deeper significance because of the lack of understanding and acknowledgement concerning the relation between the greater and the lesser orders of being at different levels. This section, then, presents the principle and an example of the Hermetic Axiom. Further examples are reserved for Volume III, Chapter 5 to demonstrate its universal application.

An understanding of 'macrocosm' and 'microcosm' is fundamental to appreciating the magnitude of the Hermetic Axiom. What exactly do these terms mean?

The Macrocosm and the Microcosm – Their Fundamental Meaning

Macrocosm and microcosm are relative terms

The macrocosm is a manifestation of any kind involving a definite structure which is activated, maintained, and vitalized according to a set of laws working invariably and consistently. A microcosm is a smaller unit of the same kind, but in an undeveloped, or unevolved state. It contains, in potentiality, all the powers and capacities that can be developed by growth and evolution (as the acorn becomes the oak tree or the human embryo the fully developed man). One may also use the example of the fractal or the hologram where the smallest unit mirrors the whole of which it is a part. The smaller the unit, the more indistinct, or fuzzy will be the appearance of the whole—but the whole is always there to a greater or lesser degree of distinctness. Hence, macrocosm and microcosm *are entirely*

Figure I-12 Hermes Trismegistus, Floor Mosaic in the Cathedral of Siena
Image Credit: Science History Images/Alamy Stock Photo

relative terms, as we shall see later. The relation of the macrocosm to the microcosm is of profound significance, not only because it elucidates many natural phenomena and processes, but also because it enables the inference of attributes or principles pertaining to the macrocosm by way of analogy with the microcosm.

The Corpus Hermeticum, the Emerald Tablet, and the Hermetic Axiom

'God *geometrizes*,' said Plato (see Plutarch, *Symposiacs*, Bk. VIII, ii. 1.). 'The laws of nature are the thoughts of God,' exclaimed Oërsted[ix] 2,000 years later. 'His thoughts are immutable,' repeated the solitary student of Hermetic lore, 'therefore it is in the perfect harmony and equilibrium of all things that we must seek the truth.'

Isis Unveiled[62]

The Hermetic Axiom is based upon the *Hermetica*, or *Corpus Hermeticum*, the esoteric teachings of Hermes Trismegistus ('Thrice Great Hermes') who, 'whether as the Egyptian Thoth or the Greek Hermes, was the God of Wisdom with the Ancients, and, according to Plato, "discovered numbers, geometry, astronomy and letters".'[63] How do we recognize a Hermetic teaching, whether orally or in text? We propose that its defining traits are: the human mind as a mirror of Divine Mind, hence the human being endowed with Divine Intellect; and the scenario of a fall into matter and a redemptive reunion with the divine. Figure I-12 above shows an inlaid floor panel mosaic in Siena Cathedral depicting the legendary god, executed in 1488 by the Italian sculptor Giovanni di Stefano (1443–*circa* 1506).

Hallmark of Hermetic teaching

It is the Principle of Correspondence (i.e., correspondences existing at all levels of nature) associated with the macrocosm/microcosm axiom that lies at the centre of esoteric science

---

ix Hans Christian Oërsted (Ørsted) (1777–1851) was a Danish physicist and chemist who discovered that an electric current in a wire can deflect a magnetized compass needle.

as well as its cardinal role in Platonism, Theosophy, and Hermeticism. This injunction lies at the heart of the *Emerald Tablet*—see Figure I-13 opposite. Based on the Hermetic writings, it is one of the oldest surviving of all alchemical documents in the alchemical tradition and the founding document of Renaissance esotericism and alchemy. What now follows is an outline of the detailed exposition reserved for Chapter 5 of Volume III.

Correspondence and analogy central to Hermetic teaching

The core meaning of the Hermetic Axiom is that there always exists a correspondence between the laws and phenomena of the various planes of existence from the densest (the terrestrial) to the subtlest (spiritual). There are planes of existence beyond our knowing since they exist in space–time orders outside the physical, but when we apply the Principle of Correspondence to them we are able to understand—by analogy—much that would otherwise remain unknown and unknowable to us. Thus, whatever happens on any level of reality (physical, emotional, mental, spiritual) also happens, correspondingly, on every other level. It is this principle that justifies the ancient sciences of astrology, alchemy, and magic by providing their theoretical basis. Correspondence should be understood as functional, not physical resemblance. We are not stating that the world we ordinarily inhabit is a sort of photocopy in four-dimensional space–time of a higher realm. Of the numerous luminaries who expounded on this sublime teaching, we give three examples, ancient and modern.

Swedenborg's science: hermetic in principle

Swedenborg taught a fundamental law governing the realization of divine life in the various realms of nature, such that there is a concordance between divine, spiritual (soul), and natural (material) things, this relationship being that between the archetype, its likeness, and its shadow.[64] His science was based on his vitalist–organic worldview that the universal soul *in*-forms matter; thus everything in nature derives its body and form from a soul which it reflects,[65] which is somewhat comparable to Sheldrake's modern theory of morphogenesis and the notion of organizing fields.

Blavatsky taught the following four-part rule:

Blavatsky's rule for applying the Hermetic Wisdom

1. 'Of a truth the aphorism of the Hermetic Wisdom, "as above, so below", applies to all esoteric instruction; but we must begin with the *above*; we must learn the formula before we can sum up the series'[66] (a simple example of this is given in Volume III, Chapter 5)
    … so because …
2. 'everything in the Universe follows analogy [correspondence]'[67]
    … we are accordingly instructed …
3. 'always argue on analogy and apply the old occult axiom "as above so below"'[68]
    … and especially to …
4. 'reduce everything to terms of consciousness.'[69]

Blavatsky's version of the Hermetic Axiom

Blavatsky's version of the Hermetic Axiom is shown in the last column of Figure I-13. She explains how: 'Tradition declares that on the dead body of Hermes, at Hebron, was found by an Ozarim, an initiate, the tablet known as the *Smaragdine*. It contains, in a few sentences, the essence of the Hermetic wisdom.' Then she warns, 'To those who read but with their bodily eyes, the precepts will suggest nothing new or extraordinary, for it merely begins by saying that it speaks not fictitious things, but that which is true and most certain.'[70]

But if all that is not convincing enough, what more resounding proof of the supreme value of the Hermetic Axiom can there be than the translation by England's legendary

THE EMERALD TABLET OF HERMES
also known as the Smaragdine Table, or Tabula Smaragdina

Image Credit: Chrysogonus Polydorus/Wikimedia Commons{PD-US}

Isis Unveiled — H. P. Blavatsky

Writer's own photograph

Image Credit: Wikimedia Commons{PD-US}

Nineveh Shadrach translation	Original Latin text	Isaac Newton translation	Isis Unveiled (Blavatsky)
True, without error, certain and most true: that which is above is as that which is below; and that which is below is as that which is above, to perform the miracles of the One Thing. And as all things were from One, by the mediation of One, so from this One Thing come all things by adaptation. Its father is the Sun, its mother is the Moon, the wind carried it in its belly, the nurse thereof is the Earth.	1. *Verum, sine mendacio, certum et verissimum.*	1. *Tis true without lying, certain & most true.*	"What is below is like that which is above, and what is above is similar to that which is below, to accomplish the wonders of one thing."
	2. *Quod est inferius est sicut quod est superius, et quod est superius est sicut quod est inferius, ad perpetranda miracula rei unius.*	2. *That which is below is like that which is above & that which is above is like that which is below to do the miracles of one only thing.*	
	3. *Et sicut res omnes fuerunt ab uno, meditatione unius, sic omnes res natae ab hac una re, adaptatione.*	3. *And as all things have been & arose from one by the mediation of one: so all things have their birth from this one thing by adaptation.*	"As all things were produced by the mediation of one being, so all things were produced from this one thing by adaptation."
It is the father of all perfection and the consummation of the whole world. Its power is integral if it be turned to Earth.	4. *Pater eius est Sol. Mater eius est Luna, portavit illud Ventus in ventre suo, nutrix eius terra est.*	4. *The Sun is its father, the moon its mother, the wind hath carried it in its belly, the earth is its nurse.*	"Its father is the sun, its mother is the moon."
	5. *Pater omnis telesmi[12] totius mundi est hic.*	5. *The father of all perfection in the whole world is here.*	"It is the cause of all perfection throughout the whole earth."
	6. *Virtus eius integra est si versa fuerit in terram.*	6. *Its force or power is entire if it be converted into earth.*	"Its power is perfect if it is changed into earth."
Thou shalt separate the Earth from the Fire, the subtle from the coarse, gently and with much ingenuity. It ascends from Earth to heaven and descends again to Earth, and receives the power of the superiors and the inferiors.	7. *Separabis terram ab igne, subtile ab spisso, suaviter, magno cum ingenio.*	7. *Separate thou the earth from the fire, the subtile from the gross sweetly with great industry.*	"Separate the earth from the fire, the subtle from the gross, acting prudently and with judgment."
	8. *Ascendit a terra in coelum, iterumque descendit in terram, et recipit vim superiorum et inferiorum.*	8. *It ascends from the earth to the heaven & again it descends to the earth & receives the force of things superior & inferior.*	
Thus thou hast the glory of the whole world; therefore let all obscurity flee before thee. This is the strong fortitude of all fortitude, overcoming every subtle [body] and penetrating every solid thing. Thus the world was created. Hence are all wonderful adaptations, of which this is the manner:	9. *Sic habebis Gloriam totius mundi.*	9. *By this means you shall have the glory of the whole world.*	"Ascend with the greatest sagacity from the earth to heaven, and then descend again to earth, and unite together the power of things inferior and superior; thus you will possess the light of the whole world, and all obscurity will fly away from you."
	10. *Ideo fugiet a te omnis obscuritas.*	10. *& thereby all obscurity shall fly from you.*	
	11. *Haec est totius fortitudinis fortitudo fortis, quia vincet omnem rem subtilem, omnemque solidam penetrabit.*	11. *Its force is above all force. For it vanquishes every subtile thing & penetrates every solid thing.*	"This thing has more fortitude than fortitude itself, because it will overcome every subtile thing and penetrate every solid thing."
	12. *Sic mundus creatus est.*	12. *So was the world created.*	
Therefore am I called Hermes the Thrice Great, having the three parts of the philosophy of the whole world. That is finished which I have to say concerning the operation of the Sun.	13. *Hinc erunt adaptationes mirabiles, quarum modus est hic. Itaque vocatus sum Hermes Trismegistus, habens tres partes philosophiae totius mundi.*	13. *From this are & do come admirable adaptations whereof the means (or process) is here in this. Hence I am called Hermes Trismegist, having the three parts of the philosophy of the whole world.*	"By it the world was formed …"
	14. *Completum est quod dixi de operatione Solis.*	14. *That which I have said of the operation of the Sun is accomplished & ended.*	

A translation bypassing the Latin by Nineveh Shadrach from the original Arabic of the *Book on the Secret of Creation* (also named *Book of the Causes*) attributed to Apollonius of Tyana.[75]

Original Latin text of the Emerald Tablet, from *De Alchimia*, Chrysogonus Polydorus, Nuremberg 1541.[76]

A translation by Isaac Newton found among his alchemical papers currently lodged in King's College Library, Cambridge University.[77]

H. P. Blavatsky, *Isis Unveiled*, ed. Boris de Zirkoff (Wheaton, Illinois, Theosophical Publishing House, 1972). Volume I: Science, 507.

Figure I-13 The Hermetic Axiom

scientist–mystic Isaac Newton, reproduced in full in Figure I-13 on page 249 alongside the original Latin text and a modern translation from the original Arabic. Note, carefully, that Newton (who figures prominently in the writings of Blavatsky, as stated earlier) came to his stupendous discoveries by applying the Principle of Correspondence. As stated by the Scottish mathematician Colin Maclaurin FRS (1698–1746) who developed and extended Newton's work in calculus, geometry, and gravitation: 'He endeavours to judge of them, by *analogy*, from what he had found in the greater motions of the system; a way of reasoning that is agreeable to the harmony of things, and to the old maxim ascribed to *Hermes*, and approved by the observation and judgment of the best philosophers, "That what passes in the heavens above is similar and analogous to what passes on earth below".'[71] And, in similar vein, regarding analogy and correspondence, we find in Book III of *Principia* in the Chapter 'Rules of Reasoning in Philosophy': 'RULE II—*Therefore to the same natural effects we must, as far as possible, assign the same causes.*' And in explanation, 'As to respiration in a man and in a beast; the descent of stones in *Europe* and in *America*; the light of our culinary fire and of the sun; the reflection of light in the earth, and in the planets [all italics in the original].'[72]

Newton's translation of the Hermetic Axiom

Examining the Hermetic Axiom in Figure I-13, note how the opening statement in Verse 2 of the original Latin and Newton's translation, 'That which is below is like that which is above & that which is above is like that which is below', popularly abbreviated to 'As Above, so Below', captures the macrocosm–microcosm correspondence. Scientists who rightfully exalt Newton's discovery of the Law of Gravity seem quite unaware (or unwilling to acknowledge) that this surely is a classic example of the great scientist–mystic applying the Hermetic Axiom—in this instance a case of 'As Below, so Above'—by reasoning that the same law that attracts the fall of the apple to Earth ('below') must also govern the motion of the heavenly bodies ('above').

Newton applies the Hermetic Axiom to gravity

The 'adaptations' in Verse 13 (second and third columns) refer to the progressive unfoldment of the universe from a state of 'wholeness and the implicate order' (to quote the title of the classic book by the metaphysical physicist David Bohm). So it is this perception of ever-simultaneous, ever-presence of the deity/universe/man trinity with the associated recognition that there is absolutely no such thing as 'dead matter'—every particle of nature is imbued with life and consciousness at its own level—that would, if imported into the mainstream scientific ethos, resolve innumerable conundrums in cosmology, evolution, and the nature of consciousness. We point out just two out of innumerable affirmations that are particularly germane to this work about man's nature in correspondence with the whole. First, 'The Universe is a Man on a large scale' has been attributed to Lao Tzu of China. Next, between 1537 and 1539, the Swiss–German physician, alchemist, and astrologer of the German Renaissance Philippus Aureolus Theophrastus Bombastus von Hohenheim, known by the name of Paracelsus, embarked on an encyclopædic work on the nature of deity and man, entitled *Astronomia Magna or the Whole Sagacious Philosophy of the Macrocosm and Microcosm*. In it he clearly stated his conviction that 'man is made out of the macrocosm and that therein lies his true nature'. 'Light of Nature' is a key Paracelsian term revealing the interconnection of all living Nature, which furnishes man with his bodies at all levels from the gross to the subtle.[73] Moreover, 'Astronomia may be called the highest wisdom of mortals in the light of nature.'[74]

Correspondence, at all levels, between Man and Universe

It is interesting to ask whether scientific research into fossils and prehistoric forms is a sort of back-to-front version of the Hermetic Axiom. In a limited sense it would appear to be, otherwise Darwin and other evolutionary biologists and palæontologists could not have come to their discoveries, which are not to be belittled. However, studying just fossils is looking backwards at inanimate, preexisting forms, either in nature or, worse still, in the artificial environment of the laboratory, whereas the proper application of the Hermetic Axiom involves participating with living nature in all her forms. In other words, concerning their different methods of investigation, the scientist observes in terms of a detached object, whereas the mystic and occultist actively participates in the inner life of the living entity. The distinction is a vital one and readers are invited to refer back to the first section of this Chapter contrasting the scientific and occult methods of investigation.

Contrast between studying fossils and engaging with living Nature

Rationale and Justification for the Principle of Correspondence

We now have to enquire: why does the Principle of Correspondence exist in all of nature and furthermore, what is the basis of its operation?

David Bohm was one of the foremost scientific thinkers and metaphysical philosophers of our time. He taught that the world is the explication of the implicate order,[78] which is a modern restatement of the perennial affirmation that just as the seed is the tree 'folded up', so the world is Divinity un-folded; hence all the world is subsumed in Divinity. Thus Proclus declares: 'Every property of divinity permeates all creation and gives itself to all inferior creatures.'[79] In similar vein Leibniz affirms, 'Every substance contains all the attributes of God, although in a manner inferior to their divine source.'[80] Thus it is seen that all forms are of one quintessential substance and all life of one universal force, and these are co-existent in the nature of the Divine Consciousness, by whatever other appellations— such as the Supreme One, or the Supreme Mind, or the Prime Author, Prime Mover and Unmoved Mover, terms coined by Aristotle—they may be known. This doctrine, also expounded by Plato, was enfleshed by his disciple, Aristotle (384–322 BC), in words worthy of his master:

All creation and every substance made of one divine essence

> We say that this Sensible World is an image of another; therefore since this world is vivid or alive, how much more, then, that other must live […]. Yonder, therefore, above the stellar virtues, stand other heavens to be attained, like the heavens of this world; beyond them, because they are of a higher kind, brighter and vaster; nor are they distant from each Other like this one, for they are incorporeal. Yonder, too, exists an earth, not of inanimate matter, but vivid with animal life and all natural terrestrial phenomena like this one, but of other kinds and perfections. There are plants, also, and gardens, and flowing water; there are aquatic animals but of nobler species. Yonder is air and life appropriate to it, all immortal. And although the life there is analogous to ours, yet it is nobler, seeing that it is intellectual, perpetual and unalterable.

Aristotle discerns the corporeal and objective from the incorporeal and subjective

> For if anyone should object and ask, How in the world above do the plants, etc. above mentioned find footing, we should answer that they do not have objective existence, for they were produced by the primal Author in an absolute condition and without exteriorization. They are, therefore, in the same case as intellect and soul; they suffer no defect such as waste and corruption, since the beings yonder are full of energy, strength and joy, as living in a life sublime and being the issue of one fount and of one quality, compounded of all like sweet savours, delicate perfumes, harmonious colour and sound, and other perfections.[81]

What Plato and Aristotle have affirmed has ever been the mystic's vision as, for example, in *The Mistress of Vision* by the English poet and mystic Francis Thompson (1859–1907):

> All things by immortal power,
> Near and Far
> Hiddenly
> To each other linked are,
> That thou canst not stir a flower
> Without troubling of a star.[82]

Quantum non-locality expressed through poetry

And then the insight of the Adept, quoted in the previous Chapter, but which bears repeating:

> Nature has linked all parts of her Empire together by subtle threads of magnetic
> sympathy, and, there is a mutual correlation even between a star and a man.

These aphorisms, however, are none other than poetical and mystical expressions—and endorsements—of the magnificent theoretical discovery backed by hard experimental proof of the principle of non-locality from modern quantum physics, the crown jewel of physics, as explained earlier in Chapter 4. And along with non-locality comes, naturally, non-local mind, or Universal Mind. It is heartening to discover how modern science is slowly corroborating the teachings of the perennial wisdom and the vision of mystics.

Hermetic Axiom Example – Cosmic Birth and Human Birth Correspondence

We have just cited the example of Newton who intuited the law of gravity from observing the fall of an apple. Another example of the Principle of Correspondence applies to the birth of cosmos—the macrocosm 'above', and human birth—the microcosm, 'below' as depicted in the accompanying Table I-1 considerably abridged from Blavatsky's *Collected Writings*.[83] Comparing human birth in a literal sense with cosmogony would be as absurd as comparing the gravitational fall of an apple with the motion of the heavenly bodies. Such comparisons are obviously not regarding actual details but in terms of the Hermetic principle of correspondences. We expand considerably on this theme in Volume III by explaining why, in the occult literature, man is said to be the measure of all things, i.e., a microcosmic representation of the universe and solar system.

Hermetic Axiom – Evidence

The following is a summary of key themes as set forth in one of the foundation documents of the Hermetic tradition—the *Corpus Hermeticum*, which brings together seventeen treatises written in Greek in the second and third centuries AD and attributed to the mythic figure of Hermes Trismegistus, a Hellenistic fusion of the Greek god Hermes and the Egyptian god Thoth:[86]

1. A complete absence of any fundamental or ontological dualism, whether between God and his creations (including Man) or between so-called good and evil.
2. On the basis of the Hermetic Axiom, the divine essence and all of the universe and nature, is reflected, holographically, so to say, in our individual minds; and since the universe is a manifestation of God, the former is a 'Book' to be 'read' by deciphering the symbols that point to its divine origin and nature.

Table I-1   The Hermetic Axiom Showing Correspondences Between Cosmogony and Human Birth

Cosmic Birth ~ Human Birth

Mahātmā Morya: 'In studying esoteric cosmogony, keep a spiritual eye upon the physiological process of human birth; proceed from cause to effect establishing as you go along, analogies between the birth of a man and that of a world.'[84]

Lao Tzu: 'Human beings are a small likeness of the great Universe.'[85]

Cosmic Process (Upper Pole)	Human Process (Lower Pole)
1. The mathematical Point, called the 'Cosmic seed', the Monad of Leibnitz, which contains the whole Universe, as the acorn the oak.	1. The terrestrial Embryo [Embryonic seed], which contains in it the future man with all his potentialities.
2. The *vis vitæ* of our solar system exudes from the Sun, called, when referred to the higher planes, Ākāśa.	2. The Amniotic Fluid exudes from the Embryo, called on the plane of matter Prāṇa (the universal Life Principle).
3. The Ether of Space, which in its external aspect, is supposed to envelop the Sun.	3. The Amnion, the membrane containing the Amniotic Fluid and enveloping the Embryo.
4. The Sidereal contents of Ether, represented in Occult and Kabalistic Mysteries by Elementals, and in physical Astronomy by meteors, comets, and all kinds of cosmic bodies.	4. Umbilical Vesicle, serving, as science teaches, to nourish the Embryo originally, but as Occult Science avers to carry to the Fœtus by osmosis the cosmic influences extraneous to the mother.
5. Life-currents in Ether, having their origin in the Sun. Vital principle of the Ether (the blood of the Cosmic Body) passes to nourish everything on the Earth and on the other planets: from minerals, from plants, to animal and man, to whom life is thus imparted.	5. The Allantois, a protrusion from the Embryo which spreads between the Amnion and the Chorion [defined in 7 below]; it is supposed to conduct the nourishment from the mother to the Embryo. It corresponds to the life-principle, Prāṇa.
6. The double radiation, psychic and physical, which radiates from the Cosmic Seed and expands around the whole Kosmos, as well as around the solar system and every planet.	6. The Allantois is divided into two layers. The interspace between the Amnion and the Chorion contains the Allantois and also an albuminous fluid.
7. The outer crust of every sidereal body, or the sphere of our solar system, of our earth, and of every man and animal.	7. The Chorion, or globular object, called *Blastodermic Vesicle*, the outer and the inner layers of the membrane of which go to form the physical man. The outer, or ectoderm, forms his epidermis; the inner or endoderm, his muscles, bones, etc.

3. We should therefore be interested in everything that is in the world. The particular and the concrete are important, as incarnations and embodiment are the ways in which God makes himself manifest to our experience.

4. Humanity spans the polarity from the spiritual to the material, namely, the divine and terrestrial realms. Hence our minds can connect with intermediary spiritual intelligences as ladders of ascent; also with guides and mentors, and the hierarchy of planetary influences, in order to reawaken our dormant spiritual nature.

5. Based on the scenario of the fall into matter, the will, both divine and human, can be summoned to the regenerative work of redemptive reintegration with the divine and the associated refinement of Earth.

Science and Occultism – Contrasted and Complemented

Recalling what was mentioned in Chapter 4, Science in its most general terms is the *study* of Truth; and Art is said to be the *practise* of what is known. The ideal scientist is therefore an artist. As an artist soul he is able to combine the analytical method *and* the holistic approach to both reveal Truth and to practise it. He understands that the analytical method *needs* the holistic approach in order to be truly appreciated and seen in its context.

The Analytical Approach of Western Science and the Holistic Approach of Occult Science are compared in Table I-2 opposite.

In science, the fundamental premise of all enquiry into life and mind is physics. Thus the movement is bottom-up from matter to mind: physics→chemistry→biology→psychology→ mind (= brain).

By contrast, occult science posits that in the movement from matter to mind, higher dimensions, or orders of being are released, or evolved—'boiled out', so to say. Conversely, in the reverse process these higher dimensions are involved—'bottled-up', so to say. Thus the top-down process from mind to matter is: mind→psychology→biology→chemistry→ physical matter, at each stage the higher dimension being increasingly involved.

Viewing the movement from physics to mind as a series of concentric spheres, each sphere is subsumed by the next adjacent outer sphere. Thus in science, biology subsumes physics as psychology subsumes biology. We can study matter using physics, but we cannot study life only by physics, even though matter is a physicalized expression of life. Similarly, the study of mind incorporates biology and physics even though mind cannot be reduced to just biological life and matter. This is the the hard problem of consciousness, the subject of phrentic scientific research and study, as detailed in Chapter 3.

And ultimately, the mystic process must necessarily incorporate the scientific—or put another way, science is completely infused by mysticism as every seer has realized and great scientists, like Newton, Planck, Schrödinger, Einstein, and Pauli have acknowledged.

This Chapter has described the complementary methods of science and occult science, followed by an overview of occult science and its essential principles and distinguishing characteristics. Considerable importance was attached to the Hermetic Axiom with a few examples of the correspondences between the 'greater' and the 'lesser'. This has prepared

Correspondence between universe, nature, man, and matter evidence of the Hermetic Axiom

Science and Art coalesce at their highest levels

Higher orders of being

Science and mysticism are mutually complementary

Table I-2 Science and Occult Science – Contrasts and Complements

Science: Aristotelian, 'bottom-up' inductive method—from particulars to universals. Analytical method, to discover the 'what' (and 'how') of nature.	**Occult Science:** Platonic, 'top down', deductive method—from universals to particulars. Holistic approach, to discover the 'how' and 'why' of nature.
1. Science provides knowledge and facts about physical nature and mind	1. Occult science maintains the whole of truth along with
2. refracted through the 'prism' of the intellect	2. consistency in all departments of nature (because of the application of the Hermetic Axiom)
3. resulting in bright and precise 'splinters' of truth about the physical behaviour and appearance of nature … but the drawback is …	… hence …
	3. the 'highest common factor'**x** of occult doctrines is the thread of universal wisdom that binds them all into an organic whole … but the limitation is …
4. an inconsistency in the various theories of science, the 'least common multiple'**x** of all scientific theories being an intellectual cul-de-sac, e.g. there is no consistency between biology and cosmology (Darwinism and 'Big Bang'); and even in physics itself, general relativity and quantum theory have not been harmonised.	4. a lack of precision and detail about individual facets of physical nature.

Summary:

- It should be clear, as previously stated, that occult science completes and complements (not replaces) the scientific picture.
- In essence, the scientist studies natural processes and is struck with wonder at the seeming intelligence that underlies these processes. He asks the question: 'what'? and occasionally, 'how'? The occultist studies natural processes and is struck by both wonder and awe at the intelligence that underlies these processes. He additionally asks the questions: 'how' and 'why'? and is therefore able to understand the inner significance, meaning, and purpose behind the intelligence and beauty of the process.
- Accordingly, the knowledge and understanding gained through occultism throws light on the inner guiding and driving forces that underlie all natural processes, thereby enriching our sensitivity and reverence towards them, albeit at the expense of the specific and detailed information about the (physical) mechanisms behind such processes that are the province of scientific knowledge.
- As science adds to our knowledge of the physical world, occultism adds to our understanding of the inner, invisible worlds which are hidden within the physical. Both avenues of exploration are complementary.

---

x 'Least common multiple' by way of a mathematical analogy with vulgar fractions; a common denominator at the most basic level as opposed to a common factor at the highest level. We suggest that the common denominator for science is dead matter (there is nothing 'lower' for science and this is where all scientific theories, whether about cosmos or man, find their common denominator); whereas the 'highest common factor' for occultism is Consciousness and Mind (the genesis of all that was, is and will be).

the ground for the next Chapter on the worldwide Mystery Teachings, ancient and modern.

Meanwhile we close with a quote that encapsulates the enduring relation at all levels between the macrocosm and the microcosm.

> *For all that happens down here is but the reflection in gross matter of the happenings on higher planes, and we may often find a crutch for our halting imagination in our studies of physical development. 'As above, so below'. The physical is the reflection of the spiritual.*

ANNIE BESANT[87]

NOTES

1 Al-Shahrazui, *Hekmat ul-Eshrâq* [Doctrine of Illumination], in Dr Massoud Homayouni, *The Origins of Persian Gnosis*, trans. F. J. Stone (London: Mawlana Centre, 1992), 16. Al-Shahrazui was a thirteenth-century Islamic physician, historian, and philosopher of Kurdish origin.

2 'The Investigation of Truth', in Edi D. Bilimoria, *The Snake and the Rope: Problems in Western science resolved by occult science* (Adyar, Madras: Theosophical Publishing House, 2006), 55–98.

3 Ilya Prigogine and Isabelle Stengers, *Order Out of Chaos: Man's new dialogue with nature*, foreword by Alvin Toffler (US and Canada: Bantam Books, 1984), xi.

4 Isaac Newton, *Opticks, Or, A Treatise of the Reflections, Refractions, Inflections & Colours of Light* (London 1730; 4th edn, New York: Dover Publications, 1979), 404.

5 G. R. Jain, *Cosmology: Old and new* (New Delhi: Bharatiya Jnanpith Publication, 1991), xxv–xxvi.

6 Leopold Infeld, *The World in Modern Science: Matter and quanta*, trans. Louis Infeld (London: Victor Gollancz, 1934), 231.

7 'A synopsis of the Prophetick ffigures', in Isaac Newton, *The First Book Concerning the Language of the Prophets, No. 8* (Keynes MS. 5, King's College, Cambridge, UK), The Newton Project [online March 2003] <http://www.newtonproject.ox.ac.uk/view/texts/normalized/THEM00005> accessed 3 August 2020. Cited also in Richard Westfall, *Never at Rest* (New York and Cambridge: Cambridge University Press, 1995), 349 n.49. Quoted substantially in Betty Jo Teeter Dobbs, *The Foundations of Newton's Alchemy or* 'The Hunting of the Greene Lyon' (1975; repr. US: Cambridge University Press, 1984), 109 n.35, citing Isaac Newton, 'The Language of the Prophets', in Newton, *Theological MS*, 119–26, quotation from pp. 119–20 (1, n.12).

8 Isaac Newton, *The First Book Concerning the Language of the Prophets, No. 8.*

9 *ibid.*

10 *ibid.*

11 *ibid.*

12 Betty Jo Teeter Dobbs, *The Foundations of Newton's Alchemy*, 109.

13 Isaac Newton, *Philosophiæ Naturalis Principia Mathematica* [Mathematical Principles of Natural Philosophy], trans. Andrew Motte, rev. Florian Cajori, 2 vols (Berkeley, Los Angeles: University of California Press, 1962), ii, 'The System of the World – General Scholium', 545.

14 *SD*-I, 'Is Gravitation a Law?', 492.

15 *SD*-I, ' "AN LUMEN SIT CORPUS, NEC NON?" ["Is Light a Body, or not?"]', 484.

16 *SD*-II, 'Scientific and Geological Proofs of the Existence of Several Submerged Continents', 794, 797.

17 *NPB*-5, 'Part 2: *The Intellect*, 'Science and Metaphysics', ¶ 106, 130.

18 Evelyn Fox Keller, *A Feeling for the Organism, 10th Aniversary Edition: The life and work of Barbara McLintock* (San Francisco: W. H. Freeman, 1983), 69, 117.

19 Spoken statement *circa* 1903, *Harper's Monthly* (September 1932).

20 'Four Letters from Sir Isaac Newton to Doctor Bentley containing some Arguments in Proof of a DEITY, in *The Correspondences of Isaac Newton*, ed. H. W. Turnbull, J. F. Scott, A. Rupert Hall, and Laura Tilling, 7 vols (Cambridge, Cambridge University Press, 1959-77), iii, 233; quoted also in Bernard Cohen and Richard S. Westfall (eds), *Newton* (US: W. W. Norton & Company, 1995), 330–9.

21 Keynes MS, 130.

22 E. F. King, *A Biographical Sketch of Isaac Newton* (2nd edn, Grantham: S. Bidge & Son and London: Simpkin, Marshall, & Co., 1858), 66.

23 'John Maynard Keynes: "Newton, the Man"'. Paper delivered posthumously by Geoffrey Keynes, brother of Lord Keynes at the Royal Society tercentenary celebrations in 1947 <http://www-history.mcs.st-and.ac.uk/Extras/Keynes_Newton.html> accessed 26 November 2019.

24 Leo Marx and Bruce Mazlish (eds), *Progress: Fact or illusion?* (Ann Arbor: University of Michigan Press, 1996), 23.

25 '"Miraculous Powers", Sutras 1–12', in Patanjali, *How To Know God: The Yoga aphorisms of Patanjali*, trans. and commentary by Swami Prabhavananda and Christopher Isherwood (US: Vedanta Press), 1996.

26 Jacobo Grinberg Zylberbaum, 'Human Communication and the Electrophysiological Activity of the Brain', *Journal of Subtle Energies*, 3/3 (1994), 25–43.

27 Stephen M. Phillips, *Extra-sensory Perception of Quarks*, introd. E. Lester Smith FRS (Wheaton, Illinois: Theosophical Publishing House, 1980), 3.

28 Annie Besant and C. W. Leadbeater, *Occult Chemistry: Investigations by clairvoyant magnification into the structure of the atoms of the periodic table and of some compounds*, ed. C. Jinarâjadâsa, assisted by Elizabeth W. Preston (1908; rev. and enl. 3rd edn, Adyar, Madras: Theosophical Publishing House, 1994).

29 Stephen M. Phillips, *Anima: Remote viewing of subatomic particles*, foreword by M. Srinivasan (Adyar, Chennai: Theosophical Publishing House, 1996). Dr Srinivasan was Associate Director of the Physics Group at the Bhabha Atomic Research Centre, Mumbai. The book was reviewed by Edi Bilimoria in *Journal of the Scientific and Medical Network*, 70 (1999), 57.

30 *SD*-I, 'The Solar Theory', 544.

31 'Nature *In Abscondito*', in Edi D. Bilimoria, *The Snake and the Rope*, 7–51 *passim*.

32 *SD*-I, 'God, Monad, and Atoms', 610.

33 *SD*-I, 'Proem', 14–18.

34 Bowen Notes, 8. The Bowen Notes are extracts from the notes of personal teachings given by H.P. Blavatsky to private pupils during the years 1888 to 1891. These are published in a pamphlet entitled *Madame Blavatsky on How to Study Theosophy* (London: Theosophical Publishing House), 1960.

35 'Of natures obvious laws & processes in vegetation', Burndy MS 16 (Sotheby lot no. 113 , now Dibner Collection MSS 1031 B, Dibner Library of the History of Science and Technology of the Smithsonian Institution Libraries, Washington, D. C). Quoted also in Betty Jo Teeter Dobbs, *The Janus Faces of Genius: The role of alchemy in Newton's thought* (New York, Melbourne, Cambridge: Cambridge University Press, 1991), 264.

36 Alain Bauer, *Isaac Newton's Freemasonry: The alchemy of science and mysticism* (Rochester, Vermont: Inner Traditions, 2003).

37 Ayval Leshem Ramati, *Newton on the Secrets of Creation Hidden in the Jewish Temple* (n.p.: Raziel Pub., 2015).

38 Ayval Leshem, *Newton on Mathematics and Spiritual Purity* (Dordrecht: Kluwer Academic Publishers, 2003).

39 Bowen Notes, 10.

40 Felisa Wolfe-Simon, Paul C.W. Davies, and Ariel D. Anbar, 'Did Nature Also Choose Arsenic?' *International Journal of Astrobiology*, 8/2 (April 2009).

41 F. Wolfe-Simon, et al., 'A Bacterium That Can Grow by Using Arsenic Instead of Phosphorus', *Science*, 332/6034 (2010), 1163–6.

42 Jesus Diaz, 'NASA Finds New Life (Updated)', *Gizmodo* (12 February 2010) <https://gizmodo.com/nasa-finds-new-life-updated-5704158> accessed 26 November 2019.

43 Paul Davies, 'The "Give Me a Job" Microbe', *Wall Street* Journal, 4 December 2010.

44 'Bacterium Calls for Biology Rewrite', 4 December 2010 <http://www.abc.net.au/radionational/programs/scienceshow/bacterium-calls-for-biology-rewrite/2959830#transcript> accessed 26 November 2019.

45 Marshall Louis Reaves, et al., 'Absence of Detectable Arsenate in DNA from Arsenate-Grown GFAJ-1 Cells', *Science*, 337/6093 (2012), 470–3.

46 Ian Tattersall and Jeffrey H. Schwartz, 'Hominids and Hybrids: The place of Neanderthals in human evolution', *Proceedings of the National Academy of Sciences of the United States of America*, 96/13 (1999), 7117–19.

47 *The Week*, 27 February 2016, 19.

48 *IU*-I, Chapter XII, 'The "Impassable Chasm" ', 427.

49 *SD*-I, 'Summing Up: The Pith and Marrow of Occultism', 277–8.

50 Freeman Dyson, *Infinite in All Directions*, Gifford Lectures Given at Aberdeen, Scotland (New York: Harper & Row, 1988), quoted in Ervin László, *Science and the Akashic Field: An integral theory of everything* (Rochester, Vermont: Inner Traditions, 2007), 110.

51 B. Goodwin, 'Meaning in Evolution', *J. Biol. Phys. Chem.*, 5 (2005), 51–6.

52 'Making Sense of *Psi*', Society for Psychical Research, Study Day No. 63 (2012).

53 Interview by Barry Rohan, *Detroit Free Press*, 25 October 1983; quoted also in *The Eclectic Theosophist* (San Diego, California, May-June 1984), 5.

54 G. T. Ladd, *Elements of Physiological Psychology: A treatise of the activities and nature of the mind from the physical and experimental point of view* (London: Longmans, Green & Co.; New York: Charles Scribner's Sons, 1887), 553; quoted also in *CW*-XII, 'Psychic and Noetic Action', 365.

55 *CW*-XII, 'Psychic and Noetic Action', 368.

56 Antoine Faivre, *Access to Western Esotericism* (Albany: State University of New York Press, 1994), 7. The book is a translation of two works first published as *Accès de L'Ésotérisme Occidental* [Access of Western Esotericism] (Paris: Gallimard, 1986); and *L'Ésotérisme* [Esotericism] (Paris: Presses Universitaires de France,1992). A similar presentation is given in Antoine Faivre, 'Introduction I', in *Modern Esoteric Spirituality*, ed. Antoine Faivre and Jacob Needleman (London: SCM Press, 1993), xv-xx.

57 B. J. T. Dobbs, 'Newton's Alchemy and His Theory of Matter', *Isis*, 73/4 (December 1982), 511–28.

58 'Psychology and Alchemy', in *Collected Works of C.G. Jung*, ed. Gerhard Adler and R. F.C. Hull, xii (Princeton: Princeton University Press), 1968.

59 Rob Iliffe, *Priest of Nature: The religious worlds of Isaac Newton* (New York: Oxford University Press, 2017), reviewed by Edi Bilimoria in *Journal of the Scientific and Medical Network*, 125 (2017), 37–40.

60 For a comprehensive exposition of the inconsistencies to be found in cosmology, consciousness, and the nature of matter, and their resolution by invoking occult science, see Edi D. Bilimoria, *The Snake and the Rope*.

61 *SD*-I, 'Summing Up: The Pith and Marrow of Occultism', 273.

62 *IU*-I, 'The Sacred Tetragram', 506–7.

63 *TSGLOSS*, 140.

64 Emanuel Swedenborg, *The Economy of the Animal Kingdom: Considered anatomically, physically and philosophically* (Philadelphia, Pennsylvania: Swedenborg Scientific Association, 1918).

65 —— *On the Worship and Love of God: Treating of the birth of the earth, of paradise, and of living creatures; also of the nativity, the infancy, and the love of the first-begotten, or Adam* (Boston: T. H. Carter, 1864).

66 *CW*-XII, 'Instruction No. III, B', 599–600.

67 *SD*-I, 'Explanations Concerning the Globes and the Monads', 177.

68 *CW*-X, 'Transactions of the Blavatsky Lodge, VII–VIII', 372.

69 *NPB*-10, *The Orient: Its Legacy to the West*, 'Related Entries', ¶ 10, 223, quoting from Blavatsky's esoteric instruction.

70 *IU*-I, 'The Sacred Tetragram', 507.

71 Colin MacLaurin FRS, *An Account of Sir Isaac Newton's Philosophical Discoveries, in Four Books*, published by Patrick Murdoch FRS from author's manuscript papers (3rd edn, London: printed for J. Nourse, et al. in Collection of Library of the University of Michigan, 1775), 22 <https:// ia800906.us.archive.org/8/items/anaccountsirisa00murdgoog/anaccountsirisa00murdgoog.pdf> accessed 7 May 2020. Quoted also in J. E. McGuire, *Tradition and Innovation: Newton's metaphysics of nature* (New York: Springer Science, 1995), n. 40.

72 Isaac Newton, *Principia*, ii, 'The System of the World: Rules of Reasoning in Philosophy', 398.

73 Matthew Wood, *Paracelsus and the Light of Nature* (Berkeley, California: North Atlantic Press, 2004).

74 Henry M. Pachter, *Magic Into Science: The story of Paracelsus* (New York: Henry Schuman, 1951), 86.

75 'The Emerald Tablet', *Endless Search* <https://www.endlesssearch.co.uk/philo_emerald_tablet.htm> accessed 6 December 2019.

76 Jabir ibn Hayyan and Roger Bacon, *Alchemiae Gebri Arabis philosophi solertissimi libri, cum reliquis, ut versa pagella indicabit* [Alchemiae Gebri Arabis philosophers solertissimi of the book, with the rest, as

it turned out pagella will indicate], ed. Chrysogonus Polydorus (Bern: 1545; repr. (Latin) Charleston, South Carolina: Nabu Press, 2010) <https://archive.org/details/alchemiaegebriar00jabi> accessed 7 May 2020.

77 'The Chymistry of Isaac Newton', ed. William R. Newman, June 2010 (Keynes MS 28, King's College Library, Cambridge University) <http://purl.dlib.indiana.edu/iudl/newton/ALCH00017> accessed 7 May 2020.

78 David Bohm, *Wholeness and the Implicate Order* (UK: Routledge, 1980).

79 *STA*, 'The Bembine Table of Isis', LIX.

80 Christia Mercer, *Seventeenth-Century Universal Sympathy: Stoicism, Platonism, Leibniz, and Conway* (2015) [Oxford Scholarship Online] doi:10.1093/acprof:oso/9780199928873.003.0007.

81 *STA*, 'The Bembine Table of Isis', LIX.

82 Francis Thompson, 'The Mistress of Vision' in *Complete Poems of Francis Thompson* (US: Andesite Press, 2017).

83 This is a highly abridged version extracted from *CW*-XII, 'Instruction No. 1 A', 523–4.

84 *ML*, Letter No. 44.

85 Chapter 1, in Lao Tzu, *Tao Te Ching*, trans. Bhikshu Wai-tao and Dwight Goddard (1935) <http://www.bopsecrets.org/gateway/passages/tao-te-ching.htm> accessed 12 January 2020.

86 Nicholas Goodrick-Clarke, *The Western Esoteric Traditions: A historical introduction* (New York: Oxford University Press, 2008), 19. Refer also to Antoine Faivre, 'Ancient and Medieval Sources of Modern Esoteric Movements', in *Modern Esoteric Spirituality*, 1–29.

87 Annie Besant, *A Study in Consciousness* (Adyar, Madras: Theosophical Publishing House, 1972), 9.

9 The Mystery Teachings About Man – Who, or What Am I?

Is it true that most men suffer from mistaken identity? That they are totally ignorant of the beautiful and virtuous, the aspirational and intuitive nature which is their higher self? The apathy which allows them to accept their lesser nature, their commonplace little self, must be found out for what it is. Since the person a man is most interested in is himself, why not get to know himself as he really is, not merely as he appears to be?

PAUL BRUNTON[1]

SYNOPSIS

Chapter 9 presents a condensed exposition on the nature of man from the Mystery Teachings of the West and the East, from archaic ages to the present century. These are the teachings of the Greeks and early Christians, the Egyptians, Persians, Indians, and the Americans of both continents. Contemporary Mystery Teachings are also included. The modern teachings of the Emerson era, namely, transcendentalism and the New Thought movement, warrant a further section since these ideas were fermented during the early years of the Theosophical Society and resonate closely with the perennial wisdom that was disseminated through the latter. A central feature of the Mystery Teachings is the double nature of the mind principle: why the average man is part-'God' and part-'Devil'. It is explained that from whatever corner of the globe these teachings emanate, their essential purpose is always to unfold the Inner nature of man—the various techniques, trials, and processes in the Mystery Schools are all directed towards that sole objective.

KEY WORDS: ancient mysteries, contemporary mysteries, Theosophical movement, transcendentalism, new thought, H. P. Blavatsky, Ralph Waldo Emerson, Thomas Troward, Ralph Waldo Trine, Walter Russell

Having described the Mystery Teachings in general in the previous Chapter, we now concentrate on the esoteric and occult doctrines, imparted through the Teachings, to elucidate the nature of man at all levels from the spiritual to the material.

As a prelude, let us reflect on the dynamic equilibrium, coherence, and organization of just our physical body (let alone our various subtle bodies) which has:

The indwelling spirit orchestrates the human body

- ❖ some million billion cells—far more than the stars in the Milky Way;
- ❖ moreover, of this cell population, 600 billion are dying and the same number are regenerating each day, which equals over 10 million cells per second;
- ❖ but no matter how diverse the cells, organs, and physiological system, they act as one unity, one orchestra organized by an intelligent master conductor, so to say.[2]

So, our outlook must be a balanced one and must also digest what is the very basis of our earthly existence. Needless to say, then, we owe a tremendous debt of gratitude to medical science and neuroscience, which has revealed for our common good so much of the wondrous workings of the physical body as the temple of the spirit.

Nonetheless, man has never ceased enquiring: What is *life*? What is *intelligence*? What is *force*? It is not fair, or reasonable, to assert that no answers have been forthcoming. Whereas we still have no satisfactory answer from mainstream science, physical medicine or orthodox religion on the profoundest questions about our existence, these are precisely the dilemmas to the solution of which the sages consecrated their temples of learning. But would the average modern man enveloped in his coats of materialistic skin understand the spiritual and transcendental qualities of the answers given? Be that as it may, there is a way of attainment: but not for the intelligentsia of the modern world who will never pass behind the veil which divides the seen from the unseen, the material from the spiritual, the phenomenal from the nomenal and transcendental, *except* in the age-old way appointed—the Mystery Teachings under various appellations such as theosophy, esotericism, and occultism.

Only the Mysteries can resolve unending impasses in science and religion on the enigmas of life

In posing that most unfathomable riddle of all that confronts man: *Who, or What Am I?* we are obviously not restricting man just to his physical body. However much scalpels and microscopes, X-rays, and MRI scans may reveal the incredible mechanisms of our body and the physical vehicles of consciousness, i.e., the physical material that we are *made of*, will these fabulous instruments of physical investigation open even a small chink into our inner nature to reveal the smallest vista into the greater aspects of our Being, namely, our subtle bodies and associated higher states of consciousness and mind?[3] For that inner vision we need other instruments of investigation: elevated faculties of consciousness, in contrast to finer physical instruments.

Physical instruments show details only of the physical body

The occult doctrines espoused in the Mystery Schools provide that necessary extra dimension to complement—not discard—the scientific picture. How shall we do this? Having expounded the Hermetic Axiom in the previous Chapter as the 'master rule' of occult investigation, we now trace its application in the Mystery Schools regarding man's true nature. These teachings, of every age and epoch, appear to be remarkably consistent in their various depictions about the composite nature of man. However varied and diverse the language, allegory or symbolism germane to the epoch in which they were disseminated, they have, without exception, invoked the Hermetic Axiom. Accordingly, we highlight this essential doctrine by following its thread uniting the teachings from the schools of antiquity—Western and Eastern—to the modern schools of our present epoch.

Mystery Teachings reveal man's inner nature

Collectively speaking, these Mystery Schools were not a unique system because they were based on the spiritual structure of the universe. Details about the initiation processes obviously varied according to the School in question, yet they were established from the same motives of compassion and reflected, or copied, as it were in miniature, what took place in those primordial times when events on Earth faithfully mirrored the wider pattern in the heavens.[4] What was the central purpose of all the Mystery Schools?

Purpose of the Mysteries – Unfolding Man's Inner Nature

Large gains all at once may occasionally succeed on the stock exchange, but spiritual illumination cannot be attained by trying to leap abruptly to a great height across intervening stages but instead must be won laboriously, step by step upwards, by a progressive purification and refinement of the lower nature towards a condition of perfection. The only exception to this is the arousal of *Kuṇḍalinī*, one of the Forces of Nature. But as Paul Brunton warns, 'unless the nature has been well purified, it may prove a highly dangerous way. Few are yet ready for it, and no teacher dare incur the responsibility of plunging into such a risky gamble with his pupil's health, sanity, morality, and spiritual future unless there is sufficient sexual stability and hardness of will in him.'[5] Any attempt, therefore, to force the process by artificially opening the psyche to 'other worldly influences', by resorting to abnormal physical and breathing practices or resorting to mind-altering drugs, for example, invariably leads to dire consequences (the reasons are explained in depth in Chapter 9 of Volume III). By lowering the threshold of the brain state (see the previous reference to William James in Chapter 6), drugs will only delude a man into a virtual reality illusion of enlightenment, but the Buddha or Christ consciousness is not attained through the *ayahuasca* drug experience,[i] for example, only by being *in consciousness* as a Buddha or a Christ—and that is a pretty tall order! It is therefore quite mistaken to think that spirituality can render a man either virtuous, rational or compassionate; in fact, quite the reverse: working on virtue, rationality, and compassionate service can make a man spiritual. This is the true alchemical process: the baseness of the lower nature transmuted into the nobility of the Higher Self. The Mysteries were therefore established for the purpose of unfolding the nature of man according to certain universally tested and strict rules which, when faithfully followed, elevated the human consciousness to a point where it was capable of cognizing its own constitution and thus the true purpose of its existence. The secret, or esoteric, or occult doctrine is thus all about how man's multifarious, multifaceted, and composite constitution could be most quickly and completely regenerated to the point of spiritual illumination.

Important for the aspirant to be patient

Psycho-spiritual significance of alchemy

The Mysteries of Antiquity

The chief Mystery Schools of antiquity, as described below, are those of the Greeks and Early Christians, the Egyptians and Persians, then the Indians and American Indians. What follows is a summary of the Mysteries from these worldwide Centres, based on a digest of the chief works of Manly Hall, Helena Blavatsky, plus other writers as referenced.

Greek and Early Christian Mysteries

The great Athenian philosopher Socrates maintained that the soul existed before the body and prior to its confinement therein, and was endowed with all knowledge. Moreover, he held that when the soul entered the material form it became confounded, but by

---

i This is not to decry the role of genuine shamans in nudging an earnest seeker to a higher level of consciousness. However, earlier cultures, like the aboriginals, who used mind-altering drugs for inner experiences worked within a family and social structure that provided mutual support, which is a far cry from modern Westerners who choose to go on a 'shamanic trip' without the necessary preparation or the social network to provide the foundation to sustain their experiences.

appropriate practices and virtuous living, was able to struggle free of its impediments and so awaken to, and recover, its lost knowledge.

The Bacchic and Dionysiac Rites of the Greek Mystery Schools are based on the allegory of the youthful god Bacchus (Zagreus, or Dionysos) being torn to pieces by the giant Titans, who then scatted the dismembered body of the god far and wide. Jupiter, the Father of Bacchus and the Demiurgus[ii] of the universe, beholding this crime, hurled his thunderbolts at the Titans and slew them, burning their bodies to ashes with heavenly fire. From the ashes of the Titans, which also contained a portion of the Bacchic body which the Titans had partly devoured, the human race was created. Thus the mundane life of every man was said to contain a part of the Bacchic (therefore godly) life.[iii] Accordingly then, the Rites taught that earthly man's composite nature comprised his lower nature, consisting of fragments of the giant Titans; and his higher, immortal, nature as the sacred life of the god Bacchus. So the Bacchic state signifies the unity of the rational soul in a state of self-knowledge; and the Titanic state, the diversity of the rational soul, which by virtue of being scattered, loses the consciousness of its own essential one-ness or unity.[iv] The giants accomplished the fall of Bacchus by getting him to become fascinated with his own image in a mirror, signifying engrossment in the sea of illusion (*māyā*)—the lower world fashioned by the Titans—which signals the downfall of Man. Hence, ordinary man is capable of either a Bacchic—rational—existence, or a Titanic—irrational—existence, and for the vast majority both existences in varying proportions.

Bacchic and Dionysiac Rites allegorize the composite nature of man

Apropos, given the hordes of holidaymakers these days thronging major tourist sites toting their 'selfie' sticks, are human narcissistic traits basically any different now?

In the Eleusinian Mysteries of the Greeks, the soul of man (frequently called *psyche*) is essentially a spiritual entity having its true abode in the higher realms where, free from the bondage of material forms and material concepts it is said to be truly alive and self-expressive at its level. The human, physical nature of man is likened to a tomb or bog and being a false and therefore an illusory and impermanent thing, constitutes the source of our suffering and sorrow. Indeed, Plato described the body as the sepulchre of the soul and he was referring to the ordinary human nature as well as the human form.

Eleusinian Mysteries on body and soul of man

Moving on to Plato then, what more does he teach? He also regarded man as constituted of two parts—one eternal, formed of the same essence as Absoluteness, the other mortal and corruptible, deriving its constituent parts from the 'minor created gods' (the various transformative forces and powers of nature intermediary between the divine and physical states). In his dialogue *Phaedrus*, Plato declares, 'In consequence of this divine initiation we became spectators of single and blessed visions, resident in a pure light; and were ourselves made immaculate and liberated from this surrounding garment which we call the body and to which we are now bound like an oyster to its shell.'[6]

Plato on eternal and mortal aspects of man

---

ii The original meaning was 'craftsman', or 'artisan', but gradually the word came to mean 'producer', and eventually 'creator'.

iii This explains why the Greek Mysteries warned against suicide. He who wilfully destroys himself raises his hand against the nature of Bacchus within him, since man's body is indirectly the dwelling of this god and consequently must be preserved with the greatest care.

iv Is it not a common experience that when we are distracted, our thoughts are scattered making us prone to erratic behaviour and faulty judgement concerning important life issues.

Blavatsky encapsulates the Platonic teaching succinctly: 'This is [also] the division adopted by Paul, another Initiate, who maintains that there is a psychical body which is sown in the corruptible (astral soul or body), and a *spiritual* body that is raised in incorruptible substance. Even *James* (iii. 15) corroborates the same by saying that the "wisdom" (of our lower soul) descendeth not from the above, but is terrestrial ("psychical", "demoniacal", *vide* Greek text); while the other is heavenly wisdom.'7

Saint Paul and Apostle James on spiritual and material aspects of man

All this shows that the Greeks and early Christians regarded man's nature as composite, hence requiring 'bodies' at various levels to express his entire nature from the material, via the intermediary (soul, or *psyche*) to the spiritual.

More details on the Greek exposition of man's composite nature are furnished in Volume II, Chapter 8 and the associated Table II-23 on page 179.

Egyptian Mysteries

The Greek Mystery Teachings were the offspring of the Egyptian Mystery Schools whose principal exponent was Thoth Hermes Trismegistus.v Like the *Emerald Tablet* described in Chapter 8, *The Divine Pymander* of Hermes is one of the earliest of the Hermetic writings now surviving. Consisting of seventeen fragmentary writings gathered together and assembled as one work, known as the *Corpus Hermeticum*, the second book is called *Poimandres*, or *The Vision*. It contains an exposition of Hermetic cosmogony and the secret sciences of the Egyptians regarding the nature and unfoldment of the human soul. These writings have greatly influenced the Western esoteric tradition and were considered to be of great importance during both the Renaissance and the Reformation. In fact, Newton (whose translation of the Hermetic Axiom was included earlier in Figure I-13, on page 249) laid great stress upon recovering from idolatry an unadulterated, pure, ancient doctrine, which he studied assiduously to aid his understanding of the physical world. What does Hermes teach about Man? Let us examine a brief extract from the sublime text of the *Poimandres* from the *Corpus Hermeticum* of Hermes Trismegistus:

> Before the visible universe was formed its mold was cast. This mold was called *Archetype*, and this Archetype was in the Supreme Mind long before the process of creation began. Beholding the Archetypes, the Supreme Mind became enamoured with its own thoughts; so taking the Word as a mighty hammer, It gouged out caverns in primordial space […] at the same time sowing in the newly fashioned bodies the seeds of living things […]. Then the Father—the Supreme Mind—being Light and Life, fashioned a glorious Universal Man in Its own image, not an earthy man but a Heavenly Man dwelling in the Light of God. The *Supreme Mind* loved the Man It had fashioned and delivered to Him the control of the creations and workmanships […]. The Man, looking into the depths, smiled, for He beheld a shadow upon the Earth and a likeness mirrored in the waters, which shadow and likeness were a reflection of Himself. The Man fell in love with His own shadow and desired to descend into it. Coincident with the desire, the Intelligent Thing [Man's high powers of mind and reason] united Itself with the unrea-soning image or shape [illusory form]. Nature, beholding the descent, wrapped herself about the Man whom she loved, and the two were [ever] mingled. For this reason earthy

Hermetic teachings on cosmogony and the human soul

Hermetic teachings on creation of man's composite nature: Heavenly and Earthly

---

v Identified by some with the Greek god Hermes and the Egyptian Thoth, or Tuti.

man is composite. Within him is the Sky Man, immortal and beautiful; without is Nature, mortal and destructible.[8]

There are two points especially noteworthy. First, that man, or rather 'Universal Man' was a Thought Form in 'Supreme Mind', obviously referring to the blueprint, or archetype of man, known as Adam Kadmon in the Qabbalah, meaning 'original man'. Hence the popular biblical aphorism that 'Man was made in the image of God'.[vi] This emphasizes the universal teaching that the universe and man are not matter but created by Mind. On this basis, readers should never presume that the quintessentially mental nature of the universe is a flight of fancy that only the ancients believed in. Indeed, the vast majority of scientists today are materialists, but there are numerous cases of modern scientists, of impeccable qualifications, who have upheld their conviction that it is Mind that creates matter, so to say. Readers may recall two seminal quotations in the Proem: first from Sir James Jeans that, 'The stream of human knowledge is heading towards a non-mechanical reality', and for that reason, 'The universe begins to look more like a great thought than a great machine. We […] ought rather to hail it [Mind] as the creator and governor of this realm'; and, second, from Sir Arthur Eddington that, 'The universe is of the nature of a thought or sensation in a universal Mind', and as a natural corollary, 'The frank realization that physical science is concerned with a world of shadows is one of the most significant of recent advances.'

Universe and Man are created by Supreme Mind

James Jeans and Arthur Eddington apprehended the mental, not material, nature of the universe

Secondly, in addition to the teaching on the twofold composite nature of man, we find the clear message, as in the Greek teachings (the god Bacchus fascinated with his own mirror image), that sorrow and suffering is the consequence of Immortal Man (our higher part) falling narcissistically in love with His own shadow, or image—indeed, mistaking this mirage cast in the mirror of deception for Himself (i.e., mistaking his body and personality for his true Self and thereby uniting his reasoning principle with his earthly desires)—so giving up Truth and Reality to dwell in appearances and illusions. In the further words of *The Vision*, 'Thus, suffering is the result of the Immortal Man's falling in love with His shadow and giving up reality to dwell in the darkness of illusion; for, being immortal, man has the power of the Seven Governors—also the Life, the Light, and the Word—but being mortal, he is controlled by the Rings of the Governors—Fate or Destiny.'

Downfall of Man caused by mistaking himself for himSelf, i.e. his form for his true Self

The Seven Governors are Spirits of the Planets. Here then we find the true esoteric rationale behind the *sciences* of astrology and psychology: the man who masters and rises above his lower nature can rule the influences associated with the Governors, but he who is enslaved by his desires is ruled by the Governors and hence experiences the result as his so-called inescapable fate. So again, *The Vision* counsels, 'Let the man endued with a Mind [the Eternal Teacher] mark, consider, and learn of himself, and with the power of his Mind divide himself [the Sky Man, or Immortal Self] from his not-self [the mortal self] and become a servant of Reality [the Delphic maxim that when a man truly understands himself, he understands his fellow human beings and the world]. The punishment of desire is the agony of unfulfillment […] At death the material body of man is returned to the elements from which it came, and the invisible divine man ascends to the source from whence he came.

Rationale behind astrology

----

vi The actual words in the Hebrew Bible, Genesis 1:26–28 are , 'And God said: 'Let us make man in our image/b'tsalmeinu, after our likeness/kid'muteinu […].'

The evil passes to the dwelling place of the demon, and the senses, feelings, desires, and body passions return to their source, namely the Seven Governors whose natures in the lower man destroy but in the invisible spiritual man give life.'[vii] So for example, a man prey to lust and sensuality finds himself helplessly victimised and dominated by the Venusian propensities, but conversely, he who has mastered his physical and sexual appetites can draw upon, at will, the Venusian influences of life-affirming universal love and compassion.

Readers should again refer to the implications of the Hermetic teachings, summarized towards the end of the previous Chapter, and amplified in Volume III, Chapter 5.

The Symbolism of Osiris and Isis

Another insight into man's physical, psychic, and spiritual natures comes from the symbolism attaching to the supreme God of Egypt, Osiris. As their solar deity, Osiris represents the material, life-giving aspect of solar activity, the sun symbolising the vital principle in nature. This vital principle—active, masculine—is the exact complement to the passive principle—inactive, feminine—represented by the deity under many names, notably Isis, signifying the principle of natural fecundity.[viii] For creation is the union of the dynamic interplay—the very highest form of Love—between the active principle of God and the passive principle of Nature. Yet again we see why man is a composite creature.

Osiris and Isis symbolize composite nature of Man

From the active principle—his Father—he inherits his Divine Spirit, his immortal part which, at death, rises out of the disintegrating clay of his mortal self. And from the passive principle—his Mother—he inherits his body, being that part of himself under control of the Laws of Nature (the material–maternal principle) and also his humanity, his (mortal) personality, appetites, emotions, and feelings. The Bulgarian sage Peter Deunov, invariably known by his spiritual name Beinsa Douno, also calls the feminine principle 'constructive' as it elaborates the form. Thus the god Osiris is blended into Man and esoterically is recognized as possessing four chief aspects: Osiris-Ptah as Light, being the spiritual aspect; Osiris-Horus as Mind, being the intellectual aspect; Osiris-Lunus, signifying the 'Lunar', or psychic (astral) aspect; and Osiris-Typhon, representing the Daimōnic, or physical and material, therefore turbulent and passional aspect. In these four aspects then, Osiris symbolises the dual (composite) nature of man: the cosmo–spiritual and the terrestrial, or the divine and the physical human.

Now for this reason, Osiris is rather curiously also identified as the god of the afterlife, the underworld and the dead. In this depiction He is represented with the lower part of his body enclosed in a mummy case (or enwrapped with funerary bandages). By now the meaning should be clear. Man's nature is a creation of distinct parts, only one of which incarnates in human form. Hence, the physical body was regarded as being a tomb, or sepulchre when inhabited by the unregenerate but in the case of an advanced person, a temple of the self-same incarnating Spirit. For this reason, Osiris, a symbol of the incarnating ego in this representation, was depicted with the lower half of his body mummified to indicate that he was the living spirit of man enclosed within the material form symbolised by the mummy case (see Figure III-4 in Volume III, Chapter 1 on page 12).

---

vii This dynamic process is explained in detail in Chapter 5 of Volume II.

viii Christianity metamorphosed Isis into the Virgin Mary. In the Vedic tradition She is known as Sīta, wife of the Lord Rāma.

Apis, the Egyptian bull of Memphis, was the emblem of the spiritual world within which was hidden the spiritual nature, Osiris. So the Apis further signified that the God–Mind is incarnated in the body of a beast and therefore that the physical beast form is the sacred vehicle of divinity. Accordingly, then, man's lower personality is the Apis in which Osiris incarnates, the result of the combination being the creation of Sor-apis (Serapis)—the material soul as ruler of the irrational material body and involved therein.

Physical body can be a tomb or a temple of the indwelling spirit

More details on the Egyptian exposition of man's composite nature are furnished in Volume II, Chapter 8 and the associated Table II-22 on page 173.

Persian Mysteries – Mithraism and Zarathuśtrianism

The Persian Mysteries incorporated the rites of the sun-god Mithras who has both a male and female aspect. As *Mithras*, He represents the masculine principle, being Lord of the Sun, radiant and powerful; as *Mithra*, this deity represents the feminine principle, Nature as receptive and terrestrial, the mundane universe as her symbol. As in the Osiris-Isis coupling, Mithra is fruitful and productive only when conjoined with the solar fire of Mithras. Mithras also stands for the God of Intelligence, mediating in the struggle for supremacy between Ahura-Mazda, or Ormuzd, the Spirit of Good, and Ahriman, initially a pure spirit who then rebelled against Ormuzd, being envious of his power.[ix] So when Ormuzd created the Earth, Ahriman entered into its gross elements; and whenever Ormuzd performed a good deed, Ahriman planted a seed of evil within it. Finally, when Ormuzd fashioned the human race, Ahriman became incarnate into the lower nature of man, such that in every human personality there is a constant war between the Spirit of Good and the Spirit of Evil, each struggling for control. This is precisely why the sacred books on the subject of yoga and self-mastery invariably propound their teachings in the form of a war, for example, the epics *Rāmāyaṇa* and *Bhagavad Gītā* of the ancient Indians. In each case the war depicted is entirely allegorical, used as a metaphor of the battle between the good and evil propensities within each man who has not reached full enlightenment. It is quite staggering how many otherwise intelligent people still foolishly deem the war in the Gītā to be an actual example of religious instruction. The fratricidal nature of the war further underscores the fact that the battle is between *different aspects and parts of one's own self*. External, physical wars are the outward projection of the internal war, where the principle of evil has, albeit temporarily, gained control. Again then, we find the Persian Mysteries teaching the composite nature of man divided into his higher immortal and spiritual self, and his lower mortal and material (personal) self.

Ormuzd and Ahriman symbolize struggle between good and evil propensities in each man

The essentially dualistic cult of Mithraism (i.e., Ormuzd and Ahriman as two principles co-existing in eternity) was taken to greater philosophical heights by the Persian religious founder Zarathuśtra, fondly known as the prophet of Iran. Consonant with the perennial wisdom, he taught a monistic doctrine of the One existence, unmanifest, from which the manifest issued forth. Thus, from Ahura-Mazda emanate two principles *that exist in potentiality in Him*. This concerns the dual, or twin-principled, nature of the mind: the first, *Spento-Mainyush*—the good twin; the second, *Angra-Mainyush*, or *Akem-Mainyu*—the evil twin, namely, the counteracting, or opposing principle of so-called evil. Note the twin

Spento-Mainyush and Angra-Mainyush symbolize good and evil tendencies in the mind of each man

---

ix Rudolf Steiner's anthroposophy expounds in depth the occult meaning behind Ahriman (counterbalancing Lucifer).

aspect of the two principles, both of which are, it is reiterated, subsumed in Ahura-Mazda, but were unfolded (explicated from the implicate order as the physicist–philosopher David Bohm might have put it) in order that a manifested universe (which of course includes man) might be brought into existence. Therefore we find each man's nature to be composite, part Spento-Mainyush and part Angra-Mainyush. The Zarathuśtrian sage Phiroz Mehta captures this wittily, thus:

> And there are those who say, 'Show me God and the Devil in flesh and blood and I'll believe in them.'

> Quite easily done. Look at yourself in a mirror. If you have clear-seeing eyes and a sound brain to interpret what you see, you will see both God and the Devil—and remember: Truth is not facetious!9

No independent, substanding principle of evil *per se*

This is not the place to delve further into the nature of evil, but let it be said that the wisdom–religion–philosophy of Persia as indeed of Greece, Egypt, India, and all great centres of esoteric learning, are united in affirming that there is no 'Evil One'—by whatever name we might care to call that shadow, e.g. Ahriman, Devil, Satan, Diabolos, Māra—as an identifiable, personal entity or being. Certainly there have been evil individuals and groups—we hardly need any convincing about that. In such cases it may be said that, apparently, the Satanic principle has completely overpowered and controlled the benevolent principle; nonetheless, there is no metaphysical principle of evil *per se*. However convenient for discussion purposes such a postulated entity or principle may be, the actual evil (as well as the good) resides to greater or lesser degrees in each and every human being.10 As Blavatsky elucidates: 'The ancients understood this so well that their philosophers—now followed by the Kabalists—defined evil as the lining of God or Good: *Daemon est Deus inversus*, being a very old adage'11 and a highly suggestive maxim. For as Blavatsky further clarifies: 'When the Occultist says that the "Demon is the lining of God" (evil, the reverse of the medal), he does not mean two separate actualities, but the two aspects or facets of the same Unity'12—see Endnote I-10 for more amplification. Refer also to Volume II, Chapter 5 for more elucidation on this thorny subject, including clarification on what is popularly known as 'hell'.

Only the Mystery Teachings can shed light on the unending paradox of good and evil

It therefore follows that as there is no independent Principle of Evil *per se*, there can be no real evil, as 'real' implies a substanding principle. There are evil conditions around us in proportion to the extent that there is a diminishment of the Good through our mis-use of free-will and consequent perversion of Providential *energies*. But of course the Good *per se* cannot be perverted as it is immutable and therefore cannot be changed. Moreover, 'good' and 'evil' are the words used to describe the two dualistic principles (issuing from the One). But they are unsatisfactory words, the esoteric meaning (the key) being given out in sacred texts like the Gāthās of Zarathuśtra (sacred hymns cast in the form of religious poetry). In them, we understand that the primal duality is not of good and evil, but is of spirit and matter, of reality and non-reality, of light and darkness, of construction and destruction, the two poles between and across which the universe is woven and without which no universe can exist.

Primal duality is spirit and matter: reality and non-reality; not good and evil

Incidentally, this general principle is elaborated in great detail by the artist and natural philosopher Walter Russell in the *Universal One* described towards the end of this Chapter. He speaks of the cosmic pendulum, of the gravitational and radiational principles, plus all the parallels just mentioned.

Good and evil, so-called, therefore come into existence only when man in his onward evolutionary march develops the power of *knowledge* and *choice*.[13] We see here, in the Zarathuśtrian teaching, a clear parallel with the biblical Adam and Eve story in the Garden of Eden, which, incidentally, the Catholic Church has ingeniously anthropomorphized, even at times, personified—as with the Devil (Satan), who has also suffered similar ludicrous treatment in the hands of those who mouth sermons without understanding their esoteric import. We say 'ingeniously anthropomorphized' because it could also be seen as a disingenuous ploy on the part of the ministry and priesthood for power and domination over the poor, uninformed masses by warning them that Satan would corrupt their souls, other than through blind obedience to the custodianship of the Church, whose control and dictates include, in large measure, parting with their money to overflow the Church coffers. It would not be an exaggeration to point out the Janus-faced scenario of past centuries where, on the one hand, the Church preached about the perils to mankind from the Devil; and on the other hand, kept the idea of Satan fully alive and well, since much of the Church's existence and its tremendous wealth depended on 'Him'.[14] It is amazing, though, that even today highly intelligent people attribute a literal meaning to the allegory of Adam and Eve in the Garden of Eden. However, given that we live in a world pervaded by duality, this is one side of the story. The other side involves acknowledging, with gratitude, the tremendous influence of the Church on music and art, the feeling of community amongst its congregation, and its care for the poor and the sick in body and soul.

Good and evil allegorized in biblical story of Adam and Eve in Garden of Eden

Reverting, then, to the Persian Mysteries, such consistency in the Mystery Teachings amongst geographically widely separated centres of esoteric learning is a measure of the authenticity of the doctrines they promulgate. Taking everything into account then, the teachings of the prophet of Iran again confirm the fundamentally composite nature of man on Earth. But the major destruction of priceless artefacts and sacred literature of ancient Iran is nothing short of a catastrophe for philosophy, wisdom, and scholarship;[x] for 'had not Alexander destroyed so many sacred and precious works of the Mazdeans, truth and philosophy would have been more inclined to agree with history, in bestowing upon that Greek Vandal the title of "the Great".'[15]

More details on the Persian exposition of man's composite nature are furnished in Volume II, Chapter 8 and the associated Table II-22 on page 173.

Indian Mysteries

Ancient India had, arguably, the most diverse, complex and richest of all the Mystery Schools and occult teachings that have provided the wellspring of the later Mystery-centres of Egypt and the West. What follows, therefore, is necessarily a cursory account of some features of the Indian Mystery Teachings that are relevant to the overall theme of this Chapter.

Given the highly individualistic character and independence of the Indian mind and the resultant tendency to doubt, challenge, and question everything in religion and philosophy, it is not altogether surprising that two great streams of divergent thought emerged

---

x However, in the deepest sense, nothing is ever lost as it can be recovered from the Akashic records by those few whose spiritual eminence qualifies them to access the tablets of Nature's universal memory.

from a single source: the Vedānta philosophy and the Sāṃkhya[xi] philosophy, representing the manifest tension between revelation and reason.

Sāṃkhya philosophy was propounded around the seventh or eighth century BC. It accepted the Vedas as canons of knowledge, but discarded, or ignored, many of its theories and ideas. Sāṃkhya philosophy propounded universal evolution out of root matter, or primordial nature (*prakṛti*) as the source of all manifestation, and postulated an infinite number of immortal souls (*puruṣa*). Its reputed founder was the sage Kapila, who propounded an atomic theory as part of his philosophical speculations on universal evolution, interestingly, along broadly similar lines, and during the same era, as the ancient Greek philosophers principally Democritus (*circa* 460–*circa* 370 BC), Plato, and Aristotle.

In the much older Vedic tradition, the Mysteries were approached and taught from two major standpoints as indeed was the case in all Mystery Schools, like the later schools of Greece. The Lesser Mysteries were given out openly, albeit entirely in allegorical and symbolical format. These were the Purāṇas, meaning 'belonging to olden times', now eighteen in number and containing the entire body of ancient Indian mythology. The underlying teaching of the Purāṇas concerned the general sequence and process of creation, and the forces in Nature, intelligent and semi-intelligent, disseminated in epic stories about the adventures of various male and female deities, such as the story of Kṛṣṇa (Krishna), the greatest of the Avatars. These teachings can broadly be classified into five themes:

Purāṇas teach the
creation and
forces in Nature
allegorized in epic
stories

1. cosmogony, i.e., the beginnings and 'creation' of the universe;
2. periodical renewals and destructions of universes;[16]
3. the genealogies of the gods, other divine beings, heroes and patriarchs;
4. the reigns of the various Manus (divine beings representative of the perfect Man);
5. a résumé of the history of the solar and lunar Races.

The Purāṇas were supposed to have been composed by the poet-sage Vyāsa, the author of the legendary *Mahābhārata*. In the *Bhagavad Gītā* (the crown jewel of the *Mahābhārata*), the Lord Kṛṣṇa symbolises the Christos principle that unfailingly brings man to the state of true individual perfection by teaching the human intelligence (represented by Arjuna) how to acknowledge, aspire to, and activate its highest and innermost principle.

By contrast, the sacred knowledge in the Vedas, meaning 'divine knowledge' (compiled by the sage Veda-Vyāsa, but whose origin is in the mists of antiquity) was accessible only to the initiated Brahmins for their individual spiritual training and instruction. The Vedas are four in number and concerned with the deepest aspects of esotericism and occult philosophy. They represent the best Sanskrit compendium of ancient sacred laws and customs of Divine origin and remotest antiquity. The Upaniṣads (Upanishads), usually reckoned today as one hundred and fifty in number, are part of the Vedic cycle constituting its esoteric doctrine—the Greater Mysteries. 'Upaniṣad' is a compound Sanskrit term signifying 'following upon or according to the teachings which were received when we were sitting down'. The implication here of course is that of *chelas* (disciples) sitting at the feet of their Master who taught them the secret wisdom orally, in private, and in forms

---

xi Also written *Sāṅkhya*.

and manner of exposition that were later written down and promulgated according to those teachings and after that style. Thus, the topics treated are highly transcendental, recondite, and abstruse. The Vedānta (perhaps the noblest of the six Indian schools of philosophy) is a mystic system of philosophy that was developed from the efforts of generations of sages to interpret the secret meaning of the Upaniṣads. 'Vedānta' is a compound Sanskrit word meaning 'the End (or Completion) of the Veda'—that is to say, instruction in the final and most perfect exposition of the meaning of the Vedic tenets. Arguably, the best example of Vedantic doctrine is the Advaita Vedānta, or Non-dualistic philosophical thought espoused by the Avatar Śrī Śaṅkarācārya (Shankaracharya). From the above we can trace a noble current of mysticism and esoteric philosophy from the Upaniṣads, Vedānta, and other lofty systems of Indian philosophy—all arising from, and rooted in, the parent Vedas.

Possibly the best known source of the secret wisdom accessible to the Brahmin initiates is what is known as the 'Laws of Manu', a work of Divine origin and immense antiquity comprising 2,684 verses, divided into twelve chapters. Its reputed author is Manu, the mythical survivor of the Flood and father of the human race, the primitive teacher of sacred rites, Sūtras (sacred writings), and laws. Esoterically, however, Manu represents the Unknowable, Eternal, and Self-existent Being who initiated Creation by forming the elements and thereby scattered the darkness of Chaos. Notwithstanding the now well-known Creation myths, little is known, even to this day, about the detailed processes and stages of initiation because the most profound teachings of the Indian Mysteries were transmitted by word of mouth alone from master to pupil. Nonetheless, we may glean some general features about the Lesser and the Greater Mysteries as outlined below.

Manu, the progenitor of the human race

A concise description of the Indian Mystery Schools from the occult perspective of the classical writings of modern Theosophy is by Grace Knoche (1909–2006), musician, artist, linguist, and leading member of the Theosophical Society in America.[17] From this, and numerous referenced sources included in it, we learn that the ancient Indians had various names for their disciples as they passed from one degree of initiation to another.[18] For instance, in one Mystery School the candidates received the names of the ten Avatars of Viṣṇu (Vishnu). The names were those of fish, animals, and deities as appropriate emblems to signify the various human and divine attributes achieved by the candidate. The first degree neophyte was termed *Matsya*, lit. 'fish', since he was yet low in the scale of spiritual mastery. The second was *Kūrma*, 'tortoise', being one step higher in evolutionary development. The third degree was called *Varāha*, 'boar', a further advance in individualization; while the fourth was termed *Narasiṁha*, lit. 'man-lion'. This fourth stage marked the turning point between the preliminary degrees of the Lesser Mysteries and the advanced degrees of the Greater Mysteries. This title of man-lion points to the choice demanded of the aspirant between the dominance of his animal soul qualities or the supremacy henceforth of his truly human attributes. In passing, note that the Mystery Schools of different cultures have their own names for depicting the nature of animal-man. For instance, in the Minoan culture of Crete, the Minotaur was the monster with the head of a bull and a body of a man, denoting the raging and unbridled passions of spiritually unregenerate man which have to be vanquished by the domination and governance of the mind (symbolised by the hero Theseus). Another symbol of the latent powers in man is the Centaur of Greek mythology as described in Chapter 3 of Volume III.

Ascending degrees of initiation in Indian Mystery Schools

Success in the fourth degree, then, insured entrance into the fifth degree called *Vāmana*, 'dwarf', in which the candidate assumed the robes of occult humanhood, though such humanhood was as yet infantile compared to full mastery. *Paraśurāma*, lit. 'Rama with an axe', was the name of the sixth-degree neophyte, suggestive of one capable of hewing his way, with equanimity, through the worlds of both spirit and matter. In the seventh degree the disciple became fully humanized, receiving the name of *Rāma*, hero of the *Rāmāyaṇa*, the shorter of the two great epics of India (the longer being the *Mahābhārata*).

While the degrees usually enumerated in the Mysteries were seven in number, hints have been given of three higher degrees than the seventh. But these would be so esoteric that only the most spiritualized of humanity could comprehend and hence undertake these divine initiations. (It could be argued that these initiations correspond to the activation of the *cākras* (*chakras*) as outlined in Chapter 9 of Volume III.)

In barest outline then, in the last three degrees, the eighth was called *Kṛṣṇa*, the Avatāra whose death ushered in the Kali Yuga (Iron Age) some five thousand years ago; the ninth was called *Buddha*, whose renunciation of *nirvāṇa* brought light and peace to a sorrowing world; and the final tenth is called *Kalkin*, or *Kalki*, the 'White-Horse' Avatāra who is yet to come. As noted in the Viṣṇu Purāṇa (Bk IV, ch. xxiv), He is destined to appear at the end of the Kali Yuga, seated on a white horse with a drawn sword blazing like a comet for the eradication of the wicked, the renewal of creation, and the restoration of purity. In ancient symbology the horse also symbolized the sun, hence the tenth Avatāra will apparently come riding the steed of solar glory to usher in the true New Age clothed with the sun of spiritual illumination. Incidentally, we need hardly warn readers to spurn anyone who loudly proclaims himself to be a messiah or an avatar of this or that deity. The list of those purporting to be so is not short![19]

Pythagoras and Paracelsus were instructed in India

Lastly in this section, we hark back to our earlier remark in Chapter 7 about Pythagoras having acquired his great learning from the initiated Brahmins during his philosophical wanderings in India. Another legendary figure who secured his esoteric knowledge, especially on occult pneumatology (the branch of occult philosophy and science dealing with spiritual substance), during his sojourn in India was Paracelsus, the Renaissance prince of Alchemists and Hermetic philosophers and true possessor of the Royal Secret.[20] In fact, as previously intimated, the Greeks and earlier Egyptians also garnered their knowledge from the Oriental sages of ancient India.[21]

More details on the Indian exposition of man's composite nature are furnished in Volume II, Chapter 8 and the associated Table II-20 and Table II-21 on pages 169 and 171.

American Mysteries

Parallels between Hiawatha and President Woodrow Wilson

Whereas the name of Hiawatha (1525–1595), the outstanding hero of North American Indian folklore is familiar to many people from school day tales, the Mystery Teachings and diverse culture of the American Indians seems to be a somewhat neglected area amongst students of esoteric philosophy. Less well known about Hiawatha is that he anticipated, by several centuries, the cherished dream of President Woodrow Wilson (1856–1924) of a League of Nations. After many setbacks, Hiawatha, a chief of the Iroquois succeeded in uniting the five great nations of the Iroquois into the 'League of the Five Nations', the purpose being to abolish war by substituting councils of arbitration.

Every idealist, sage or great reformer, irrespective of time or race, has met with fierce opposition from those who preferred to preserve the status quo (see Chapter 7), and Hiawatha's struggles were no exception.

We now touch upon the Mysteries of the Americas and later on underscore their commonality with other Mystery-centres of the world. For convenience, the narrative is divided into North, Central, and South America; however, this is done purely for descriptive convenience and the underlying philosophies apply in a general sense to both American continents as a whole. However, from a historical and cultural standpoint the case is otherwise. It is important to distinguish between the completely different goals of the colonization of North America and the conquest of Central and South America. In the former, the European immigrants who went to North America were first the Huguenots (French Protestants) in the middle sixteenth century, followed in the seventeenth century by the British. Their intention was to build a new, free country based, in the latter case, on the principles of Rosicrucianism and Freemasonry. Although they were not free of blame for having taken the native lands by force and disbanded or annihilated many tribes, yet their primary aim was to colonize the continent and seek new opportunities for prosperity and religious freedom. In the latter case, the Spaniards discovered the wealth of the Inca Empire in the 1520s and went to Central and South America with the express purpose of plundering the Inca Empire of its wealth, ransacking the natural resources, and subjugating the populations by crushing their cultural and religious traditions.[22] The conquest took place under the guise of religious conversion as the Spanish Inquisition regarded the religious beliefs and practices of the Inca, Maya, and Aztec peoples as profane and blasphemous to Catholicism.

Colonization of North America versus plundering of Central and South America

North American Mysteries

This section is based mainly on the exposition by Manly Hall[23] and other sources as referenced. The Mysteries of North America were the outcome of the nature of its peoples, innately drawn to symbolism and mystical philosophy. Like the aboriginal peoples of Australia, Africa, and elsewhere, the red man's native instincts about elemental creatures resulted from his intimate contact with nature. Thus, the whole sky, rivers, and forests were inhabited with myriads of superphysical and invisible beings. His mystical philosophy had much in common with other world cultures, as we shall see shortly. The Indians of North America considered the Earth (the Great Mother) to be an intermediate plane, bounded above by a heavenly sphere (the dwelling place of the Great Spirit) and below by a dark and terrifying subterranean world (the abode of shadows and of sub-mundane powers). They divided the interval between the surface of Earth and heaven into various strata, one consisting of clouds, another of the paths of the heavenly bodies, and so on. The underworld was similarly divided. Those creatures capable of functioning in two or more elements were considered as messengers between the spirits of these various planes. The abode of the dead was presumed to be in a distant place: in the heavens above, the Earth below, the distant corners of the world, or across wide seas. Sometimes a river flowed between the world of the dead and that of the living. Significantly, the number four was especially sacred to the Indian, being a key to the creation of the universe. The legendary narratives of the strange adventures of intrepid heroes who, while in the physical body, penetrated the realms of the dead prove beyond question the presence of Mystery cults

Subdivisions of underworld, Earth, and heavens

among the Indigenous Peoples of North America. Wherever the Mysteries were established they were recognized as the philosophic equivalents of death, for those passing through the rituals experienced all after-death conditions while still in the physical body. (A similar experience by Paul Brunton is described towards the close of this Chapter.) At the consummation of the ritual the initiate actually gained the ability to pass in and out of his physical body at will. This is the philosophic foundation for the allegories of adventures in the Indian Shadow Land, or World of Ghosts.

Figure I-14 The Great Serpent Mound

Picture Credit: Terry/Wikimedia Commons/Serpent Mound, Peebles, Ohio 01.jpg

The American Indians recognized the difference between the ghost and the actual soul of a dead person, a knowledge restricted to initiates of the Mysteries. They also understood the principles of an archetypal sphere wherein exists the patterns of all forms manifesting on the Earth plane. The theory of 'Group', or 'Elder Souls' having supervision over the animal species is also shared by them. The red man's belief in guardian spirits would certainly have met with the approval of Paracelsus. Moreover, as Hall avers, 'who can doubt the presence of the secret doctrine in the Americas when he gazes upon the great serpent mound in Adams County, Ohio, where the huge reptile is represented as disgorging the Egg of Existence?'[24] Figure I-14 shows an aerial picture of this 1,348-foot-long, three-foot-high prehistoric effigy mound on a plateau of the Serpent Mound crater along Ohio Brush Creek.

Central American Mysteries

The *Popol Vuh* is the story of creation according to the Quiché (K'iche') Maya of the region known today as Guatemala, the Central American country south of Mexico. No other sacred book, according to Hall, sets forth so completely as the *Popol Vuh* the initiatory rituals of a great school of mystical philosophy. This volume alone is sufficient to establish incontestably the philosophical excellence of the red race.[25] The *Popul Vuh* was discovered in the seventeenth century by the Dominican priest Father Ximinez (1666–*circa* 1729) who designated the volume 'The National Book'. The title, however, is variously translated, each version providing different insights into its enigmatic characteristic. A literal version is probably 'The Book of the Mat', because of the woven mats the people would sit on to hear the work recited at the council house (council of arbitration). According to the Scottish poet, folklorist, and occult scholar Lewis Spence (1874–1955) the correct title is 'The Collection of Written Leaves', *Popol* signifying the 'prepared bark' and *Vuh*, 'paper', or 'book' from the verb *uoch*, to write.

In his articles on the *Popol Vuh* appearing in the fifteenth volume of *Lucifer* (the journal published by Helena Blavatsky on philosophical, theosophical, scientific, and religious topics), the American author, publisher, and Theosophist James Morgan Pryse (1859–1942) approached the subject from the standpoint of the mystic, calling this work 'The Book of the Azure Veil'. 'The Red "Children of the Sun" ' writes Pryse, 'do not worship the One God. For them that One God is absolutely impersonal, and all the Forces emanated from that One God are personal.' *Note that this is the true mystic and esoteric philosophy of all ages. It is the exact reverse of the popular Western conception of a personal (even anthropomorphized) God and impersonal forces in nature working according to mindless mechanical laws—the cause of no end of confusion and strife in orthodox religion and establishment science.*

The Xibalbian Mysteries are found in the second book of the *Popol Vuh*, which is largely devoted to the initiatory rituals of the Quiché nation. These ceremonials are of seminal importance to students of Masonic symbolism and mystical philosophy, since they establish, beyond doubt, the existence of ancient and divinely instituted Mystery schools on the American Continent. The actual ordeals of the Xibalbian Mysteries were seven in number. There would be little value in outlining all of them as details can be found in quality reference books.[xii] However, as with the initiatory trials in any Mystery School, the Xibalbian processes were intended to test, to the very limit, the character and mettle of a candidate before he could be entrusted with the innermost secrets of nature. An example of just one of the ordeals: Hunahpu and Xbalanque (the heroes of the second book of the *Popul Vuh*), are depicted undergoing the torment of the Bat House. Camazotz, the Lord of the Bats, emerging suddenly from the gloom, strikes with his great sword at the intrepid invaders of his domain. The test here is the realization that the animal soul of man is likened to a bat because, like this creature, it is blinded and can only be restored to sight by the light of the spiritual, or philosophic sun—the spiritual soul. (The animal soul, and spiritual soul are fully defined and explained in Volume II, Chapters 2 and 3.)

Xibalbian Mysteries

Merit of candidate tested to the extreme

Then, as time passed, we learn from the available native records the abundant evidence that the later civilizations of Central and South America degenerated into the Left-Hand Path, and then were hopelessly dominated by the black arts of their priestcraft—a similar trend that can clearly be perceived elsewhere, such as in the latter days of the Egyptian dynasty, and in India as in the *Rāmāyaṇa* epic about the titanic war and eventual victory by the divine prince Rāma over Rāvana, king of the demonic beings, the Rākṣasas (Rakshasas). The abominable sanguinary rites practised by many of the Central American Indians possibly represent remnants of the later Atlantean perversion of the ancient sun Mysteries. According to the secret tradition, it was during the later Atlantean epoch that black magic and sorcery overpowered the esoteric schools, resulting in the bloody sacrificial rites and gruesome idolatry which ultimately overthrew the Atlantean empire and even penetrated the Aryan world,[xiii] large fragments of which may be discerned even to this day—recall the Nazi atrocities and the recent abominations of the Taliban and the Islamic State of Iraq and Syria (having nought to do with Islam, *per se*) epitomizing the degradation of occultism and religion at their worst. But what of the keys to the Mysteries of Xibalba? They will shortly be summarized. Meanwhile, we move southwards.

Degeneration of Mysteries into sorcery and black magic

---

xii For example by Albert Soria, Kenneth S. Guthrie, Brother Philip (George Hunt Williamson), Heinrich Arnold Krumm-Heller, Augustus Le Plongeon, and many others, extracts from whose writings are referenced in this section.

xiii Many details and copious references are scattered throughout *The Secret Doctrine* (especially Volume II: 'Anthropogenesis') by H. P. Blavatsky and *The Secret Teachings of All Ages* by Manly P. Hall.

South American Mysteries

It is well said that the history of a nation is written by its conquerors. This certainly applies to Latin American history written under the censorship of the Spanish Inquisition, which in itself spanned nearly four centuries from 1478 to 1834. Much of the recorded information about the great Inca, Maya, and Aztec civilisations and empires was therefore distorted. However, as periodically intimated in this work, the means to recover the true history of any civilisation is through its myths, legends, and chronicles. And, in addition, regarding the history of the Incas, the fragmentary documents left behind by the Spanish invaders in the sixteenth century and the tales of the mestizos (persons of mixed racial or ethnic ancestry, in this case the descendants of the union of a Spaniard with a Peruvian native). The history of the civilizations of the Andes therefore needs to be rewritten based on information available from the studies of archæology, anthropology, and, primarily, mythology. We find scattered amongst these sources hints and traces of information about the real dimension of the pre-Inca and Inca cosmovision, or worldview.[26] There appears to be a persistent theory that the Incas embodied the final phases of a highly evolved culture which started around the eleventh century.[27]

Various sources of Inca Mysteries

In a comprehensive and well referenced paper *The Cosmovision of the Incas*[28] used as the basis of this section and much of the following, the contemporary Latin-American sociologist, social theorist, and cultural critic Dr Albert Soria informs us that a highly organized state religion existed in the Inca Empire. The Inca priests resided at important shrines and temples. The official priesthood maintained temples and convents in the main cities of Tahuantinsuyo, the name of the Inca Empire in Quechuan. The Sun god, known as 'Inti' in the Quechuan language, was the most important deity and is usually portrayed as a gold disc with a human face from which rays and flames extended. The second most important deity was the Moon, 'Mama Killa', who was Inti's sister and consort, represented as a silver disc with human features. Their offspring were the stars and thunder. Then came the Earth Mother, 'Pachamama' (from *Pacha*, Earth and *mama*, Mother). She was regarded as a living entity and mother of all earthly life, plus the personification of fertility and growth.

Inca temples and deities

The common characteristic in the mythologies among the Inca, Maya, and Aztec civilizations is their accounts of supernatural beings coming out of water—a lake or sea. These are, of course, the Elementals associated with the Water Element in esotericism. The rituals of these peoples indicate that they worshipped the Sun. This was particularly the case with the Incas, who considered themselves Children of the Sun; and even to this day, the Inti Raymi festival is celebrated on 21 June[xiv]—the winter solstice in the southern hemisphere—in Cusco, Peru in front of the site of Koricancha, the Temple of the Sun, which was ransacked of its gold and then demolished by the Spaniards. Cusco was the capital of the empire and Koricancha, meaning 'Place of Gold' in Quechuan, was the main temple of the Incas. The great Solar Disc was displayed in the shrine of this temple but was removed ahead of the Spanish invaders and secreted away for safe keeping to the Monastery of the Seven Rays deep within the remote cordillera (parallel mountain ranges with intervening plateaux) of the Andes.[29] There, the Inca high priests

Inca Temple of the Sun

---

xiv The day was moved to 24 June, Catholicism being the fundamental religion in the Spanish-speaking countries.

who escaped to this remote village secretly kept safe the ancient knowledge and wisdom of the Solar Brotherhood. The Organization of American States booklet *The Incas* provides some details of the Solar Disc: 'The chroniclers, who saw the Temple of the Sun before it was completely stripped of its treasurers by the Spanish conquerors, described its interior as literally a mine of gold. From the western wall of the temple, the face of the Sun God looked down from a massive golden disc, thickly encrusted with emeralds and precious stones; the rays of the morning sun irradiated directly on the great plaque, lighting up the interior with dazzling brilliance.'[30] But when, and how, did the Solar Disc arrive in Peru in the first place before it was suspended in the shrine of Koricancha?

The American metaphysical author George Hunt Williamson (1926–1986, pen name 'Brother Philip') writes about the legend of a highly evolved civilization that was destroyed by a series of cataclysms around 11,500 years ago. (There is considerable scientific evidence for worldwide cataclysms during this time.[31]) Survivors of these disasters migrated to different parts of the world, some moving to the Andean Cordillera through the Eastern Islands of the Pacific. The legend further relates that an initiate by the name of Amaru Muru—from whose name 'America' is derived—brought the Solar Disc with him and established a highly spiritual society on the shores of Lake Titicaca at Puno in Peru. This was the Brotherhood of the Seven Rays which had become the leading force in the spiritual lives of the Incas, who learned about the esoteric significance and use of the Disc from ancient records left by the pre-Incas. 'The Inca Emperor at the time was a divine Mystic or Saint, and he made a pilgrimage to the Monastery at Lake Titicaca, and there Aramu-Muru [Amaru Muru], as Spiritual Head or Abbot of the Brotherhood, gave the Disc to the Emperor.'[32]

How the Solar Disc arrived in Peru

Serge Raynaud de la Ferrière (1916–1962), the French initiatic philosopher and scholar on religion, cosmobiology, medicine, and hermetic science, appeared to be acquainted with the Andean mystical brotherhood and their Mystery-centre. Writing in *The Great Messages* about an esoteric fraternity hidden in the Peruvian Andes, he maintained that Inca spirituality was highly evolved. According to him, the Andean Cordillera has a special regenerative energy for the Americas such as Tibet used to have, and possibly still does, for Asia. He refers to the safety of an old Inca temple, a Mystery-centre in the Andean Plateaux as a 'sacred place where the profane have never come, in spite of the different organized expeditions.'[33] The existence of a hidden monastery in the Andes is endorsed by several other writers like Mark Amaru Pinkham in *The Return of the Serpents of Wisdom*, explicitly affirming that this hidden monastery is the headquarters of the Brotherhood of the Seven Rays.[34] Serge Raynaud de la Ferrière along with his disciple, the Japanese born Mexican philosopher David Ferriz de Olivares (1921–1992) and a few others, believed that in the same way that Tibet and India were once the focus for pilgrims in search of enlightenment, the Andes is now entrusted with this function in the coming age.[35] Hence, nowadays, different mystical and esoteric groups make their pilgrimages to the Andes and to Urubamba Valley for spiritual renewal. An opinion similar to that of Serge Raynaud de la Ferrière is affirmed by the American spiritualist Earlyne Chaney (1916–1997), spiritual leader of the esoteric group *Astara* in *Lost Empire of the Gods*: 'The old Peruvian said that in these lost inner-world cities, hidden behind the cordilleras of the Andes, dwell these emissaries from an ancient civilized race.'[36] Finally, in evidence of the Mysteries of South America we mention the case of

Hidden location of Andean Mystery-centres

the German doctor, Rosicrucian, and occultist Heinrich Arnold Krumm-Heller (1876–1949), who founded a traditional Hermetic order, the *Fraternitas Rosicruciana Antiqua* (the Brotherhood of the Ancient Rosy Cross), in Mexico in 1927 and created and promoted branches of this society in several South American countries, including Brazil. A member of the Theosophical Society in Paris, he was also a German naval intelligence agent during the Mexican Revolution and World War I. A prolific writer, he published twenty-five esoteric books, novelettes, history books, biographies, as well as countless articles in his magazine *Rosa Cruz* and similar publications. Krum-Heller openly claimed to have been initiated into the secret wisdom of the Andes (Peru) by an esoteric fraternity.[37]

A Closing Note on the Mysteries of Antiquity

The universality and self-consistency of the *philosophia perennis* and its teachings was mentioned in the Proem on pages xxxviii–xli; and indeed, one of the imperatives of this work is to justify our claims with examples from diverse cultures and ages. Appropriately, then, having just outlined the American Indian Mysteries, we use them as the basis for comparison with other Mysteries of the West and the East, before moving on to comparisons of a more general nature.

Stratification of underworld, Earth, and heavens common to all Mystery traditions

The Mysteries of the North American Indian had much in common with the mystical philosophy of other world cultures. Their view of the Earth as an intermediate plane, bounded above by a heavenly sphere and below by a subterranean world, was similar to the cosmovision of the early Scandinavians. Like the Chaldeans, the interval between the surface of the Earth and heaven was divided into various strata; and like the Greeks, the underworld was similarly divided. The river that flowed between the world of the dead and that of the living, paralleled the Egyptian, Greek, and Christian theologies. Their understanding of archetypes as universal patterns of all pre-existing forms that manifested on Earth was in common with the Platonists. Significantly, like the veneration accorded the *tetrad* by the Pythagoreans, who held it to be a fitting symbol of the Creator, the number four was sacred to the American Indians because the Great Spirit was supposed to have created His universe in a square frame. The square in this context has nothing to do with literal geometrical proportions but is a philosophical symbol when considering earth as an *element* and not as a *body*. Thus, the American Indians, like the Brahmins, Egyptians, and Greeks always referred to its four corners although they were perfectly aware that planet Earth itself was, geometrically speaking, spherical.

Parallels of Mayan Mysteries with Egyptian, Greek, Indian and Christian Mysteries

In the classic volume *Sacred Mysteries among the Mayas and the Quichés* the French–American photographer, archaeologist, and antiquarian Augustus Le Plongeon (1825–1908) compared the mythology and spiritual belief systems of the Mayans and those of other cultures, such as the ancient Egyptians, Indians, Chaldeans, and on to the Christians. He illustrates how entirely human many sacred mysteries are, and just how closely bonded people and communities are—no matter how far apart. He writes about the Mysteries of Xibalba: 'Do they not seem an exact counterpart of what happened in a milder form at the initiation into the Eleusinian mysteries? [*sic*] and also the greater mysteries of Egypt, from which these were copied? Does not the recital of what the

candidates to the mysteries in Xibalba were required to know, before being admitted ***
[*sic*] call to mind the wonderful similar feats said to be performed by the Mahatmas, the
Brothers in India, and of several of the passages of the Book of Daniel, who had been
initiated to the mysteries of the Chaldeans or Magi which, according to [the Athenian
poet of mythological subjects] Eubulus [450–350 BC] were divided into three classes or
genera, the highest being the most learned?'[38]

An English translation of the *Popol Vuh* by the eclectic Scottish philosopher and writer
Kenneth S. Guthrie (1871–1940) appeared in *The Word* Magazine beginning in October
1905 (Vol. 11, No. 1) and contained a valuable commentary. In his introductory notes to
the *Popol Vuh*, Dr Guthrie presented a number of important parallels between this sacred
book of the Quichés and the sacred writings of other great civilizations. In the tests
through which Hunahpu and Xbalanque are forced to pass he finds analogies with the
signs of the zodiac as employed in the Mysteries of the Egyptians, Chaldeans, and Greeks.
In 'his effort to identify Xibalba with the ancient continent of Atlantis', writes Manly Hall,
his astonishing conclusion is that, 'He sees in the twelve princes of Xibalba the rulers of
the Atlantean empire, and in the destruction of these princes by the magic of Hunahpu
and Xbalanque an allegorical depiction of the tragic end of Atlantis. To the initiated,
however, it is evident that Atlantis is simply a symbolic figure in which is set forth the
mystery of origins.'[39]

Parallel teachings in sacred books worldwide

The French writer, ethnographer, historian, and archæologist Abbé Charles-Étienne
Brasseur de Bourbourg (1814–1874) was a specialist in Mesoamerican studies. His writings, publications, and recovery of historical documents contributed much to knowledge
of the languages of the region, its history, and culture, particularly of the Maya and Aztec
civilizations. In 1861 he published a significant work: a French translation of the *Popol
Vuh*.[40] He also produced a grammar of the K'iche' (Quiché) language and an essay on
Central American mythology.[41] Brasseur de Bourbourg was first attracted to the study of
religious parallelisms in the *Popol Vuh* by the fact that the temple, together with the black
stone which it contained, was named the 'Caabaha', a name astonishingly similar to that
of the 'Temple', or 'Caaba', which contains the sacred black stone of Islam.

Analogies between Mayan, Aztec and Islamic religious traditions

The exploits of Hunahpu and Xbalanque take place before the actual creation of the
human race and therefore are to be considered essentially as spiritual mysteries. Xibalba
doubtless signifies the inferior universe of Chaldean and Pythagorean philosophy; and
the princes of Xibalba are the twelve Governors (Cosmocreators, or lesser Spiritual
Prototypes) of the lower universe.

Creation of human race and main human centres of consciousness

The descent of Hunahpu and Xbalanque into the subterranean kingdom of Xibalba by
crossing over the rivers on bridges made from their blowguns has a subtle analogy to the
descent of the spiritual nature of man into the physical body through certain superphysical
channels that may be likened to the blowguns or tubes. The musical instrument known
as the *sabarcan* is also an appropriate emblem of the spinal cord and the (psycho-spiritual)
power resident within its tiny central opening. To that end (the descent of spiritual nature
of man into the physical body), and concerned primarily with the problems of mystical
anatomy, James Morgan Pryse relates the various symbols described in the *Popol Vuh* to
the occult centres of consciousness in the human body. (These centres are elaborated in
Chapters 3 and 9 of Volume III.) Accordingly, he sees in the pineal gland, and in Hunahpu
and Xbalanque, the dual electric current directed along the spinal column.

That the Quichés possessed the keys to the mystery of regeneration is evident from an analysis of the symbols appearing upon the images of their priests and gods. In Vol. II of the Anales del Museo Nacional de México is reproduced the head of an image generally considered to represent Quetzalcoatl (the Feathered–Serpent deity of ancient Mesoamerican culture). The sculpturing is distinctly Oriental in character and on the crown of the head appear both the thousand-petaled sunburst of spiritual illumination and the serpent of the liberated spinal fire. The Hindu *cākra*, *Sahasrāra*, is unmistakable and it frequently appears in the religious art of the three Americas. One of the carved monoliths of Central America is adorned with the heads of two elephants with their drivers. No such animals have existed in the Western hemisphere since prehistoric times and it is evident that the carvings are the result of contact with the distant continent of Asia. Among the Mysteries of the Central American Indians is a remarkable doctrine concerning the consecrated mantles or, as they were called in Europe, magic capes. Because their glory was fatal to mortal vision, the gods, when appearing to the initiated priests, robed themselves in these mantles.

Spiritual links between Mystery-centres in the Americas, Europe, and Asia

In *The Cosmovision of the Incas* Albert Soria argues that esoteric writings suggest there was a spiritual link between the Incas and the Western Mystery Tradition—indeed, one that may still exist.[42] Among these orders are the Alpha and Omega, the Order of Melchizedek, and the Order of the Essenes, as well as, in South America, the Brotherhood of the Seven Rays, and the Solar Brotherhood located in Urubamba Valley, the Sacred Valley of the Incas, near Cusco in Peru. Regarding the connection between the Incas and the Orders comprising the Great White Brotherhood dispersed all over the world (see Chapter 7) it would appear that there was some sort of contact between the mystical organizations of Europe and the secret societies of the Andes. A remarkable hint is found in a manifesto of the authentic Rosicrucian Order of Christian Rosenkreutz from Germany. In the *Confessio Fraternitatis* (1616)—written during the time when South America was in its early stages of bloody colonisation and the power of the Spanish Inquisition immense—appears this incredible statement: 'Were it not excellent you dwell in one place, that neither the people which dwell beyond the River Ganges in the Indies could Hide anything, nor those which in Peru might be able to keep secret their counsels from thee?'[43] The clue to understanding the Rosicrucian pronouncement comes from the American occultist and Qabbalist Paul Foster Case (1884–1954) when he wrote that the *Confessio* 'was published by the European branch of the worldwide occult society we call the Inner School. Note that it refers to those "beyond the … Ganges" and "those in Peru". Here is a hint that the anony-mous writers who published the *Confessio* in 1616 were in communication with the Himalayan Brotherhood "beyond the … Ganges", and with the strong [mystical] [*sic*] centre, located in the Andes, which had been in contact with both the Asiatic and the European groups since long before Columbus sailed to find the Indies.'[44]

Rosicrucian contact with Himalayan Brotherhood

It is not difficult to see in the stars and thunder—the offspring of the Sun god Inti and the Moon god Mama Killa of the Incas—the creation of the universe of stars and planets, not from a primeval 'Big Bang', but more philosophically, from the eternal interplay of Consciousness and its Activity—Spirit and its polarity, Matter. Moreover, the Inca desig-nation of gold to the Sun and silver to the Moon has obvious parallels with European alchemy and also similarities with the Osiris-Isis polarity of the Egyptians. Pachamama, the Inca Earth Mother, has similarities with the goddess Isis of the Egyptians, and Sīta, wife of the Lord Rāma, of the Indians.

Finally, in this brief comparative review of the worldwide Mystery Teachings, the most authoritative accounts come from Blavatsky. In her various writings she provides copious and well referenced details showing how the spiritual tradition of the Inca culture was related to the Great White Brotherhood. The following extract, illustrating the self-consistency of the (mythologically narrated) wisdom-teachings (obviously stated highly allegorically) of the Indian Brahmins, the Egyptians, and the Incas, is all that can reasonably be offered at present:

> The Incas, judged by their exclusive privileges, power, and 'infallibility', are the antipodal counterpart of the Brahmanical caste of India. Like the latter, the Incas claimed direct descent from Deity, which, as in the case of the Sûryavansá dynasty of India, was the Sun. According to the sole but general tradition, there was a time when the whole of the population of the now New World was broken up into independent, warring, and barbarian tribes. At last, the 'Highest' deity—the Sun—took pity upon them, and, in order to rescue the people from ignorance, sent down upon earth, to teach them, his two children Manco Capac and his sister and wife, Mama Oella Huaca—the counterparts, again, of the Egyptian Osiris, and his sister and wife, Isis, as well as of the several Hindu gods and demi-gods and their wives. These two made their appearance on a beautiful island in Lake Titicaca […] and thence proceeded northward to Cuzco, later on the capital of the Incas, where they at once began to disseminate civilization. […] As the direct descendants of the Sun, they were exclusively the high priests of the state religion, and at the same time emperors and the highest statesmen in the land; in virtue of which, they, again like the Brahmans, arrogated to themselves a divine superiority over the ordinary mortals, thus founding like the 'twice-born' an exclusive and aristocratic caste—the Inca race.[45]

One has but to transcend the limitations of dry academic scholarship to apprehend the striking similarities between the teachings of the Intic Churincuna in the South American Andes with the Egyptians of north-eastern Africa, the Greeks throughout the Hellenistic period, the Rosicrucians in Europe, and the Mahātmas (Masters) of Asia. So it is evident that the universal, esoteric and mystical tradition, from its primeval origins in the mists of antiquity, has spread out to fecundate Mystery-centres around the world, principally in Asia, Egypt, Greece, Europe, and the Americas.

Inca, Indian, and Egyptian wisdom—the outpouring from the Great White Brotherhood

Very little of the actual details is known—rather, has been revealed—about the mystical Orders that reportedly dwell in the fastness of the Himalayas and the Andes or in other remote regions of the world. This is entirely as it should be, for authentic spiritual societies have no need for marketing, self-promotion or public recognition. Their teachings are generally orally transmitted to qualified and genuine seekers and, apparently, the first contact is usually made on levels that are non-physical (astral). That is the way to contact such as the True and Invisible Rosicrucian Order in Europe, the mystical Order of the Andes or the Mahātmas of India. Paul Foster Case writes truly when he states that the Order is 'a state of mind [namely, a state of *consciousness*]'; one may not join it by applying for membership, paying fees or going through ceremonies.[46] In point of fact, it is said that the contact is actually made the other way round. No one can make contact with the Order; members of the Order contact the candidate when he is ready, in accordance with the initiatic tradition: 'When the disciple is ready the master appears.'

How contact with the mystical Orders is attained

Here, the writer feels obliged to reproduce and pass on to readers the following warning from Blavatsky, which he feels should be taken in earnest by all seekers, however sincere they may be, but who may, over-enthusiastically, rush headlong into territory 'where angels fear to tread':

Blavatsky's warning to over enthusiastic seekers

> Magic is a dual power: nothing is easier than to turn it into Sorcery; *an evil thought suffices for it.* Therefore while theoretical Occultism is harmless, and may do good, practical Magic, or the fruits of the Tree of Life and Knowledge, or otherwise the 'Science of Good and Evil,' is fraught with dangers and perils. For the study of theoretical Occultism there are, no doubt, a number of works that may be read with profit, besides such books as the *Finer Forces of Nature*, etc., the *Zohar, Sēpher-Yetzīrāh, The Book of Enoch*, Franck's *Kabalah*, and many Hermetic treatises. These are scarce in European languages, but works in Latin by the mediæval Philosophers, generally known as Alchemists and Rosicrucians, are plentiful. *But even the perusal of these may prove dangerous for the unguided student* [emphasis added]. If approached without the right key to them, and if the student is unfit, owing to mental incapacity, for Magic, and is thus unable to discern the Right from the Left Path, *let him take our advice and leave this study alone; he will only bring on himself and on his family unexpected woes and sorrows* [emphasis added], never suspecting whence they come, nor what are the powers awakened by his mind being bent on them. Works for advanced students are many, but these can be placed at the disposal of only sworn or 'pledged' chelas (disciples), those who have pronounced the everbinding oath, and who are, therefore, helped and protected. For all other purposes, wellintentioned as such works may be, they can only mislead the unwary and guide them imperceptibly to Black Magic or Sorcery—if to nothing worse.[47]

Newton's experience with the arcane teachings

It is highly significant that Newton, who expended gargantuan time and energy studying the 'works in Latin by the mediæval Philosophers, generally known as Alchemists and Rosicrucians', had a nervous breakdown in mid-life at age fifty-one because of, in the opinion of the writer, 'the powers awakened by his mind being bent on them.'[48] That he made a full recovery can only be attributed, again according to the writer, to his deeply religious nature and chaste life, his tremendous mental discipline, and massive will power.

Timeless Truths are always enrobed

In concluding, then, this major exposition on the ancient Mysteries, what is so utterly perplexing to the literal-minded, matter-of-fact intellectualist, but so completely natural to the mystic and esoteric philosopher whose mind is not clouded by materialism, is simply this: allegory and fable, myth and mythology, symbols and metaphors are the various outer (exoteric) veils in which the *philosophia perennis*—the esoteric wisdom, the Secret Doctrine—is ever enveloped. Just as the pearl is concealed within the oyster, such magic robes conceal the hallowed books of divine inspiration such as the Bible, Virgil's *Aeneid*, Ovid's *Metamorphoses*, Dante's *Divina Commedia*, the *Confessio Fraternitatis*, the *Mahābhārata* and *Rāmāyaṇa* of India, the *Popol Vuh* of the Quichés—deep within whose folds sit the gods of Eternal Wisdom.

Contemporary Mystery Teachings – The Theosophical Movement

We mentioned in Chapter 7 the location of modern centres of Mystery Teachings, emphasizing that they are needed now more than ever due to the present turbulent world situation. How have these centres promulgated the *philosophia perennis* in an updated format to answer to modern needs for spiritual sustenance? There are, apparently, three principal inter-related distributions of this esoteric life-flow from the Shamballic heart-centre through the Lesser and Greater Mysteries.[49]

The first, as the American scholar and esoteric philosopher Gottfried de Purucker informs us, comprise the Lesser Mysteries that are now 'largely replaced by the different activities of the Theosophical Movement which itself is exoteric as a Movement'.[50] This point is taken up by the American John Algeo (1930–2019) Professor Emeritus of English at the University of Georgia, a Senior Freemason, and former Vice President of the Theosophical Society. He states that whereas the Theosophical Society works within the (Western) Mystery tradition, it is not a mystery organization as such, as it lacks the formality and structures pertaining to the latter. The study of its principal tenets is a form of *Jñāna* Yoga (Yoga of the Mind), which is the path of yoga best suited to the Western student. Furthermore, no similar organization makes such supreme demands on its members on all levels, not least of all, intellectually. Blavatsky did not mince her words on this score. 'Theosophy', she said, 'is for those who can think, or for those who can drive themselves to think, not mental sluggards.' 'Dumskulls!' used to be her name for the average student.[51] Even a cursory look at the massive and erudite doctrines will swiftly endorse her remark. However, as she stressed in no uncertain terms, one should never imagine that the teachings in her monumental book, *The Secret Doctrine* are meant to give any such final verdict on existence, but to *lead towards the truth*.

Relation of the Theosophical Society to the 'Lesser' Mysteries

Notwithstanding this, the worldwide teachings set out in her book are laid out in breathtaking depth and detail but there is no directive on what to think, how to feel, and how to act. What is clearly stated however, is the goal—Self-realization, to discover who we truly are—and the overriding imperative—respect for the unity of all life. Theosophists are thrown entirely on their own resources to work this out independently for themselves through their own study, meditation, and service, plus whatever help or guidance they may obtain from the teachings on the means to attain that goal.[xv] On that score, many Theosophists, even senior members of the Society, it has to be admitted, have occasionally succumbed to the pull of their lower proclivities for not having heeded sufficiently the dire warning given in the teachings that attention directed towards the hidden powers in nature and man can stoke the sensual nature, which, if not stabilized by the appropriate disciplinary practices, can run amok.[52] 'Let sleeping dogs lie' is an old proverb containing a world of occult meaning that needs to be taken seriously by students of the Mysteries.

Self-reliance and enormous demands made on Theosophists

Far more carefully concealed because of the weight of matter eclipsing the world-consciousness, that is to say, because of excessive materialism in science and philosophy blinding humanity to spiritual insights, are the Greater Mysteries comprising the Esoteric Section of the Theosophical Society and the still more recondite Inner Group Instructions of the Esoteric Section (and other independent centres). Even though virtually all of these teachings are now publicly available, members at the time (including Annie Besant) were bound by a solemn pledge of conduct due to the gravity of what was imparted and the attendant dangers of their misuse in wrong hands.[53] A small selection of these teachings relevant to the theme of this work is provided in Volume III, Chapter 7. But note that there are no grounds for assuming that the Greater and Lesser Mysteries are the sole

Relation of the Esoteric Section of the Theosophical Society to the 'Greater' Mysteries

---

xv Communicated in a lecture, entitled 'Mysteries: Ancient and Modern', given to the Theosophical Society in England on 31st July 1996 by former Vice President of the Theosophical Society John Algeo.

prerogative of the Theosophical (or Anthroposophical) movements. They undoubtedly do subsist in unrelated or offshoot movements that have propounded similar doctrines and ideals through their leaders, books, and teachings (though perhaps not with the breadth and profundity of the principal esoteric centres of learning).

Spiritual centres of all nations

The second 'distribution centre' is through the spiritual centres of the nations acting as organic focal points for the circulation of spiritual influences, since all countries are in magnetic and sympathetic vibration with Śambhala (Shamballa). Thus every country has its own secret spiritual protectors, who, as a body, form a true esoteric centre. It cannot be too strongly emphasized that these national Occult Guardians do not meddle in political affairs. As Purucker states, their work is 'purely spiritual, moral, intellectual, and wholly benevolent, and indeed universal, and is a silent guide to the intuitive minds of the different races.'[54] As the sage Phiroz Mehta eloquently puts it:

Spiritual, not earthly, Utopia the only motive of all Great Teachers

> Not one of the Great Teachers allowed this Truth to be soiled by the lure of establishing any earthly Utopia, or his life-energy to be wasted in inventing techniques and systems for dealing with the muddlement and evil of the world's politics, economics and unregenerate everyday life at their own level. Each of them saw with unerring insight that man the world over is himself the prolific spawner of ubiquitous ugliness and suffering, and that there is only one way to redeem the world situation: the way of purity and truth, wisdom and love; the way of the unselfed, of the transformed man.[55]

Finally, the third channel of esoteric work is one of the most fascinating, albeit least recognized. It is that of preserving the knowledge from age to age. Purucker says: 'There are actually groups whose sole business is forming occult centres of Initiation, preparing of students for esoteric work in the world, and for the safeguarding of priceless treasures, the heirlooms of the human race, treasures both intellectual and material.'[56]

Principal esoteric nerve centres in five countries

Furthermore, according to Purucker, the chief of these veiled centres—with their parental home in Śambhala—has branches in Syria, Mexico, Egypt, the United States, and Europe, each one 'subordinate to the mother-group of the Occult Hierarchy in Śambhala.'[57] It might seem incongruous at first sight that a country like Syria, currently so woefully war-torn, would have an esoteric centre of spirituality. But on reflection this must be so, for as we have said earlier, it is precisely the darkness of ignorance and stupidity that calls forth a compensating centre of truth and illumination as an indispensable agency. And in any case, some of the world's greatest illuminators were born in ancient Syria—Pythagoras and Jesus, to name but two. As seen in the treatise *Anacalypsis* by the religious historian Godfrey Higgins: 'The first striking circumstance in which the history of Pythagoras agrees with the history of Jesus is, that they were natives of nearly the same country; the former being born at Sidon, the latter at Bethlehem, both in [ancient] Syria.'[58]

It appears, then, that all that is of essential spiritual value is preserved in the secret archives of the planet, for the generations of seers are not wasteful, nor are the grand systems of philosophy and religion lost in the darkness of receding ages. As Blavatsky avers:

Pearls of wisdom are never lost

> There are, scattered throughout the world, a handful of thoughtful and solitary students, who pass their lives in obscurity, far from the rumors of the world, studying the great problems of the physical and spiritual universes. They have their secret records in which are preserved the fruits of the scholastic labors of the long line of recluses whose successors they are. The knowledge of their early ancestors, the sages of India, Babylonia, Nineveh, and the imperial Thebes; the legends and traditions commented upon by the

masters of Solon, Pythagoras and Plato in the marble halls of Heliopolis and Sais; traditions which, in their day, already seemed to hardly glimmer from behind the foggy curtain of the past—all this, and much more, is recorded on indestructible parchment, and passed with jealous care from one adept to another.[59]

Someday, worthy explorers will recover the lost keys, the Mystery Teachings, and the secrets of the human race such as are allegedly concealed in the secret chambers of the Great Pyramid. As spoken (telepathically) by one of the Guardian spirits of the Great Pyramid, as recorded by Paul Brunton:

> In this ancient fane lies the lost record of the early races of man and of the Covenant which they made with their Creator through the first of His great prophets. Know, too, that chosen men were brought here of old to be shown this Covenant that they might return to their fellows and keep the great secret alive.[60]

Secret records hidden in the Great Pyramid

When will this happen? Not by man's whim or fancy, but at the appointed hour, the hour when an awakened intuition reveals the light of perennial truths: a light always bright but clouded by the leaden weight of selfishness and materiality until the latter are finally sloughed off.

The Issue of Śambhala

As expounded by the international exponent of Vedic philosophy, the Hindu–American David Frawley (*b*.1950), honoured by the President of India with the Padma Bhushan, the third highest civilian award granted by the Government of India for 'distinguished service of a high order to the nation':

> According to the Tibetan Buddhists, there was an earlier Buddhist kingdom in Central Asia from which their teaching derives, called Shamballa, which appears to have been in the Tarim basin, northwest of Tibet […]. This earlier Buddhist culture was, by Tibetan accounts, also a culture in which [an earlier, original version of] Sanskrit, the 'language of the gods', was spoken.[61]

Here, according to the most ancient traditions, lived those great Intelligences (*Kumāras*) who are the real Guides of our planetary life as a whole, keeping watch over the evolution of the various kingdoms of our planetary nature, seen and unseen—not just mankind. These Intelligences were known in antiquity as 'Lhas', from which, apparently, the Islamic god-name 'Allah' is derived. Moreover, the name Śambhala is itself an agglutinative compound derived from either T'schamba-Lha or Skambha-Lha. According to occult sources, these same Intelligences are those who have, several aeons ago, passed beyond the range of human existence into the superhuman realm known as 'Planetary Spirits'. The same high sources inform us that there was a time, several millions of years ago, when at least some of the Shamballic inhabitants took on physical bodies as their outer vestures and moved openly among the prototypal humanity of the time (the Third, or Lemurian Root Race) in order to assist with the nurturing of the full human type.[62, 63] This was at a time when, apparently, an earlier equivalent of Śambhala existed in the area of what is now central South America—see the earlier section on the Mysteries of the Americas and refer also to the accounts by Alice Bailey (1880–1949), the prominent English Theosophist and prolific esoteric writer who founded the Lucis Trust and the Arcane School in the 1920s.[64]

Shamballic impulse to the early human race

Once the full individualization of self-conscious man had been achieved, the Śambhala location moved to the other side of the world, to await and assist the development of the next great racial types—the Fourth, or Atlantean Root Race, and the Fifth, or Aryan Root Race. The latter, also known as the Indo-Caucasians, is the racial type of the vast majority of present day humanity. At some intermediary stage, the objectively visible land of Śambhala and its inhabitants, transferred to a higher state of being, which, to ordinary mortal sight, is invisible. And it is for this reason that modern travellers or archaeologists have found no physical or objective trace of it. This sphere of operation in unseen realms of the Shamballic guardianship and evolutionary guidance is confirmed in the cryptic writings of occult fraternities such as the Rosicrucians—see the numerous references to this scattered through the pages of Manly Hall's *The Secret Teachings of All Ages* and the references quoted therein.

Śambhala, once objective now invisible on higher planes

In the same way as a family or corporation, a kingdom or an empire has its organizational structure, Śambhala is organized along four chief areas of activity with regard to the three superior (unseen) Kumāras governing the higher Kingdoms of our planetary Nature:

Inner governance of the world

- ❖ SEVENTH KUMĀRA: governing the Mineral Kingdom and Element of Earth (via the Devas)

- ❖ SIXTH KUMĀRA: governing the Plant Kingdom and Element of Water (via the Devas)

- ❖ FIFTH KUMĀRA: governing the Animal Kingdom and Element of Air (via the Devas)

- ❖ FOURTH (SANAT) KUMĀRA: governing the Human Kingdom via the Adept Hierarchy concerning man's Higher Principles; and Element of Fire (via the Devas) concerning man's terrestrial nature.[65]

Related Nineteenth Century Spiritual Teachings

In this section we outline the chief tenets of New Thought and its precursor, Transcendentalism. Whilst not in the sublime category of the Mystery teachings, these philosophic-religious nineteenth century movements in the United States more or less prepared the esoteric groundwork and paved the way for the emergence of the complex occult doctrines promulgated through the Western occult tradition in the nineteenth century, like the Hermetic Order of the Golden Dawn,[xvi] and the worldwide Theosophical Society founded also in the United States in the late nineteenth century.

Exponents of Transcendentalism and New Thought in America

We then summarize the teachings of arguably the greatest Transcendentalist whose ideas strongly influenced New Thought and later generations of thinkers and philosophers— Ralph Waldo Emerson. Finally, we sketch the main ideas of later exponents of New Thought like Thomas Troward, Ralph Waldo Trine, and Walter Russell.

By synchronicity, these latter-day nineteenth century teachings also appeared on the American continent and it is a matter of pure speculation whether they were in any way subliminally influenced by the Mystery Schools of the red man just described. To trace

---

xvi The British occultist MacGregor Mathers (1854–1918) was a principal founder.

such a link would however be a useful subject of research because, if established, it would provide further substantiation to that already adduced about the diversity of the worldwide schools of esoteric philosophy being tributaries of the primordial mystery teachings.

Transcendentalism

Transcendentalism was a major American intellectual movement and inspired succeeding generations of American intellectuals and literary notables.[66] (However, it was certainly not the first of its kind. For example, as the French occult author and ceremonial magician Éliphas Lévi (1810–1875) has noted, the Italian visionary mystic Comte di Cagliostro (1743–1795) was believed to have been an emissary of the Knights Templar, a late Middle Age society in Europe with strong transcendentalist tenets.[67]) The movement in America directly influenced the growing movement of 'Mental Sciences' of the mid-nineteenth century, which later became known as the 'New Thought movement' of which Emerson is widely regarded as its philosophical and intellectual father.[68]

The aim of Transcendentalists was to base their religion and philosophy on transcendental principles, i.e., principles drawn from the inner spiritual and mental essence of the person and not based on, therefore not contradictable by, physical experience. One can discern three principal influences that gave birth to the movement: first, as an upshot to the biblical criticisms of the German philosophers and theologians Gottfried von Herder (1744–1803) and Friedrich Daniel Ernst Schleiermacher (1768–1834), and the scepticism of the Scottish philosopher and historian David Hume (1711–1776); second, German and especially English Romanticism; and third, the mystical spiritualism of Emanuel Swedenborg along with the strong bearing of Indian sacred literature.[69] The American Arthur Versluis (b.1959) professor of American Thought and Language at Michigan State University detailed the immense impact that the Euro-American discovery of Asian religions had not only on European Romanticism but, above all, on American Transcendentalism. Regarding the latter, he argued that the discovery of the *Bhagavad Gītā*, the Vedas, the Upaniṣads, and other world scriptures by the Transcendentalists, was critical in the entire movement, pivotal not only for the well-known figures like Emerson and the American essayist, poet, and philosopher Henry David Thoreau (1817–1862), but also for lesser known figures like the English writer, literary critic, poet, and essayist Samuel Johnson, often referred to as Dr Johnson (1709–1784), and William Rounsville Alger (1822–1905) the Unitarian minister whose writings were important to the development of comparative religious studies. Versluis explicitly states, 'That Transcendentalism emerged out of this new knowledge of the world's religious traditions I have no doubt.'[70] Thoreau in *Walden* spoke of the debt that Transcendentalists owed to Indian religions directly.[71] It is highly significant that American Transcendentalism was inspired by many of the same august sources as was modern Theosophy, namely, Eastern and Western religions, esotericism, spiritual science, and universal ethics.

Influences on Transcendentalism

New Thought

The 'New Thought' (sometimes known as 'Higher Thought') movement was, and still is, a spiritual movement with an emphasis on a mind-healing that originated in the United

States in the early nineteenth century (1830s).[72] Note that in England the term 'Higher Thought' was preferred at first, and this name was chosen for the Higher Thought Centre, the first organization of its kind in England. This name did not however represent a change in point of view, and the movement in England has been similar to the movement elsewhere. It originated from the overall milieu of transcendentalism and therefore has similar religious and philosophical ideals and precepts. New Thought was based on religious and metaphysical ideas and in a general sense, like the Transcendentalist movement in the United States—it bears repeating—prepared the ground (directly or indirectly) for the profound doctrines promulgated through the Theosophical Society. The influence of the New Thought movement survives to this day in the form of a loosely allied group of spiritual and religious denominations, writers, and philosophers, not only in the United States, but also in the United Kingdom, Europe, Asia, Africa, and Australia. Although their diversity of views and life styles are difficult to describe because of their variety, one can still discern a common creed concerning metaphysics, positive thinking, the law of attraction, healing, the life force, creative visualization, and personal power. So the reason for including the movement at this juncture is to demonstrate that teachings concerning man's relationship with deity, cosmos, and nature are not confined to the Mystery Schools of antiquity or their modern versions, like the Theosophical or Anthroposophical movements, but also to related and parallel movements that have propounded similar doctrines and ideals through their leaders, lectures, journals, and books (albeit not with the breadth and profundity of the principal esoteric centres of learning).

The origins of New Thought (born out of the earlier Transcendentalist movement as just stated) may also be traced to the romanticism and idealism of the nineteenth century combined with a growing dissatisfaction with scientific materialism and empiricism; also a reaction to the religious scepticism of the seventeenth and eighteenth centuries. Phineas Quimby (1802–1866), the American spiritual teacher, magnetizer, and mesmerist is usually cited as the earliest promoter of the movement. He developed his concepts of mental and spiritual healing and health based on the view that illness is a matter of the mind. His influence may be seen in the writings of the woman Mark Twain thought was the 'most interesting that ever lived': Mary Baker Eddy (1821–1910), Christian religious reformer and founder of the religious denomination known as Christian Science. Although she is supposed to have retracted acknowledgment of dependence on her teacher, Quimby's influence was, however, readily acknowledged by others like the American Methodist and later Swedenborgian minister Warren F. Evans (1817–1889) who was leader of a movement based on the teachings of Swedenborg.

The tenets of New Thought may easily be traced to the transcendentalist philosophical ideals drawn from the West and the East: to the Idealism of Platonism which holds that the realm of ideas is more real than that of matter; to Swedenborgianism, especially the view that the material realm is one of effects whose causes are spiritual and whose purpose is divine; to Hegelianism, especially those ideas concerning the external world, mental phenomena, and the nervous organism as the meeting ground of the body and the mind; to the concept and system of transcendental philosophy of the German Idealist Friedrich Schelling (1775–1854); to Orientalism, involving spiritual teachings of Eastern philosophies and religions, especially Vedānta; and, particularly, to the transcendentalism of the nineteenth century American philosopher and poet Ralph Waldo Emerson, whose

New Thought a
progeny of
Transcendentalism
based on eternal
principles

Early influences
on New Thought
movement

Christian Science
and New Thought

Influences on
New Thought

teachings are summarised below in the context of the theme of this work. New Thought is essentially positive and optimistic about life and its outcomes. But it should be noted that the movement does not maintain any dogma or just one belief system; moreover, apart from individual proponents like Baker Eddy who opposed medical science, New Thought in general is not opposed to any form of science. Furthermore, truth is viewed as a matter of continuing revelation, and no one leader or institution can have the final word on the nature of truth. All this resonates well with the perennial philosophy as outlined earlier (see Chapter 8).

In 1916 the International New Thought Alliance (formed in 1914) agreed upon the following purpose that embraces some central ideas of most New Thought groups:

> To teach the Infinitude of the Supreme One; the Divinity of Man and his Infinite Possibilities through the creative power of constructive thinking and obedience to the voice of the indwelling Presence which is our source of Inspiration, Power, Health and Prosperity.[73, 74]

New Thought is an international movement

Then in 1917, at the St. Louis (Missouri) Congress, the alliance adopted a 'Declaration of Principles'. It was modified in 1919 and was published in *New Thought* until revised in the 1950s. (Interestingly, the English mystic and author Henry Thomas Hamblin (1873–1958) was at the forefront of New Thought, or Right Thinking, the parallel movement in England. He started a magazine 'The Science of Thought Review', first published in October 1921. It was aptly renamed 'New Vision', which should come as no surprise since Hamblin was once an optician.)

We can see that there is not even a whiff of materialist concepts in these principles. On the contrary, they emphasize the primarily spiritual character of the universe, the immanence of God ('the Supreme One'), hence, the divine nature of man ('the Divinity of Man'), the immediate availability of God's Power to man, and that sin, human disorders, and human disease are basically the consequences of incorrect thinking. Moreover, according to New Thought, all human beings can live in oneness with God in love, truth, peace, health, and plenty. But unlike Quimby, New Thought leaders have increasingly stressed material prosperity as one result of New Thought. Concerning religious affiliation, many groups and individuals happen to be Christians, but there are no established patterns of worship and there is no stipulation to profess Christianity or any other faith. In fact, New Thought implies a sort of monism, or view of the oneness of the world, and possesses strong Gnostic undertones.

Spiritual tenets of New Thought

In summary, New Thought promotes the idea that the Divine is omniscient and omnipresent, transcendent and immanent in everyone and everything. Moreover it holds that Infinite Intelligence is ubiquitous, Spirit is the totality of real things, true human selfhood is divine, Divine Thought is a force for good, sickness originates in the mind, and right thinking has a healing effect. It is open to all religions, since spiritual healing and strength of mind and body are available to all who follow, live their lives, and marshal their thoughts according to nature's universal laws.

The Debasement of New Thought

It is patently clear, then, that the New Thought movement is not a panacea for satiating personal desires. Many individuals and groups have, regrettably, seen it that way; so the core of the teachings about the indissoluble bond between Divine Power and man has degenerated into the popular modern egoistical and highly commercial, self-glorification culture of trying to get just what one desires—invariably power, sensual gratification, riches, and celebrity status—simply by wishfully 'thinking the right way' or by meaningless, mechanical chanting of sacred words, but with no attendant self-effort, arduous discipline or stern character analysis. The 'gospel of the prosperity preachers' now in America is deplorable. Moreover, one in five Americans are estimated to follow a prosperity gospel church led by maestros of high-tech religious marketing—like Joel Osteen, whose personal fortune is estimated at $60 million and his mansion, with three elevators, a pool, and parking for twenty cars, valued at $10.7 million;[75] and Jesse Duplantis, the American televangelist who is asking his followers to help buy his fourth private jet—a Falcon 7X tri-jet for $54m—because God had told him to buy one.[76] Latest in this line of televangelists is Paula White, spiritual advisor to former President Donald Trump, an appointment she calls an 'assignment from God'. Claiming that the Lord wanted her to go on national television, she practices the school of thought known as 'prosperity theology'. Clearly, Ms White is duty bound to prove that her particular brand of theology works in her own life and this she has seemingly done by manifesting 'God's gift' of a multimillion-dollar home in a gated community and, of course, a private jet.[77] Perhaps the prosperity theology has failed to acknowledge the salutary lesson, recounted in the Gospel of Matthew, where Jesus reprimands hypocrites for saying one thing and doing another. To drive the point home, below is the writer's abridged version:

> Whatever they [the Pharisees] tell you to observe, *that* observe and do, but do not do according to their works; for they say, and do not do. For they bind heavy burdens, hard to bear, and lay *them* on men's shoulders; but they *themselves* will not move them with one of their fingers. But all their works they do to be seen by men. They love the best places at feasts, the best seats in the synagogues, greetings in the marketplaces, and to be called by men, 'Rabbi, Rabbi'. And whoever exalts himself will be humbled, and he who humbles himself will be exalted.

> Woe to you, scribes and Pharisees, hypocrites! For you cleanse the outside of the cup and dish, but inside they are full of extortion and self-indulgence. Blind Pharisee, first cleanse the inside of the cup and dish, that the outside of them may be clean also.

> Woe to you, scribes and Pharisees, hypocrites! For you are like whitewashed tombs which indeed appear beautiful outwardly, but inside are full of dead *men's* bones and all uncleanness. Even so you also outwardly appear righteous to men, but inside you are full of hypocrisy and lawlessness.[78]

It is true to say that in certain quarters of American society, where Mammon reigns supreme, the 'Almighty dollar' has become the idol, and limitless economic growth the mantra, underpinning the society as a whole. Fuelled by advertising and television commercials, it is not difficult to see how material opulence has become the counterfeit coin of spiritual riches. According to a 2015 report on average daily TV viewing in countries around the world, users in the United States lead the world in daily TV watching time with some 274 minutes, the equivalent of more than four and a half hours or nearly twenty per cent of the day.[79] In 2009, an average hour of monitored prime-time US network TV programming comprised over 36 per cent (almost 22 minutes) of commercial messages, according to TNS Media Intelligence.[80] Now the figure is closer to 50 percent (30 minutes).[81] This is the ideal environment for charismatic imposters to supercharge their egos and fatten their wallets—like bloodthirsty vampires—feeding on the gullibility of their followers mesmerized by the mind numbing effects of hype, a barrage of advertising, and massive overdoses of daily television viewing containing stories extolling celebrity glamour. Surely this utterly meretricious religion, this worshipping at the altar of materialism is the true 'opiate of the masses'?

> **A spiritual vacuum either in individuals or in society is all too easily filled with materialistic or sensual cravings—generally both.**

Regrettably also many self-styled gurus, several of them in what is known as the 'New Age movement', have tarnished their image by hitching their stars to this glamorous 'quick fix' bandwagon.[82] However, many New Age groups are genuinely concerned (if somewhat naïvely on occasions) with service towards human welfare and planetary ecology, so the New Age movement should not be tarnished as a whole due to some of its superficial and misguided proponents.

Let us revert to New Thought in the charge of its worthy proponents.

Ralph Waldo Emerson – The Over-Soul

We first turn to Ralph Waldo Emerson of whom his contemporary, the American poet, essayist, and journalist Walt Whitman (1819–1892) said: 'I was simmering, simmering, simmering. Emerson brought me to a boil.'[83] Emerson was the cardinal exponent of Transcendentalism and New Thought; and a supreme example also of Higher Thought in the best sense of the term. But what should be our basis of evaluation? What is the foundation upon which we may validate and authenticate his ideas and teachings that are germane to the overall theme of this work? The straightforward answer is this: by setting them against the ethical precepts and universal doctrines of the Eternal Wisdom of the ages—of all ages—known by terms such as *philosophia perennis*, or *theosophia* (refer to the Proem, page xxxviii f. and see Figure I-6 in Chapter 6, page 167). To reiterate, the arcane wisdom is not *a* philosophy, and neither is it *a* religion, nor *a* science; rather, it is the *root-source* from which all philosophies, religions, and sciences have sprung. It is not the result of one man's speculation, but the synthesis and integration of the knowledge of the ages which has been accumulated, recorded, and preserved by a long line of adepts. It is a complete *whole*, and admits of no comparison with anything less than itself. Moreover, it also reconciles the various and apparently contradictory systems of science, religion, and philosophy, and shows some of them to be necessarily correct, since they are corroborated in the arcane records. All that can be done in the case of a single philosopher, like Emerson, is to examine the fruit of his mind in order to see if it was grown in the Garden of Wisdom.

Yardstick for evaluating Emerson's philosophy

To continue with the simile, there have been several Gardeners who have tended the Tree of Knowledge growing in the midst of this Garden. The occultists and theosophists know of Them as Adepts or Mahātmas. How does Emerson refer to Them?

Emerson's reverence for 'great spiritual Lords'

> I cannot recite the laws of the intellect without remembering that lofty and sequestered class of men who have been its prophets and oracles, the high priesthood of pure reason, the Trismegisti, the expounders of the principles of thought from age to age. This band of grandees, Hermes, Heraclitus, Empedocles, Plato, Plotinus, Olympiodorus, Proclus, Synesius, and the rest, have somewhat so vast in their logic, so primary in their thinking, that it seems antecedent to all the ordinary distinctions of rhetoric and literature, and to

be at once poetry, and music, and dancing, and astronomy, and mathematics. The truth and grandeur of their thought is proved by its scope and applicability, for it commands the entire schedule and inventory of things for its illustration.[84]

Comparing
Emerson's
thoughts with
the Three
Fundamental
Propositions in
*The Secret
Doctrine*

In the teachings of these 'great spiritual lords', as Emerson refers to Them,[85] (regarding whom the current crop of American multi-millionaire preachers are quite likely to be clueless), certain fundamental ideas appear as the axis around which his entire system of philosophical thought revolves. We may compare them with what has been epitomized in a few pages of Blavatsky's *The Secret Doctrine* as the 'Three Fundamental Propositions, or Axioms' (see Chapter 8). Emerson's entire output, but especially his three celebrated and widely read works: *Compensation, Self-Reliance*, and *The Over-Soul* strongly presage these Propositions. (Note: *The Secret Doctrine* was published six years after Emerson died in 1882.) Accordingly, we shall appraise Emerson's teaching against the backdrop of the Three Fundamental Propositions in order to demonstrate the essentially metaphysical and esoteric tenor of his thoughts about the universe and man.

The *First Fundamental Proposition*, treating of that Unity behind all diversity, is the affirmation of What IS; it is not a hypothesis, theory, or what is fashionably known as a 'model of reality'. Emerson realized the philosophical necessity of such a proposition, but finding no satisfactory expression of it in the religious or scientific teachings of his own day and race, he sought for it within the philosophy of the ancient Aryans. The term 'Aryan' derives from Arya, meaning holy and truthful. The Aryans were that august race of Rishis, or Adepts, who intoned the sacred literature of ancient India (the Vedas, Upaniṣads, Brahmanas, and Purāṇas). Here we must impress upon readers that 'Aryan' has absolutely nothing in common with the monstrous distortions that the twisted Nazi racial ideology gave to this sacred term—refer back to Chapter 7.

This extract from the Kāṭhaka Upaniṣad outlines the method Emerson pursued in his search for the 'Causeless Cause' behind all causes:

> Than the powers, the impulses are higher;
> Than the impulses, Mind is higher;
> Than Mind, Soul is higher; than Soul, the Great Self.
> Than the Great Self, the Unmanifest is higher;
> Than the Unmanifest, Spirit is higher;
> This is the end, the supreme way.[86]

Emerson's Westernized version of this Eastern teaching is found in his essay on Plato which expresses the movement from 'without' to the deepest centre 'within'. He writes:

> The mind is urged to ask for one Cause of many effects;
> then for the cause of that;
> and again the cause, diving still into the profound;
> self-assured that it shall arrive at an Absolute and sufficient one;
> a One that shall be All.[87]

Emerson realizes
the limits, and
limitations, of
thought

In that 'potency' (for want of a better term) he says, the last fact beyond which analysis cannot go, all things find their common origin. Being above the power of analysis, beyond the range of thought, and outside the faculty of speech, Emerson was too wise to attempt to describe it. Instead he points towards what cannot be defined in words or known by the mind, what is generally known as the apophatic approach, or *via negativa*, which is an approach to describe what is unutterable and indescribable by negation. Hence to speak of the ineffability of God ('the Divine Dark') only in terms of what cannot be said, owing to the absolute unknowability of God—thus, the 'apophatic', or 'negative' approach. It stands in contrast to the cataphatic approach, or *via positiva*, the path of affirmation that ascribes to the Divine the highest attributes that one can conceive.

Emerson realized that when we try to describe God in words, both language and thought desert us since the ineffable essence refuses to be recorded. As the American Unitarian minister, writer, and lecturer George Willis Cooke (1848–1923) states in his excellent biography of Emerson, 'When we try to define God, however, we cannot; he is beyond all definition, because he includes all definitions. Of that ineffable essence which we call Spirit […] he that thinks most [meaning of course, deeply contemplates, not left-brain ratiocinates] will say least.'[88] Emerson realized that, 'Of this pure nature every man is at some time sensible. Language cannot paint it with colours. It is too subtle. It is undefinable, unmeasurable, but we know that it pervades and contains us.'[89] (Interestingly, religions have dealt with the ineffability of God in two ways: the Hindu scriptures, for example, refer to God simply as 'THAT', alluding to apophatic theology; whereas others, like Islam, speak of the ninety-nine Names of God or, in the case of Zarathuśtrianism (Zoroastrianism), the one hundred and one Names of God—ninety nine and one hundred and one being, of course, purely figurative ways of alluding to the infinite potentiality of the Divine, which obviously is the way of cataphatic theology.

Emerson realizes when thought must be transcended

'What is the aboriginal Self, on which a universal reliance may be grounded?' asks Emerson.[90] This aboriginal Self, that single source from which all human beings emerged, is none other than the Over-Soul as elucidated in arguably his finest work by that name, which opens with a poem by the English philosopher of the Cambridge Platonist school Henry More FRS (1614–1687).[91] This classic essay bears close scrutiny. The several themes treated may be grouped into the following four general categories: (*a*) the existence and nature of the human soul; (*b*) the relationship between the soul and the personal ego; (*c*) the relationship of one human soul to another; and (*d*) the relationship of the human soul to God, i.e., how the Over-Soul manifests in individuals. The essay is a fine integration of the influence of Eastern religions, including Vedānta, with the philosophy of Western traditions, such as the works of Plato, the Greek–Roman biographer and essayist Plutarch (45–127), and Neoplatonists like Plotinus and Proclus, in addition to the inspiration gained from Swedenborg. We find a similar commentary on the thoughts and ideas of great men that have profoundly influenced the world (such as Swedenborg) in Emerson's *Representative Men*,[xvii] which is a collection of seven lectures published as a book of essays in 1850.[92]

Emerson's perception of the Over-Soul

Emerson described the Over-Soul as, 'that great nature in which we rest, as the earth lies in the soft arms of the atmosphere; that Unity, that Over-soul, within which every man's particular being is contained and made one with all other […].' 'All is One' he repeats again and again, 'the act of seeing, the thing seen, the seer and the spectacle, the subject and the object.'[93] But it is significant that although Emerson attempts to define the

---

xvii The essays are on Plato ('the Philosopher'), Emanuel Swedenborg ('the Mystic'), Michel de Montaigne ('the Skeptic'), William Shakespeare ('the Poet'), Napoleon ('the Man of the World'), Johann Wolfgang von Goethe ('the Writer').

Over-Soul, he admits that ultimately *it cannot be known through language and definitions, but only through moral actions*. This is highly significant on two counts pertaining to spirituality and science. First, it fully endorses what the German Theosophist Franz Hartmann has said about several spiritual and religious societies being anything but exemplars of the love and brotherliness that they freely profess and preach (see Chapter 7, page 220 f.). Rather, it would seem that such organisations are self-serving, unable to actualize such high ideals by 'walking their talk', i.e., by bringing forth latent divine faculties into objective and active manifestation through moral actions. Instead they prefer to rest content with pious platitudes and sermons, prestigious lectures or quoting from scholarly books. Second, Emerson's words express important truths that materialistic scientists need to take on board. Instead of jeering at those who find it impossible to 'define' the soul or God or provide physical evidence about God (so concluding that the 'God Delusion' is an illusion of gullible minds), they would do better to understand the meaning of such terms through the path laid down by Emerson and the long and illustrious generations of seers and sages long before, and after him—*the path of moral actions*.

Over-Soul cannot be defined but must be known through moral actions

Starting, then, with that basic Unity as a postulate, Emerson traced the movement from within to without, the One become many, and thus affirmed the absolute necessity of both unity and diversity. 'Every chemical substance, every plant, every animal in its growth', he writes, 'teaches the Unity of Cause, the variety of appearance.'[94]

Emerson discerns unity behind diversity

Nature appeared to him as the manifold forms assumed by the One or the various shadows cast by the One light, suggesting the Absolute, yet never defining it. The various substances out of which nature's forms are compounded might seem to be divided at their base, yet in their summits they are all united. 'The Same, the Same' he declares; 'friend and foe are of one stuff; the ploughman, the plough and the furrow are of one stuff; and the stuff is such, and so much, that the variations of form are unimportant.'[95]

There is no doubt that Emerson's thoughts were entirely consonant with the most fundamental maxim of occult science as stated in *The Secret Doctrine*.

The *Second Fundamental Proposition* speaks of eternal periodicity and cyclicity as of the alternation of day and night, diastole and systole, in-breath and out-breath. In his speech 'The American Scholar' given to the Phi Beta Kappa Society of Harvard College in August 1837, Emerson says: 'There is never a beginning, there is never an end, to the inexplicable continuity of this web of God, but always *circular power returning into itself* [writer's emphasis]. Therein it resembles his own spirit, whose beginning, whose ending, he never can find.' Emerson's insight into universal periodicity paved the way for his understanding that the whole of manifested nature is pervaded by duality: the whole of nature was bisected by an inexorable duality, so that each thing perceived is only one half, and demands another half to make it a whole. He continues in the same address: 'Polarity, or action and reaction, we meet in every part of nature; in darkness and light; in heat and cold; in the ebb and flow of waters; in male and female; in the inspiration and expiration of plants and animals; in the systole and diastole of the heart; in the centrifugal and centripetal gravity; in the undulations of fluids and of sound; in electricity, galvanism and chemical affinity.'[96]

Emerson discerns cyclicity in all manifestation

Turning to the human mind, he recognised that, 'with its separative tendency [the mind], constantly tries to dissociate these two halves [of any question] and to consider one without its relation to the other' (a remarkable prevision of the dangers to our society of the excessive dominance of left-brain over right-brain thought[97]). But nature refuses to be thus divided (permanently) as, for example, 'The parted water reunites behind our hand'.[98] So we can no more act without feeling the reaction than we can hope to find an inside without an outside, a top without a bottom. Not even spirit and matter can be thought of as things in themselves, for they are but two aspects of one and the same thing: 'Once men thought Spirit divine, and Matter diabolic; one Ormuzd, the other Ahriman. Now science and philosophy recognize the parallelism, the approximation, the unity of the two: how each reflects the other as face answers to face in a glass: nay, how the laws of both are one, or how one is the realization.'[99]

Emerson warns of dangers of thinking in dichotomies

Emerson was fully aware of periodicity as manifested through the Law of Karma when he states, 'What we call Retribution is the universal necessity by which the whole appears whenever a part appears. The causal retribution is in the thing, and is seen by the soul. The retribution in the circumstance is seen by the understanding; it is inseparable from the thing, but is often spread over a long time, and so does not become distinct until after many years. Cause and effect, means and end, seed and fruit, cannot be severed; for the effect already blooms in the cause, the fruit in the seed.'[100] The wise man, he counsels, will extend this lesson to every department of his life, and realize that *it is the part of wisdom to pay his debts on whatever plane.* Persons and events may seem to stand for a time between a man and justice, but this is only a postponement, for sooner or later the debt must be settled. On this subject, Paul Brunton, who was a great admirer of Emerson, had this to say to a seeker concerning the role of time in settling karmic debts—or credits: 'What really happens does not take place in time, but it will unfold for you in time because you are in time.'[101]

Discharging karmic debts central to Emerson's philosophy

These ideas, then, are a glowing poetic-cum-philosophical elucidation and precursor of the Second Fundamental Proposition of occultism stated in *The Secret Doctrine.*

The *Third Fundamental Proposition* proclaims the fundamental identity of all souls with the Universal Over-Soul, like the sparks from a central fire, and the force in each entity impelling it to unite with the parent flame. Earlier, on the theme of evolution, we mentioned Emerson's criticism of science as being superficial because it limited its speculations solely to physical matter (see the last section of Chapter 3, page 57). So it is not surprising that his radical ideas about 'living matter', as opposed to the 'dead matter' theory of the science of his day (as indeed nowadays in the mainstream), were not in the least perturbed by the publication of Darwin's *On the Origin of Species* in 1859 (which looked at evolution from a purely materialistic, 'dead matter' standpoint). He continually asserted that science, by ignoring Spirit, could never reach ultimate truth; and that religion, by limiting itself to Spirit and ignoring Matter, was in the same position. He saw that something was needed which took both into account and offered a basis of reconciliation. This basis was his overall philosophy which he bequeathed to the world. He turned again to the East for a corroboration of scientific theories and prophesied that 'The avatars of Brahma will presently be text-books of natural history.'[102] (Stated prosaically, the truth disseminated by spiritual emissaries about the impersonal, supreme, and incognizable Supreme Consciousness, from which all emanates, will one day be recorded facts in the annals of history.) In his Journal of 1866 he gives a dissertation on the Eastern views of science, and shows how science can perform its real function only when it learns to separate

Emerson identifies weaknesses in science and religion and turns to Eastern wisdom

the real from the unreal and arrives at the contemplation of the One Life and the One Cause. (Apropos on the question of reconciliation of both sides of the coin, so to speak, this is why the school of Indian Mahayana Buddhism and Taoism known as Zen is helpful because it unites subjective and objective, releasing the nameless truth in the paradox.)

As both nature and man are rooted in the same identical Essence, as both emanate from the same neutral centre to re-merge into it at the end of the cycle, where then lies the difference between the two? It is contained in a single, hyphenated word: the kingdoms below man are conscious; man is *self*-conscious.

Thus far we have focussed on the parallels between the Three Fundamental Propositions in Emerson's thoughts on the origin and genesis of the universe and sentient beings, including man. What does Emerson explicitly have to say about man and his soul? In his essay *The Over-Soul*,[103] he again clearly states his conviction that, 'the soul in man is not an organ, but animates and exercises all organs; is not a function, like the power of memory, of calculation, of comparison, but uses these as hands and feet; is not a faculty, but a *light*; is not the intellect or the will, but the *master* of the intellect and the will; is the vast background in which they lie, an immensity not possessed and that cannot be possessed [writer's emphases].' Clearly, then, Emerson regards the Soul as that permanent principle in man which does not change, but which is able to perceive the changes going on around him.

Emerson explains the meaning of 'Soul'

Emerson refers to the Soul by various names, such as 'the Thinker and Actor', 'the Observer', 'the Perceiver' and 'the Revealer of Truth', considering it to be immutable, superior to its knowledge, the God Within. 'When it [the Soul] breathes through his [the ordinary man's] intellect', he declares, 'it is genius; when it breathes through his will, it is virtue; when it flows through his affection, it is love; and the blindness of the intellect begins when it would be something of itself [in other words, when intellect arrogantly denounces its source in Soul—alas, a common failing amongst many scientists].'

Emerson clearly identifies immortal and mortal aspects of man

The composite nature of man—one part divine and immortal, other part mortal and corruptible—on which we have laid particular stress, did not escape Emerson's acuity. For he warns us, '[to] hold fast to the man and awe the beast; stop the ebb of thy soul—ebbing downward into the forms into whose habits thou hast now for many years slid.'[104] This is nothing other than an eloquent, poetic rendition of the teachings of Plato in the West, and the Vedāntic and Esoteric schools in the East (described in detail in Chapter 8 of Volume II), about the choice facing the soul of each man: either to align with spirit and reap the fruits of wisdom by virtue of such contact, or to attach to his desire-driven personal nature and risk much suffering. So in this sense life is indeed a battleground and each man must fight his own personal *jihad*—a *psychological* holy war against his own base nature and ignoble thoughts until the final victory has been won from storm to peace when, 'The soul raised over passion beholds identity and eternal causation, perceives the self-existence of Truth and Right, and calms itself with knowing that all things go well.'[105] Here we cannot stress sufficiently that terms like '*jihad*' and 'holy war' have been pathetically corrupted. The writer personally heard the Dalai Lama say at a public gathering that *jihad* has nothing to do with killing people; that the 'holy war' is to be fought on the battle ground within the psyche to overcome one's own internal enemies.[106] Incidentally, this is also the primary message of the *Bhagavad Gītā*, a book which Emerson studied assiduously.

It is clear, then, that Emerson's thoughts are perfectly in accord with the Third Fundamental Proposition of occultism stated in *The Secret Doctrine*.

Reincarnation figures strongly in Emerson's thoughts on the basis that he considered the Soul as an evolving, *becoming* entity. Its advances, he says, are not made by gradation, such as can be expressed by motion in a linear fashion, but rather by an ascension of state (namely, higher planes of consciousness). There are innumerable steps on the stairway of evolution, he explains, which we have already climbed; but there are steps above us, many a one, which go upward and out of sight. How can these steps be climbed save through the process of reincarnation? In terms of the Soul's unfoldment, it is apparent that Emerson considered this idea as the only logical one. He says: 'The soul having often been born, having beheld the things that are here, those which are in heaven and those which are beneath, there is nothing of which she has not gained the knowledge. No wonder that she is able to recollect [re-collect] what formerly she knew.'[107] This is the meaning behind the paradoxical saying that one can only learn what one already knows. Soul-growth means a growth in perception, in knowledge, and in the realization of our own inherent perfection. The way to this realization lies within ourselves, and can be brought about only through our own 'self-induced and self-devised efforts'.[108] In passing, we may note that Emerson's ideas on reincarnation were followed by those of Alfred Russel Wallace.[109] As we mentioned earlier, Wallace published the theory of evolution by natural selection jointly with Darwin but whereas Darwin is a household name synonymous with the theory, Wallace's more forward looking and esoteric ideas have been all but forgotten. However, there are signs of a welcome comeback. The English veteran broadcaster and naturalist Sir David Attenborough FRS (*b*.1926) is a great Wallace admirer and on 7 November 2013 (on the 100th anniversary of Wallace's death) unveiled a statue of Wallace at the Natural History Museum in London. There is also now a portrait of Wallace in the Linnean Society, where the joint paper with Darwin was read in 1858.

Emerson on evolution through successive reincarnations

Finally then, to summarize the essence of Emerson's ideas and ideals we revert to his classic Essay *The Over-Soul*, from which the following quotations are taken. What exactly did Emerson mean by the term 'man'? Is man just the physical body and nothing else as main-stream science pronounced in his time and continues to do so even to this day? In this seminal passage he clearly states that what we commonly call man is a mere parody of his true nature, for in the mundane sense of the term, 'What we commonly call man [the outer appearance or façade], the eating, drinking, planting, counting man does not, as we know him, represent himself, but misrepresents himself'—a misrepresentation that forces man to 'live in succession, in division, in parts, in particles'. However, in the deeper sense, 'a man is the fasade [façade] of a temple wherein all wisdom and all good abide. Within man is the soul of the whole; the wise silence; the universal beauty, to which every part and particle is equally related; the eternal ONE. Him [the ordinary eating-drinking man] we do not respect, but the soul, whose organ he is, would he let it appear through his action, would make our knees bend.' It is for precisely this reason in order to distinguish clearly between the outward appearance and the enduring spiritual entity that, throughout this work and even at the expense of occasional pedantry, we have carefully distinguished between 'man' (common noun) and 'Man' (proper noun) as explained in detail in the Definitions in Volume IV. In our moments of contemplation and intuition we may experience a direct knowing of the deeper, (impersonal) soul of humanity—the Over-Soul. The resounding

Emerson distinguishes corporeal man from his soul and spirit

call for self-reliance supported by the Divine Power rings through the entire philosophy of Ralph Waldo Emerson and he promulgated it throughout his entire life.

A summary of these striking similarities between Emerson's thoughts and the arcane wisdom (as cited above and exemplified in *The Secret Doctrine*) is shown in Table I-3 on the next page.

We restate our earlier contention for the emphasis that we have just laid on Transcendentalism and New Thought, especially through the philosophical lens of Emerson. These strongly related movements prepared (indirectly) the cultural and mental climate for the grand occult doctrines promulgated later through the Theosophical Society by:

How Emerson loosened the stranglehold of dogmatic science and religion

1. establishing the intellectual, moral, and spiritual foundations of esotericism;

2. loosening the stranglehold of both scientific materialism and religious dogmatism, and in so doing prepared the cultural and intellectual climate for the investigation of mediumship and psychic abilities which could not be explained satisfactorily by physical science;

3. drawing attention to the unity of existence expressing through infinite diversity;

4. showing how man can align himself with the Higher Power;

5. alerting America, and the remaining Western world, to the wisdom of the East (at a time in history during the British Raj when the Englishman, by virtue of being white, was automatically regarded as superior to the Indian without question[110]).

The above preparatory influences were the precursor to the two pillars supporting the massive edifice of occult teachings of both East and West that issued from the pen of H. P. Blavatsky: *cosmogenesis* and *anthropogenesis*—the origin and generation of cosmos and man, respectively, at all levels (seen and unseen, objective and subjective).

But it was Emerson, above all, who established most closely the same bond of similarity of aim, purpose, and teaching that unites Transcendentalism with Theosophy. His aims and purpose were essentially similar to the Three Objects of the Theosophical Society in that he constantly reiterated the brotherhood of humanity, its First Object; he always encouraged the study of comparative religions, sciences, and philosophies, and followed himself the advice he gave to others along these lines, as per the Second Object; and he continually pointed to the spiritual powers latent in man and urged their development, as per the Third Object.

Emerson's teaching was entirely in accord with the quintessence of esotericism as expressed by the Three Fundamental Propositions as we have just shown. Furthermore, he revivified the case for esotericism by:

How Emerson prepared the ground for esotericism

1. his reading of the Eastern scriptures and epics like the Vedas and the *Bhagavad Gītā*, respectively;

2. turning the Western mind back towards Plato and the Buddha, and showing the connection of their teachings with the more ancient ones of Kṛṣṇa in the *Gītā*;

3. calling attention to the contribution of the Alexandrian School (from which the term 'theosophy' derives—see Chapter 7 earlier).

Table I-3 Emerson's Thoughts Upheld by the Perennial Wisdom

What Emerson Affirmed (abridged)	What *The Secret Doctrine* Later Confirmed (paraphrased)
In his essay on Plato:	The *First Fundamental Proposition*:
The mind seeks for one Cause of many effects; then for the cause of that, and so on towards an Absolute One that shall be All. Although undefinable and unmeasurable, we know that It pervades and contains us.	An Absolute Principle of Unity behind diversity. The Causeless Cause behind all causes, unthinkable and unpronounceable.
EPITOME: Unity in diversity, One Life present in all Nature.	
In 'The American Scholar':	The *Second Fundamental Proposition*:
There is never a beginning or an end to the inexplicable continuity of this web of God, but always circular power returning to itself. Therein it resembles man's own spirit.	Eternal Periodicity and Cyclicity. Universes appear and disappear, i.e., from subjectivity to objectivity (the explicate, or manifestation) and from objectivity withdrawn into subjectivity (the implicate, or dissolution).
EPITOME: Periodicity manifested through polarity, a fundamental Law of the Universe.	
In his Essay on Nature:	The *Third Fundamental Proposition*:
There is a latent omniscience not only in man, but in every particle. A force in every creature that impels it to ascend to higher forms of life. Plants are the young of the world, but they grope ever upward towards [self-] consciousness.	The fundamental identity of all souls with the Universal Over-Soul, which itself is an aspect of the Unknown Root; and the necessity for every Soul to realize and re-claim, in full consciousness, its intrinsic Divinity.
EPITOME: God within man himself, man's evolution can proceed only by self-effort.	

We now touch upon the New Thought teachings that followed in the wake of Emerson's philosophy and generally in parallel with the outpouring from the Theosophical Society.

Post-Emersonian New Thought During the Era of Theosophy

It is a matter of conjecture as to the degree to which post-Emersonian thinkers, like Thomas Troward, Ralph Waldo Trine, and Walter Bowman Russell, were also influenced by the doctrines of the contemporary Theosophical movement. Nonetheless our objective is to show that their ideas were entirely congruent with the occult philosophy, hence making our case that:

1. The occult doctrines (from whatever source) are not an outmoded, antediluvian theory dressed up in modern clothing by way of fanciful inventions put out by the Theosophical Society, but constitute the profound conviction of all thinkers, based on their personal experience (irrespective of affiliation to the Theosophical Society), who were able to penetrate the veil of physical existence into the deeper realms of life and existence.

Wisdom comes from both the West and the East

2. Any complete teaching must embrace the wisdom of both the West and East.

Regarding 2. above, it is necessary to point out that Blavatsky has been wrongly charged (by the likes of Rudolf Steiner, no less) with over-emphasizing the Eastern occult tradition at the expense of the Western tradition. This is untrue as any student who takes the trouble to examine her works will find out for himself. For example the Qabbalah constitutes a significant binding thread within *The Secret Doctrine* and shows Theosophy to be a Universal Teaching, rather than an essentially Eastern tradition. What she, and a few others like the German-born philologist and Orientalist Max Müller (1823–1900), did during the late nineteenth century, when the supremacy of Western learning was presumed without question, was to restore the balance between the Western and Eastern doctrines at a time when the latter were virtually ignored and therefore largely unknown.

Thomas Troward

The English author Thomas Troward (1847–1916) was by profession a divisional Judge in British–administered India. One of the finest spiritual guides and the most important writer in New Thought of his time, his clarity of style, insight, and compassionate approach influenced several other writers like Emmet Fox (1886–1951), the Irish spiritual leader of the early twentieth century, during the Great Depression. Troward's works were the outcome of solitary meditation and profound study, and represented a fusion of the world religions and scriptures, notably the Bible, Islam, Buddhism, and the Hindu teachings. The great philosopher and psychologist William James characterized Troward's Edinburgh Lectures on Mental Science as 'far and away the ablest statement of philosophy I have met, beautiful in its sustained clearness of thought and style, a really classic statement.'[111]

Influences on Troward's thought

Let us refer to some seminal remarks made in his books and lectures. The pre-eminence of mind and the supreme importance he placed upon mental hygiene, correct thinking, and living according to nature's laws runs like four closely intertwined threads linking his entire teaching.

Troward discriminates truth from falsehood

First, we deal with his thoughts about universal principles: spirit as truth and one of its inherent laws—beauty. In his book *The Creative Process in the Individual* he writes, 'A lie is a statement that something is, which is not. Then, since the Spirit's statement or conception of anything necessarily makes that thing exist, it is logically impossible for it [the Spirit] to conceive a lie. Therefore the Spirit is Truth. Similarly disease and death are the negative of life, and therefore the Spirit, as the Principle of life, cannot embody disease or death in its Self-contemplation. In like manner also, since it is free to produce what it will, the Spirit cannot desire the presence of repugnant forms, and so one of its inherent Laws must be Beauty. In this threefold Law of Truth, Life and Beauty, we find the whole underlying nature of the spirit, and no action on the part of the individual can be at variance with the Originating Unity which does not controvert fundamental principles.'[112] Such discrimination between a lie and a truth coming from a renowned judge should be taken seriously!

In the next extract Troward speaks of the universality of fundamental principles and the urgent need to engage with them in the 'here and now' of our thoughts. 'The principle being thus universal there is no reason why we should postpone its application till we find ourselves in another world, and the best place and time to begin are Here and Now. *The starting point is not in time or locality, but in the mode of Thought* [writer's emphasis]; and if we realize that this Point of Origination is Spirit's power to produce something out of nothing, and that it does this in accordance with the natural order of substance of the particular world in which it is working, then the spiritual ego in ourselves, as proceeding direct from the Universal Spirit, should be able first, to so harmoniously combine the working of spiritual and physical laws in its own body as to keep it in perfect health, secondly to carry this process further and renew the body, thus eradicating the effects of old age, and thirdly to carry the process still further and perpetuate this renewed body as long as the individual might desire.'[113]

Troward's reference to the 'spiritual ego' as an emanation from 'Universal Spirit' is absolutely in line with the occult teaching on the constitution of man, described in detail in Chapter 2, Volume II of this work. Moreover, it is quite reasonable to propose that Troward was influenced by the leaders and doctrines of the Theosophical Society then in its heyday during the same period as his judicial tenure in India.

Possible Theosophical influences on Troward

Dealing with the mind, Troward states in his *Edinburgh Lectures*: 'The action of Mind plants that nucleus which, if allowed to grow undisturbed, will eventually attract to itself all the conditions necessary for its manifestation in outward visible form.'[114] Note carefully how Troward distinguishes mind from thought by referring to the latter as the action of the former. This again is entirely consistent with the arcane wisdom, but flies in the face of a materialistic neuroscience that either conflates the two, or regards thought as generated by the physical brain, otherwise equated with mind.

In the next extract from the same lectures, it is again not difficult to discern the sharp legal mind applied to metaphysical principles when he refers to karma in these words: 'It is an enduring truth, which can never be altered, that every infraction of the Law of nature must carry its punitive consequences with it. We can never get beyond that range of cause and effect. There is no escaping from the law of punishment.'[115] We might add that working with nature's laws reaps abundance aplenty as Troward has also been at pains to show, for example, when he affirms in his *Dore Lectures* that, 'My mind is a centre of Divine operation. The Divine operation is always for expansion and fuller expression […].'[116] Troward's notion of 'a centre' is essential to his teaching, as is his understanding of 'I Am'. Of course, by 'my mind' is meant the minds of each one of us because the Supreme Power works through us owing to Its inherent nature. Hence, we will be given, Troward continues, 'opportunities to produce new conditions, always in advance of any that have gone before' for the simple reason that this operation of Divine Mind is within us. We are a centre of it. It is operating in and within us because we are part of the universal Consciousness. He explains the Divine as the generating centre and us as distributing centres, an apt analogy with a central power station and transformer substations.

Troward on universal principles for living

In essence, then, Troward's teaching was a perfectly balanced fusion of Eastern and Western philosophy. Notwithstanding the stress he laid upon correct thinking, he never underplayed the importance of the physical life. As succinctly stated by his only private student, the French-born Genevieve Behrend (1881–1960): 'A difference between Troward's teaching and that of Christian Science is that he does not deny the existence of a material world. On the contrary, he teaches that all physical existence is a concrete corresponding manifestation of the thought which gave it birth. One is a complement of the other.'[117] The kernel of his thought however, as expressed to Behrend, was Christian. When Behrend then asked her teacher how one could impart to others the deep truths which he taught, 'By being them', Troward answered, 'My motto is, "Being, and not possessing, is the great joy of living".'[118]

Troward also acknowledges the importance of physical life

We continue this section on seminal figures in the New Thought movement with some remarks about another 'Ralph Waldo'—but with the surname Trine!

Ralph Waldo Trine

The American philosopher, author, and teacher Ralph Waldo Trine (1866–1958) was much influenced by the writings of the German Johann Gottlieb Fichte (1762–1814), the founding figure of the philosophical movement known as German idealism, the Scottish scientist and evangelist Henry Drummond (1851–1897), and Emerson. His seminal book *In Tune with the Infinite*[119] was launched in 1897. Hailed as a classic of Western spirituality, it has sold well over one million copies. It was read by such personages as Queen Victoria (1837–1901), the American self-help author Napoleon Hill (1883–1970), the industrialist Henry Ford (1863–1947), and the American film, stage, and television actress and painter, Janet Gaynor (1906–1984).

Influences on Trine's thought and his influence on others

Why has this remarkable book stood the test of time? Because in its pages we find perennial truths that have indeed been restated in many other forms during his time and even nowadays, but perhaps never so clearly. 'To point out the great facts in connection with, and the great laws underlying, the workings of the interior, spiritual, thought forces', writes Trine in the introduction, 'to point them out so simply and so clearly that even a child can understand, is the author's aim. To point them out so simply and so clearly that all can grasp them, that all can take them and infuse them into everyday life […].'[120] As with Emerson and Troward, we shall evaluate Trine's philosophy against the backdrop of the perennial wisdom.

Trine's goal of utter simplicity

We have periodically asserted that one of the striking characteristics about the wisdom tradition is its remarkable consistency: whether we look to the West or to the East, to remotest antiquity or to modern expositions, there is a common thread that strings them all together like pearls on one necklace of wisdom. Let us remind ourselves of the function of the 'thread doctrine' mentioned in Blavatsky's words in Chapter 8:

> The Esoteric Doctrine may well be called the 'thread-doctrine,' since […] it passes through and strings together all the ancient philosophical religious systems, and reconciles and explains them all. We say now it does more.[121]

Thus, the significance of the thread-doctrine is not limited just to Eastern occultism. It is the common provenance of all who work in the perennial wisdom tradition. In the West we have the glorious example of Newton who delved for decades into the alchemical and esoteric literature. The *Expanding Force in Newton's Cosmos* is a condensed edition of a four volume treatise containing the fruits of some thirty years of work and research by the solitary Spanish historian and Cambridge researcher David Castillejo (1927–2020) on Newton's unpublished alchemical and prophetic papers from the manuscripts bequeathed to King's College, Cambridge by Lord Keynes. It shows that 'Newton's entire work—his mechanics, optics, alchemy and church history—forms a single body of thought.'[122]

What, then, along similar lines do we find in the opening sentences of the introduction to Trine's book to which we have just referred?

> There is a golden thread that runs through every religion in the world. There is a golden thread that runs through the lives and the teachings to all the prophets, seers, sages, and saviours in the world's history, through the lives of all men and women of truly great and lasting power. All that they have ever done or attained to has been done in full accordance with law.

> What one has done, all may do. This same golden thread must enter into the lives of all who today, in this busy work-a-day world of ours, would exchange impotence for power, weakness and suffering for abounding health and strength[,] pain and unrest for perfect peace, poverty of whatever nature for fullness and plenty.[123]

Trine sees the connection between teachers and teachings

Here we find a stirring affirmation in simple language of the thread-doctrine which puts Trine's thoughts very much on an esoteric footing. As we have shown in this Chapter and numerous other sections of this Volume, the composite nature of man has been a recurrent theme of all the Mystery Teachings. It finds its endorsement in this key sentence from the New Thought Movement introducing the original 1897 publication of Trine's book: 'By recognizing the power of our thoughts and by harmonizing our own [will] with the Divine will, we attract perfect peace, health, love, prosperity and success'.[124] Three teachings may be gleaned. First, the need to align our mortal self of matter with our immortal Divine counterpart. Next, we are again reminded of the primal importance of thoughts. Finally, we understand the need to build our lives first from thought, from inside to outside, from within to without. And the reason is because, 'Each is building his own world. We both build from within and we attract from without. Thought is the force with which we build, for thoughts are forces. Like builds like and like attracts like. In the degree that thought is spiritualized does it become more subtle and powerful in its workings. This spiritualizing is in accordance with law and is within the power of all.'[125]

Trine's three teachings

Like all initiates and adepts, Plato taught that everything is 'worked out', so to speak, in Divine Mind as ideal archetypes (Divine, or Primordial Thought) before its appearance in the world: that creation, better understood as emanation, is the whole movement from Being to Becoming, from Unmanifest to Manifest, from noumena to phenomena. Trine says as much: 'Everything is first worked out in the unseen before it is manifested in the seen, in the ideal before it is realized in the real, in the spiritual before it shows forth in the material.'[126] Then follows the crucial insight, stated briefly in the Introduction and later reinforced in the Chapter, 'The Supreme Fact of Human Life':

Trine traces the movement from cause to effect: from eternal to transient

> The realm of the unseen is the realm of cause. The realm of the seen is the realm of effect. The nature of effect is always determined and conditioned by the nature of its cause.[127]

> Everything exists in the unseen before it is manifested or realised in the seen, and in this sense it is true that the unseen things are the real, while the things that are seen are the

unreal. The unseen things are the cause, the seen things are *effect* [emphasis added]. The unseen things are the eternal[,] the seen things are the changing, the transient.[128]

Why is this: Because, 'thought is a force, and it has occult power of unknown proportions when rightly used and wisely directed.'[129] It cannot be stressed too strongly, then, that the visible, tangible mundane world we ordinarily inhabit is the world of effects, or phenomena; the causes, or noumena, lie in the realm of the invisible. This is something that mainstream science has yet to appreciate, as also the whole matter of cosmogenesis and evolution, other than on the physical plane (refer back Chapter 8).

Trine's inspiration from the Christ

What has Trine to say about evolution on realms not limited to physical matter and therefore not limited merely to mutations and natural selection? Drawing his inspiration from the Christian scriptures, he says: 'But long ago there came one who with a great aptitude for discerning the things of the mind and the spirit, a great clarity of perception that enabled Him to understand the reality of life, the One Life, and to identify His own life with it—the Infinite Spirit of life and power that is back of all, animating and working through all, the life of all. So direct and intimate was His understanding of it that He used the term Father: I and my Father are one. And to make it of value in that it was not for Him alone, He said: As I am you shall be. My consciousness of the One Life shall be your consciousness, My insight and power shall be your insight and power, if you will receive My message and do the things I tell you. And truly He handled the stuff of life with a wonderful artistry. This is the message that the Master, Jesus of Galilee, tried so hard to get over into the world. It is through this that He becomes the supreme Way-revealer, the Way-revealer to us men of earth. The Way He showed is what men so sadly need for a higher and a more efficient individual life, and what the world needs for a more efficient and harmonious and cooperative life.'[130]

Evolution applies to all kingdoms of nature

Note, with every care, the words: 'As I am you shall be. My consciousness of the One Life shall be your consciousness.' *They speak of the evolution of consciousness—mind and spirit.* It affirms that mankind, quickened by individual effort, will, in the fullness of time, attain to the supreme, holistic consciousness of such as the Christ. Here we must stress that evolution in nature is both inter-kingdom and intra-kingdom. The former concerns evolution from one kingdom of nature to another, for example, the mineral kingdom to the plant kingdom. The latter concerns evolution within each kingdom of nature. There are innumerable species of plants ranging from rudimentary to complex types—like the fungus to the oak tree. In the animal kingdom there is a vast difference in body types and behaviour between the mouse and the tiger. So why should humanity not display a vast range of characteristics depending on evolution (primarily of mind and spirit rather than body type) within the human kingdom? This is certainly the case. We find the evolutionary arrow ranging from basic and simple human types, to cultured and sophisticated varieties, and finally to the highest exemplars of the human kingdom epitomized by the great messengers and saviours of humanity.

From these brief extracts it is clear that Trine's teaching about the human condition and its evolution is fully in consonance with the *philosophia perennis*; moreover, that he expresses it, as was his wish, 'simply and so clearly that even a child can understand'.

Finally, it is most significant that Trine co-authored a book with the American captain of industry and business magnate Henry Ford (to whom we referred above) in which they presented an intimate account of the inner side of life, matters of the mind and spirit, and the inner powers and forces that make for achievement.[131] In fact, Ford attributed his success directly to having read *In Tune with the Infinite*. The message from this is that the industrialist Ford, notwithstanding his phenomenal worldly success, would pay heed to the inner life; and Trine, despite his bent towards Christianity and mysticism, should acknowledge the indispensable worth of the material life. However, both these great men owed their success to their conviction that physical existence is the imperative physical counterpart to the thought which gave it birth. Interestingly, Henry Ford was one of the interviewees suggested by the Scottish–American industrialist Andrew Carnegie (1835–1919) to the motivation author Napoleon Hill; but Ford felt that too many of the valuable principles had been given away by Hill in the first edition of his *The Law of Success*.[132]

Henry Ford acknowledges the inner life as Trine does the material life

Walter Bowman Russell

A Renaissance man for the twentieth century described by the *New York Herald Tribune* as 'the modern Leonardo',[133] Walter Bowman Russell (1871–1963) was an American natural philosopher, musician, author, painter, sculptor, and builder. His books and lectures place him firmly in the New Thought Movement.[134] Although some considered him a polymath, Russell was not, and is not generally thought of as an academic, which had the advantage that his highly intuitive and visionary forays into territory hitherto unexplored by science were not moulded, or congealed, by the materialistic concepts in mainstream scientific academia then prevailing. His unique contribution to the New Thought movement was his quintessentially Mind-centric explanation of cosmogony (the origin of the universe) uniting spiritual cause and scientifically observable effect.

Russell connects the spiritual and scientific

This went so far as to venture a critique of Kepler's First Law of planetary motion and Newton's Mathematics concerning the orbit of the moon, which he defended in the pages of the *New York Times* in 1930–1931,[135] although in the latter case, exposure to Newton's vast alchemical treatises, practically unknown at the time, might have caused Russell to temper his criticisms, which in all probability were based on Newton's mathematical and mechanical writings. Nonetheless, Russell's cosmogony and related ideas about the nature of man's relationship to the universe and divinity, in terms of varying degrees of consciousness, are of particular relevance to this work since they are much in line with the *philosophia perennis*. But it is a matter of conjecture whether Russell was in any way influenced by similar doctrines promulgated by the Theosophical Society in the last quarter of the nineteenth century.

Russell's criticism of Kepler and Newton

Russell's ideas were first expressed in his books *The Universal One*[136] and *The Russell Genero-Radiative Concept*,[137] and further developed in *The Secret of Light*[138] and *A New Concept of the Universe*[139] where his fundamental premise was that, 'gravity and radiativity are opposite pressure conditions. They perpetually void themselves by giving to the other.'[140] Here we find a striking parallel with Newton's *esoteric* cosmogony to which, regrettably, Russell could not have had access. Recall the exhaustive treatise by David Castillejo, mentioned above, showing that Newton's entire work forms a single body of thought. Castillejo further shows that in his work, Newton 'was identifying two fundamental forces in Nature: the contracting force of gravitation, and a single expanding force which operates in the radiation of light, in chemical composition and biological growth,

Russell identifies two polar opposite forces in nature

and also governs the mind and behaviour of human beings.'[141] Like Newton, Russell seems to have realized that gravitation and radiation are two fundamental polar opposite forces: gravitation, the law in the material world being the impulse towards the centre of materiality; and radiation, or levitation, the law in the spiritual world being the impulse towards the centre of spirituality.

The Russell Cosmogony, albeit on a much smaller scale than Newton's works, was never-theless, a new concept of the universe, explaining the relationship between matter and energy, and between electricity and magnetism that was publicly available.[142] An engineer who learned of the Russell Cosmogony in 1930 commented, 'If Russell's theories are sound, they will be of utmost value, as he shows that there can be but one substance, and that the difference [among the elements] is a dimensional difference and not a difference of substance. In other words, if Russell's theories are right, transmutation can be reduced to a practical reality.'[143]

It is a *sine qua non* of the *philosophia perennis*, 'that there can be but one substance' known by various terms like *Æther* in the West or *Ākāśa (Akasha)* in the East; and one of the main purposes of Volumes II and III of this work is to describe the various processes and mechanisms of esoteric science that demonstrate how the manifested universe arises from differentiation and modifications within the One universal substance.

Russell's forward looking ideas

Russell's advanced ideas have fired some of the finest minds in science and philosophy. For example in 1929, the British physicist and inventor Sir Oliver Lodge FRS (1851–1940) wrote that future investigations will result in 'no merely material prospect that will be opening on our view, but some glimpse into a region of the universe which Science has never entered yet, but which has been sought from afar, and perhaps blindly apprehended, by painter and poet, by philosopher and saint.'[144]

In March 1947, when *The Secret of Light* was published, the American writer and popular historian Francis Trevelyan Miller (1877–1959) sent Russell an unsolicited letter of praise about the 'tremendous magnitude of thought expressed in this little volume', and the 'courage and vision' to explore the natural laws which science, hitherto, 'has not attempted to define'.[145] Trevelyan might well have been struck by this passage: 'For within the secret of Light is vast knowledge not yet revealed to man.'[146] Some three quarters of a century later, part of the 'vast knowledge' was by slow degrees becoming an open secret—the mystery of consciousness, spurred in large measure by the discoveries of quantum physics. Unfortunately, Russell did not live to see the day when eminent physicists would be using words like mind, light, and consciousness not exactly as synonyms, but in the same breath, so to speak.

Russell discerns unity expressed in cyclicity and multiplicity

On the first page of the Prelude to *The Universal One*, Russell postulates: 'The universe is a multiplicity of changing effects of but One unchanging cause. All things are universal. Nothing is which is not universal. Nothing is of itself alone. Man and Mind and all creating things are universal. No man can say: "I alone am I". There is but One universe, One Mind, One force, One substance. When man knows this in measurable exactness then will he have no limitations within those which are universal.' The essential idea supported by observation based experiment is, 'This belief of unity of force, expressed in a continuous cycle of integration following disintegration, of generation succeeding degeneration, of the visible lifting itself out of the invisible in forever repeative [*sic*] cyclic intervals.'[147]

Universal periodicity and cyclicity are key tenets of the *philosophia perennis*, as stated periodically in this Chapter.

Russell worked for a full seven years on *The Universal One*, subtitled: *An exact science of the One visible and invisible universe of Mind and the registration of all idea of thinking Mind in light, which is matter and also energy*. The book was to be given only to the leading scientists of the day, so a limited number were printed. Later on, owing to the destructive manner in which humanity was heading, his wife Lao Russell felt it was necessary to release it to the public. Indeed, it was she who wrote the preface to this eminent book pointing out on the first page that 'Civilization is in reverse. Science is being used to destroy instead of to build.'[148] The celebrated Russian inventor, engineer, physicist, and futurist Nikola Tesla (1856–1943) 'recognized the wisdom and power of Russell's work and urged him to lock up his knowledge in a safe for one thousand years until man was ready for it.'[149] What Tesla and Lao Russell might well have been alluding to was that mankind (or perhaps, more to the point, the scientific community) was not yet ready to take on board Russell's key insight about the cardinal error of science as expressed by Russell in an 'Open Letter To The World Of Science':

> Man has for too long left the Creator out of His Creation, thinking He cannot be proven in the laboratory. God not only can be proven in the laboratory, but because of the facts of that proof man can solve many heretofore hidden mysteries of the universe—such as that of the seed and growth—life and death cycles—the purpose of the inert gases as electric recorders of all repetitive effects—and the true process of atomic structure.[150]

Can God be 'proven in the laboratory'? Yes, but only by the chemist or biologist gifted with mystic vision who, peering into his microscope, can sense the divine impress in every particle of nature—the 'image of God in matter', a theme that will become clearer as we progress through Volume II and Volume III.

Needless to say, 'the Creator', or 'God' was never an anthropomorphic god, but rather that 'God is the invisible, motionless, sexless, undivided, and unconditioned white Magnetic Light of Mind'[151]—an utterance that is consonant with, however differently expressed, the pronouncements of legendary scientists, mystics, and sages since time immemorial.

A Closing Note on Contemporary Mystery Teachings and Nineteenth Century Spiritual Teachings

The reader should never be under the impression that such emphasis on the primacy of thought was the province of gullible nineteenth century make-belief, without scientific justification. It has every scientific support, and we previously cited a few examples as evidence from legendary modern scientists, especially Sir James Jeans who shifted the emphasis of scientific thinking about primary realities from matter to mind.[152] It is worth pointing out that everything that the reader can see looking around the place in which he is reading was once a thought—as indeed was this work! So the unequivocal conclusion is the primacy of thought: this has been the doctrine of arcane wisdom transmitted through the great sages and occultists since time immemorial, which has found such magnificent corroboration, clear written expression and living proofs from

Nikola Tesla's admiration for Russell's work

Russell identifies root cause of malaise in society

Divine Mind and primacy of thought are omnipresent

such as Emerson, Troward, Trine, Russell and others who have actively engaged with Divine Mind and not just indulged in empty, evangelical word-spinning, or 'get-rich-quick' quackery, but *lived their lives with the discipline afforded by their inner convictions.*

Accordingly, we maintain that the contemporary Mystery Teachings, and their reflection in New Thought, as expounded in this major section are fully consonant with the worldwide mystery teaches of all ages, from hoary antiquity or from our modern age.

The Consummate Achievement of the Mysteries – Man, United With Him-Self

Earlier we stressed that the Mystery Teachings never teach that spirituality ever makes men either virtuous, rational or compassionate; on the contrary, that virtue, rationality, and compassionate service rendered are the qualities that in due course make men spiritual.

Accordingly, the Mysteries teach that spiritual illumination is attained only by raising the lower nature towards the highest grade of perfected functioning and purity. This knowledge of how man's composite nature can be most speedily and completely unfolded and regenerated to the point of spiritual illumination constitutes the secret, or esoteric doctrine of all ages and main objective of the Mysteries. In passing, it may be suggested that the safest and surest way to develop genuine clairvoyance is again by raising the lower perception, that is by bringing the normal physical faculties to their ultimate standard of refined functioning—not by means of drugs or other artificial methods with all the dangers involved. A clue to this suggestion can be gained from scientific and anecdotal evidence indicating that people who suffer a decline in one of the senses, for example vision, often report the heightening of another sense, such as hearing.[153] Otherwise stated, the highest levels of consciousness can be contacted only by letting go of the lowest. According to Lester Smith FRS, who has spent a lifetime in science, Theosophy, and psychical investigation (see Chapter 4): 'Drugs can induce euphoria and other altered states of consciousness. This shortcut is not desirable on account of side effects; nor are the experiences so gained as satisfying as those arising from long-continued meditative practices.'[154]

Safest means of attaining illumination is by slow degrees

Hence, through the gradual purification of his vehicles and the ever-increasing sensitiveness resulting from that refinement, man, by gradual degrees, overcomes the limitations of matter and disentangles himself from the limitations imposed by the mortal coil. At the point of deepest materialism, therefore, man is at the greatest distance from Himself; but the trend of man's evolutionary growth through all his incarnating cycles of struggles and trials is inexorably toward his own essential Selfhood.

The Mysteries accelerate the natural evolutionary process

The Secret Doctrine of all ages further teaches that after aeons of incarnations on Earth, the evolutionary cycle for our present humanity will have completed its physical evolution, and man will have attained his own essential Selfhood. Thereafter the empty shell of materiality left behind will be used by other life waves as stepping-stones to their own evolutionary cycle. (This is an enormous and complex subject of occult science and will not be expounded in this work. Nevertheless, the highest sources of evidence are all there to be studied by one who seeks understanding—see Endnote I-9.) However, those desiring to do so may enormously accelerate the natural evolutionary process by determined self-effort, which has nothing to do with egoistic striving. These are, of course, the initiates and earnest students of occultism, who have decided to take their spiritual development into their own hands instead of leaving it to the natural course of events. By initiation into the Mysteries, then, they learn that man becomes aware of, and consciously reunited with, the divine source of Himself without tasting of physical dissolution. This is at once the primary purpose and the consummate achievement of the Mysteries.

One of the best modern, authentic accounts of such an initiation is the experience of Paul Brunton during an entire night in the darkness of the King's Chamber of the Great Pyramid. The process commenced with a severe and terrifying ordeal to test his mettle and resolve before the climax, when Brunton was given actual proof about death, the soul, and the body, in what could be described in popular terms as an out-of-body experience. In his words, looking down upon his own body, he realized:

The body dies: Man never does

> *This is the state of death. Now I know that I am a soul, that I can exist apart from the body. I shall always believe that, for I have proved it.*[155]

It cannot be sufficiently stressed that the pyramids were not burial chambers, as prosaic Egyptology would have us believe, but ancient fanes of initiation into the Mysteries stretching far back to Atlantean times. The initiation process was conducted, as Brunton recounts in his case, by the guardian-spirits of the Pyramid—High Priests of an ancient Egyptian cult. They conveyed (telepathically, of course) the following message to him:

> Thou hast now learned the great lesson. *Man, whose soul was born out of the Undying can never really die.* Set down this truth in words known to men. Behold![156]

Needless to say, the sceptics will mock all this as laughable nonsense and, to use their favourite term when all else fails, 'delusion'. They are entitled to their opinions as long as they remain—just opinions. But Truth, ever patient, is not perturbed in the least and forever smiles with compassion at those who fancy themselves as the omniscient scientific and intellectual salt of the earth.

This Chapter represents the acme of Volume I of this work, for which the previous Chapters have been as stepping stones. The main theme has been to show that the Mystery Teachings, whether from the East or the West, whether ancient or modern, are as a network of choruses in spiritual resonance and thus 'sing' with a united voice, albeit in different tongues, about man's true nature, his sense of purpose, and his glorious destiny. 'Human ambition may produce the tyrant; divine inspiration will produce the adept.'[157] The closing quote to this Chapter leaves us in no doubt about this.

The following Recapitulation draws together the core precepts of Volume I.

The soul of man has not been deprived of its wings; they are merely folded under its garment of flesh. Philosophy is ever that magic power which, sundering the vessel of clay, releases the soul from its bondage to habit and perversion.

The criers of the Mysteries speak again, bidding all men welcome to the House of Light. In this era of 'practical' things men ridicule even the existence of God. They scoff at goodness while they ponder with befuddled minds the phantasmagoria of materiality. The great institution of materiality has failed. Only transcendental philosophy knows the path. Only the illumined reason can carry the understanding part of man upward to the light. Only philosophy can teach man to be born well, to live well, to die well, and in perfect measure be born again. Into this band of the elect—those who have chosen the life of knowledge, of virtue, and of utility—the philosophers of the ages invite YOU.

THE SECRET TEACHINGS OF ALL AGES[158]

NOTES

1   *NPB*-6, Part 1: *The Ego,* 'What Am I?', ¶ 3, 4; ¶ 4, 4.

2   Ervin László, *Science and the Akashic Field: An integral theory of everything* (Rochester, Vermont: Inner Traditions, 2007), 45–6.

3   A paraphrased version of Blavatsky's incisive remark: 'Scalpels and microscopes may solve the mystery of the material parts of *the shell of man*: they can never cut a window into his soul to open the smallest vista on any of the wider horizons of being,' *CW*-VIII, 'The Science of Life', 241.

4   For more details consult G. de Purucker, *Fundamentals of the Esoteric Philosophy* (West Hills, California: Wisdom Religion Press), 1996.

5   *NPB*-4, Part 2: *The Body,* 'Kundalini', ¶ 3, 142–3.

6   Plato, *Phaedrus,* trans. Benjamin Jowett (US: CreateSpace Independent Publishing Platform, 2012) [online facsimile] The Internet Classics Archive <http://classics.mit.edu/Plato/phaedrus.1b.txt> accessed 13 December 2019.

7   *KT,* 'Theosophical Teachings as to Nature and Man', 91.

8   Considerably abridged from *STA,* 'The Life and Writings of Thoth Hermes Trismegistus', XXXIX–XL.

9   Phiroz Mehta, *Holistic Consciousness: Reflections on the destiny of humanity* (UK: Element Books, 1989), 119.

10 For profound insights into this thorny problem see 'Evil and Suffering', in Phiroz Mehta, *The Heart of Religion* (UK: Compton Russell Element, 1976), 148–208.

11 *SD*-I, 'Daemon Est Deus Inversus: Death is Life', 413.

12 *SD*-I, 'Stanza VII: The Parents of Man on Earth', 235–6.

13 Annie Besant, *Seven Great Religions* (Adyar, Madras: Theosophical Publishing House, 1972), 65–6.

14 A fine sardonic story on this theme, appropriately titled 'Satan', is in Martin L. Wolf (ed.), *The Secrets of the Heart, Selected Works by Kahlil Gibran,* trans. Anthony Rizcallah Ferris from Arabic (Bombay, India: Jaico Publishing House, 1947), 35–60.

15 *TSGLOSS,* 385.

16 Better understood in the Sanskrit terms *manvantara* and *pralaya,* meaning cosmic awakening and cosmic slumber. The unsophisticated terms 'Big Bang' and 'Big Crunch' in modern cosmogony are faint echoes of this principle of periodic and endless cosmic emergence (awakening) and cosmic withdrawal (slumber)—see Edi D. Bilimoria, *The Snake and the Rope: Problems in Western science resolved by occult science* (Adyar, Madras: Theosophical Publishing House, 2006), 204.

17 Grace F. Knoche, *The Mystery Schools* (2nd edn, rev., Pasadena, Califorña: Theosophical University Press, 1999).

18 ——*op. cit.,* Chapter 6, 'Degrees of Initiation' [online facsimile] <https://www.theosociety.org/pasadena/mysterys/mystsch1.htm> accessed 16 January 2020.

19 'List of Messiah Claimants', Wikipedia (last modified 15 January 2020) <https://en.wikipedia.org/wiki/List_of_messiah_claimants> accessed 13 December 2019.

20 Arthur Edward Waite, 'Paracelsus', in *Lives of Alchemystical Philosophers: Based on Materials Collected in 1815 and Supplemented by Recent Researches with a Philosophical Demonstration of the True Principles of the Magnum Opus, Or Great Work of Alchemical Re-construction, and Some Account of the Spiritual Chemistry* (London, G. Redway, 1888).

21 Sarvepalli Radhakrishnan, *Eastern Religions and Western Thought* (Delhi: Oxford University Press India,1990).

22 Organization of American States (OAS), *The Incas* (booklet) (Washington, DC, 1975), 3.

23 *STA*, 'American Indian Symbolism', CXCIII–CXCVI.

24 *STA, op. cit.*, CXCIII.

25 *STA, op. cit.*, CXCIV.

26 Evidence of Inca and pre-Inca spirituality can be traced in: Brother Philip [George Hunt Williamson], *Secret of the Andes: Brotherhood of the Seven Rays* (London: Corgi, 1973); Antón Ponce de León Paiva, *The Wisdom of the Ancient ONE* (California: Bluestar Communications, 1995); Antón Ponce de León Paiva, *In Search of the Wise ONE* (California: Bluestar Communications, 1996); Mark Amaru Pinkham, *The Return of the Serpents of Wisdom* (Kempton, Illinois: Adventures Unlimited Press, 1996).

27 B. F. de Costa, *The Pre-Columbian Discovery of America by the Northmen* (Albany, New York: Joel Munsell's Sons, 1980) <http://tinyurl.com/ya4asfk8> accessed 14 December 2019.

28 Albert Amao Soria, 'The Cosmovision of the Incas', *NEXUS* (August–September 2017), 48–54, 75.

29 Brother Philip, *op. cit.*, 13–14 [online facsimile] <http://tinyurl.com/y8s9nr2u> accessed 16 January 2020.

30 Organization of American States (OAS), 5.

31 One of many authentic accounts is by D. S. Allan and J. B. Delair, *Cataclysm! Compelling Evidence of a Cosmic Catastrophe in 9500 B.C.* (Rochester Vermont: Bear & Company), 1997. See also: Paul A. LaViolette, *Earth Under Fire* (NewYork: Starlane), 1997; *Genesis of the Cosmos* (Rochester, Vermont: Bear & Company), 2004.

32 Brother Philip, *op. cit.*, 13.

33 Serge Raynaud de la Ferrière, 'Message 1: The Coming of the Great Instructor of the World – The Order of Aquarius' <http://tinyurl.com/y8suo25u> accessed 13 June 2018.

34 Mark Amaru Pinkham, *The Return of the Serpents of Wisdom* (Illinois: Adventures Unlimited Press, 1996), 56–7.

35 David Ferriz de Olivares, *Teoría Científica de la Cosmobiología* [Scientific Theory of Cosmobiology] (Peru, Trujillo: Universidad Nacional de Trujillo, 1976).

36 Earlyne Chaney, *Lost Empire of the Gods* (California: Astara Inc. 1994), 137.

37 Arnoldo Krumm-Heller – Huiracocha, '*Ordo Templi Orientis Phenomenon Fraternitas Rosicruciana Antiqua Baphomet and Rosycross*' ['Order of Eastern Phenomenon Temple of the Brotherhood of the Ancient Rosy Cross Baphomet and Rosycross'], compiled by Peter-Robert Koenig (April 1996) <http://www.parareligion.ch/fra.htm> accessed 10 May 2020.

38 Augustus Le Plongeon, *Sacred Mysteries Among the Mayas and the Quichés* (New York: Cosimo Classics, 2007), 45. Quoted also in *STA*, 'American Indian Symbolism', CXCVI.

39 *STA, loc. cit.*

40 Charles Étienne Brasseur de Bourbourg, *Popol Vuh: Le livre sacré des Quichés, &c* [The Popol Vuh: Sacred Book of the Quichés], *Collection de documents dans les langues indigènes, pour servir à l'étude de l'histoire et de la philologie de l'Amérique ancienne,* i (Paris: Arthus Bertrand, 1861). The complete title is *Popol Vuh: Le livre sacré et les mythes de l'antiquité américaine, avec les livres héroïques et historiques des Quichés. Ouvrage original des indigénes de Guatémala, texte quiché et traduction française en regard, accompagnée de notes philologiques et d'un commentaire sur la mythologie et les migrations des peuples anciens de l'Amérique, etc.* [Popol Vuh: The sacred book and the myths of American antiquity, with the heroic and historical books of the Quiches. Original work by the natives of Guatemala, quiche text and French translation opposite, accompanied by philological notes and a commentary on the mythology and migrations of the ancient peoples of America, etc.].

41 Charles Étienne Brasseur de Bourbourg, *Grammaire Quichée et le drame de Rabinal Achí* [A Quiché Grammar and the Dance of Rabinal Achi] (Paris, 1862) [online facsimile]

<https://openlibrary.org/works/OL1546423W/Gramatica_de_la_lengua_quiche> accessed 15 December 2019. Refer also to Carroll Edward Mace, 'Charles Étienne Brasseur de Bourbourg, 1814–1874', in Howard F. Cline and John B. Glass (volume eds), *Handbook of Middle American Indians, Vol. 13: Guide to Ethnohistorical Sources, Part II.*, ed. R. Wauchope (Austin: University of Texas Press, 1973), 298–325.

42 Albert Amao Soria, *op. cit.*, 48–54, 75.

43 *The Rosicrucian Manifestos: Fama Fraternitatis* and *Confessio Fraternitatis* (Cincinnati, Ohio: Emperor Norton Books, 2000; Benjamin Rowe, Acrobat Edition), 21 [online facsimile] <http://www.nommeraadio.ee/meedia/pdf/RRS/Rosicrucian%20Manifestos.pdf> accessed 16 December 2019.

44 Paul Foster Case, *Tarot Interpretation* (Los Angeles, California: Builders of the Adytum, 1961), Correspondence Lesson 3:3, in Albert Amao Soria, *op. cit.*, 53.

45 *CW*-II, 'A Land of Mystery', 306–7.

46 Paul Foster Case, *The True and Invisible Rosicrucian Order: An interpretation of the Rosicrucian allegory and an explanation of the ten Rosicrucian grades* (US: Weiser Books, 1927), 5.

47 *CW*-XIV, 'The Dangers of Practical Magic', 59–60.

48 There are many authentic and scholarly accounts of this episode. See for example, Frank E. Manuel, *A Portrait of Isaac Newton* (Cambridge, Massachusetts: Da Capo Press, 1968), 213–25.

49 Grace F. Knoche, *op. cit.*

50 G. de Purucker, *Studies in Occult Philosophy* (UK: Theosophical University Press, 1973), 637.

51 '*The Secret Doctrine* and Its Study', in *Madame Blavatsky on How to Study Theosophy* (London: Theosophical Publishing House, 1960), 9 from the Bowen Notes, being extracts from the notes of personal teachings given by H.P. Blavatsky to private pupils during the years 1888 to 1891.

52 Paraphrased from 'Pledged Chelas and Lay Chelas', *The Theosophist*, iv, Supplement to No. 10 (July 1883), 10–11; repr., *CW*-IV, 'Chelas and Lay Chelas', 611, which states: 'One who undertakes to try for Chelaship [a candidate who has offered himself or herself as to learn, practically, the hidden mysteries of Nature and the psychical powers latent in man] by that very act rouses and lashes into desperation every sleeping passion of his animal nature [which is not restricted just to sexuality but includes avarice, lust for power, selfishness, and much else].

53 Henk J. Spierenburg (compiled and annotated), *The Inner Group Teachings of H. P. Blavatsky* (2nd edn, rev. and enl, San Diego, California: Point Loma Publications, 1995), 27.

54 G. de Purucker, *Studies in Occult Philosophy*, 638.

55 Phiroz Mehta, *The Heart of Religion*, 125.

56 G. de Purucker, *Studies in Occult Philosophy*, 637.

57 *ibid.*

58 Godfrey Higgins, *Anacalypsis, An Attempt to Draw Aside the Veil of the Saitic Isis; Or, an Inquiry into the Origin of Languages, Nations, and Religions,* 2 vols (London: Longman, 1836), i, 150. Quoted also in *STA*, 'The Life and Philosophy of Pythagoras', LXV.

59 *IU*-I, 'Egyptian Wisdom', 557–8.

60 Paul Brunton, *A Search in Secret Egypt* (London: Rider and Company, 1954), 75.

61 David Frawley, *Gods, Sages, and Kings: Vedic secrets of ancient civilizations* (US: Lotus Press, 2001), 295.

62 *SD*-I, 'The Theogony of the Creative Gods', 424 et seq.

63 Alice Bailey, *A Treatise on White Magic* (2nd rev. edn, London: Lucis Press, 1951), 378.

64 —— *op. cit.*, 379–80.

65 John Gordon, *The Path of Initiation: Spiritual evolution and the restoration of the Western mystery tradition* (Rochester, Vermont: Inner Traditions, 2013), 511.

66 See: Peter Coviello, 'Transcendentalism', in *The Oxford Encyclopedia of American Literature* (New York: Oxford University Press, 2004); 'Transcendentalism', Wikipedia (last modified 10 January 2020) <https://en.wikipedia.org/wiki/Transcendentalism> accessed 16 January 2020.

67 Aubrey Sherman, *Wizards: The Myths, legends, and lore* (US: Adams Media, 2014).

68 'New Thought', *MSN Encarta*, Microsoft (retrieved 16 November 2007), accessed 11 May 2020.

69 Arthur Versluis, *American Transcendentalism and Asian Religions* (New York: Oxford University Press, 1993).

70 —— *The Esoteric Origins of the American Renaissance* (New York: Oxford University Press, 2001), 3.

71 Henry David Thoreau, *Walden* (Boston: Ticknor & Fields, 1854), 279.

72 Horatio Willis Dresser, *A History of the New Thought Movement* (New York: TY Crowell, 1919), 154.

73 J. Gordon Melton, Jerome Clark, and Aidan A. Kelly, *New Age Almanac* (New York: Visible Ink Press, 1991), 343.

74 Paul K. Conkin, *American Originals: Homemade varieties of Christianity* (North Carolina: The University of North Carolina Press, 1997), 269.

75 'A Preacher for Trump's America: Joel Osteen and the Prosperity Gospel: Lakewood Church's $60m "smiling pastor" holds up worldly success as proof of God's favour', *Financial Times*, 18 April 2019.

76 'US Preacher Asks Followers to Help Buy Fourth Private Jet', BBC News, 30 May 2018.

77 Poppy Noor, '"Satanic Wombs": the outlandish world of Trump's spiritual adviser', *The Guardian*, 27 January 2020 <https://www.theguardian.com/us-news/2020/jan/27/satanic-pregnancies-trump-spiritual-adviser-paula-white-outlandish-acts> accessed 8 September 2020.

78 Extract from Matthew 23, New King James Version.

79 'Radio, TV & Film Daily On-Demand TV Viewing Time' <https://www. statista.com > Media & Advertising > Radio, TV & Film> accessed 16 December 2019.

80 'Average Hour-Long TV Show is 36% Commercials' (7 May 2009) <http://www.marketingcharts.com/television/average-hour-long-show-is-36-commercials-9002> accessed 16 December 2019.

81 'Does American Television have More Adverts than any other Country?' <http://forums.digitalspy.co.uk/showthread.php?t=1616147> accessed 16 December 2019.

82 Typical examples are: Rhonda Byrne, *The Secret* (UK: Simon & Schuster, 2006); Wallace Wattles, *The Science of Getting Rich* (New York: Palmera Publishing, 2016).

83 David S. Reynolds, *Walt Whitman* (New York: Oxford University Press, 2005), 11.

84 Ralph Waldo Emerson, 'Essay XI: Intellect', in *Essays: First Series* (US: BiblioLife, 2009). See *Ralph Waldo Emerson* for online access to the complete essays and poems of Emerson <https://emerson-central.com/texts/essays-first-series> accessed 8 August 2020.

85 —— *op. cit.*

86 'Precursors of H.P.B. – The Three Fundamental Concepts of Emerson's Philosophy', *Theosophy*, 24/2 (December 1935), 49–54 <http://blavatsky.net/Wisdomworld/setting/emersontwo.html> accessed 17 December 2019.

87 Ralph Waldo Emerson, 'Lecture II: Plato; or, the Philosopher', in *Representative Men: Seven Lectures* (Boston: Phillips, Sampson and Company, 1850).

88 George Willis Cooke, 'The New Career', in *Ralph Waldo Emerson: His life, writings, and philosophy* (Germany: Hansebooks, 2017).

89 Ralph Waldo Emerson, 'Essay IX: The Over-Soul', in *Essays: First Series* (US: BiblioLife, 2009).

90 —— 'Essay II: Self-Reliance', in *Essays: First Series* (US: BiblioLife, 2009).

91 —— 'Essay IX: The Over-Soul'.

92 —— *Representative Men*.

93 —— 'Essay IX: The Over-Soul'.

94 —— 'Essay I: History', in *Essays: First Series* (US: BiblioLife, 2009).

95 —— 'Lecture II: Plato; or, the Philosopher'.

96 —— 'The American Scholar: An Oration delivered before the Phi Beta Kappa Society, at Cambridge [Massachusetts], August 31, 1837' <https://emersoncentral.com/ebook/The-American-Scholar.pdf> accessed 17 December 2019.

97 This is fully explained in the classic book by Iain McGilchrist, *The Master and His Emissary: The divided brain and the making of the Western world* (rev. edn New Haven and London: Yale University Press 2019). The implications are fully discussed in Volume II, Chapter 7.

98 Ralph Waldo Emerson, 'Essay III: Compensation', in *Essays, First Series* (US: BiblioLife, 2009).

99 —— 'The Sovereignty of Ethics', *North American Review*, x (1878), 12.

100 —— 'Essay III: Compensation'.

101 Kenneth Thurston Hurst, *Paul Brunton: A personal view* (New York: Larson Publications for Paul Brunton Philosophic Foundation, 1989), 191.

102 *The Journals and Miscellaneous Notebooks of Ralph Waldo Emerson*, ed. William H. Gilman, et al., 16 vols (Cambridge: Harvard University Press, 1960, 1982), ix, 211–12.

103 Ralph Waldo Emerson, 'Essay IX: The Over-Soul'.

104   —— 'Essay I: History'.

105   —— 'Essay II: Self-Reliance'.

106   Edi Bilimoria, 'The Alchemy of Religion: From inner illumination to love and service in action', in *Multiculturalism and the Convergence of Faith and Practical Wisdom in Modern Society*, ed. Ana-Maria Pascal (US: IGI Global, 2017), 38.

107   Ralph Waldo Emerson, 'Lecture III: Swedenborg; or, The Mystic', in *Representative Men: Seven Lectures*.

108   —— *Compensation and Self-Reliance* (New York: Cosimo Classics, 2005).

109   Alfred Russel Wallace, 'A Substitute for the Reincarnation Theory (S285a: 1878)', *The Spiritualist (London)* (25 January 1878), 43 <http://people.wku.edu/charles.smith/wallace/S285A.htm> accessed 17 December 2019. See also *The Alfred Russel Wallace Page* <http://people.wku.edu/charles.smith/index1.htm> accessed 17 December 2019.

110   Refer to the several correspondences with the Englishman Alfred Percy Sinnett (1840–1921) included in *The Mahatma Letters to A. P. Sinnett in chronological sequence* (Manila, Philippines: Theosophical Publishing House, 1993). Sinnett was the Editor of *The Pioneer*, the leading English Daily of India. He became an ardent Theosophist, wrote major works on the Ancient Wisdom and was Vice-President and Acting President of the Theosophical Society during the late nineteenth and early twentieth century.

111   Quoted in Richard Lanoue, *The Science of Living the Life You've Always Wanted* (Richard Lanoue, 2007), 207.

112   Thomas Troward, *The Creative Process in the Individual* (US: Arc Manor, 2008), 34.

113   —— *op. cit.*, 42.

114   —— *The Edinburgh Lectures on Mental Science* (US: Arc Manor, 2008), 42.

115   —— *op. cit.*, 51.

116   —— *The Dore Lectures on Mental Science* (US: Arc Manor, 2008), 29.

117   Genevieve Behrend, *Attaining Your Desires* (Radford, Virginia: Wilder Publications, 2008), 11.

118   *ibid*.

119   Ralph Waldo Trine, *In Tune with the Infinite* (Radford, Virginia: Wilder Publications, 2007).

120   —— *op. cit.*, 6.

121   *SD*-I, 'Gods, Monads, and Atoms', 610.

122   David Castillejo, *The Expanding Force in Newton's Cosmos, as Shown in His Unpublished Papers* (Madred: Ediciones de Arte y Bibliofilia, 1981), back cover. This book is the summary of a four volume treatise.

123   Ralph Waldo Trine, *In Tune with the Infinite*, 6.

124   —— *In Tune with the Infinite: The New Thought movement* (New York: Dodge Publishing Company, 1897), 6.

125   —— *In Tune with the Infinite* (Radford, Virginia: Wilder Publications, 2007), 6.

126   —— *op. cit.*, 6.

127   —— *ibid*.

128   —— *op. cit.*, 18.

129   —— *op. cit.*, 87.

130   —— *op. cit.*, 9.

131   Ralph Waldo Trine and Henry Ford, *Power That Wins* (US: Kessinger Pub Co, 2003).

132   Napoleon Hill, *The Law of Success in Sixteen Lessons* (US: Tribeca Books, 1928). The work was originally commissioned at the request of the Scottish–American industrialist and philanthropist Andrew Carnegie (1835–1919).

133   *New York Herald Tribune*, 20 May 1963, 22.

134   Charles S. Braden, *Spirits in Rebellion: The rise and development of New Thought* (Dallas: Southern Methodist University Press, 1963), 376.

135   'Scientist and Artist Dispute Newton and Kepler Findings', *New York Times* (3 August 1930).

136   Walter Russell, *The Universal One*, ed. Louise Russell, preface by Lao Russell (Swannanoa, Virginia: University of Science & Philosophy, 1927; facs. repr., 1974) [online facsimile] <https://bluestarenterprise.com/files-outside-wordpress/walter-russell/49306379-Walter-Russell-the-Universal-One-Alchemy-Chemistry.pdf?fbclid=IwAR0xDDRQouV8dAiNWmwTMWkn1sW wa3nUIWvFikqK1t34EUjPSszRo8CYW8w> accessed 16 February 2020.

137 —— *The Russell Genero-Radiative Concept or The Cyclic Theory of Continuous Motion* (New York: Press of L. Middleditch Co., 1930).

138 —— *The Secret of Light* (Swannanoa, Virginia: University of Science & Philosophy, 1947).

139 —— *A New Concept of the Universe* (Swannanoa, Virginia: University of Science & Philosophy, 1953).

140 —— *The Secret of Light*, 228–9.

141 David Castillejo, *The Expanding Force in Newton's Cosmos, loc. cit.*

142 Walter Russell, *A New Concept of the Universe*, xi.

143 C. W. Kelsey, 'Walter Russell and the Atom,' Letter to the *New York Sun*, 5 March 1930.

144 Sir Oliver Lodge, *The Ether of Space* (New York: Harper and Brothers,1929), 28–9.

145 Dr. Francis Trevelyan, 'Letter to Walter Russell, March 1947', in Walter Russell, *The Secret of Light* <https://www.philosophy.org/store/p7/The_Secret_of_Light.html> accessed 17 December 2019.

146 Walter Russell, *The Secret of Light* (3rd edn, Swannanoa, Virginia: University of Science & Philosophy, 1974), xi.

147 *The Russell Genero-Radiative Concept*, 4.

148 Preface by Lao Russell, in Walter Russell, *The Universal One*.

149 'School of the Holy Science' <https://www.facebook.com/Astrotheology/photos/a. 308319812561844.70741.118019521591875/1355938601133288/?theater> accessed 16 January 2020.

150 Walter Russell, *A New Concept of the Universe*, 9.

151 Walter Russell and Lao Russell, *Atomic Suicide?* (US: University of Science & Philosophy, 1957), 106.

152 James Jeans, *The Mysterious Universe* (Cambridge: Cambridge University Press, 1937), 137.

153 Maria Cohut, 'How the Brain Adapts to Hear Better after Vision Loss', *Medical News Today* (25 April 2019) <https://www.medicalnewstoday.com/articles/325032> accessed 5 August 2020.

154 E. Lester Smith, *Inner Adventures* (Wheaton, Illinois: Theosophical Publishing House, 1988), 131.

155 Paul Brunton, 'A Night Inside the Great Pyramid', in *A Search in Secret Egypt* (London: Rider and Company, 1954), 74.

156 *ibid.*

157 Henry L. Drake, in foreword to Manly P. Hall, *The Secret Teachings of All Ages* (Diamond Jubilee Edition, Los Angeles, Philosophical Research Society, 1988).

158 *STA*, 'Conclusion', CCIV.

Recapitulation:
Unifying Consciousness Through Science and the Mystery Teachings

'SCIENCE SHOULD HAVE NEITHER DESIRES NOR PREJUDICES. TRUTH SHOULD BE HER SOLE AIM.'

SIR WILLIAM GROVE FRS FRSE[1]

SYNOPSIS

The recapitulation stresses the need for a *science of consciousness*, not consciousness as a subject within mainstream science. We enquire whether science is an enemy of reason, when experimental evidence does not fit the accepted theoretical norms, or an impartial enquiry into truth and the investigation of the still unknown. We also contrast the role and context of the connected and convergent pattern of explanations with the concordance of evidence from multiple unrelated sources (consilience), as different ways of investigating truth. Also explained is the meaning of soul and subtle bodies, in simple terms at this stage, thus providing a bridge for the full exposition in Volume II.

KEY WORDS: spirit of Science, scientism, convergence, consilience, science of consciousness, soul, beyond the brain, Galileo Commission Report, Richard Dawkins, Rupert Sheldrake, Steven Weinberg, Robert Jahn

The highest ideal of Science was quoted in Chapter 3 in the words of Sir William Grove, the British physicist and a justice of Britain's High Court. Its seminal importance warrants that Grove's injunction be repeated in the epigraph. However, it is sobering to consider that his recognition that this was not the case in the nineteenth century (indicated by his use of the word 'should' in two short sentences) is still clearly not the case some two centuries on.

Volume I of this work has been at pains to show that excepting a few legendary scientists, mainstream science has, unfortunately, fallen far short of adopting Grove's inspired injunction—what ought, in fact, to be the motto of Science. For this reason, unshackling scientific enquiry from materialistic encrustations into consciousness has never been more pressing than now. Thus, throughout Volume I, and indeed throughout this entire work, the primacy of consciousness and mind is shown to be a *sine qua non* of Science, not restricted to the objective science of physical matter. The writer demonstrates how Mind constitutes the fundamental reality of the universe and its inhabitants. Notwithstanding its wonderful discoveries in the physical domain, the inability of modern science to explain the nature of consciousness, or to account for innumerable cases of what it refers to as 'paranormal' or 'anomalous' (such as ESP or *psi*), is undoubtedly due to its self-limiting paradigm of materialism. In justifying this stance, we have first underlined the deficiencies and limitations (as well as the strengths) in the philosophy, metaphysic, and methodology of science, and then shown the indispensable need of a complementary esoteric component drawn from the thoughts of legendary scientists and mainly from the *philosophia perennis* and the Mystery Teachings of All Ages at its heart.

Mainstream science unable to explain consciousness due to its overtly materialistic paradigm

316

On the other hand, we have also provided examples from scientists of the quantum era to show how modern science is slowly, but incontrovertibly, uniting with esoteric and occult science as to the central role of mind. Chapter 3 provided examples of this from scientists of the calibre of Sir Arthur Eddington and Sir James Jeans, both of whom regarded the universe, not as a machine, but as an Idea, or a great Thought, hence pointing to the primacy of Universal Mind over matter. But in fairness, we have to admit that such forward thinking, metaphysically minded scientists are still very much in the minority— the vast majority of mainstream scientists uphold the machine paradigm as the earlier portions of this Volume have been at pains to show. Nonetheless, it would not be labouring the point to highlight key obstacles that prevent the realization of the crucial importance of consciousness and mind.

Arthur Eddington and James Jeans invoke the truth of esotericism and the ideal of science

The Spirit of Science or Scientism?

In earlier chapters we drew upon the insights of William James in order to elucidate the whole question of how we perceive reality and the various factors that inhibit such clear and undistorted perception. In the penultimate Chapter, 'Percept and Concept' of his last book *Some Problems of Philosophy*, published after his death in 1910, he rounded out his philosophical work with a treatise on metaphysics with this insight: 'The intellectual life of man consists almost wholly in his substitution of a conceptual order for the perceptual order in which his experience originally comes.'[2] This is equivalent to saying that the theoretical model which tends to hold sway over the living experience ultimately dominates the latter. One of the best of many recent such examples of the 'map ruling the territory' is the unwarranted attacks on the work of Robert Jahn at the PEAR laboratory (summarized in Chapter 4). The American Nobel physicist Philip Anderson (1923–2020), also from Princeton, wrote an article in the journal *Physics Today*, the magazine of the American Physical Society, containing an oblique attack on Jahn's work citing it as an example of 'those who call themselves physicists' yet engage in experiments studying the possibility of ESP, thus having 'abandoned healthy scepticism in favour of bigotry.'[3] But who is the real bigot: Jahn or Anderson? Anderson's objection was not on the grounds of the actual experimental findings (the true scientific ethos) but on the basis that if the findings were not in consensus with the expectations and paradigm of mainstream science, then they could not possibly be right. This is a glaring example of refusing to 'look through the telescope' at the evidence, just like the professor of philosophy at Padua University in Galileo's day (see the epigraph to Chapters 2 and 5).[4] And like Galileo, Jahn has been castigated for his discoveries, albeit far less harshly. In his book *Dreams of a Final Theory*, another committed sceptic and Nobel physicist, the American Steven Weinberg refers to Jahn's complaint[5] that 'although his [Anderson's] [*sic*] office is only a few hundred yards from my own, he has not visited our laboratory, discussed any of his concerns with me directly or apparently even read with care any of our technical literature.'[6] However, Anderson was later obliged to retract his position with a defensive response in order to avoid having to comment on the numerous issues raised in discussions about his article that appeared in the journal's correspondence column. (A very similar case of not bothering to inspect the evidence on a priori grounds will shortly be described in connection with the aborted televised debate between Rupert Sheldrake and Richard Dawkins when the

Nobel laureates
Philip Anderson
and Steven
Weinberg uphold
scientism despite
every evidence to
the contrary

latter declined to look at evidence given to him in peer-reviewed journals about telepathy and related matters.)

In similar vein to Anderson, Weinberg disparaged Jahn's findings on the basis of the 'syndrome' we have already outlined, namely that the nature of the supposed phenomenon is enough in itself to condemn a work as being wrong (see 'Weinberg's syndrome' in Chapter 4, page 120). According to Weinberg, if such things as telekinesis, or other such (quoting Jahn's words) 'consciousness-related anomalous phenomena',[7] did exist then 'one would be turning one's back on all of modern science',[8] throwing away everything we know, and having to start all over again. Weinberg further opines, 'Now, the conventional answer would be that this evidence must be tested with an open mind and without theoretical preconceptions. I do not think that this is a useful answer, but this view seems to be widespread'[9] because 'what Jahn […] and others who agree with them are missing is the sense of the connectedness of scientific knowledge. We do not understand everything, but we understand enough to know that there is no room in our world for telekinesis […].'[10]

How Weinberg
justifies the
stance of
scientism

As an example to support this contention, Weinberg mentions the Spanish settlers in Mexico who began in the sixteenth century to push northwards into the country known as Tejas, led on by rumours of cities of gold, the seven cities of Cibola. At the time, when few Europeans had been to Tejas, that did not seem so unreasonable. However, if someone today reported evidence that there are seven golden cities somewhere in modern Texas, would we open-mindedly mount an expedition to search every corner of the state from the Red River to the Rio Grande to look for these cities, or would we judge that the geophysics and layout of the modern state is so well explored and known that it is simply not worthwhile to look for golden cities? 'In the same way', he reasons, 'our discovery of the connected and convergent pattern of scientific explanations has done the very great service of teaching us that there is no room in nature for astrology or telekinesis […] or other superstitions.'[11] We have no quarrel with this judgement insofar as it applies to hunting for golden cities in the modern state of Texas, and would of course answer in the negative. Nor would we wish to disagree that the convergent (but not necessarily the connected) pattern of scientific explanations is a valid criterion for overlooking (but not necessarily disbelieving) phenomena that do not fall strictly within the legitimate boundaries of physical science based upon a materialistic paradigm. But, in today's world, it is completely mistaken to apply this line of reasoning when there is substantive evidence on so-called 'anomalous phenomena', including telekinesis, coming from eminent physicists such as Weinberg's colleague, Robert Jahn, Professor of Aerospace Science, and Dean of Engineering at Princeton University,[12] and others, as cited in Chapter 4.

Moreover, note Weinberg's words 'in our world' and 'no room in nature'. This surely is a perfect example of fixed preconceptions dictating, on a priori grounds, what can be allowed as constituting evidence in the world of the materialistic scientist. Furthermore, Weinberg is entirely mistaken about the 'connectedness of scientific knowledge'. It was precisely such an attempt at 'connectedness', between the results of quantum experiments and classical theory, that caused considerable disquiet to Einstein because of the complete *disconnection* between the theories of classical physics and quantum physics (see Chapter 4). That Weinberg, ironically, received the Nobel Prize (along with physicists

Abdus Salam and Sheldon Glashow) for his contributions to the unification of the weak force[i] and electromagnetic interaction between elementary particles—very much in the realm of quantum physics—only goes to show that famous scientists can sometimes make poor philosophers (and philosophy is in any case a subjected that Weinberg appears to disdain[ii]).

Preconceptions and prejudice overrule evidence in mainstream science

So, in essence, both Anderson and Weinberg have both unwittingly, but admirably, demonstrated a perspicuous observation of another Nobel physicist from Princeton—Albert Einstein. Objecting to the placing of observables at the heart of the new quantum mechanics, during Heisenberg's 1926 lecture at Berlin, Einstein remarked: 'Whether or not you can observe a thing depends upon the theory you use. It is the theory that decides what can be observed.'[13] (It is a matter of speculation whether this comment represented Einstein's mature reflection on his difficulties in fitting the results of quantum experiments within the framework of classical physics—see again Chapter 4.) Nonetheless, recent casualties like Eric Laithwaite, Thomas Nagel, and Robert Jahn (to mention but a few) have all discovered the truth of Einstein's observation for themselves to their bitter cost. With exceptional scientists it is otherwise, as with Jahn, who was more interested in integrity and truth than pre-established theories, or what repercussions on his career his anomalous discoveries might have. Anderson's and Weinberg's objections (and those from others of similar hubristic self-superiority) when added to Einstein's corrective, perfectly demonstrate what Arthur Ellison's 'flower bowl experiment' showed so dramatically (see again Chapter 4, page 68): that only in exceptional cases of complete inner clarity do we see truly; invariably otherwise, we see only what we want to see, our cherished beliefs dictate our version of reality, and we 'force-fit' reality into our conceptual thought-maps, instead of the other way around, which is the hallmark of the true scientist but not necessarily the famous one despite his numerous accolades (see the epigraph).

Convergence and Consilience Contrasted – A Matter of Proof

In addition to the connected and convergent pattern of explanations, there is also another form of convergence used as a valid test of truth. Known as 'consilience', it is the synthesis of knowledge from different specialized fields of human endeavour, defined by the American biologist and naturalist Edward Osborne Wilson as 'literally a "jumping together" of knowledge by the linking of facts and fact-based theory across disciplines to create a common groundwork of explanation.'[14] Consilience (also referred to as 'convergence of evidence' or 'concordance of evidence') is thus the principle that evidence from independent, unrelated sources can 'converge' to confirm the same truth from different perspectives, thereby not only validating the truth but, in the process, each other. The veracity of a principle is of course strengthened to the degree that it is confirmed by several sources. That is to say that *when multiple sources of evidence are in agreement, the conclusion reached is stronger than would be the case were individual sources relied upon with a significantly weaker evidential claim.* In addition to its application to science, consilience

The case for invoking evidence from multiple sources

---

i The 'weak force' is one of the four fundamental forces of physics through which particles interact with each other. It underlies some forms of radioactivity and governs the decay of unstable subatomic particles.

ii Chapter VII of *Dreams of a Final Theory* is entitled 'Against Philosophy'. The implications are explored in Volume III, Chapter 11 of this work.

is especially suited to gaining a consensus in natural history, anthropology, pre-history, and theology.

As described in Chapter 8, this was the method used in a broad sense by Newton and Blavatsky. Regarding the former, we gave the example of how he compared, and brought together, diverse tracts from prophetic, philosophical, and theological texts to affirm, in the General Scholium of *Principia*, the omnipresence of God (see pages 231–232). Likewise, Blavatsky garnered an abundance of ancient and modern evidence, from widely-separated periods of history and tradition, all tending to show the common origin of the diverse esoteric teachings of worldwide civilizations and cultures. She likened these to 'so many streams of the same water' which she said, 'must have had a common source [the Mystery Teachings] from which they started.'

The Need for a Science of Consciousness

Moreover, to assert—as do Weinberg, and Dawkins (see below)—that evidence for *psi* phenomena, like telekinesis, would entail having to jettison all we know in science and start afresh is complete nonsense. It just goes to show the virtually bulletproof armour of opinion worn even by Nobel physicists who are wedded to an impregnable materialistic paradigm having no truck with consciousness (other than as an epiphenomenon of physical brain activity). It does not mean that mainstream science would have to jettison all it knows; but it forcefully indicates the urgent need to rejuvenate its fossilized opinions and expectations, scrutinize its metaphysical foundations, widen its perspective, and fully embrace consciousness and mind as subjects in themselves, not as subsets within mainstream science (see the earlier reference to the Galileo Commission Report).

The near-impregnable psychological armour of scientism

Perhaps Anderson has not come across the penetrating reflection (quoted above) of his Princeton colleague—Einstein. But also, so it would seem, he has not come across, or chosen to ignore, what other legendary Nobel physicists of the quantum era had to say about the dominance of expectations and theory over observed facts, for example: 'All ideas we form of the outer world are ultimately only reflections of our own perceptions', Max Planck;[15] 'All new experience makes its appearance within the frame of our customary points of view and forms of perception', Niels Bohr;[16] and 'The same organizing forces that have shaped nature in all her forms are also responsible for the structure of our minds', Werner Heisenberg.[17]

So is Science An 'Enemy of Reason' Because 'I don't want to discuss evidence'?

Still on the subject of telekinesis and related areas, *The Enemies of Reason* was a two-part television documentary. Written and presented by Richard Dawkins, his aim was to expose 'those areas of belief that exist without scientific proof, yet manage to hold the nation under their spell', including mediumship, acupuncture, and psychokinesis. It was first broadcast in 2007 on Channel 4 in the UK, and constituted, in effect, a sequel to his life-long tirade against religion in his documentary of the previous year, *The Root of All Evil?*

Shortly before *The Enemies of Reason* was filmed, the production company, IWC Media, informed Rupert Sheldrake that Richard Dawkins wanted to visit him to discuss his research on unexplained abilities of people and animals with an assurance that this would be an entirely more balanced affair than *The Root of All Evil?* had been, adding that it was intended as a discussion between two scientists about scientific modes of enquiry.

The following extract is highly significant. It is taken from Sheldrake's website, 'Richard Dawkins Comes to Call' https://www.sheldrake.org/reactions/richard-dawkins-comes-to-call/

> 'He [Dawkins] said that if it [i.e., telepathy] really occurred, it would "turn the laws of physics upside down," and added, "Extraordinary claims require extraordinary evidence."
>
> "This depends on what you regard as extraordinary", I [Sheldrake] replied.
>
> The previous week I had sent Richard copies of some of my papers, published in peer-reviewed journals, so that he could look at the data.
>
> Richard seemed uneasy and said, "I don't want to discuss evidence". "Why not?" I asked. "There isn't time [Richard responded]. It's too complicated. And that's not what this programme is about." The camera stopped.
>
> The Director, Russell Barnes, confirmed that he too was not interested in evidence. The film he was making was another Dawkins polemic.
>
> I said to Russell, "If you're treating telepathy as an irrational belief, surely evidence about whether it exists or not is essential for the discussion. If telepathy occurs, it's not irrational to believe in it. I thought that's what we were going to talk about. I made it clear from the outset that I wasn't interested in taking part in another low grade debunking exercise."
>
> Richard said, "It's not a low grade debunking exercise; it's a high grade debunking exercise."
>
> In that case, I replied, there had been a serious misunderstanding, because I had been led to believe that this was to be a balanced scientific discussion about evidence. Russell Barnes asked to see the emails I had received from his assistant. He read them with obvious dismay, and said the assurances she had given me were wrong. The team packed up and left.'

Richard Dawkins disregards evidence in favour of preconceptions

Three factors are noteworthy in Dawkins's mind-set: first, the refusal to examine evidence from papers published in peer-reviewed journals; second, the predictable mantra about 'extraordinary evidence' uttered in desperation when materialistic scientists cannot provide a reasoned argument or be bothered to think—see Chapter 4, page 103 et seq., for an exposition on why such vacuous utterances are meaningless; third, the unsupported assumption that all the laws of physics are fully known and therefore there are no hidden laws of a (physical) nature to be discovered (the same sort of assumption made by classical physicists of the nineteenth century before Max Planck ushered in the quantum era).

Public understanding of science vitiated by scientism

In view of this episode, we are entitled to ask: given that Dawkins at the time held the Simonyi Professorship Chair for the Public Understanding of Science, was his crusade, in reality, to convert the public to regard science as a vehicle of prejudice in order to promote a fundamentalist belief-system, any different, in principle, from religious fundamentalism—in which case, would not a better alternative title to *The Enemies of Reason* be *Opponents of Truth and Adversaries of Common Sense*? Or should the 'public understanding of science' be a method of engaging the public by popularizing scientific enquiry into unchartered territory through impartial examination of the hitherto unexplained laws of nature supported by any available evidence, extraordinary, or otherwise?

The section title above is illuminating in this respect. Is science, then, an 'enemy of reason'?

Or Is Science a Humble Enquiry into Truth and the Unknown?

It is fitting to conclude this section with the following quotation from Brian Josephson, another Nobel physicist, also a member of the Scientific and Medical Network. In the concluding paragraph to his article about another BBC television series 'Heretic' regarding the responses of the scientific community to ideas generally considered unacceptable, and the treatment meted out to the scientists advocating such ideas, Josephson has this to say:

> The benefits of the most crucial discoveries could be unnecessarily lost to mankind if these ways of dealing with unusual results were the norm [i.e., scorning the evidence without first examining it, and attacking the scientist], as they indeed appear to be. What is it that causes such reactions? My model for what goes on is that science involves not only facts and theories but a collection of 'defence mechanisms', intended to maintain the 'purity' of science. Science is viewed as a good that can be threatened if adequate standards are not maintained. So far, so good, but problems start when scientists start to think of themselves as experts who know better than others what is true and what is in error. Experts do not need to go into details; they 'know' what is wrong with a field and become authorities that others can look up to know what is the truth. At the level of detail, if the going gets bad in an argument one can always call upon the universal mantra 'extraordinary claims require extraordinary proof', to extricate oneself from further discussion, or the need to think.[18]

Brian Josephson castigates defence mechanisms of science used to rebut unusual evidence

The fallacy of the 'universal mantra' to forestall 'the need to think' has, to reiterate, been fully exposed in Chapter 4. But here, Josephson has neatly encapsulated the four interrelated components of the problem:

1. The suppression of potentially new discoveries and fresh ways of looking at the world though science that could potentially be of benefit to humanity.

2. The prevailing mainstream reaction to new ideas.

3. The defensive mechanisms used to preserve the 'purity' and status quo of science.

4. The appeal to authority to explain away the problem with a superior hand-waving attitude when pressed for details regarding the criticisms levied.

What, then, are these defence mechanisms brought into play to preserve the ostensible purity and sacrosanctity of natural science? They are purely psychological reactions to unusual phenomena; in fact, none other than the interposing of the knowledge filter between the new evidence and what is allowed to filter through (as described at the close of Chapter 4 on page 115). The 'filter media' comprise established theories and fixed concepts, in other words, unalterable mind structures, left-brained 'conceptual maps confused with the territory' as in this terse quotation (partly stated in Chapters 6 and 7) from the little book (see Figure I-15) presented by Blavatsky to Leo Tolstoy—*The Voice of the Silence*, derived from *The Book of the Golden Precepts*:

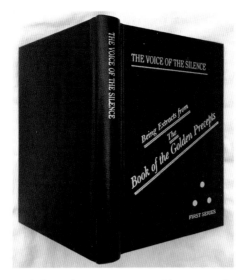

Figure I-15 *The Voice of the Silence* presented by H. P. Blavatsky to Leo Tolstoy
Writer's own photograph

Having become indifferent to objects of perception, the pupil must seek out the *rajah* [overlord] of the senses, the Thought-Producer, he who awakes illusion.

The Mind is the great Slayer of the Real.

Let the Disciple slay the Slayer.[19]

Psychological blocks to clear perception

What happens when we manage to slay the illusion-producer and peer into the Real?

Man – Consciousness Enfleshed

We then discover that our physical body provides the temporary tabernacle for the enduring Self. Physical man is consciousness enfleshed: immortal in essence, though mortal in form. This theme is illustrated in Table I-4 on page 325 being a recapitulation of the teachings, so far, on man's overall constitution for a terrestrial life. The twofold division is underscored with five succinct observations: from three legendary Nobel physicists—Albert Einstein, Max Planck, and Erwin Schrödinger; from David Bohm, one of the most significant physicists and philosophers of the twentieth century; and from the British philosopher, author and educator C. E. M. Joad (1891–1953) who candidly commended Blavatsky's trailblazing ideas of her time (summarized later in the Coda of Volume II). Note, especially, their unanimous pronouncement about the mind principle being unamenable to physical investigation by science because its action is noetic and therefore not directly associated with a brain or body organ. Their joint assertions of: (*a*) an independent mind reality neither body- nor brain-dependent (and therefore not amenable to investigation by science); and (*b*) manifesting through a body- and brain-dependent physical reality, could arguably be comparable to the A-consciousness and B-consciousness, respectively, that Lord Geddes experienced—see Chapter 6, page 171.

Legendary scientists understand the hard problem of consciousness

This being so, mainstream neuroscience is simply wasting its time trying to fathom the mystery of mind and consciousness on a physical and material basis—the brain. Why keep looking for a non-existent needle in a haystack?

In which case and in simple terms, what is the meaning of soul; and what is its relation to spirit and body?

The Soul – What Does it Mean?

From the Mystery Teachings the world over, it should be apparent that in absolutely no sense can the mind be perceived as being just the product of the material brain of the mortal self, bereft of its parent principle. This will become clearer in Volume II where we elucidate the meaning of what is known as the Higher Mind and the Lower mind. Moreover, we need not labour the point that even a brief survey of the Mysteries of all epochs furnishes ample testimony as to the composite nature of man: part spirit, and part corporeal (i.e., comprising his spiritual and animal natures). But when two such dissimilar parts—one immortal and the other mortal—are brought together in one entity (man) there has got to be an interface, or intermediary, that necessarily partakes of the nature of both parts. 'Soul' is the common term used for this intermediary, or mediator between the spiritual and material parts of man, as depicted in the threefold division shown in Table I-4. Note however, that soul, used without qualification, is a *generic* term and its meaning at different levels from the spiritual to the material is fully explained in Volume II, Chapter 3. For the moment, note that soul is not restricted to man; the animals and vegetables also possess a soul at their level.

'Soul' is essentially a mediator

Accordingly, the most fundamental esoteric taxonomy of man's principles derived from his two parts, as we find in all the religious philosophies, is the trinity of spirit, soul, and body. These again are all generic terms. In Volume II we explain, in depth, the functions of the soul. (The derivation, enumeration, and significance of man's sevenfold division are reserved for Chapters 2 and 3 of Volume II. However, it is shown in outline below, in Table I-4 opposite, in order to display its relationship with the more elementary ways of dividing man's constitution into a duality and a triplicity.)

Meanwhile, let us again recall Plato's teaching, mentioned in Chapter 9, and further add that the great initiate affirmed that man is composed of three principles: (*a*) an immortal principle; (*b*) a mortal body; and (*c*) a 'separate mortal kind of Soul'.[20] It is that which we have respectively referred to above as the spirit, the physical body, and the soul (*psyche*); and this tripartite enumeration follows directly from his teaching about the *interior* man as constituted of two parts—one immutable and always the same, formed of the same substance as Deity, and the other mortal and corruptible.[21] Very significantly, Plato counsels about *psyche*, the soul in general, in its two aspects:

Dual functions of the soul

1. Functioning as *Nous*, the rational soul, (Spiritual Soul) 'rising' to ally herself with the divine part of man, whereupon she does everything aright and felicitously.

2. However, when 'sinking' to attach herself to man's unbridled desire nature she functions as *Anoia*, folly, or the irrational soul (Animal soul) and in the extreme, runs towards eventual annihilation of the physical man and personality.[22]

That man throughout history has displayed the whole range of characteristics and behaviour, from sublime genius to depraved monster, is surely fitting evidence about the truth of Plato's dictum. Moreover, such extremes of human behaviour can neither be wholly explained by Darwinism, nor by materialistic neuroscience proclaiming (as per Francis

Table I-4 An Outline of the Constitution of Man on Earth

Man as One Unified Entity	Twofold Constitution						Threefold Constitution	Sevenfold Constitution
Individuality or Higher Self (Immortal) • noetic • no brain or body organ	"The upper half plans and thinks	'I regard consciousness as fundamental. We cannot get behind consciousness. Everything that we talk about, everything that we regard as existing, postulates consciousness.'	'Consciousness is absolutely fundamental. It cannot be accounted for in terms of anything else.	'The observing mind is not a physical system. And it might be better to reserve the term "subject" for the observing mind. For the subject, if anything, is the thing that senses and thinks.	'The ultimate perception does not originate in the brain or any material structure. The subtle mechanism of knowing the truth does not originate in the brain,	'The "Higher Self" has no special organ as its counterpart in the body. It is not, therefore, located in the brain, and it has no counterparts in brain movements.	**Spirit** / **Soul**	**Upper Triad** 1, 2, 3
Personality or Lower self (Mortal) • psychic • brain and body-dependent	while the lower half determines our fate.' Albert Einstein[23]	I regard matter as derivative from consciousness.' Max Planck[24]	Consciousness cannot be accounted for in physical terms.' Erwin Schrödinger[25]	It cannot interact with any physical system. Sensations and thoughts do not belong to the [physical] "world of energy".' Erwin Schrödinger[26, 27]	although a material structure is necessary to manifest it.' David Bohm[28]	The "Lower Self" is body-dependent. It manifests itself, through our organic system.' C. E. M. Joad[29]	**Soul** / **Body**	**Lower Quaternary** 4, 5, 6, 7

Crick and his school) that our entire behaviour and nature is governed solely by the oscillations of neurons across the neocortex of our brains (see Chapter 2). We need hardly give examples or dwell on the *Anoia* end of the spectrum. But concerning *Nous* let us enquire what the Christ meant by: 'I am the way, the truth, and the life: no man cometh unto the Father, but by me' (John 14:6, King James Version). This sublime saying has been ludicrously anthropomorphized and turned into a dogma by the Christian Church who interpret it to mean that mankind's sole way to salvation is through the way of the historical Jesus and none else—'but by me' because 'I [Jesus] am the [only] way'. Esoterically what do 'I am the way' and 'but by me' mean? The Christ stands for the impersonal principle, *in each man*, of the Spiritual Soul (*Nous*, or *Christos*). In respect of *Nous*, an insightful biblical quotation is: 'Let this mind be in you, which was also in Christ Jesus' (Philippians 2:5, King James Version). Krishna is the equivalent Eastern term deriving from the same root. Recasting the Christ's words in their esoteric connotation we may suggest the following: 'The Spiritual Soul (*Nous*) of each man is the way, the truth, and the life: therefore, no man (be he Christian, Hindu, Muslim, or any other religious denomination) cometh to the Father (i.e., his immortal Self) but by me—the Spiritual Soul.' For this reason, the Christ is sometimes referred to as 'the Mediator' (the soul of man being 'the Mediator' as explained above). It was the Christ's spiritual status that made him at-one with truth. Indeed, he said, 'I and My Father are one' (John 10:30, King James Version). But this oneness with truth was also the case with Zarathuśtra, Kṛṣṇa, and Buddha, to name but three more examples of divine incarnation, where the man-god, for their allotted time on earth, displayed the perfect tripartite union of the immortal spirit with Nous and the mortal human vehicle.

How does this tripartite union function in the man of flesh and blood on Earth?

How the Church misunderstands the meaning of Nous

Spirit-Soul-Body – Their Role and Function in Man

We have spoken at length about the Hermetic Axiom. So let us now apply the principle of correspondences to understand the communal role and function of spirit, soul, and body in man. Generically speaking, in the macrocosmic realm the spiritual world is the sphere of causation, the material world that of effects, and the soul world is the world of mediation (see Chapter 8 on pages 245 and 249 regarding the spectrum of mediations acknowledged by esotericism). By correspondence then, man's divine nature partakes of the heavens, his animal nature of the earth, and his strictly human nature, or soul, of the intermediate realms. Thus we find the spiritual and material universes are both reflected in the constitution of the composite human being who partakes of both divinity and nature. But if it seems that we are attaching excessive importance to the soul and spirit, this is only to readjust the balance because they are unjustly neglected at the expense of the body, which is mistakenly regarded as the sole vehicle of life. We stress that the body is just as important because, 'A seed is useless and impotent unless it is put in its appropriate matrix', for, as the Rosicrucian axiom proclaims: 'A soul cannot develop and progress without an appropriate body, because it is the physical body that furnishes the material for its development.'[30] What this effectively means is that the 'currents' of the soul must be 'earthed', to use a simplistic electrical analogy.

Man is a creature of heaven and earth

What happens to man after death when his physical body disintegrates, turns to dust and returns to the earth? The simple answer is: 'The spirit shall return unto God who gave it'

(Ecclesiastes 12:7, King James Version). The enormous implications of this terse maxim will be explained in detail in Chapter 5 of Volume II. For now, suffice it to say that an errant soul is destructible, but Spirit is forever indestructible, as this further extract from the Scriptures makes plain: 'Then shall the dust return to the earth as it was' (Ecclesiastes 12:7, King James Version) and 'the soul that sinneth [i.e., *Anoia* as stated above], it shall die' (Ezekiel 18:20, King James Version); but as just stated, 'the spirit shall return unto God who gave it'.

The above is just a bare outline of what will all be fully elaborated in Volume II. But even at this stage it is apparent that it is hardly viable to define a clean line of demarcation between soul and spirit, even though the above quotations make it plain that the two terms are not synonymous.

So whether we refer to Divine Mind in its aspect as transcendence, or as immanence in individual minds, the unequivocal inference is that consciousness is primary: this has been the doctrine of arcane wisdom through its emissaries, having also percolated the minds of eminent scientists of metaphysical inclination willing to embrace realms of existence not necessarily limited to the physical domain, as we have shown. The natural corollary to the primacy of Divine Thought would appear to be the consistent and unequivocal message given out by the sages and occultists since time immemorial:

1. that the material nature is a dimmed reflection of the Divine Nature;
2. and for this reason, the material sciences and arts are shadows of Divine Wisdom;
3. hence, the path to understanding and reality is through penetrating the physical veil of nature into her innermost and secret recesses.

The timeless message of the sages

These are the three principal strands of that golden thread uniting all wisdoms—whether we look: (*a*) to the Vedas, Upaniṣads, and Purāṇas of the East; or (*b*) in the West, to the Hermeticism of Egypt, the Platonism of Greece, and then the long Platonic succession through the Qabbalistic, Gnostic, and Rosicrucian movement in Europe, and to New Thought in America; or (*c*) to the modern Theosophical doctrines that subsume the Eastern and Western teachings.

Afterword

In concluding Volume I of this work we revert to Sir William Grove's maxim cited in the epigraph. Coming from a man eminently qualified in both science and the law, his words remain as true today, for all fields of knowledge, as they were in the nineteenth century. Indeed, they represent the clarion call that all true scientists hear and are working hard to manifest. The day will surely come when what 'should' be the 'sole aim' of science is exchanged for reality—when Science has become free of the bonds of prejudice and Truth becomes unquestioningly its sole aim.

With the same allegiance to Truth, Volume II of this work comprises an in-depth exposition from the perennial wisdom on man's complete constitution and nature. It extends considerably the scope of Volume I on this subject by progressing well beyond general remarks about soul and spirit, or mind and consciousness, in favour of a detailed exposition of man's bodies of consciousness (subtle and physical) manifesting on all levels from the spiritual to the physical. The post-mortem states of consciousness are detailed with evidence from science, literature, and music; and of course, the *philosophia perennis*. This begs the question whether the brain is analogous to a computer and therefore generates consciousness. This topic is explored in depth with robust evidence from diverse sources, scientific, philosophical, and esoteric, adduced to show the fatal error of equating the brain with a computer. A major theme of this work is the unity of the *philosophia perennis*. This is especially so with regard to the totality of man's being, as shown from the testimony of world cultures since time immemorial.

Meanwhile, we close Volume I with the words of another scientist who, in the writer's consideration, worked in the true spirit of scientific enquiry: one who recognized the strengths of Western science as well as its limitations, which can only be alleviated by—

> **some blood transfusion from the East to the West to save Western science from spiritual anaemia.**

ERWIN SCHRÖDINGER[31]

NOTES

1   *SD*-I, 'The Masks of Science', 509. Quoted also in I. M. Oderberg, *Sunrise* (August/September 2000) in book review of Robert Nadeau and Menas Kafatos, *The Non-Local Universe: The new physics and matters of the mind* (Oxford: Oxford University Press, 1999) <https://www.theosociety.org/pasadena/sunrise/49-99-0/sc-imo11.htm> accessed 3 February 2020.

2   William James, *Some Problems of Philosophy: A beginning of an introduction to philosophy* (New York: Longmans, Green: 1911; repr. 1916), 51.

3   P. Anderson, 'On the Nature of Physical Law', *Physics Today* (December 1990), 9. Quoted also in Thomas Brophy, *The Mechanism Demands a Mysticism: An exploration of spirit, matter and physics* (US: Medicine Bear Publishing, 2001), 6.

4   Harald Walach, *Galileo Commission Report: Beyond a materialist worldview towards an expanded science* (The Scientific and Medical Network, 2019).

5   R. G. Jahn, letter to the editor, *Physics Today* (October 1991), 13.

6   Steven Weinberg, *Dreams of a Final Theory: The search for the fundamental laws of nature* (London: Hutchinson Radius, 1993), 37. Quoted also in Thomas Brophy, *The Mechanism Demands a Mysticism*, 6.

7   R. G. Jahn and B. J. Dunne, *Foundations of Physics*, 16 (1986), 721, quoted in Steven Weinberg, *Dreams of a Final Theory*, 37.

8   Steven Weinberg, *op. cit.*, 37.

9   *ibid.*

10 *ibid.*

11 Steven Weinberg, *op. cit.*, 38–9.

12 Robert Jahn, 'The Persistent Paradox of Psychic Phenomena: An engineering perspective', *Proceedings of the IEEE*, 70/2 (1982).

13 'Albert Einstein Quotes', *Biography Online* <https://www.biographyonline.net/scientists/albert-einstein-quotes.html> accessed 19 December 2019.

14 Edward Osborne Wilson, *Consilience: The unity of knowledge* (New York: Vintage Books, 1998), 7.

15 Max Planck, *A Survey of Physical Theory*, trans. R. Jones and D. H. Williams (New York: Dover Publications, 2003), 53.

16 Makoto Katsumori, *Niels Bohr's Complementarity: Its structure, history, and intersections with hermeneutics and deconstruction* (Boston Studies in the Philosophy of Science, 2011), 286.

17 Werner Heisenberg, *Physics and Beyond* (Cambridge: Cambridge University Press, 1971), 101.

18 Brian Josephson, *Times Higher Education Supplement* (12 August 1994).

19 *VS*, 'The Voice of the Silence: Fragment I', 1.

20 *KT*, 'Theosophical Teachings as to Nature and Man', 91.

21 Plato, *Timaeus*, xxxi, 69 c.

22 Rephrased from *KT*, 'Theosophical Teachings as to Nature and Man', 92–3.

23 *The Sunday Times*, 16 July 2006.

24 *The Observer*, 25 January 1931.

25 Erwin Schrödinger, 'General Scientific and Popular Papers', in Collected Papers, iv (Vienna: Austrian Academy of Sciences. Friedr. Vieweg & Sohn, Braunschweig/Wiesbaden, 1984), 334.

26 —— 'Nature and the Greeks' from the Shearman Lectures delivered at University College, London, 1948, in *Nature and the Greeks* and *Science and Humanism*, foreword by Roger Penrose (Cambridge: Cambridge University Press, 1961), 157.

27 —— 'Mind and Matter: The Mystery of the Sensual Qualities' from the Tarner Lectures delivered at Trinity College Cambridge, 1956, in *What is Life?* with *Mind and Matter* and *Autobiographical Sketches*, foreword by Roger Penrose (Cambridge: Cambridge University Press, 1993), 127.

28 David Bohm, Lecture at the University of California, Berkley, 1977, in 'Papers and Correspondence of David Joseph Bohm, 1917–1992', *Birkbeck Library Archives and Special Collections, University of London, Reference GB 1832 BOHM* <https://archiveshub.jisc.ac.uk/search/archives/be7987a8-d6d9-33f5-a620-130995145068> accessed 19 January 2020.

29 C. E. M. Joad, 'What is the Soul?' *The Aryan Path*, 8/5 (Bombay, India: Theosophy Company, May 1937), 201–3.

30 'Alchemy', in Franz Hartmann, *In the Pronaos of the Temple of Wisdom* (UK and US: Theosophical Publishing Society, 1890; facs. edn, London: Banton Press, 1991), 133 § 37 [online facsimile] <https://archive.org/details/inpronaostemple00hartgoog/page/n4/mode/2up> accessed 12 May 2020. Quoted also in *STA*, 'The Sun in Alchemical Symbology', LII.

31 Michel Bitbol CNRS, Paris, France, 'Schrödinger and Indian Philosophy': transcript of a conference given at the French embassy in India, New Delhi, January 1998 (Allahabad, India: Cahiers du service culturel de l'ambassade de France en Inde, August 1999) <http://michel.bitbol.pagesperso-orange.fr/Schrodinger_India.pdf> accessed 5 February 2020. Quoted also in: Phil Mason, *Quantum Glory:The science of heaven invading earth* (US: XP Publishing, 2010), 39; Yogendra Singh Sikarwar, 'Common Ground between Physics & Indian Philosophy (3): Schrödinger & Vedanta', *Indian Wisdom, Physics, Physics & Indian Philosophy* (17 July 2014) <https://profyogendra.wordpress.com/2014/07/17/common-ground-between-physics-indian-philosophy-3-schrodinger-vedanta> accessed 5 February 2020.

Appendix I-A:
Timeline of the Progression of the Physical Sciences – Physics and Cosmology

There is an interesting and radical difference between developments in the physical sciences compared with the life sciences. Physicists, without exception, fully recognize and accept Newton's laws as a limiting case of Einstein's laws, so there is no question of a dichotomy between a 'back to Newton' or a 'drop Newton and only Einstein'. Both laws are seen to be valid within their rightful context. So for terrestrial physics, and even space travel, Newton's laws are used. However, for intergalactic computations involving stellar objects millions of light years distant from Earth, Einstein's laws (relativity theory) are used.

Mainstream physics and cosmology have progressed beyond Newton's theories

However, with few exceptions, as explained further in Appendix I-B, there is no notion amongst mainstream biologists of Darwinism being a rudimentary version of the more enlightened views now emerging on life and evolution that incorporate such ideas as consciousness and organizing fields.

The Situation at the Close of the Nineteenth Century and the Opening of the Twentieth Century

The scientific paradigm then prevailing was well encapsulated by the famous scientist Lord Kelvin OM (William Thomson), past President of the Royal Society and also President of the Royal Society of Edinburgh. In a famous speech delivered on 27 April 1900 before the Royal Institution of Great Britain and published in *Philos. Mag.* (ser. 6) 2, 1 (1901) Lord Kelvin said that most scientific problems were solved. But there were only two 'clouds' on the horizon of physics: the problem of black-body radiation, and the failure of the Michelson-Morley experiment to detect the luminous ether. These were the final two lacunae that needed to be filled before having a complete understanding of the thermodynamic and energy properties of the universe, explained in classical terms of the motion of particles. Furthermore, these two clouds signalled the end of the era beginning with Galileo and Newton. Kelvin suggested that if we knew the mass and the velocity of every particle in the universe then we should know in principle the whole future of the universe. So, in essence, the scientific paradigm at the close of the nineteenth century was bottom-up, reductionist, mechanistic, quantitative, and deterministic.

There were, however, notable exceptions to the mainstream paradigm. For example, even as early as 1826, the German physician and astronomer Heinrich Wilhelm Olbers (1758–1840) posited Olbers' paradox: the argument that the darkness of the night sky conflicts with the assumption of an infinite and eternal static universe. It is one of the early pieces of evidence for a non-static universe such as postulated by the current Big Bang model.

Nonetheless, later in the same year as Lord Kelvin's famous pronouncement, Max Planck solved the black-body problem and along with Einstein, Schrödinger, and a galaxy of other physicists, ushered in the quantum era of the twentieth century. Serious contradictions and confusion then ensued because relativity theory, and especially quantum theory and its supporting experimental results, implied a holistic worldview and the fundamental nature of reality as a mental rather than a physical construct.

The New Insight Emerging During the Early Twentieth Century

In his Gifford Lectures, delivered in the University of Edinburgh (January–March 1927) and his book *The Nature of the Physical World* (1928), Sir Arthur Eddington spoke of the source and condition of physical reality, from which brief extracts were cited in Chapter 3 and a fuller version given below:

> The universe is of the nature of a thought or sensation in a universal Mind [...]. To put the conclusion crudely—the stuff of the world is mind-stuff. As is often the way with crude statements, I shall have to explain that by 'mind' I do not exactly mean mind and by 'stuff' I do not at all mean stuff. Still that is about as near as we can get to the idea in a simple phrase. The mind-stuff of the world is something more general than our individual conscious minds; but we may think of its nature as not altogether foreign to feelings in our consciousness [...].
>
> It is difficult for the matter-of-fact physicist to accept the view that the substratum of everything is of mental character. But no one can deny that mind is the first and most direct thing in our experience, and all else is remote inference—inference either intuitive or deliberate. [...] The frank realization that physical science is concerned with a world of shadows is one of the most significant of recent advances.

A Timeline Showing How Physics and Cosmology have Progressed since the Turn of the Twentieth Century

Chronological highlights for physics are shown to the left hand margin; and parallel highlights for cosmology are shown indented.

Physics	Cosmology
1900	Max Planck discovers energy quanta and was the originator of quantum theory, which revolutionized human understanding of the terms 'atomic' and 'subatomic'.
1905	Albert Einstein publishes the Special Theory of Relativity, positing that space and time are not separate but a continuum.
1911	Sir John Arthur Thomson in *Introduction to Science* declares that the vulgar belief that science has explained everything is a hopeless misunderstanding, and that it would be nearer the truth to say that science has explained nothing—other

Physics **Cosmology**

than in the limited sense of reducing complex systems to simpler units and by relating the observed facts to a general formula or equation, both of which, in the final analysis, do not really get beyond a description.

1915 Albert Einstein publishes the General Theory of Relativity, showing that an energy density warps space–time.

> 1917 Willem de Sitter derives an isotropic static cosmology with a cosmological constant, as well as an empty expanding cosmology with a cosmological constant, termed a 'de Sitter universe'.
>
> 1922 Vesto Slipher summarizes his findings on the systematic redshifts of spiral nebulae.
>
> 1922 Alexander Friedmann finds a solution to the Einstein field equations which suggests a general expansion of space.

1924 Louis de Broglie in *Recherches sur la théorie des quanta* [Researches on the quantum theory] demonstrates the fact of matter waves. This demolishes the classical paradigm about matter being solid and impenetrable.

1925 Alfred North Whitehead in *An Anthology* reduces matter to a mode of vibratory motion which can, in principle, be mathematically expressed.

> 1925 Arthur Eddington in *Why I believe in God: Science and religion, as a scientist sees it* pictures the universe, not as a machine, but as an Idea, or a great 'Thought' in the Mind of God.
>
> 1927 Georges Lemaître discusses the creation event of an expanding universe governed by the Einstein field equations. From its solutions to the Einstein equations, he predicts the distance-redshift relation.

1927 Werner Heisenberg formulates the uncertainty principle which showed that indeterminacy is an inherent phenomenon in physical nature having nothing to do with any errors in measurement. The entirety of nature cannot be known with certainty, but only approximately, i.e. as a matter of principle, the present in all it details cannot be known.

> 1928 Howard Percy Robertson briefly mentions that Vesto Slipher's redshift measurements, combined with brightness measurements of the same galaxies, indicate a redshift-distance relation.

1928 Sir Arthur Eddington in *The Nature of the Physical World* considers that the universe is a 'Thought' or sensation in a universal Mind and that the substratum of everything is of a mental character.

1929 Louis de Broglie in his Nobel Lecture *The Wave Nature of the Electron* shows the wave aspect of particles, further undermining the classical paradigm.

Physics   Cosmology

> 1929   Edwin Hubble demonstrates the linear redshift-distance rela-
> tion and thus shows the expansion of the universe.

1930   Sir James Jeans in *The Mysterious Universe* states the tendency of modern physics
to resolve the whole material universe into waves, and nothing but waves, which
concept reduces the whole universe to a world of light, potential or existent, so
that the whole story of its creation can be told with perfect accuracy and
completeness in the six words: 'God said, Let there be light'.

1932   John von Neumann in *The Mathematical Foundation of Quantum Mechanics*
shows that there are two ways in which physicists regard quantum mechanics.
Employing scientific rigour, this book introduces the notion of the 'observer
effect' and shows the role of personality and how different ideas emerge from
'thing' minds and 'people' minds.

> 1933   Edward Milne names and formalizes the cosmological principle.

1932   Max Planck in *Where is Science Going?* prologue by Albert Einstein, explicitly
maintains that there can never be a fundamental opposition between religion
and science; for the one is the complement of the other. Every serious and reflective person realizes that the religious element in his nature must be recognized
and cultivated if all the powers of the human soul are to act together in perfect
balance and harmony. And it was not by any accident that the greatest thinkers
of all ages were also deeply religious souls, even though they made no public
show of their religious feeling.

1934   Karl Popper in *The Logic of Scientific Discovery* argues the concept of falsifiability:
that a theory in the empirical sciences can never be proven, but it can be falsified
in that it can be scrutinized by appropriate experiments.

> 1934   Georges Lemaître interprets the cosmological constant as due to
> a vacuum energy with an unusual 'perfect fluid' equation of state.

1935   Max Born in *The Restless Universe* signals the difference between the mathematical description (map) and the real (territory).

This was the same warning that Newton stated in *Principia* which H. P. Blavatsky,
nearly half a century earlier, specifically quotes and references in *The Secret
Doctrine*: 'At the outset of his *Principia*, Sir Isaac Newton took the greatest care
to impress upon his school that he did not use the word "attraction" with regard
to the mutual action of bodies in a physical sense. To him it was, he said, a purely
mathematical conception involving no consideration of real and primary physical causes.'[1]

1938   Alfred North Whitehead in *Modes of Thought* presents a panpsychism view that
mental operations should be included among the factors that make up the
constitution of nature.

1938   Paul Dirac suggests the 'large numbers' hypothesis. This holds that the gravitational constant may be small because it is decreasing slowly with time.

Physics   Cosmology

The variability with time of the fundamental physical constants of nature is also mentioned nearly half a century earlier in *The Secret Doctrine*;[2] and at the close of the twentieth century by Rupert Sheldrake in *Seven Experiments that Could Change the World*.[3]

1940   Gustaf Strömberg in *The Soul of the Universe* (endorsed by Einstein in its second, 1948 edition) describes how the structure of the material and immaterial worlds, and the 'World Soul' elucidate the problem of memory regardless of death, i.e., independent of matter. He provides *scientific evidence* of human immortality and the non-physical realm as the ultimate origin of all things; hence his conviction that consciousness is rooted in a non-physical world, so our mental characteristics and faculties originate in a world not built of atoms.

1942   Luigi Fantappiè coins the term 'syntropy', now slowly gaining currency amongst a few scientists, to stress the need to extend the scientific paradigm of his time.

1942   Albert Einstein coins the term *ubercausalitat* (supercausality) to stress the need to extend the scientific paradigm of his time.

        1948   George Gamow, et al. examine element synthesis in a rapidly expanding and cooling universe, and suggest that the elements were produced by rapid neutron capture.

        1948   Hermann Bondi, Thomas Gold, and Fred Hoyle propose steady state cosmologies based on the perfect cosmological principle.

        1948   George Gamow predicts the existence of the cosmic microwave background radiation by considering the behaviour of primordial radiation in an expanding universe.

        1950   Fred Hoyle derisively coins the term 'Big Bang'.

1951, 54 Erwin Schrödinger in *Science and Humanism* (1951) and *Nature and the Greeks* (1954) laments the deficiency of the scientific picture of the real world: whereas it gives considerable factual information and consistent order, 'it is ghastly silent about all and sundry that is really near to our heart, that really matters to us' such as subjective experiences, God, and eternity.

1955   Carl Jung and Wolfgang Pauli in *The Interpretation of Nature and the Psyche* show how physics is veering towards the study of the structure of consciousness.

1957   Hugh Everett III in *Reviews of Modern Physics* proposes his 'Many Universes' idea that there are many worlds coexisting with our own, but there is no communication between the various universes. This strongly alludes to the powerful and succinctly stated occult doctrine of a plurality of globes 'in COADUNITION [united, or linked together] *but not* IN CONSUBSTANTIALITY [not of the same substance] WITH OUR EARTH [*because they*] pertain to quite another state of consciousness'.[4]

1958   Werner Heisenberg in *Physics and Philosophy: The revolution in modern science* reasserts the old concept of 'potentia' in Aristotelian philosophy. The quantum concept of a 'probability wave', describing the likelihood of different possible

Physics   Cosmology

outcomes of a measurement, was a quantitative version of Aristotle's potential: 'It introduced something standing in the middle between the idea of an event and the actual event, a strange kind of physical reality just in the middle between possibility and reality.'

This alludes to the esoteric idea that intelligence comes first, an idea explored in the Theosophical classic of similar name edited by E. Lester Smith.[5]

In the same book, Heisenberg states the observer effect as 'what we observe is not nature herself, but nature exposed to our method of questioning.'

1958   Richard Feynman in *Selected Papers on Quantum Electrodynamics* describes the difference between the real state and virtual state of a photon as a matter of perspective: 'What looks like a real process from one point of view may appear as a virtual process occurring over a more extended time'. This shows similarities between physics and the esoteric doctrine of *māyā*.

    1961   Robert Dicke argues that carbon-based life can only arise when the gravitational force is small, because this is when burning stars exist—the first use of the weak anthropic principle.

1964   John Bell in *On the Einstein Podolsky Rosen Paradox* states the fact of nonlocality, or that 'existence is ONE THING' as Blavatsky put it.[6]

    1965   Martin Rees and Dennis Sciama analyse quasar source count data and discover that the quasar density increases with redshift.

    1965   Arno Penzias and Robert Wilson, astronomers at Bell Labs, discover the 2.7 K microwave background radiation, which earns them the 1978 Nobel Prize in Physics. Robert Dicke, James Peebles, Peter Roll, and David Todd Wilkinson interpret it as a relic from the Big Bang.

    1966   Stephen Hawking and George Ellis show that any plausible general relativistic cosmology is singular.

    1967   Andrei Sakharov presents the requirements for 'baryogenesis', a baryon-antibaryon asymmetry in the universe.

    1968   Brandon Carter speculates that perhaps the fundamental constants of nature must lie within a restricted range to allow the emergence of life; the first use of the strong anthropic principle.

1970   Evan Harris Walker in his paper, 'The Nature of Consciousness', published in *Mathematical Biosciences* speculates that consciousness may be associated with all quantum mechanical processes.

1970s Arthur Ellison conducts an experiment to demonstrate the importance of the mental model of the observer: that simple phrases like 'physically observed' and 'independent repeatable experiments' have deeper implications and cannot always be relied upon for the 'real test' of a scientific theory. We see only what we expect to see; and overlook what does not accord with our beliefs.

Physics   Cosmology

1971   Henry Stapp in *Physical Review* states, 'An elementary particle is not an independently existing, unanalysable entity. It is, in essence, a set of relationships that reach outward to other things.' This strongly veers towards psychology, a holistic and organic outlook, and the role of consciousness.

Henry Stapp in 'Mind, Matter, and Quantum Mechanics', further states: 'The conclusion here is not the weak conclusion that there *may* not be a substantive physical world but rather that there definitely is not a substantive physical world.' (unpublished paper).

1973   Edward Tryon proposes that the universe may be a large scale quantum mechanical vacuum fluctuation where positive mass-energy is balanced by negative gravitational potential energy.

1974   Werner Heisenberg in *Across the Frontiers* states how even the most eminent of scientists find great difficulty in changing their thought patterns when forced by the discovery of phenomena not comprehensible in terms of the old theories.

1974   David Bohm and Basil Hiley in 'On the Intuitive Understanding of Non-Locality as Implied by Quantum Theory' show how we are led to a new notion of *unbroken wholeness* which denies the classical idea of analysability of the world into separately and independently existent parts. This is again one of many statements from cutting-edge science that corroborates Blavatsky's dictum: 'Existence is ONE THING, not any collection of things linked together. Fundamentally there is ONE BEING.'7

1974   John Wheeler in his article, 'Perspectives: The Universe as Home for Man: Puzzles attached to consciousness, the quantum principle, and how the universe came into being suggest that the greatest discoveries are yet to come', published in the magazine *American Scientist*, puts the case for a participatory universe. Observers participate in order to make the universe consistent and orderly. Observers are necessary to bring the universe into being.

1975   Isidor Rabi (Nobel laureate) in *The New Yorker Magazine* says, 'I don't think that physics will ever have an end. I think that the novelty of nature is such that its variety will be infinite—not just in changing forms but in the profundity of insight and the newness of ideas.' Contrast this with Lord Kelvin's 1901 speech cited on page 331.

1977   Steven Weinberg in *The First Three Minutes: A modern view of the origin of the universe* states his conviction that the universe appears increasingly pointless the more it is comprehensible through modern science.

1977   David Bohm in a Lecture at the University of California at Berkeley says:

'We must turn physics round. Instead of starting with parts and showing how they work together we start with the whole.' This unequivocally affirms the primacy of unity.

Physics   Cosmology

Bohm continues with: 'Description is totally incompatible with what we want to say. This is because our thinking is based upon an ancient Greek mode of thought that only Being *is*. Therefore, Non-being is *not*. Whereas it furnishes a practical tool for dealing with the ordinary world, but it does not describe what happens. In point of fact, Non-being also *is*. And both Being and Non-being are that-which-is. So *everything*, even so-called "emptiness" is that-which-is. There is nothing which is not that-which-is.'

What Bohm refers to as 'so-called "emptiness"' is none other than the 'fullness of the Void' in Blavatsky's *The Voice of the Silence*, which thus finds its perfect scientific corroboration in this further pronouncement from Bohm: 'Space is not empty. It is full, a plenum as opposed to a vacuum, and is the ground for the existence of everything, including ourselves. The universe is not separate from this cosmic sea of energy.'

Then comes this seminal insight: 'The ultimate perception does not originate in the brain or any material structure, although a material structure is necessary to manifest it. The subtle mechanism of knowing the truth does not originate in the brain.' This points to consciousness beyond the brain, that the brain does not produce or generate consciousness, rather that it is the vehicle of consciousness.

1977   Henry Stapp in his paper, 'Are Superluminal Connections Necessary?' in the scientific journal *Nuovo Cimento*, states: 'Everything we know about Nature is in accord with the idea that the fundamental processes of Nature lie outside space–time but generate events that can be located in space–time. The theorem of this paper supports this view of Nature by showing that superluminal transfer of information is necessary, barring certain alternatives. . . that seem less reasonable.' This alludes to the esoteric doctrines about the variability of the physical constants of nature (the non-constancy of the velocity of light, in this case) and of space and time being the vesture and vehicle of the divine.

1977   Sir Karl Popper and Sir John Eccles in *The Self and Its Brain: An argument for interactionism* argue that in its attempts to explain matter and its properties, modern physics transcended the original programme of materialism; and, ironically, physics itself has produced by far the most important arguments against classical materialism.

1979   Bernard d'Espagnat in *The Quantum Theory and Reality* states the case for nonlocality.

    1979   Bernard Carr and Martin Rees in 'The Anthropic Principle and the Structure of the Physical World' propose the philosophical consideration that observations of the universe must be compatible with the conscious and sapient life that observes it, posited as a necessity, because if life were impossible, no living entity would be there to observe it, and thus it would not be known.

    1981   Alan Guth proposes the inflationary Big Bang universe as a possible solution to the horizon and flatness problems.

Physics   Cosmology

1980   David Bohm in *Wholeness and the Implicate Order* contends that manifested existences are explicate versions of a fundamental undivided wholeness and implicate order.

1980   Cambridge theoretical physicist Stephen Phillips in *Extra-Sensory Perception of Quarks* shows a remarkable correlation between the facts of modern particle physics and paranormal observations of subatomic particles carried out by two occult researchers in the Theosophical Society (Charles Leadbeater and Annie Besant) as reported in detail in their book *Occult Chemistry*.

1981   Alain Aspect, et al. in 'Experimental Tests of Realistic Local Theories via Bell's Theorem' proves nonlocality.

1982   Alain Aspect, et al. in 'Experimental Realization of Einstein-Podolsky-Rosen-Bohm Gedankenexperiment: A New Violation of Bell's Inequalities', further demonstrates the fact of nonlocality.

1982   Alain Aspect, et al. in 'Experimental Test of Bell's Inequalities Using Time-Varying Analyzers' provides more proof of nonlocality.

1983   Brian Josephson in an interview for Detroit Free Press states his conviction that every atom of matter may contain elements of intelligence.

1984   Ilya Prigogine in *Order Out of Chaos: Man's new dialogue with nature* discusses the problems ensuing purely from dissection (analysis) of problems and shows how two great themes of classical science, order and chaos, are being reconciled in a new and unexpected synthesis.

1986   Alain Aspect in 'Quantum Concepts in Space and Time' proves nonlocality between particles twelve meters apart.

1986   Renée Weber in *Dialogues with Scientists and Sages: The search for unity* declares that the Grand Unified Theory is, in a sense, pursued more aptly by mysticism, than by science, because the mystic leaves nothing out of his reckoning, whereas the scientist detaches himself, the observer, from his observations. Furthermore, that in quantum mechanics, the observer and observed are admitted to constitute a unit but the full meaning of this has not yet caught up with most of the community of scientists who, despite quantum mechanics, believe they can stand aloof from what they work on.

        1986   John Barrow and Frank Tipler in *The Anthropic Cosmological Principle* draw together a collection of ideas upholding the view that the existence of intelligent observers determines the fundamental structure of the universe. They ask, if life is not a product of chance and necessity, then is it a product of design? In which case the universe must be purposive, made in such a way as inevitably to evolve sentience.

        1988   I. Prigogine, J. Geheniau, E. Gunzig, and P. Nardone in *Proceedings of the National Academy of Sciences U.S.A.* propose

Physics   **Cosmology**

> that matter-creating bursts, similar to our Big Bang, occur periodically. This alludes to the Second Fundamental Proposition and the doctrine of 'Rounds' in *The Secret Doctrine*.

1988   Freeman Dyson in *Infinite in All Directions* states that in quantum mechanics, matter is not an inert substance but an active agent and it appears that mind, as manifested by the capacity to make choices, is to some extent inherent in every electron.

> 1990   Preliminary results from NASA's Cosmic Background Explorer (COBE) mission confirm that the cosmic microwave background radiation has a near-perfect, isotropic black-body spectrum to an astonishing one part in 105 precision, thus eliminating the possibility of an integrated starlight model proposed for the background by proponents of the steady state hypothesis.

> 1990s   Ground-based cosmic microwave background experiments measuring the first peak, determine that the universe is geometrically flat.

> 1993   Fred Hoyle, Geoffrey Burbidge, and Jayant Narlikar in *The Astrophysical Journal* propose cyclicity and periodicity in the creation of universes. This also alludes to the Second Fundamental Proposition[8] and the doctrine of 'Rounds' in *The Secret Doctrine*.

1994   Willis Harman in *New Metaphysical Foundations of Modern Science* advocates the integration of the spiritual and the intellectual, and the need for global transformation. He discusses the observer effect (that mere observation of a phenomenon inevitably changes the latter) and the role of causality in our understanding of what constitutes reality, and how things happen.

> 1997   Alan Guth in *The Inflationary Universe: The quest for a new theory of cosmic origins*, advances the idea of multiple universes and new universes created inside black holes. This again alludes to the Second Fundamental Proposition and the doctrine of 'Rounds' in *The Secret Doctrine*.

1998   W. Tittel, J. Brendel, and N. Gisin in *Phys. Rev. Lett.* perform a similar experiment to Alain Aspect (1986) but between particles more than ten kilometres apart, showing that connection between particles is not transmitted by a signal but is intrinsic to the particles themselves—they are entangled, their correlation being independent of time and space.

1998   Controversial evidence for the fine structure constant varying over the lifetime of the universe is first published.

> 1998   Riess, et al. discover the cosmic acceleration in observations of Type Ia supernovae providing the first evidence for a non-zero cosmological constant.

Physics   **Cosmology**

1999   Measurements of the cosmic microwave background radiation (most notably by the BOOMERANG experiment) indicate that the geometry of the universe is flat. Together with large scale structure data, this provides complementary evidence for a non-zero cosmological constant.

1999   Robert Taormina in 'A New Consciousness for Global Peace' in Proceedings, Third International Symposium on the Culture of Peace, Baden Baden, Germany is one of an increasing number of scientists who seriously consider the possibility of life on other planets.

1999   Cambridge theoretical physicist Stephen Phillips in *ESP of Quarks and Superstrings* provides more demonstrable consistency about the remote viewing of subatomic particles using the yogic siddhi (psychic faculty) known as 'anima', as reported in *Occult Chemistry*, with the established facts of nuclear physics and the theories of quarks and superstrings, with the qualification that not all interpretations can be taken at face value.

2002   Paul Steinhardt and Neil Turok in 'A Cyclic Model of the Universe' propose a cosmological model comprising Big Bang and Big Crunch. This further alludes to the Second Fundamental Proposition and the doctrine of 'Rounds' in *The Secret Doctrine*.

2003   NASA's Wilkinson Microwave Anisotropy Probe (WMAP) obtains full-sky detailed pictures of the cosmic microwave background radiation. The image can be interpreted to indicate that the universe is 13.7 billion years old (within one percent error) and confirms that the Lambda-CDM model and the inflationary theory are correct.

2003   Jacob Bekenstein in *Scientific American* posits a holographic universe in that the entire universe could be considered a many-dimensional hologram.

2004   M. D. Barret, et al. in *Nature* shows teleportation which is a form of nonlocal connection whereby any disturbance to one particle of a coupled pair is instantly registered by the other particle.

2004   M. Riebe, et al. in *Nature* also demonstrates teleportation. Teleportation could in principle provide one explanation of telepathy which crosses all boundaries of space.

2004   Andrei Linde in *Science and Ultimate Reality: From quantum to cosmos* advances the hypothesis of 'metaverse'[i] including the

---

i Metaverse, refers to the array of all mathematically precise and consistently describable objects and structures. Comparable terms are 'omniverse' and 'multiverse'.

Physics   Cosmology

> concept of a cyclical universe in which our universe was 'birthed' from a previous one. This provides more substantiation to the Second Fundamental Proposition and the doctrine of 'Rounds' in *The Secret Doctrine*.

2005   Marvin Goldfried, John Pachankis, and Alissa Bell in *A Handbook of Psychotherapy Integration*, state how the importance of experience alludes to the central importance of consciousness which, if left out, will render all theories incomplete.

> 2006   Amanda Gefter in *New Scientist* suggests an observer-created universe so the present determines the past—the causal chain of events is reversed.

2006   Ervin László in *Science and the Reenchantment of the Cosmos: The rise of an integral vision of reality* is one of an increasing number of scientists who provide mounting evidence for the reality of the physical vacuum as a complex and real medium in the nature of a field of all-information similar to the Akasha. (This strongly echoes the aphorisms about the 'fullness of the Void' found in Buddhist scriptures and Blavatsky's *The Voice of the Silence*.)

2007   Ervin László in *Science and the Akashic Field: An integral theory of everything*, shows, like the geneticist Mae-Wan Ho, that no matter how diverse the cells, organs and system in a complex organism such as the human body, dynamic equilibrium is staggering and they act as one unity, one orchestra.

> 2007   Bernard Carr (editor) in *Universe or Multiverse?* collates recent developments in cosmology, particle physics, and string theory that have led to the realization that our universe—rather than being unique—could be just one of many universes. The multiverse proposal is postulated as an explanation for the origin of the universe and the fine tuning of physical constants, which can be different in other universes, but which appear necessary for the emergence of life.

2012   Brian Josephson, in an address to the Society for Physical Research on *psi*, states that agents are the source of physics and that physics, which currently has things back to front, needs to come to terms with agents.

2014   *Manifesto for a Post-Materialist Science* issued by a group of internationally acclaimed scientists from a variety of scientific fields—biology, medicine, neuroscience, psychology, and psychiatry—highlights the importance of a shift from materialist science to a post-materialist paradigm for science, spirituality, and society.

> 2016   The Rosetta spacecraft orbiting Comet 67P/Churyumov-Gerasimenko detects glycine (an amino acid) and phosphorus, both ingredient of proteins, in the thin atmosphere of the Comet, as reported in *Science Advances* by Kathrin Altwegg at the Centre of Space and Habitability of the University of Bern.

Physics   Cosmology

2017   The *Business Insider* (July) reports that a new Chinese experiment shows that quantum teleportation works between the ground and space—a huge leap toward developing technologies that could reshape the modern world. J. C. Séamus Davis, a physicist at Cornell University who studies quantum mechanics, said that the implications were 'profound' because it demonstrated the basis of a fully 'quantum internet'—a technology likely to make our World Wide Web obsolete.

        2018   Stephen Hawking and Thomas Hertog in their paper *A Smooth Exit from Eternal Inflation?* reportedly provide mathematical evidence for the theory that there have been multiple Big Bangs, of which our own universe is just one such event; hence the possibility of universes that exist well beyond our own with completely unknown galaxies, stars, and planets. This provides yet more substantiation to the Second Fundamental Proposition and the doctrine of 'Rounds' in *The Secret Doctrine*.

2019   Harald Walach on behalf of The Scientific and Medical Network publishes the *Galileo Commission Report: Beyond a Materialist Worldview Towards an Expanded Science* (www.galileocommission.org). The Report argues that the world today is dominated by science and its largely unexamined philosophical assumptions that are associated with a mechanistic and materialistic worldview where humans are just complex biological machines devoid of free will and living in a purposeless universe. The Report seeks to liberate the spirit of scientific enquiry by opening up public discourse and to find ways to expand the scope of science so that it is no longer constrained by an outmoded view of matter and physical reality, and can explore and accommodate significant human experiences, especially evidence indicating that consciousness may go beyond the brain.

2019   Iain McGilchrist in the Foreword to the *Galileo Commission Summary Report: Beyond a Materialist Worldview – Towards an Expanded Science*, emphasizes that science needs to be more scientific in that the science establishment makes unscientific and inconsistent assumptions which are ignored by the mainstream who assume that they make no assumptions. He cites the example that there is no single shred of evidence that matter gives rise to consciousness, and good reason from the stance of contemporary physics that consciousness is prior to matter.

2020   The Venera 13 and 14 spacecraft detect the biosignature gas phosphine—indicating possible signs of life—in the hostile clouds around Venus, as reported in *Nature Astronomy* and *National Geographic*.

NOTES

1   *SD*-I, 'Is Gravitation a Law?' 490.
2   *SD*-I, 'Reasons for these Addenda', 478.

3   Rupert Sheldrake, *Seven Experiments that Could Change the World: A do-it-yourself guide to revolutionary science* (London: Fourth Estate, 1994), 164–90. Refer to 'Variability of Fundamental Physical Constants of Nature', in Edi D. Bilimoria, *The Snake and the Rope: Problems in Western science resolved by occult science* (Adyar, Madras: Theosophical Publishing House, 2006), 229–32, showing the data from Sheldrake's book on the variation with time of the gravitational constant, Planck's constant, and the velocity of light, supported with an occult commentary by Bilimoria.

4   *SD*-I, 'Theosophical Misconceptions', 166.

5   E. Lester Smith (ed.), *Intelligence Came First*, rev. Patrick Milburn (1975; 2nd edn, Wheaton, Illinois: Theosophical Publishing House, 1990).

6   '*The Secret Doctrine* and Its Study', in *Madame Blavatsky on How to Study Theosophy* (London: Theosophical Publishing House, 1960), 8 from the Bowen Notes, being extracts from the notes of personal teachings given by H.P. Blavatsky to private pupils during the years 1888 to 1891.

7   *ibid.*

8   *SD*-I, 'Proem', 16–17.

Appendix I-B:
Timeline of the Progression of the Life Sciences – Biology and Evolution

In the eighteenth century, the German chemist, physician, philosopher, and supporter of vitalism George Stahl (1659–1734), proposed the followed challenges to a materialist biology looking at life in purely mechanistic terms:

1. the impossibility of making organic molecules from inorganic ones;

2. that life is not mechanistic physical machinery, but transmutational;

3. that living organisms cannot be machines because they suffer.[1]

Remarkable developments in biology over the last quarter of a century have increased the plausibility of the hypothesis of formative causation (morphic resonance associated with morphic fields) by exposing the limitations of the conventional mechanistic approach, including the much vaunted science of molecular biology and genetics.

However, what we find is that the timeline for life sciences has a two-pronged fork: one prong towards the 'bottom-up' establishment theories of the mechanistic paradigm where chance and necessity are dogmatically regarded as sufficient to explain life, evolution, and consciousness; and the other prong, more or less in parallel, upwards towards the 'top-down' newer ideas that emphasize holism and consciousness. As explained in Appendix I-A, there is a fundamental difference between the development of biology compared with that of physics.

In physics it is recognized that Newton's laws are a limiting case of Einstein's laws, so there is no question of a dichotomy between them. Both laws are recognized as valid within their context of application. However, in biology there is virtually no notion amongst mainstream biologists of Darwinism being a limiting case of more enlightened views on evolution that incorporate such ideas as consciousness, organizing fields, and teleology. So we have the two-pronged fork just mentioned. The vast majority of biologists (mainstream, by definition) subscribe to Francis Crick's aspiration that all of biology will one day be explained in terms of reductionism to physics and chemistry. These are the molecular biologists whose mind-set is entirely mechanistic.

Mainstream biology and evolutionary science has progressed little beyond Darwin's theories

Only the enlightened biologists, very much in the minority, have seen that the mechanistic paradigm and Darwinian theory is but a partial view that needs to be supplemented and complemented by a much deeper organic and holistic outlook in order to incorporate the latest discoveries in quantum theory whereby all life and matter are regarded as the various forms and expressions of the primary element—unitary consciousness. Such are the

345

scientists and developmental biologists who adopt a more holistic approach. This enlightened approach to biology and evolution comes from the work of physicists like the contemporary Indian–American physicist Amit Goswami (*b.*1936), who has placed consciousness and quantum theory squarely within evolutionary theory, and biologists like Brian Goodwin, Rupert Sheldrake, and their forerunners, who collectively have argued the case for organicism, vital fields, and morphogenesis, together with the importance of entelechy, the chreode, and attractors (refer to Chapter 4, page 69ff). These scientists along with psychologists and mystical philosophers such as Ken Wilber, Teilhard de Chardin, and Śrī Aurobindo affirm the primacy of consciousness and the role of involution, which hardly figure in the concepts of most mainstream biologists.

The Situation from the Mid to Late Nineteenth Century

1858   Alfred Russel Wallace publishes a joint paper with Darwin 'On the Tendency of Species to form Varieties; and on the Perpetuation of Varieties and Species by Natural Means of Selection'. It was communicated to the Linnean Society by the Scottish geologist Sir Charles Lyell FRS (1797–1875) who stated that both Wallace and Darwin had 'independently and unknown to one another, conceived the same very ingenious theory to account for the appearance and perpetuation of varieties and of specific forms on our planet.'

1859   Charles Darwin publishes his *On the Origin of Species by Means of Natural Selection or the Preservation of Favoured Races in the Struggle for Life* in which he argues that evolution is driven by chance and necessity, i.e. random mutations and natural selection of favourable genes over unfavourable ones in the struggle of the survival of the fittest. (There are numerous references to Darwin's theories in *The Secret Doctrine* and other writings of H. P. Blavatsky.[i])

1871   Darwin publishes *The Descent of Man in Relation to Sex* on evolutionary theory following his 1859 work, *On the Origin of Species*. In *The Descent of Man*, Darwin applies evolutionary theory to human evolution, and details his theory of sexual selection. The book discusses many related issues, including evolutionary psychology, evolutionary ethics, differences between human races, differences between sexes, the superiority of men to women, and the relevance of the evolutionary theory to society.

1871   Alfred Russel Wallace in the final essay, 'The Limits of Natural Selection as Applied to Man' of *Contributions to the Theory of Natural Selection*, asserts that either all matter is conscious, or consciousness is something distinct from matter; and in the latter case, its presence in material forms is a proof of the existence of conscious beings outside of, and independent of, matter.

1874   Ernst Haeckel on 'Ontogeny Recapitulates Phylogeny' posits that the physical, cultural, moral, or intellectual development of each individual passes through stages similar to the developmental stages of that individual's species, society,

---

i Numerous references to Darwin's theories by H. P. Blavatsky are in: *Isis Unveiled, The Secret Doctrine* (especially in Volume II: Anthropogenesis), and the *Collected Writings*.

or civilization. (There are several references to Haeckel's ideas in *The Secret Doctrine* and other writings of H. P. Blavatsky.[ii])

1870s   Sir Benjamin Ward Richardson in *Theory of a Nervous Ether* postulates the *vital principle* which he calls 'nervous ether' with its fountainhead in the sun, and in the human body, being a direct product from blood. (There are several referenced quotations to Richardson in *The Secret Doctrine* and other writings of H. P. Blavatsky.[2])

1882   In *Beiträge zur Descendenzlehre* [Contributions to the Theory of Descent], August Weismann veers towards the teachings of the Vedas on reincarnation and sets aside Darwin's theory. Weismann uses the term 'germ plasm' to refer to the immortal portion of our bodies. (Weismann's theory is expounded in *The Secret Doctrine*.[3])

1889   Alfred Russel Wallace in *Darwinism: An Exposition Of The Theory Of Natural Selection – With Some of Its Applications* demarcates the parameters of the theory of natural selection and the limitations of its application, citing, as an example, the enormous development of the mathematical faculty as being wholly unexplained by natural selection, and therefore due to some altogether distinct cause.

1892   Hans Driesch, one of the proponents of vitalism, separates the individual cells of a two-cell sea urchin embryo and shows that each cell develops into a complete individual unit, thus disproving the theory of preformation and showing that each cell is 'totipotent', containing all the hereditary information necessary to form an individual unit.

A Timeline Showing How Enlightened and Mainstream Life Sciences have Progressed since the Turn of the Twentieth Century

Chronological highlights for enlightened and mainstream life sciences (biology and evolution) are shown to the left hand margin and idented, respectively.

Enlightened	Mainstream	
	1900	Gregor Mendel's work regarding the new science of genetics is rediscovered. His study of certain traits in pea plants shows that the inheritance of these traits follows particular laws.
	1905	William Bateson coins the term 'genetics' to describe the study of biological inheritance.
	1910	Thomas Hunt Morgan advances his gene theory of inheritance.

---

ii As with Darwin, there are numerous references to Haeckel's theories by H. P. Blavatsky in: *Isis Unveiled, The Secret Docrine* (especially in Volume II: Anthropogenesis), and the *Collected Writings*.

Enlightened   Mainstream

1914   Hans Driesch in *The History and Theory of Vitalism* postulates the existence of a non-physical causal factor (entelechy), which acts on the physical system but is not itself a part of it, to account for the fact that there are some aspects of living organisms that remain whole even though parts of the physical whole could be damaged, mutilated or removed.

1914   Sir John Arthur Thomson in his Gifford Lectures, and his books written with Sir Patrick Geddes, argues for a form of holistic biology in which the activity of the living organism could transcend the physical laws governing its component parts.

1917   Sir D'Arcy Wentworth Thompson in *On Growth and Form* proposes that biological form can reflect physical and mathematical principles so that initial conditions that determine the shape of the anatomical structures of organisms might well reflect some aspects of natural selection, but the resulting morphology does not.

> 1924   Raymond Dart discovers the Australopithecus Africanus.
>
> 1924   J. B. S. Haldane in *Daedalus; or, Science and the Future* predicts that great benefits would come from applications of advanced sciences to human biology, especially eugenics (selective breeding), ectogenesis (creating and sustaining life in an artificial environment), and the application of genetics to improve human characteristics, such as health and intelligence; and that every such advance would first meet with the objection of being unnatural or perverted.

1935   Alexis Carell in *Man, the Unknown* compares the quantity of liquid necessary to keep artificially alive a piece of living tissue which has been reduced to pulp, with the quantity of blood doing the same within the living organism. He estimates that if all the tissues of the human body were treated in this way, it would take 45,000 gallons of circulating fluid to keep them from being poisoned in a few days by their own waste products but within the human body the blood achieves the same task with 1½ gallons.

1937   Theodosius Dobzhansky in *Genetics and the Origin of Species* notes that the sudden origin of a new species by random mutation might be an impossibility because with the known mutation rates, the probability of such an event would be negligible.

1940   Śrī Aurobindo in *The Life Divine* states the primacy of consciousness and the role of involution (which hardly figure in mainstream biology).

> 1940s   Modern neo-Darwinism is established together with one of the twentieth century's strongest taboos in biology against the inheritance of acquired characteristics—Lamarckian inheritance.
>
> Note: Darwin himself was a convinced Lamarckian.

1942   Ernst Mayr in *Systematics and Origin of Species* states that instead of looking at the mystery and the mechanisms of fast tempo evolution, establishment biology

Enlightened   Mainstream

looks for chance and necessity theory to explain away the fossil gaps and invents theories such as the theory of geographical isolation.

1950   Karl Lashley in 'In Search of the Engram' establishes that memories are not localized in one part of the brain but are widely distributed throughout the cortex; therefore, it is not possible to demonstrate the isolated localization of a memory trace anywhere within the nervous system. (Lashley's discovery is based on the results of numerous experiments conducted on trained animals.)

> 1950s   Francis Crick and James Watson dogmatize Weismann's idea in molecular biology that information only flows from gene to protein, never protein to gene as Lamarckism would imply. Crick then elevates Weisman's 1893 idea to 'the central dogma of molecular biology'.

> 1952   American developmental biologists Robert Briggs and Thomas King clone the first vertebrate by transplanting nuclei from leopard frog embryos into enucleated eggs.

> 1952   Alan Turing in 'The Chemical Basis of Morphogenesis' offers a molecular explanation of morphogenesis through chemistry and theorizes that identical biological cells differentiate, change shape, and create patterns through a process of intercellular reaction–diffusion.

> 1953   The double-helix model of the DNA structure is published in the journal *Nature* by James Watson and Francis Crick. The term 'double helix' enters popular culture with the publication by James Watson in 1968 of The Double Helix: A Personal Account of the Discovery of the Structure of DNA.

> 1953   Stanley Miller experiment produces amino acid in 'possible primitive earth conditions'.

1953   Julian Huxley in *Evolution in Action* and his later books, alludes to a teleological aspect to evolution. (*The Secret Doctrine* and other works of H. P. Blavatsky contain numerous references to the materialistic theories of Julian Huxley's grandfather, Thomas Henry Huxley known as 'Darwin's Bulldog' for his dogmatic advocacy of Charles Darwin's theory of evolution.[iii])

1957   Conrad Waddington in *The Strategy of the Genes* suggests an extension of the idea of morphogenetic fields to include the temporal aspect of development which new concept he calls the 'chreode'.

1960s   James Lovelock proposes the Gaia hypothesis that living and non-living parts of the Earth form a complex interacting system that can be thought of as a single

---

iii As with Darwin, there are numerous references to Huxley's theories by H. P. Blavatsky in: *Isis Unveiled, The Secret Docrine* (especially in Volume II: Anthropogenesis), and the *Collected Writings*.

Enlightened   Mainstream

> organism. Named after the Greek goddess Gaia, the hypothesis postulates that the biosphere has a regulatory effect on the Earth's environment that acts to sustain life. This constitutes a departure from a mechanistic notion of life towards a more organic view.

1961   Teilhard de Chardin in *The Phenomenon of Man* affirms the primacy of consciousness and the role of involution (which are both ignored by virtually all mainstream biologists).

1963–65   Alister Hardy's Gifford Lectures at Aberdeen University published as *The Living Stream* and *The Divine Flame*, the former containing a chapter entitled 'Biology and Telepathy' where he explains that the process of evolution might possibly be influenced by something akin to telepathy.

> 1965   Genetic code fully cracked through trial-and-error experimental work.

> 1974   First totally successful fertilization of human ovum outside human body. (A letter making reference to cloning can be discerned in *The Mahatma Letters to A. P. Sinnett*.)

> 1972   Stephen Jay Gould and Niles Eldredge in *Paleobiology* reconsider the tempo and mode of evolution and propose an idea they call 'punctuated equilibrium'; that the fossil record is an accurate depiction of the pace of evolution, with long periods of 'stasis' (little change) punctuated by brief periods of rapid change and species formation (within a lineage).

> 1974   Stanley Miller in *The Heritage of Copernicus: Theories 'pleasing to the mind'* produces the first laboratory synthesis of organic compounds under primitive conditions.

> 1976   Richard Dawkins publishes *The Selfish Gene* forcefully promoting the neo-Darwinian ideas of adaptation and natural selection, that all life and behaviour is dependent upon the genetic program, the term 'selfish gene' being a way of expressing the gene-centred view of evolution as opposed to concepts that consider the organism and the group.

1977   Robert Efron in *Logic, Laws and Life: Some philosophical complications* thinks biologists miss something by objectifying subjective phenomena; that the reductionist stratagem to circumvent or surmount the problem is to take life out of the living and the living out of the life they are trying to explain.

1978   Louise Brown born—the first person in the world to be born through in vitro fertilization (IVF).

> 1980   Mechanistic theory (i.e. neo-Darwinism plus molecular biology) allegedly on the verge of ultimate triumph. Genetic code discovered and techniques developed for genes to be cloned.

Enlightened   Mainstream

1980   Humberto Maturana and Francisco Varela in *Autopoiesis and Cognition* propose holistic models concerning the self-organization of life.

1980   Ilya Prigogine in *From Being to Becoming* proposes holistic models of the self-organization of life.

1981   Rupert Sheldrake publishes *A New Science of Life* (revised and expanded as *Morphic Resonance*) putting forward the hypothesis of formative causation and morphogenetic fields as an alternative explanation to an exclusively mechanistic biology. Sir John Maddox, the editor of the prestigious journal *Nature*, condemns these ideas in an attack stating that even books like Hitler's *Mein Kampf* should not be burned, but Sheldrake's book would be 'the best candidate for burning there has been for many years.'

1981   Brian Josephson, a Nobel laureate counters the attack against Sheldrake stating that the editor showed 'a concern not for scientific validity but for respectability' and that 'the fundamental weakness is a failure to admit even the possibility that genuine physical facts may exist which lie outside the scope of current scientific descriptions.'

1981   Ken Wilber in *Up from Eden* affirms the primacy of consciousness and the role of involution (again ignored by virtually all mainstream biologists).

1982   Dialogue between Rupert Sheldrake and David Bohm on morphic fields and the implicate order published in ReVision Journal and as Appendix B in *Morphic Resonance: The nature of formative causation* (4th edn, 2009).

1982   Francis Hitching in *The Neck of the Giraffe* shows that an organismic approach is needed to account for the evolutionary lengthening of the giraffe's neck. Slow, accumulated variations and their selection by cumulative step-by-step chance and necessity is not credible, nor is a 'neck lengthening gene' a viable explanation.

1987   Robert Shapiro in *Origins: A skeptic's guide to the creation of life on earth* gives detailed reasons and probability calculations questioning the validity of Darwinism as the sole mechanism for producing complicated non-linear designs, despite all the time available for chance and necessity to act.

1987   John Searle in *Mindwaves: Thoughts on intelligence, identity and consciousness* provides evidence that matter cannot process meaning.

1988   J. Cairns, J. Overbaugh, and S. Miller in 'The Origin of Mutants' provide experimental verification of directed mutation in favour of Lamarck's basic idea, plus evidence in favour of downward causation.

1988   Rupert Sheldrake in *The Presence of the Past* develops some of the important ideas published in his first book, *A New Science of Life*, regarding morphogenetic fields, such that formative causation is not solely the product of molecular interactions but presupposes an independent organizing principle whereby all natural systems from minerals to human society are influenced by their past experiences

Enlightened   Mainstream

and therefore inherit a collective memory that influences their form and behaviour in the present.

1989   Roger Penrose in *The Emperor's New Mind* also provides evidence that matter cannot process meaning.

       1990   'Decade of the brain' inaugurated by President George Bush Sr. leads to further growth in neurosciences.

       1990   Human Genome Project launched with a projected budget of $3 billion.

1991   Robert Wesson in *Beyond Natural Selection* proposes holistic models of the self-organization of life.

1992   Gerald Edelman in *Bright Air, Brilliant Fire: On the matter of the mind* on how the mind originates in the brain argues that it is puerile to reduce a theory of the behaviour of an individual solely to a theory of molecular interactions due to the many different levels of physical, biological, and social interactions that must transpire for higher order consciousness to emerge.

1993   Mae-Wan Ho in *The Rainbow and the Worm: The physics of organisms* proposes an organismic approach to biology arguing that evolutionary emergence of a new trait cannot be gradual. She argues that no matter how diverse the cells, organs, and systems in a complex organism like the human body are, dynamic equilibrium is staggering and they act 'in concert' as one.

1993   Amit Goswami in *The Self-Aware Universe* argues that it is consciousness that creates the material world.

1993   Michael Cremo and Richard Thompson in *Forbidden Archeology: The hidden history of the human race* (and its condensed edition *The Hidden History of the Human Race*) provide a massive amount of detailed data and facts, assembled with meticulous scholarship, demonstrating the enormous antiquity of the human race in accord with the great esoteric and occult traditions of the world, especially the Vedas; and that such worldwide anomalous archæological evidence has been systematically suppressed by mainstream science in order to preserve its status quo on evolutionary theory based on Darwinism.

1994   Francis Crick in *The Astonishing Hypothesis: The scientific search for the soul* asserts that all our joys and sorrows, memories and ambitions, mental activities, sense of personal identity and free will, 'are in fact no more than the behaviour of a vast assembly of nerve cells and their associated molecules.'

1994   Brain Goodwin in *How the Leopard Got Its Spots* states, 'I don't think biology at the moment is a science at all, at least in the sense that physics and chemistry are sciences. We need to know the universal ordering principles just as Newton provided them for the inanimate world.'

1995   David Chalmers in *Towards a Theory of Consciousness* provides evidence that matter cannot produce consciousness.

Enlightened   Mainstream

1995   Daniel Dennett in *Darwin's Dangerous Idea* claims that Darwinian adaptive evolution itself brings about the capacity of evolvability in a canalized manner; and explains away meaning-processing, self-consciousness, and appreciation of beauty as Darwinian adaptation.

1995   Publication of the first complete genome of a free-living organism.

1996   Dolly the sheep is the first clone of an adult mammal.

1996   John Horgan's best-selling book *The End of Science* maintains that 'one must accept the possibility—even the probability—that the great era of [pure] scientific discovery is over'.

   Note: this remark is astonishingly similar to Lord Kelvin's statement a century earlier that physics had little else to discover—before Max Planck ushered in the scientific revolution of the quantum era.

1996   Michael Behe in *Darwin's Black Box: The biochemical challenge to evolution*, like Robert Shapiro in *Origins*, shows detailed reasons and probability calculations questioning the validity of Darwinism as a mechanism for producing complicated non-linear designs, despite all the time available for chance and necessity to act.

1996   Fritjof Capra in *The Web of Life: A new scientific understanding of living systems* proposes holistic models of the self-organization of life.

1997   Hans-Peter Dürr states that whereas in microphysics the fundamental limitations of the fragmenting, reductionist approach are giving way to holistic ideas, in biology the main thrust is still in the opposite direction: to reduce the phenomena of life and mind to the mechanistic physics of the nineteenth century.

1997   Amit Goswami and Dennis Todd in *Integrative Physiological and Behavioral Science* also provide direct experimental verification of directed mutation in favour of Lamarck's basic idea, together with evidence in favour of downward causation based on quantum measurement theory.

1997   Amit Goswami in 'A Quantum Explanation of Sheldrake's Morphic Resonance' argues the case for morphic resonance.

1997   Hans-Peter Dürr and Franz-Theo Gottwald in *Rupert Sheldrake in der Diskussion. Das Wagnis einer neuen Wissenschaft des Lebens* [Scientists discuss Sheldrake's theory about morphogenetic fields].

1997   Andrew Maniotis in *Proceedings of the National Academy of Sciences U.S.A.* shows by laboratory experiments the direct connection between the genome and soma in support of Lamarckian inheritance.

1997   Roger Sperry in his article for *The Nobel Prize* describes how after separating the two hemispheres of the brain by cutting the corpus callosum connecting

Enlightened   Mainstream

them, each remained a conscious system in its own right at a characteristically human level, which demonstrates a radical departure from the prevalent orthodox view that the human mind is an illusion or, at best, a powerless by-product of physical brain processes.

1998   Michael Lieber in *Fundamental and Molecular Mechanisms of Mutagenesis* uses laboratory experiments to demonstrate the direct connection between the genome and soma in support of Lamarckian inheritance.

1998   Paul Davies in *The Cosmic Blueprint* states that biology is an incomplete science needing new non-physical, non-material organizing principles to explain the difference between life and non-life.

1998   Willis Harman and Elisabet Sahtouris in *Biology Revisioned* show that chaos theory and complexity theory have undermined the strictly materialistic paradigm by introducing the concept of Self into an understanding of life.

1999   Paul Davies in *The Fifth Miracle* states that after initial success, the molecular synthesis of life in a laboratory remains elusive. He questions whether molecular biology can ever explain what life is or how it originated.

2000   Marco Bischof in *Biophotonics and Coherent Structures* sums up the insights emerging at the frontiers of life sciences as: 'Quantum mechanics has established the primacy of the inseparable whole. For this reason, the basis of the new biophysics must be the insight into the fundamental interconnectedness within the organism as well as between organisms, and that of the organism *with the environment* [emphasis by Bischof].'

    2001   First draft of human genome sequence published by NIH. Astonishing result emerges that the fruit flies, sea urchins, many animals much simpler than humans, and many species of plants, rice for example, have far more genes than humans.

    2001   Svante Paabo, the director of chimpanzee genome project anticipates 'the profoundly interesting genetic prerequisites that make us different from other animals.'

    2001   Publication of the first drafts of the complete human genome sequence in *Nature*.

    Note: Post-2000 there is a dramatic drop in optimism in the explanatory power of molecular biology and genetics with the realization that all life cannot be understood merely from the genetic 'program'. Realizing the huge gap in knowledge between the molecular approach and gene sequences, and the way that living organisms grow and behave, paves the way for alternative hypotheses such as formative causation.

2001   Amit Goswami in *Physics of the Soul* affirms the primacy of consciousness and the role of involution (anathema to most mainstream biologists).

Enlightened   Mainstream

2002   William Dembski in *No Free Lunch: Why specified complexity cannot be purchased without intelligence* shows that complexity theories, like chaos theories, can produce simple types of order but not coded information as in the genetic code.

2002   Steven Kaufman in *Unified Reality Theory: The evolution of existence into experience* states that life arises from self-organization that goes beyond the mechanisms of molecular biologists.

2003   Human Epigenome Project launched. Evidence in favour of Lamarckian inheritance continued to accumulate throughout the twentieth century but was generally ignored until soon after the turn of the millennium with the growing recognition of epigenetic inheritance.

2003   Arne Wyller in 'Beyond Darwin's Paradigm' proposes a consciousness-driven evolution.

        2004   Eli Minkoff and Pamela Baker in *Biology Today: An issues approach* still champion the standard textbook-materialist characteristics of 'life' comprising: organization, metabolism, homoeostasis, selective response, growth and biosynthesis, genetic material, reproduction, population structure.

        2005   After the complete chimpanzee sequence was published, Svante Paabo, the director of the chimpanzee genome project states, 'we cannot see in this why we are so different from chimpanzees.'

2005   Bruce Lipton in *The Biology of Belief* maintains that establishment biologists assume that only the genes have all the programs for cell functioning. However the programs also exist in the soma. This is the idea moving in the direction of the new biology.

        2005   Marc Kirschner and John Gerhart in *The Plausibility of Life: Resolving Darwin's dilemma* claim that Darwinian adaptive evolution itself brings about the capacity of evolvability in a canalized manner; and explain away meaning-processing, self-consciousness, and appreciation of beauty as Darwinian adaptation.

2005   Eva Jablonska and Marion Lamb in *Evolution in Four Dimensions: Genetic, epigenetic, behavioral, and symbolic variation in the history of life* propose a broader definition of inheritance involving a two-way flow, which opens new possibilities for neo-Lamarckism.

2005   Brian Goodwin in 'Meaning in Evolution' challenges neo-Darwinist reductionism as an exclusive explanatory mechanism and maintains that natural selection is a 'too weak force' on its own to explain evolution fully.

2008   Amit Goswami in *Creative Evolution* proposes that consciousness is the ground of being. He therefore advocates a biology within consciousness.

Enlightened   Mainstream

2009	Rupert Sheldrake in the fourth, revised and expanded edition of *A New Science of Life* (renamed *Morphic Resonance: The nature of formative causation* in the US) updates his earlier work and adds Appendices regarding new tests for morphic resonance and his dialogue with David Bohm.
2010	NASA scientist Felisa Wolfe-Simon and her team discover a bacterium whose DNA is completely alien to what we know today, working differently to other organisms on the planet. Instead of using phosphorus, the newly discovered microorganism, GFAJ-1 found in Mono Lake, California, uses the poisonous *arsenic* for its building blocks. It is unlike *anything* currently living in planet Earth. NASA is saying that this is 'life as we do *not* know it'. This strongly alludes to the occult tenet that there is no dead matter and all is life using different vehicles of expression.
2010	Despite the mountains of data in molecular biology, the sequencing of the human genome, advances in neurosciences, and the physics of superstrings, we find that science has not come to an end—not with the discovery that some ninety-five per cent of the universe is made up of dark matter and dark energy, whose nature is quite literally ambiguous.
2012	Thomas Nagel in *Mind and Cosmos: Why the materialist neo-Darwinian conception of nature is almost certainly false* rebuts the materialist neo-Darwinian theory as an adequate explanation of nature and evolution.
2012	John Dupré in *Processes of Life: Essays in the philosophy of biology* highlights the limitations of the mainstream viewpoint with a wealth of evidence to show that biology cannot be explained solely by a reductionist approach using the laws of physics and chemistry.
2017	Brenda Dunne and Robert Jahn (eds), and Larry Dossey (contributor) in *Being & Biology: Is consciousness the life force?* argue that despite modern advances in epigenetics and complexity theory, the mindset of mainstream biology is still dominated by the mechanistic thinking of the 1920s, underpinned further in the 1950s when vitalism was banished and replaced by the central dogma of molecular biology making the gene and DNA into the 'elementary particles' of biology, thus assuming a strictly one-way process from DNA to RNA to proteins to function.

2019	Templeton Foundation World Charity Foundation launch the first phase of a $20 million project at the Society for Neuroscience meeting in Chicago, Illinois to compare two theories of the neurological and physiological mechanisms that produce consciousness by scanning the brains of participants during cleverly designed tests.
2019	Michael Graziano in *Rethinking Consciousness: A scientific theory of subjective experience*, and a related *New Scientist* article, states that the final solution to the hard problem of consciousness is imminent. How the brain generates consciousness can

Enlightened   Mainstream

be discovered through evolutionary theory and an engineering analogy with machines; that 'in this account, consciousness isn't so much an illusion as a self-caricature.' He proposes how 'to engineer human-like consciousness into a machine' and offers the prospect of the natural consciousness of a person uploaded into a machine for a digital afterlife.

2021   Anil Seth in *Being You: A science of consciousness* posits that our brain hallucinates our conscious reality; so once we start explaining our own unique experience in terms of the properties of what happens inside our brains and bodies, the apparently insoluble mystery of consciousness should start to fade away.

NOTES

1   See: 'Georg Ernst Stahl', *Encyclopedia.com* <https://www.encyclopedia.com/people/science-and-technology/chemistry-biographies/georg-ernst-stahl> accessed 18 January 2020; 'Georg Ernst Stahl Facts', *Your Dictionary – Biography* <http://biography.yourdictionary.com/georg-ernst-stahl> accessed 18 January 2020.
2   See: *SD*-I, 'Life, Force, or Gravity', 529–40 *passim*; *SD*-I, 'Forces – Modes of Motion or Intelligences?' 603; *CW*-IX, 'The Life Principle', 78–9.
3   *SD*-I, 'Stanza VII: The Parents of Man on Earth', 223.

Endnotes to Volume I

Endnote I-1 Evidence for the hypothesis of morphic fields and morphic resonance

The following is a representative selection of wide-ranging evidence in support of the hypothesis of the nature of formative causation.

Shown below is a list, extracted from Appendix A of *Morphic Resonance*, of new tests for the hypothesis of formative causation using two approaches: (*a*) through morphic fields, which connect together parts of morphic units in space; and (*b*) through morphic resonance and its cumulative influence in time.

Morphic fields

❖ Bose-Einstein condensates
❖ Melting points
❖ Crystal transformations
❖ Adaptations in cell cultures
❖ Heat tolerance in plants.

Morphic resonance

❖ The transmission of aversion
❖ The evolution of animal behaviour
❖ Collective human memory
❖ Improving human performance
❖ Resonant computers.

The following is a representative selection of peer reviewed papers by Rupert Sheldrake and co-workers in support of the hypothesis of morphic resonance in connection with two especially noteworthy areas of research: animal powers and telepathy. They have been extracted verbatim.

Animal Powers

❖ 'Listen to the Animals: Why did so many animals escape December's tsunami?', *The Ecologist*, March 2005.[i]
❖ 'Testing a Language – Using a Parrot for Telepathy', *Journal of Scientific Exploration* 17, 601–615, 2003.

---

i It would be instructive to know if a similar study will be done regarding the appalling loss of wildlife during the devastating bushfires in Australia in 2019.

❖ 'A Dog That Seems To Know When His Owner is Coming Home: Videotaped Experiments and Observations', *Journal of Scientific Exploration* 14, 233–255, 2000.

❖ 'Testing a Return-Anticipating Dog, Kane', *Anthrozooes*, 13, 203–212, 2000.

❖ 'The "Psychic Pet" Phenomenon: Correspondence', *Journal of the Society for Psychical Research* 64, No 859, 2000.

❖ 'Commentary on a Paper by Wiseman, Smith and Milton: on the "Psychic Pet" Phenomenon', *Journal of the Society for Psychical Research* 63, October 1999.

❖ 'A Dog That Seems To Know When His Owner is Returning: Preliminary Investigations', *Journal of the Society for Psychical Research* 62, 220–232, 1998.

❖ 'Perceptive Pets: A Survey in London', *Biology Forum* 91, 57–74, 1998.

❖ 'Perceptive Pets: A Survey of North-West California', *Journal of the Society for Psychical Research* 62, 396–406, July 1998.

❖ 'Perceptive Pets with Puzzling Powers: Three Surveys', *ISAZ* The Newsletter No. 15, l99E 1998.

❖ 'Psychic Pets: A Survey in North-West England', *Journal of the Society for Psychical Research* 61, 1997.

Telepathy

❖ 'Automated Tests for Telephone Telepathy Using Mobile Phones', Explore: *The Journal of Science and Healing* 11 No. 4, 310–319, 2015.

❖ 'Telepathy in Connection with Telephone Calls, Text Messages and Emails', *Journal of International Society of Life Information Science* 32 No. 1, 7–15, 2014.

❖ 'An Automated Test for Telepathy in Connection with Emails', *Journal of Scientific Exploration* 23 No. 1, 29–36, 2009.

❖ 'Sensing the Sending of SMS Messages: an automated test', Explore: *The Journal of Science and Healing* 5, 272–276, 2009.

❖ 'A Rapid Online Telepathy Test', Psychological Reports, Vol 104 957-970, 2009.

❖ 'An Automated Online Telepathy Test', *Journal of Scientific Exploration*, Vol 21 No 3, 511–522, 2007.

❖ 'Testing for Telepathy in Connection with E-Mails', *Perceptual and Motor Skills*, 101, 771–786, 2005.

❖ 'Videotaped Experiments on Telephone Telepathy', *Journal of Parapsychology* 67, 147–166, 2003.

❖ 'A Filmed Experiment on Telephone Telepathy with the Nolan Sisters', *Journal of the Society for Psychical Research* 68, 168–172, 2004.

❖ 'Investigaciones Experimentales En Telepatía Por Teléfono' (in Spanish), *Revista Argentina de Psicología Paranormal* 15 No. 3–4, Julio-Octubre 2004.

❖ 'Experimental Tests for Telephone Telepathy', *Journal of the Society for Psychical Research* 67, 184–199, July 2003.

❖ 'Apparent Telepathy Between Babies and Nursing Mothers: A Survey', *Journal of the Society for Psychical Research* 66 181–185, 2002.

❖ 'The Anticipation of Telephone Calls: A Survey in California', *Journal of Parapsychology* 65, 145–156, 2001.

❖ 'Telepathic Telephone Calls: Two Surveys', *Journal of the Society for Psychical Research* 64, 224–232, 2000.

❖ 'Do You Know Who is Calling? : Experiments on Anomalous Cognition in Phone Call Receivers', *The Open Psychology Journal*, 2, 12–18, 2009.

❖ 'Who's Calling At This Hour? : Local Sidereal Time and Telephone Telepathy', Paper presented at the *Parapsychology Association Annual Convention*, Vienna, August 2004.

Endnote I-2 Scientific bodies and references to psychical research and paranormal phenomena

The following principal scientific bodies in the West are associated with investigating the whole field of psychical and paranormal phenomena, including claims of mediumship.

Learned Societies

1. The (British) Society for Psychical Research
   Founded 1882 by Professor Henry Sidgwick, Frederic Myers, and Edmund Gurney. Past presidents have included philosophers William James and Henri Bergson, scientists William Crookes, Lord Rayleigh, and Charles Richet, and British Conservative Prime Minister Arthur Balfour.
   http://www.spr.ac.uk/

   ❖ Libraries and Archives
   https://www.spr.ac.uk/about/libraries-and-archives
   The full archive of the SPR's *Journals and Proceedings* (1884–2011) and *Psi Researcher/Paranormal Review* (1991–2006) is housed within Lexscien, an independent online library (https://www.spr.ac.uk/online-library). Also included are the archives of the *Journal of Parapsychology* and other leading *psi* research journals.

2. The American Society for Psychical Research
   Founded 1885 by Professor William James and others.
   http://www.aspr.com/

   ❖ Library
   http://www.aspr.com/virtuallobby.htm#library
   An extensive parapsychological library containing overs 10,000 volumes and over 300 periodical titles. The works in the collection extend from the eighteenth century to the present. The library collection is international, containing publications in over fourteen languages.

   ❖ *Journal of the American Society for Psychical Research* providing scholarly reports, research findings, discussions of implications and applications of psychic functioning, and book reviews.
   http://www.aspr.com/jaspr.htm

   ❖ Newsletters
   http://www.aspr.com/ullm.htm

3. The Scottish Society for Psychical Research
   Founded 1987 by Professor Archie Roy.
   www.sspr.co.uk

   ❖ Library Book List – The full list in alphabetical order can be seen on:
   http://media.wix.com/ugd/b1af60_0a405f2a32b34746897eae472de3dd50.pdf

Further Reading

❖ *Parapsychology: A Handbook for the 21st Century*, (Edited by Etzel Cardeña, John Palmer and David Marcusson-Clavertz), McFarland, Jefferson, NC, 2015.
❖ W. J. Crawford, *Experiments in Psychical Science*, Watkins, 1919.
❖ W. J. Crawford, *The Reality of Psychic Phenomena*, Watkins, 1916.
❖ J. W. Dunne, *An Experiment with Time*, Macmillan, 1927.
❖ A. Ellison, *The Reality of the Paranormal*, Harrap, 1988.
❖ P. Fenwick, et al. ' "Psychic sensitivity", mystical experience and brain pathology', *British Journal of Medical Psychology*, Vol. 58, 1985.
❖ R. G. Jahn and B. J. Dunne, *Margins of Reality*, USA, 1987.
❖ R. G. Jahn, 'The Persistent Paradox of Psychic Phenomena: an Engineering Perspective', *Proc. IEEE*, Vol. 70, 1982.
❖ L. LeShan, *The Medium, the Mystic, and the Physicist*, Turnstone, 1974.
❖ R. A. Monroe, *Journeys Out of the Body*, Doubleday, 1971.
❖ F. W. H. Myers, *Human Personality and Its Survival of Bodily Death*, Longmans Green, 2 vols, 1903.
❖ I. Stevenson, See Endnote I-5 below.
❖ R. Targ, and Puthoff, H.E., *Mind-Reach*, Delacorte Press/Eleanor Friede, 1977.

Endnote I-3   Remote viewing and clairvoyance

Representative literature on remote viewing and clairvoyance is cited below.

❖ Frederick Bligh Bond, *An Architectural Handbook of Glastonbury Abbey: With a historical chronicle of the building*, Glastonbury : 'Central Somerset Gazette', 1920.
❖ Frederick Bligh Bond, *The Gate of Remembrance: The story of the psychological experiment which resulted in the discovery of the Edgar Chapel at Glastonbury*, B. H. Blackwell, 1918.
❖ W. E. Butler, *How to Develop Clairvoyance*, Samuel Weiser Inc.,1979.
❖ J. Goodman, *Psychic Archeology: Time machine to the past*, Putnam Publishing Group, 1977.
❖ D. Moorhouse, *Psychic Warrior: The true story of the CIA's paranormal espionage programme*, Clairview Books, 2013.
❖ J. Schnabel, *Remote Viewers: The secret history of America's psychic spies*, Dell, 1997.
❖ S. A. Schwartz, *The Secret Vaults of Time: Psychic archaeology and the quest for man's beginnings*, Universe, 2001.
❖ J. White, *Psychic Warfare: Fact or fiction?*, Aquarian Press, 1988.

Endnote I-4   Literature on reincarnation

Arguably, the finest single resource of representative literature on reincarnation from both Western and Eastern sources is the following anthology:

> *Reincarnation: The Phoenix Fire Mystery – An East-West dialogue on death and rebirth from the worlds of religion, science, psychology, philosophy, art, and literature, and from great thinkers of the past and present*, compiled and ed. Joseph Head and Sylvia Cranston with a foreword by Elizabeth Kübler-Ross, MD, Theosophical University Press, 1994.

Other anthologies are:

❖ *Reincarnation – An East-West anthology* (compiled and ed. Joseph Head and Sylvia Cranston), The Theosophical Publishing House, 1968.

❖ Joel Bjorling, *Reincarnation: A bibliography*, Garland Publishing, 1996.

❖ Sylvia Cranston and Carey Williams, *Reincarnation – A new horizon in science, religion, and society*, Theosophical University Press, 1999.

Comprehensive, but shorter volumes are:

❖ John Algeo, *Reincarnation Explored*, Theosophical Publishing House, 1995.

❖ John Algeo, 'Reincarnation: the Evidence', *Quest* 89.2, March-April 2001, 44–50.

❖ Annie Besant, *Death – and After?* Theosophical Manual No. 3, Theosophical Publishing House, 2006.

❖ Annie Besant, *Reincarnation*, Theosophical Manual No. 2, Theosophical Publishing House, 1915.

❖ David Lorimer, *Whole in One: The near-death experience and the ethic of interconnectedness*, Penguin Books 1991.

❖ Eben Alexander and Ptolemy Tompkins, *The Map of Heaven: How science, religion, and ordinary people are proving the afterlife*, Simon and Schuster, 2014.

See also Endnote I-5 below.

Endnote I-5   Further publications by Ian Stevenson

These references to Ian Stevenson's publications are in addition to those cited in Chapter 4.

❖ *Twenty Cases Suggestive of Reincarnation*, University of Virginia Press, 1966.

❖ *The Psychiatric Examination*. Little, Brown, 1969.

❖ *Telepathic Impressions: A review and report of 35 new cases*, University Press of Virginia, 1970.

❖ *The Diagnostic Interview* (2nd revised edition of Medical History-Taking), Harper & Row, 1971.

❖ *Twenty Cases Suggestive of Reincarnation* (second revised and enlarged edition), University of Virginia Press,1974.

❖ *Xenoglossy: A review and report of a case*, University of Virginia Press, 1974.

❖ *Unlearned Language: New studies in xenoglossy*, University of Virginia Press, 1984.

Endnote I-6 Further academic sources on Western esotericism

Academic References

Antoine Faivre and Wouter J. Hanegraaff (eds), *Western Esotericism and the Science of Religion*, Peeters Publishers, 1998.

> This book is based upon papers read during the innovative section 'Western Esotericism and the Science of Religion' organized at the 17th International Congress of the International Association for the History of Religions (IAHR) in Mexico City, August 5–12, 1995. It was created in order to fill a long-standing hiatus in the academic study of religions: whereas subjects such as Gnosticism, Hermeticism, and the occult sciences in antiquity have long been recognized as subjects worthy of serious investigation, the history of similar and related subjects in more recent periods has hardly received the same measure of scholarly attention and recognition. Hence, this book is devoted to the academic emancipation of these areas as constituting a legitimate domain of contemporary research. It is preceded by an introductory essay on the birth of this new discipline in the study of religion and a sample of current research in the field.

Antoine Faivre, *Access to Western Esotericism*, State University of New York Press, 1994.

> This book is the first systematic treatment of esotericism to appear in English. It includes an historical survey, beginning with the Alexandrian period, of the various esoteric currents, such as Christian Kabbalah, Theosophy, Alchemy, Rosicrucianism, and Hermeticism, showing their common characteristics of universal interdependency and the experience of spiritual transformation. Furthermore, it establishes a rigorous methodology and provides clarifying definitions of such key terms as 'gnosis', 'theosophy', 'occultism', and 'hermeticism', with an analysis of contemporary esotericism based on three distinct pathways. It goes on to present studies on several important figures, works, and movements in Western esotericism.

Antoine Faivre, trans. Christine Rhone, *Western Esotericism: A concise history*, State University of New York Press, 2010.

> This book comprises an overview of Western esoteric currents since late antiquity, with an emphasis on the last six centuries. It is an historical and pedagogical guide providing a chronological overview of Western esoteric currents from ancient and medieval sources (Alexandrian Hermeticism, Gnosticism, Neoplatonism), through the Renaissance up to the present time.

Antoine Faivre, trans. Christine Rhone, *Theosophy, Imagination, Tradition: Studies in Western esotericism*, State University of New York Press, 2000.

> This book presents the current state of research in esotericism, plus an exploration of three main aspects of the field from the Renaissance to the twentieth century tracing the history of the theosophical current, its continuity and shifts, against the background of social and cultural events. Also included are the Paracelsian movement, the romantic Philosophies of Nature and the Occultist movement, and the role of tradition in major exponents of Western esotericism.

Antoine Faivre, *Eternal Hermes: From Greek god to alchemical magus*, Weiser, 2000.

Hermes, the messenger of the gods, eloquent revealer of hidden wisdom, and guardian of occult knowledge, has played a central role in the development of esotericism in the West. Drawing upon many rare books and manuscripts, this highly illustrated work explores the question of where Hermes Trismegistus came from, how he came to be a patron of the esoteric traditions, and how the figure of Hermes has remained lively and inspiring to our own day.

Wouter J. Hanegraaff, *Esotericism and the Academy: Rejected knowledge in Western culture*, Cambridge University Press, 2014.

This publication is a meticulous study of primary and secondary sources to show that academics tend to look on 'esoteric', 'occult' or 'magical' beliefs with contempt, but are usually ignorant about the religious and philosophical traditions to which these terms refer, or their relevance to intellectual history. It also shows the clash between the progressive and the establishment: how intellectuals since the Renaissance have tried to come to terms with a cluster of polytheistic ideas from late antiquity that challenged the foundations of biblical religion and Greek rationality.

Dictionary of Gnosis & Western Esotericism, ed. Wouter J. Hanegraaff, in collaboration with Antoine Faivre, Roelof van den Broek, and Jean-Pierre Brach, Brill, 2006.

This book provides a comprehensive coverage of Gnosticism, Hermeticism, astrology, magic, the occult sciences, and esoteric religion, in the form of pagan, Jewish, and Christian religious discourses and phenomena. It also contains articles about the life and work of all the major personalities in the history of Gnosis and Western Esotericism, discussing their ideas, significance, and historical influence.

Wouter J. Hanegraaff, *Western Esotericism: A guide for the perplexed*, Bloomsbury Academic, 2013.

This is an accessible guide providing the basic knowledge and techniques to navigate the complex field of Western esotericism from late antiquity to the present day. Hence it works to remove misconceptions and prejudice that are the reasons for the disdain and disregard of more modern scholars. The book also shows what unites diverse subjects like Gnosticism and Hermeticism, the occult sciences comprising astrology, alchemy, and magic, Rosicrucianism and Christian mysticism, and contemporary New Age spiritualities; and what their study can teach us about our common cultural and intellectual heritage, and how they are relevant to contemporary concerns.

Arthur Versluis, *Wisdom's Book: The sophia anthology*, Paragon House, 2000.

This is an outstanding collection of rare texts that reveal what may well be referred to as the Nag Hammadi Library of modern times. Non-sectarian, often suppressed, this lay mystical tradition is the Christian equivalent of Sufism in Islam, and of Qabbalah in Judaism. This spiritual tradition has developed since the seventeenth century and still exists today. Revealed for the first time in a single volume, many of these texts of this rare tradition have never before been published.

Nicholas Goodrick-Clarke, *The Western Esoteric Traditions: A historical introduction*, Oxford University Press, 2008.[1]

> Western esotericism has now emerged as an academic study in its own right, combining spirituality with an empirical observation of the natural world while also relating humanity to the universe through a harmonious celestial order. This introduction to the Western esoteric traditions offers a concise overview of their historical development, from their roots in Hermeticism, Neoplatonism, and Gnosticism in the early Christian era, up to their reverberations in current scientific paradigms. This book includes modern esoteric thought in the light of new scientific and medical paradigms along with the analytical psychology of Carl Gustav Jung.

Further reading

❖ Arthur Edward Waite, *The Occult Sciences: A compendium of transcendental doctrine and experiment*, Kegan Paul, Trench, Trubner & Co., 1891.

❖ Brian Copenhaver, *Magic in Western Culture: From antiquity to the enlightenment*, Cambridge University Press, 2015.

❖ Dion Fortune [Violet Frith], *Principles of Hermetic Philosophy*, Thoth Publications, 1999.

❖ Frances Yates, *The Occult Philosophy in the Elizabethan Age*, Routledge, 2001.

❖ Frances Yates, *The Rosicrucian Enlightenment*, Routledge, 2001.

❖ Kocku von Stuckrad, *Western Esotericism: A brief history of secret knowledge*, (translated and with a foreword by Nicholas Goodrick-Clarke), Routledge, 2014.

❖ S. L. MacGregor Mathers, *Selected Occult Writings Of S. L. MacGregor Mathers*, Kessinger Publishing, LLC 2014.

Endnote I-7 The field of cognitive science

This section provides a bare outline of the field of cognitive science taken from a digest of several sources.[2] The objective is to show how science examines physical consciousness.

Cognitive science is a generalized term for the interdisciplinary study of mind and intelligence. Mental faculties of concern to cognitive scientists include language, perception, memory, attention, reasoning, and emotion. Hence to understand these faculties, cognitive scientists borrow from fields such as:

Multi-disciplinary input to cognitive science

❖ Neuroscience—The study of the anatomy and physiology of the brain and central nervous system

❖ Artificial Intelligence—The theory and development of computer systems to simulate and be able to perform tasks that normally require human intelligence

❖ Psychology—The study of the mind including its development, organization, and functions, particularly those relevant to behaviour

❖ Philosophy of mind—The study of the fundamental nature of knowledge, reality, and existence

❖ Linguistics—The study of language in form, meaning, and context

❖ Anthropology—The scientific study of the origin, development, and varieties of human beings and their societies.

Topics of interest include:

❖ Attention
❖ Change blindness (a perceptual phenomenon that occurs when a change in a visual stimulus is introduced and the observer does not notice it)
❖ Consciousness
❖ Decision-making
❖ Learning
❖ Memory
❖ Language
❖ Mirror neurons—directly observed in primate species, a neuron that fires both when an animal acts and when the animal observes the same action performed by another. Thus, the neuron 'mirrors' the behaviour of the other, as though the observer were itself acting. The function of the mirror system in humans is a subject of much speculation.[3]

Spectrum of cognitive science

❖ Perception
❖ Social cognition
❖ Emotions.

Methods generally used by cognitive scientists are both theoretical and experimental, such as:

❖ Computational Modelling
❖ Psychophysics (the branch of psychology that deals with the relations between physical stimuli and mental phenomena)
❖ Experimental methods of specific psychology fields, typically:
  – Functional magnetic resonance imaging (a functional neuroimaging procedure using MRI technology that measures brain activity by detecting changes associated with blood flow, relying on the fact that cerebral blood flow and neuronal activation are coupled)

Techniques of cognitive science

  – Transcranial Magnetic Stimulation (a magnetic method used to stimulate small regions of the brain)
  – Electroencephalography (a test used to detect abnormalities related to electrical activity of the brain by tracking and recording brain wave patterns)
  – Electrocorticography (a type of electrophysiological monitoring that uses electrodes placed directly on the exposed surface of the brain to record electrical activity from the cerebral cortex).

Two points should be plain to the reader. First, that consciousness is regarded as one of many subsets of the overall field of mental faculties. Secondly, the multi-disciplinary fields engaged, topics of interest, and methods of investigation are all based upon the assumption that there is a physical basis for mental faculties and the brain generates or produces the latter. There is nothing intrinsically wrong with this, except when such assumptions (and they are no more than assumptions) are taken as proven fact, such that other modes of enquiry and evidence to the contrary are excluded a priori.

Overriding basis of cognitive science

Endnote I-8 The evidence for prehistoric continents

The massive tomes by H. P. Blavatsky, Rudolf Steiner and Manly Hall provide the fullest details. However, the following books provide more digestible descriptions:

J. S. Gordon, *The Rise and Fall of Atlantis: And the true origins of human civilization*, Watkins Publishing, 2008.

> Whereas Plato's account of the lost continent and people of Atlantis has been dismissed by many as phantasy, this book, based primarily on the doctrines of modern Theosophy, argues that Atlantis is both a true account of a forgotten civilization, and a complex metaphor for cosmic creation. In presenting the evidence for Atlantis and its fate, controversial questions about the flawed logic of Darwinian theory are raised, demonstrating that neither this, nor literal Creationism is the only option for a credible theory of evolution.

Joscelyn Godwin, *Atlantis and the Cycles of Time: Prophecies, traditions, and occult revelations*, Inner Traditions, 2010.

> This publication is a comprehensive study of the major occult writings on Atlantis by a renowned scholar, author, editor, and translator of more than 30 books comprising a thorough examination of the many occult teachings on Atlantis, including those from G. I. Gurdjieff, Madame Blavatsky, Julius Evola, Edgar Cayce, Antoine Fabre d'Olivet, and Dion Fortune. The book goes on to show how these writings correlate with the concept of cyclical history, such as the Mayan calendar with its 2012 end-date, the Age of Aquarius, and the four Yugas.

Graham Hancock, *Underworld: The mysterious origins of civilization*, Three Rivers Press, 2003.

> Guided by cutting-edge science, innovative computer-mapping techniques, and the latest archæological scholarship, this book seeks to examine the mystery at the end of the last Ice Age with astonishing revelations that challenge long-held views about the existence of sunken continents. The author includes accounts of discoveries of underwater ruins exactly where the ancient myths stated they should be in the submerged kingdoms that archæologists never thought existed.

Edgar Cayce, *Edgar Cayce on Atlantis*, Grand Central Publishing, 1988.

> This book by the legendary mystic and clairvoyant, nicknamed 'The Sleeping Prophet', discusses the Atlantean civilization, advanced Atlantean technology, the wars of Atlantis, the exodus from Atlantis to Egypt both before and during the destruction of the continent, and the incarnations of the Atlanteans.

Refer also to the sources cited in Endnote I-9.

Endnote I-9   Source references to the occult description of the evolutionary cycle for our present humanity.

The massive tomes by H. P. Blavatsky, Alice Bailey, and Rudolf Steiner, provide the fullest details. However, the following books provide more digestible descriptions:

- ❖ Geoffrey A. Barborka, *The Divine Plan*, The Theosophical Publishing House, 1980.
- ❖ Geoffrey A. Barborka, *The Peopling of the Earth*, The Theosophical Publishing House, 1975.
- ❖ Geoffrey A. Barborka, *The Story of Human Evolution*, The Theosophical Publishing House, 1980.
- ❖ Gottfried de Purucker, ed. Trevor Barker, *Fundamentals of the Esoteric Philosophy*, Kessinger Publishing, 2007.
- ❖ Basil Crump, *Evolution as Outlined in the Archaic Eastern Records*, Luzac & Co., 1930.

Endnote I-10   Extract from The Secret Doctrine on *Daemon East Deus Inversus*

'Indeed, evil is but an antagonizing blind force in nature; it is *reaction, opposition* and *contrast*—evil for some, good for others. There is no *malum in se* [evil in itself]: only the shadow of light, without which light could have no existence, even in our perceptions. If evil disappeared, good would disappear along with it from Earth. […] Everywhere the speculations of the Kabalists treat of Evil as a FORCE, which is antagonistic, but at the same time essential, to Good, as giving it vitality and existence, which it could never have otherwise. There would be no *life* possible (in the *Māyāvic* sense) without *Death*, nor regeneration and reconstruction without destruction. Plants would perish in eternal sunlight, and so would man, who would become an automaton without the exercise of his free will and aspirations after that sunlight, which would lose its being and value for him had he nothing but light. Good is infinite and eternal only in the eternally concealed from us, and this is why we imagine it eternal. On the manifested planes, one equilibrates the other.'[4]

NOTES

1   The book was reviewed by Edi Bilimoria, *Journal of the Scientific and Medical Network*, 102 (2010), 49–50.
2   See: *Stanford Encyclopedia of Philosophy* <http://plato.stanford.edu/index.html> accessed 18 January 2020; Cognitive Science Society <http://www.cognitivesciencesociety.org> accessed 18 January 2020; 'Cognitive science', Wikipedia (last modified 5 January 2020) <https://en.wikipedia.org/wiki/Cognitive_science> accessed 18 January 2020.
3   G. Rizzolatti and C. Sinigaglia, *Mirrors in the Brain. How we share our actions and emotions* (Oxford: Oxford University Press, 2008). See also Michael A. Arbib, *How the Brain Got Language: The mirror system hypothesis* (Oxford: March 2015) [Oxford Scholarship Online] <https://www.oxfordscholarship.com/view/10.1093/acprof:osobl/9780199896684.001.0001/acprof-9780199896684> accessed 18 January 2020.
4   *SD*-I, 'Daemon Est Deus Inversus: Death is Life', 413–14.